The POLYTECHNIC WOLVERHAMPTON

Main site: ROBERT SCOTT LIBRARY, St. Peter's Sq.,
Wolverhampton WV1 1RH   Tel: 313005 ext. 2300

WALSALL CAMPUS
LIBRARY
& LEARNING RESOURCES

Gorway, Walsall WS1 3DD
Walsall (0922) 720141

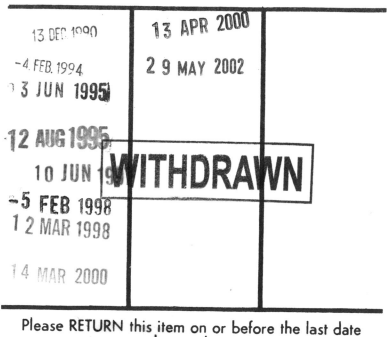

13 DEC 1990

13 APR 2000

-4. FEB. 1994

2 9 MAY 2002

3 JUN 1995

12 AUG 1995

10 JUN 19 **WITHDRAWN**

-5 FEB 1998

1 2 MAR 1998

14 MAR 2000

Please RETURN this item on or before the last date
shown above   L I

dn 73077860

CARLTON R. MEYERS, Ed.D., Teachers College, Columbia University, is Professor of Physical Education and Education at the State University of New York at Buffalo. He has also taught at Yale University. Dr. Meyers has contributed a number of articles in the area of measurement to various journals and periodicals in the field.

MEASUREMENT IN
PHYSICAL EDUCATION

CARLTON R. MEYERS

STATE UNIVERSITY OF NEW YORK
AT BUFFALO

SECOND EDITION

THE RONALD PRESS COMPANY • NEW YORK

Library of Congress Catalog Card Number: 73–77860
PRINTED IN THE UNITED STATES OF AMERICA

To My Wife
Eleanor

Preface

Recognizing that a teacher can be more effective if he or she understands and uses measurement properly, this book has been written to meet the need for a text presenting a functional approach in teaching measurement for physical education. It is designed to serve as a basic textbook in professional physical education and for in-service education, and also as a comprehensive resource for teacher use in the field.

This Second Edition has been revised extensively to stress more thoroughly those aspects essential for the teacher—as both a consumer and a prospective producer—to be a constructive critic of tests as devices and measurement as a process.

The material is organized and presented as it will actually be used in teaching. Seemingly, physical education measurement publications have been written more for research-oriented than teaching-oriented individuals. The focus of this book, teacher application, is specifically intended to enhance thorough understanding and effective utilization of measurement by teachers.

The book is organized into three parts to facilitate integration of the material into meaningful relationships. Part I emphasizes the selection and construction of tests and what the teacher needs to know about elementary statistical procedures. In addition to the general principles and considerations implicit in selection and construction presented, considerations specific to the different types of tests and different measurement areas are incorporated in Parts I and II. Part II explains the various areas of measurement in physical education and the function and relationship of these areas in the overall appraisal of the individual. Many available tests are included for different educational levels, together with reported test development statistics. Preference is given to tests deemed most practical for teacher use. When appropriate, tests are designated as to the particular grade level and sex for which they are intended. Part III deals with the application of measurement, including description of illustrative school testing programs and a directive approach to grading. Appendix A contains definitions and appropriate descriptions of commonly used terms in measurement. Brief descriptions of selected basic strength and motor

performance test items are presented in Appendix B to facilitate reference usage for test construction and analysis and to avoid repetition
of common descriptions in the textual reports of tests. The remaining
appendices (C, D, and E) contain normative data for three fitness tests,
a popular physical education attitude inventory, and a table of squares
and square roots.

The book organization is structured to direct attention to five measurement tasks that the teacher encounters—test selection, construction and
administration, and analysis and application of the results. While much
material is interrelated, and Chapter 7 on overall appraisal sets the stage
for this, the teacher interested in one or more of these functions is guided
by content and check lists through procedural steps and salient considerations. Chapter 3 is the resource for test selection, Chapters 4 and 5
for test construction, Chapter 6 for test organization and administration,
Chapter 2 for analysis of results, and Chapter 16 for application.

Essentially, this book contains no norm tables or the equivalent, which
warrants explanation, particularly for the reader who might not otherwise
delve into the text. Obviously, the inclusion of norms would necessarily
reduce the number of tests that could be reported and thus not permit
inclusion of many tests available for teacher consideration. But apart
from that, norms possess serious shortcomings and are subject to gross
misuse by the person unsophisticated in measurement. The writer has
been appalled upon numerous occasions to hear a teacher cite, "norms are
included," as the basic reason for selecting a particular test, even though
they may be totally inappropriate for the given situation. In a constructive vein, the approach herein is to foster two concepts: the importance
of the individual as his or her own best norm; and the ease of development of norms by the teacher (for self-made or published tests) from the
two basic statistics (mean and standard deviation).

Acknowledgment is accorded to the many persons who have contributed to this book either directly by publishing a test or as one of the
many aiding in continued development of measurement tools and techniques. Special gratitude is extended to Dr. S. David Farr of the State
University of New York at Buffalo for his assistance in developing the
initial presentation of statistical concepts and analysis and to Dr. T. Erwin
Blesh of Yale University for his formative influence as collaborator on the
first edition.

CARLTON R. MEYERS

Buffalo, N. Y.
January, 1974

Contents

PART III

APPLICATION OF MEASUREMENT

APPENDIX

Part I

UNDERSTANDING OF MEASUREMENT IN TEACHING

This Part is directed to the development of an understanding of measurement as an integral part of teaching physical education. The teacher who fails to understand and properly employ measurement, comparatively speaking, knows neither where he is going nor why. To give intelligent direction to the physical education program necessitates information that the teacher can derive from properly organized and discreet use of measurement. In achieving the purpose stated, the chapters in this Part are intended to depict a desirable approach to measurement, to foster a comprehension of basic statistical concepts for which the teacher has need, to describe test selection and construction meaningfully, and to discuss considerations implicit in the organization of a program of measurement. An understanding of these fundamental concepts of physical education measurement will provide the basis for presentation of specific tools and their application in the ensuing Parts.

1

Approach to Measurement

BASIC PHILOSOPHY AND NEED

Measurement and the evaluation based upon it provide a more scientific and objective basis for the physical education program. Accordingly, measurement might well be regarded as the backbone of the physical education program and should serve as the dynamic force in the development of such programs. The desired approach to measurement is in terms of the fullest realization of its potential in contributing as a teaching device to the education of children and youth. Its concern is to provide information pertaining to the abilities, capacities, and needs of children and youth in physical education so as to guide the teaching of physical education and later serve to ascertain the effectiveness of this teaching. Measurement affords the basis for deciding where to begin in teaching a particular skill to a given individual or group and to provide direction toward realization of the desired objectives, as well as to determine progress toward these goals. Thus, measurement enables the teacher to guide the course of experience in physical education intelligently and deliberately toward the desired goals in a most efficient and effective manner.

The individuality of each student in his innate capacity, ability, needs, and interests as influenced by varied environmental backgrounds presents many differences to be heeded in teaching and, consequently, to be divulged by measurement. The teacher learns what the student can do now, including recognition of any limiting factors, and what he may be expected to achieve. Then with this information, the teaching can be planned to enhance the overall development of the individual to the greatest extent possible. Guided by these "vital statistics" of the learner, along with the "blow-by-blow" description obtained through continued use of tests during the instructional experience, the teaching becomes noticeably improved and more nearly approaches its full potential. So conceived, it becomes apparent that the basic purpose of measurement can be viewed as the improvement of instruction in order to foster and facilitate learning in physical education. Testing is an integral part of teaching, not merely associated with it, and entails planning and supervision, as does any other activity that is used to promote more effective guidance of learning.

Reliance upon measurement in physical education differs in no way from circumstances found in the routine of ordinary living. In everyday life measurement is all around us. We rise according to the clock and begin a day in which it is difficult to find any activity not affected by or involving measurement, directly or indirectly. Water, fuel, electricity, food, clothing, and other essential are all measured in appropriate units and paid for at a given amount for each unit. The money used to purchase necessities and luxuries is received as payment for service performed on the basis of a specific wage for a given period of work, such as hourly or weekly. The average person is surrounded by measuring devices, such as time pieces, weight scales, rulers, barometers, thermometers, and speedometers, and such dependency establishes the importance of measurement in our lives.

Progress in scientific endeavor and education is related to and dependent upon the utilization of measurement. A driect and positive relationship has been noted between the status of a particular science or field of endeavor and the degree to which measurement has developed in it; that is, the more a branch of science utilizes exact measurement, the more highly developed it is. This is illustrated by the advancement during recent years in the different areas of responsibility in education —instruction, supervision, and administration—which has been fostered by the increasing application of the scientific approach to education problems.

A skilled carpenter is thoroughly familiar with the use of scales found on the framing square for work with wood. The competent machinist works with great accuracy on metal with the aid of a micrometer. The physician employs the best available measuring devices in looking after our health, the most valuable resource of all. Likewise, in dealing with people, all fields of education should employ the best available means of measurement in guiding and ascertaining the results of their efforts, as well as continually striving to develop better measuring instruments. Many educational measurements appear crude in comparison with physical measurements of weight and length. However, as has been shown by recent developments that have occurred since the concerted application of scientific methodology to educational problems, these crude beginnings afford a starting point toward meeting complexities found in educational problems. It should be recognized that there are many limitations in existing measuring instruments; but these limitations in no way detract from the importance of measurement, though they may make it more difficult. In fact, this presents a challenge for, and places a premium on, skillful use of these instruments. Generally speaking, the cruder a tool is, the greater the skill of applying it must be to obtain satisfactory results. As an illustration, the modern automobile requires little spill to operate compared to the early production models.

Thus it is noted that measurement is not peculiar to any area of interest or of living in general but constitutes a definite part of living, and the degree of development of any field of study is directly related to the extent to which measurement is utilized. The development of tests and measurement in physical education is not a recent innovation but from its beginnings has given guidance and direction to the growth of physical education. Measurement provided the impetus for national interest and attention to the overall fitness—physical, mental, emotional, and social— which has resulted in concerted and continuing effort on the part of government, social agencies, and schools to meet this definite need.

THE HISTORY OF MEASUREMENT IN BRIEF

Measurement is nothing new, but has been serving man since his origin. Likewise, in the field of education, measurement in some form has long been utilized in formal instruction. Shortly after the middle of the nineteenth century, a discernible movement in tests and measurement was initiated in education, educational research, and physical education. About this time, written and objective tests came into existence in education in this country. The first experimental psychological laboratory was opened by Wilhelm Wundt in Germany in 1879 and marked the start of the development of statistical and research techniques applied to educational problems.

The establishment of a Chair of Physical Education at Amherst College in 1861 and the man who first occupied it, Edward Hitchcock, may be credited with the beginning of the testing movement in our physical education. Hitchcock, together with his successor, Phillips, compiled a series of anthropometric measurements over a period of 50 years. These and other pioneers endeavored to apply anthropometry to practical work in the gymnasium. The study of anthropometric measurement led quite naturally from symmetry and size to the measurement of strength; and, at Harvard in 1880, Dr. Dudley Allen Sargent developed a strength test that was widely adopted by colleges and universities. Kellogg's interest in strength testing led to his invention of a dynamometer to clear up some basic misconceptions, such as the fact that the large man may not necessarily be the strong man, and the man who has great endurance may not necessarily be the strong man.

Beginning in 1885, at the first meeting of the American Association for Health, Physical Education, and Recreation, which was then known as the Association for the Advancement of Physical Education, tests and research techniques upon which they are based were proffered and were recognized as a vital force in physical education. At this first meeting, the problems of uniformity in testing and the application of averages or norms were discussed at great length. Also, Hitchcock presented a plan in which the physical education program for individual students would be scientifically determined by medical examinations and physical measurements of the anthropometric type.

About 1900, interest in cardiac function was manifested in the development of cardiovascular tests. A number of physiologists contributed to this area through study of the efficiency of the circulatory system, based on heart reaction to activity, beginning with the publication by Crampton in 1905 of a test of this type. The aforementioned tests—anthropometric, strength, and cardiovascular—reflected attention to physical development and capacity. Shortly after 1900, interest in ability became manifested when Sargent devised a six-item test designed to indicate physical efficiency. Consequently, as in ancient civilizations, a change in emphasis was made from strength and size to skill, speed, accuracy, and endurance. Meylan of Columbia also provided leadership to this cause through the development of a comprehensive test involving the fundamental skills, such as running, jumping, and climbing. Interest in ability testing became very great and many tests were devised. Finally, about 1920, attention was directed to the desirability of a measure or indicant of physical efficiency; and this presented a new challenge in the areas of both performance and capability.

The turning point and line of demarcation between early and modern physical education measurement appeared to be about 1925. At this time attention was given to physical education as a part of education in light of its contributions and desirable research and statistical techniques were beginning to be used in the development of measurement tools—thus the scientific approach was given recognition. Then professional educators developed an interest in the characteristics of learners instead of limiting their concern only to subject matter, which in turn stimulated the development of more intricate techniques of educational measurement.

The *Research Quarterly* of the American Association for Health, Physical Education, and Recreation, which was first published in March, 1930, has been an important factor in the development of the testing movement. This publication has afforded a means of disseminating information concerning recently constructed tests and of generally encouraging teachers to participate in the conduct of research studies, through which interest in the scientific side of physical education has been stimulated. In 1936, the Administrative Measurements Section of the AAHPER was officially recognized. Its purpose has been to demonstrate already proven and usable tests in physical education and to show the practical application of tests and testing devices.

Realization of the place of physical education in education led to ways of determining its contributions in terms of three basic types of learning: *technical,* entailing physical development and performance; *associated,* which includes knowledge and understanding; and *concomitant,* concerning attitudes and behavior. In the late 1940s educational psychologists focused attention on these three types of learning by initiating efforts that led to the development of a taxonomy of educational objectives relating to each type, termed the psychomotor, cognitive and affective domains, respectively. Today, measurement in physical education is continually striving to improve devices in the technical learning area, where already good tests exist; to find better measures of associated learning; and at the same time to develop better techniques for determining the more intangible characteristics and objectives encompassed in concomitant learning. Contemporary physical education is deemed to make significant contributions to education through fostering desirable social, mental, and emotional development; hence, there is the challenge to discover satisfactory means of ascertaining the extent of existence of these "intangibles." Recent measurement led to national interest and desire to encourage people to attain and maintain fitness in all of its aspects (physical, mental, social, and emotional). This has made two significant contributions. First, it has directed attention to the unity of man, a whole of inseparable parts. Second, it has spotlighted a "do-it-yourself stage" of physical activity wherein individuals are seeking out physical recreation for participation and the accruing benefits, rather than merely being spectators.

Thus, it can be shown that now, as before in history, measurement continues to play a vital role.

THE VALUE OF MEASUREMENT IN PHYSICAL EDUCATION

Inasmuch as the fundamental purpose of measurement has been depicted as the improvement of instruction, it follows that the basic value of the measurement program may be stated as the determination of the efficacy of the program in light of desired outcomes, so that needed adjustment can be made to approximate more nearly the realization of the aim of the physical education program. Succinctly, the major value of measurement lies in informing the teacher how effectively the teaching is attaining the established goals with a view toward continual improvement.

To elucidate, measurement in relation to the physical education program is analogous to the compass and map that have guided the travel of men for many years. By taking compass bearings of identifiable landmarks on the map, one is able to establish his position on the map at any time and, thereby, note progress toward the desired destination or aim; and measurement serves as the compass to reveal one's position and progress at desired intervals in his travel toward an established educational goal. The landmarks or guideposts upon which sights are set for bearings are the objectives of the physical education program. If the direction of travel varies from the desired course in attaining the goals of the program, needed alteration can be made to redirect the effort on course; in purposeful direction of the physical education program, measurement becomes indispensable.

THE OBJECTIVES OF PHYSICAL EDUCATION

Inasmuch as the purpose and value of our measurement lie in the improvement of the physical education program, the characteristics that define and describe physical education should be clearly delineated. Physical education can be described as a medium for education, an integral part of education, a phase of educating the whole individual, a program of activity by which goals in personal and social development may be met, and that part of education that proceeds predominantly through physical or motor activity. Concisely stated, physical education is the particular phase of education that is concerned with engendering maximum physical, physiological, psychological, and social development of all individuals through participation in properly selected and controlled motor activities. The general objectives of physical education are embodied in this definition as developmental areas. As shown earlier, objectives serve to guide the course of educative experience and, thereby, give direction to the program. These objectives that function to shape the program should be based upon and derived from the prevailing philosophy of education and physical education. They point out the specific ways in which physical education makes its contribution to education.

While different physical educators may express objectives in various ways, it is quite generally recognized that physical education has a definite responsibility in four areas of individual development:

1. Physical and organic development.
2. Development of physical skills.
3. Psychological development.
4. Social and moral development.

This general classification of objectives of physical education should lead to the specific attributes to be achieved at various grade levels. In so doing, a problem that has existed previously may be avoided, wherein the objectives of physical education are stated in such general terms that the teachers feel no sense of responsibility for accomplishing specific things. The statement of objectives indicates that, while this phase of education proceeds largely through physical activity, by the very nature of physical activity individuals interact with others in a social situation and, thereby, may acquire concomitant learning that fosters the development of responsible human beings as well as the learning and other benefits associated directly with physical skills.

These objectives provide specific points of reference and emphasis to guide the teaching of physical education toward making its greatest possible contribution to the education of youth and the fundamental purpose of education—the fullest possible development of the individual within the framework of society. Regardless of the delineation of the objectives as developmental areas, it should be recognized that the teaching of physical education is concerned with an integrated and unified human being, and that any given experience may influence development in more than one area. These areas are not distinct, separate entities but intertwined aspects of human activity and behavior. In dealing with specific emphases in teaching, it is not difficult to lose sight of the concept of the unity of the individual. The concept of diverse and specific functions provides the approach for teaching; that is, specifics are taught to the whole child who goes to school.

So in measurement, a device for teaching physical education, attention should be directed toward maintaining the whole relationship of the individual in appraising his development in the areas indicated by the objectives.

THE FUNCTION OF MEASUREMENT IN TEACHING

Briefly and precisely stated, the function of measurement in physical education is to ascertain status or capacity in a given quality or skill at a particular time. Yet through this simple function, measurement provides the information vital to efficient and effective teaching in physical education. This simple measurement of status or capacity yields information to indicate present ability, weaknesses and strengths, and potential.

Thus, the results of measurement give the basis for determining achievement or progress, classifying individuals according to similar qualities, diagnosing particular defects, and predicting educability in given qualities. Furthermore, the results of measurement provide evidence for motivating students and teachers, for guidance in terms of performance, for research in physical education which is so vital to progress, to serve as an indicant of teacher and program efficacy, and to furnish a sound and informative basis for the interpretation of physical education to the public as well as to educational administrators and other teachers.

Explanation of what is accomplished through measurement can best be made by listing the objectives to be realized in a measurement program. Justification for such a listing, other than purposes to be served herein, lies in the fact that much of the retardation of measurement in physical education is attributable to the vague statement of objectives. Certainly, comprehension of physical education measurement can be facilitated by depicting its scope and content through an enumeration of what is encompassed. In general, a measurement program in physical education should attempt:

1. To measure the status and capacities of individuals in terms of the stated objectives of physical education—physical and organic development, development of physical skills, psychological development, and social and moral development.
2. To provide information to determine and motivate improvement over a period of time in the qualities comprising these development areas.
3. To provide data for diagnosing specific strengths, weaknesses, and other needs of individuals.
4. To furnish information for determining the efficacy of the physical education program.

Full understanding of the scope and realization of the function of physical education measurement can best be achieved through a further delineation of these general objectives, that is, by listing the specific objectives included within these general objectives. The following objectives constitute a broadly conceived and developed measurement program, and it is not to be implied that they must be implemented in their entirety. The purpose herein is to describe the entire scope of the program. Specifically, the program of measurement in physical education should serve:

1. *To determine the status of the physical fitness* [1] *of each individual*

---

[1] Physical fitness as used herein refers to the condition of the body that permits one to meet daily demands of living, including recreational activity, and still possess physical stamina and strength to meet unforeseen demands.

as the basis for planning a program to foster his optimum development. In order to provide a program conducive to promoting desired physical and organic development, it becomes necessary to determine the existing level of physical fitness. Desired information relative to physical fitness can be provided by tests of strength and physical or motor fitness, and measures of cardiovascular efficiency. Although it neither is administered by nor is the responsibility of the physical education teacher, the medical examination and recommendations based thereupon provide valuable information for guidance of the physical education teachers in this context. Consequently, pertinent information from the health appraisal record warrants inclusion with physical education tests in ascertaining the status of physical fitness.

2. *To measure the abilities and capacities of each student in physical education activity as a basis for determining the appropriate scope and content of the physical education program, in addition to providing a means of classifying students for instruction and participation.* If the teaching of physical education is to be adapted to the needs of students, a determination of their abilities and capacities as individuals becomes a necessity. Not only does such information help to shape the program, but it also provides meaningful facts upon which to base proper guidance. Revelation of ability in relation to one's own capacity is usually more valuable and meaningful than a comparison of one's ability with that of others. Classifying students for instruction and participation on the basis of this type of measurement facilitates teaching and learning in all aspects—technical, associated, and concomitant. Such classification affords a practical and valuable approach to providing instruction geared to individual differences, which is extremely important in the realm of physical performance. In particular, however, classification according to ability and capacity is especially important in enhancing concomitant learning, that is, providing optimum conditions for the development of desirable attitudes and behavior. A student will be more likely to develop a favorable disposition toward and interest in activities that he learns and plays initially with persons of comparable ability. As a result, in addition to advantages concerning the learning of the skill itself, the student becomes more inclined to pursue this activity further.

3. *To determine specific strengths, weaknesses, and limitations of individuals in physical education activity.* At a cursory glance, this objective may appear to be mere repetition of functions covered in the aforementioned two specific objectives. However, the purpose here is to indicate the place of tests specifically intended to divulge strong or weak points, that is, tests of diagnostic purpose. Some tests might well serve as measures of both status and peculiarity. The diagnostic type

of test is invaluable as a source of information upon which to base individualized instruction. For class purposes, the results of such testing can direct decisions in program content and the time allotted to particular skills or activities, so as to meet particular needs adequately.

4. *To measure achievement or proficiency in motor skills that will be useful to the student in the present and future.* Viewed in relation to one's capacity, achievement takes on special significance. Tests of achievement also reveal particular points which need improvement, and give direction to teaching and learning. Similar beneficial direction accrues from divulging areas of notable progress. Regarding proficiency, such tests represent a relatively recent and seemingly very promising innovation in physical education, paralleling the concept of advanced placement tests and proficiency examinations applied to the various academic disciplines. Illustrative of this is the College Proficiency Examination Program initiated by New York State in 1961, which affords individuals the opportunity to qualify for credit in a variety of courses. In physical education, tests of proficiency are utilized either as the basis for student exemption from or to grant credit for a particular physical education activity course. While outside the scope of this objective, it warrants mention that, broadly conceived, proficiency tests entail knowledge related to the activity as well as performance of the motor skill itself. It is anticipated that increasing use will be made of proficiency tests at both secondary school and college levels as a means of individualizing the physical education of students by permitting them to satisfy performance requirements in skill areas in which they display proficiency and free them to select activity areas in which they have less, if any, proficiency.

5. *To act as a guide to better body mechanics and as a means of improving the functional postures of those individuals needing attention.* Much of the indifference and uncertainty concerning the need for understanding the fundamental concepts and considerations of body mechanics can be eliminated through the application of informative measures of body mechanics. Experience indicates that the motivational value of techniques of measures in posture and body mechanics is amazing, even before the significance of results has been fully explained. This, of course, is due largely to the general esthetic impression obtained by observing the results of measurement in body mechanics.

6. *To determine student knowledge of physical education activities and, accordingly, to serve as a guide to knowledge in sports appreciation.* The associated learning—knowledge and understanding—involved with technical or skill learning is most important not only in terms of knowl-

edge and understanding per se but also in light of their influence on the development of attitudes and behavior. This associated learning provides the basis for lasting, permanent values embodied in concomitant learning—habits, attitudes, and appreciations. A thorough knowledge and understanding of physical education activities enhances the likelihood of developing favorable appreciations, attitudes, and behavior which will contribute to a fuller life for the individual.

7. *To provide the best available evidence concerning an individual's social efficiency, so that effort can be efficiently directed toward affecting better social adjustment.* Measurement in the realm of social and moral development has not achieved the stage of development enjoyed by skill and knowledge testing. This is attributable not to the lack of study and research but rather to the characteristics and intangibility of the traits involved. Physical education purports to make a significant contribution toward fostering better social adjustment and, consequently, should endeavor to gather the best information possible to ascertain the relative degree of effectiveness. Progress in developing measuring instruments results from use and experimentation with the best instruments available. Ogburn provides further substantiation for this measurement, stating, "Where data are fragmentary and emotions strong, it is almost impossibe to do a good piece of approximating." [2] Thus, the more evidence available, the more certainty can be affixed to the findings.

8. *To measure individual accomplishment in the physical education program and provide a more objective basis for grading.* The amount and rate of progress made by students warrant serious consideration in the development of teaching ability and methodology. The resultant effects of the use of varied techniques can be determined. Student accomplishment also gives direction to need in emphasizing various parts or aspects of the program. Overall, accomplishment in relation to one's own ability and potential, along with the relation to one's peers, affords a basis for appraisal of student, teacher, and program.

9. *To guide the establishment of appropriate achievement standards in the areas of physical fitness, general motor or athletic abilities, and specific skills or achievement in a variety of activities.* Meaningful achievement standards should serve to stimulate student effort toward realization of goals within their capacity. Furthermore, such standards would provide comprehensible information conducive to promoting public understanding of the place and value of physical education. A prime

[2] William F. Ogburn, "Considerations in Choosing Problems for Research," *Essays on Research in the Social Sciences* (Washington, D.C.: The Brookings Institution, 1931).

need in physical education is to identify the characteristics of a physically educated individual at the various grade and age levels. Obviously, measurement is indispensable in endeavoring to satisfy this need. An excerpt from a treatise on tests and measurement written almost three decades ago still remains timely and expressive of this need today.

In addition to using available scales, we need to develop many more achievement levels scaled to age, height, weight, and "motor age" of students so that both teachers and students can judge accomplishment objectively in relation to what can be expected in performance for each individual pupil. If teachers had such instruments readily available and felt the need to keep all students up to the accomplishment level normal for them, we should no doubt have programs considerably superior to those we have at present. Herein lies another important area for the future of tests and measurements. . . .[3]

10. *To act as a motivating device for effective learning and teaching.* With proper orientation, measurement procedures should motivate students to put forth their best efforts and capture their interest and understanding. When used in conjunction with teaching, testing procedures do much to enhance the satisfaction derived from improvement in the program. Measurement facilitates perception of objectives and also in this way contributes to motivation. While the motivational value of measurement is appreciable in both teaching and learning, heed should be paid to insure that the use of test results presents the major reason for testing and that motivation remains secondary in purpose. As a word of admonition it should be mentioned that a well-conceived and well-organized testing program will afford intrinsic motivation and obviate the need for or desirability of extrinsic motivational factors. Particularly with physical performance tests, when extrinsic motivation is used, considerable evidence exists to infer that the tests are measuring the effects of the motivational factors rather than giving a reliable indicant of performance.

11. *To determine the relative value of various types of programs or emphases in a program.* This objective contributes to continual evaluation of programs with a view toward providing the best balance and meaningfulness. In many instances justification for varied emphasis on different aspects of the physical education program is merely speculation. Too many teachers have opinions that they cannot substantiate with facts. An effort to reveal the facts might in an appreciable number of cases indicate lack of justification for their opinion, while in others substantiation would be provided.

[3] Aileen Carpenter, "The Future of Tests and Measurements in the Elementary Schools," *Journal of Health and Physical Education,* **15,** No. 9 (November, 1944), 479.

12. *To provide an indicant of teacher effectiveness.* The good teacher is interested in improving teaching methods and will utilize the objective evidence derived from tests to evaluate the merits of different methods and phases or aspects of the program. Objective self-appraisal constitutes one of the most important steps that must be often taken by the teacher who wishes to grow. Since the teacher looms large as a determinant of both the quantity and the quality of learning derived by students in the learning situation, it is imperative that pertinent information be obtained to afford a reading of teacher efficacy.

13. *To contribute to research in improving the program content and by developing better means of testing in some areas and devising more satisfactory tests in areas where beginnings are meager.* Attention is directed here to the contribution of the measurement program to research and not to the role of measurement per se in research. The previously stated objectives indicate ways in which measurement provides the data and related information regarding the physical education program and the specific characteristics or skills involved. This information lends itself to analysis and appraisal with which to further a development and refinement of the program and its measuring instruments. Implicit in this objective is the challenge to utilize appropriate means of dissemination of such research findings, meaningfully interpreted, to other teachers and administrators. Astute observation of physical education programs confirms that many important findings, both positive and negative, as disclosed by measurement programs, are not being made known to other teachers whose programs might well benefit appreciably from such knowledge.

14. *To furnish objective data and related information concerning program results for use as a tool in interpreting physical education to the public, educators, and students.* Teachers of physical education are convinced that the purposes stated for physical education are achieved but need to produce unquestionable evidence that this is so. Each teacher should be ready, willing, and able to show evidence of the results of his program. This is fundamental to fostering an understanding of what physical education is and purports to achieve. Concrete illustrations do much more to interpret and further an understanding of physical education than simple figurative speech. It is not uncommon for administrators to request information, preferably tangible evidence of what physical education accomplishes and not just a statement of its intentions, as a means for interpreting the school program or justifying needed financial support. Programs that can furnish evidence of results garner additional support. Selection of tests in the light of desired objectives, and the keeping of careful records, supply basic information to show

just what physical education is doing and for substantiating requests for additional equipment and personnel in terms of need. The inclusion of testing as an integral part of the program noticeably increases the importance of physical education for students and parents as well as tending to place physical education on a par with other school subjects that employ periodic testing as general practice.

Conducted in the perspective of the foregoing objectives, measurement affords the physical education program a more scientific and objective basis than is otherwise possible, gives it purposeful direction, and generally serves to benefit physical education.

To complete the discussion of the function of measurement and to dispel the possibility of construing measurement as the panacea for program ills in physical education, recognition should be given to the limitations of measurement. It is often said that one can prove anything he wishes by astute use of figures. This suggests that interpretation of measurement must be grounded upon a thorough and objective analysis and precludes reading extraneous effects or conclusions into the results. Measurement presents the hazard of making things appear oversimplified, such as a single score or index as an indicant of physical fitness or any similar quality. A baseball score may be used to illustrate this very effectively; a game may be scoreless for eight, nine, or even ten innings; yet a final score of 4 to 0 would fail to express this actuality. A common tendency in the use of measurement is to place more reliance on scores or results than can be justified by the original measurement. For example, in scoring diving competition, the final results are sometimes expressed to the nearest hundredth to determine places, when original awards for each dive are made as the number of points to the nearest half-point and multiplied by the degree of difficulty to the nearest tenth. Thus, more accuracy is presumedly derived from results than had characterized the original measurement.

As depicted previously, measurement of certain qualities is in a beginning stage and may be comparatively crude. Cognizance should be made of this difficulty in measurement, and the use of results should be tempered by knowledge of the evasiveness of the characteristics in question. The fact that effective means of measurement have not yet been devised for certain qualities should in no way detract from the significance of such qualities or the best available means of measuring them. Finally, in the application of results, it should be remembered that decisions are made on the evidence of measurement; but measurement can never eliminate the need for judgment whenever human welfare is involved. There may be certain reasons or factors associated with a particular test score. A proper and just decision must be based upon judgment of the significance of all circumstances involved.

WHAT THE TEACHER SHOULD KNOW ABOUT MEASUREMENT

The answer to the question "What does the teacher need to understand about tests and measurement in order to be more effective?" is essential in order to achieve the purpose of measurement—the improvement of instruction. The teacher should understand the place of measurement in teaching if he is to be expected to use it. The approach to measurement here is in terms of its serving as a medium to facilitate an understanding of these needs or basic competencies for the teacher so as to realize more nearly the fullest potential of measurement as a teaching device in physical education.

The perspective to be maintained throughout entails the unity concept of man, his indivisibility, and recognizes the "whole relationship" of man despite the fact that he can also be described as a composite of many diverse and interrelated functions. Measurement of the wide variety of physical skills, associated knowledge, and accompanying habits and attitudes that are encompassed in physical education is viewed as related to the individual as a whole, which in itself entails the interrelatedness of parts or function.

Accordingly, the teacher should understand and develop competence in the following aspects of measurement in his quest to be more effective in teaching.

1. *Analyzing and interpreting the results of measurement in physical education.* In essence this involves an understanding of a few basic statistical tools and concepts and of expeditious means (from manual to electronic) of computing and interpreting results. Teacher competence in this aspect has been impeded in the past by ineffective learning approaches to necessary statistical concepts and by inclusion of a number of unnecessary statistical tools and concepts.
2. *Factors and considerations involved in test selection.* Implicit here is comprehension of the characteristics of a good test as they relate to the particular quality being measured.
3. *Factors and considerations included in scientifically constructing tests that involve technical, associated, and concomitant learning, that is, skills, knowledge, and attitudes.* This deals with the wherewithal requisite to development of tests that meet the criteria for a good test.
4. *Efficiently organizing and administering testing as an integral part of teaching in a challenging, interesting and meaningful manner, including explanation of the use and meaning of the results.* The importance of this phase of measurement resides in the fact that the inherent value of a test is not guaranteed but depends upon its proper use.
5. *Available and suggested tests for use in appraising the various aspects of development in the four areas that constitute the objectives of physical education—physical and organic, physical skills, psychological, and social and moral.* A knowledge of the historical development of each type of test in relation to its usage is desirable for fullest understanding.

This competency is envisaged as encompassing awareness of sources of suitable existing tests, as well as the procedure for being informed of new and revised tests as they become available.

6. *Application of the results of measurement in teaching physical education, individual appraisal, and program evaluation, and the need for the interest and desire to apply measurement and to foster continued development of the scientific approach in physical education.* The prime importance here resides in the fact that, unless the teacher is competent in it, the effort spent in testing will be to no avail and the potential value of measurement will never be realized. Unless use is made of the results, there is no need for measurement. This reflects the basic principle of measurement,[4] that tests are useful only if they help in making educational decisions.

Substantiation that these needs or basic competencies are essential for effective teaching can be afforded by different studies. In a survey of measurement programs to which 381 teachers responded, Wilson [5] noted that only 25 percent of the teachers utilized measurement pertaining to the four developmental areas or objectives of physical education. Other noteworthy findings were: in most instances teachers devised their own measuring instruments; the limited use of measurement was attributable to the lack of understanding of measurement possibilities in school programs, suggestive of inadequate exposure in their professional preparation to the extensive variety of tests and measurement devices available; and definite preference was expressed for instruments and techniques that are applicable for mass testing.

Roundy [6] conducted a survey involving 700 teachers and administrators in Californit and Utah in which 21 problems were identified and ranked together with their associated competencies. Two of the four general areas in which teachers were most often lacking competence were grading and reporting pupil progress, and evaluating the effectiveness of the physical education program. Ranked at the middle of the problems was the using of tests and other devices to measure progress. In an educational measurement project involving 2,900 seniors in 86 colleges and a follow-up of 541, Mayo [7] observed a strong implication that a measurement course should be compulsory for every prospective

---

[4] Jum C. Nunnally, *Educational Measurement and Evaluation* (New York: McGraw-Hill Book Co., 1964), p. 4.

[5] C. B. Wilson, "A Survey of Measurement Devices Used in Health and Physical Education Programs and Their Applications in Programs of the Central Western and Western Zones of New York State," Unpublished Ed.D. Project, University of Buffalo, 1955.

[6] Elmo S. Roundy, "Problems of and Competencies Needed by Men Physical Education Teachers at the Secondary Level," *Research Quarterly*, 38, No. 2 (May, 1967), 274.

[7] Samuel T. Mayo, *Pre-Service Preparation of Teachers in Educational Measurement* (Chicago: Loyola University, U.S. Dept. of HEW Project, 1967).

teacher, since some measurement is needed by all teachers, and students who have taken course-work will tend to show superior competency. It is indeed appalling to note Mayo's further comment that some teachers habitually construct poor tests, without realizing how poor they are, and without knowing first that they should improve and, second, how they can improve. All in all, the implications of these and similar studies, which can be corroborated empirically manifold, reveal the specific needs to enhance understanding of measurement and its use as a vital teaching device.

It is intended that the presentation of material in the ensuing chapters will engender the development of an understanding of measurement and its role in physical education, so as to increase the effectiveness of the teacher. The chapters have been organized to foster comprehension of the aforementioned specific needs in sequential order as listed. Continual attention should be directed to the fact that measurement in and of itself will not guarantee more effective teaching. Measurement merely comprises the means of, or device for teaching and learning, and the basic principles of good teaching must nevertheless be applied to insure more effective teaching.

2

Basic Statistical Concepts and Analysis

WHAT THE BASIC STATISTICAL CONCEPTS TELL THE TEACHER

Teachers of physical education, if they are to be most effective in teaching boys and girls, if they wish to construct and use tests in their classes, and if they are to be able to understand and interpret research in the field, must have a working knowledge of some of the basic statistical concepts. It is not the purpose of this chapter to attempt a detailed analysis of these concepts but merely to help toward a better understanding of some of the commonly used procedures and to equip the teacher to make a meaningful analysis of test results.[1]

What are some of these basic concepts? Suppose, for instance, that the teacher has administered the push-up test to a class of boys. What would he like to know about the results of that test? The fact that a particular boy scored 25 push-ups in itself is meaningless as far as disclosing how that boy scored in comparison to other members of the group. If the score of 25 denotes the mean score of the group, or maybe the point below which 75 percent of the group performed, or leads to some other index that would establish his performance in relation to others who took the test, then this score would begin to have meaning. Consequently, understanding certain measures of central tendency or

---

[1] The reader is urged to become familiar with the glossary of commonly used terms in measurement and in research reports, appearing in Appendix A, to facilitate comprehension of the material in this and ensuing chapters.

average score and such tools as percentiles and quartiles becomes essential.

In addition to knowing how to determine these statistics, it is necessary for the teacher to know the scatter or spread of the individual test performances in the group test distribution. The range of scores (lowest to highest) gives some indication of this spread but does not afford much information as to how the scores cluster around a measure of central tendency. To find the variability of the data, the standard deviation and the quartile deviation are most often used, particularly the former. In addition the standard deviation affords the basis for the teacher to derive scoring scales to facilitate comparison and averaging of different tests for the same or similar groups.

The measures of central tendency, measures of variability, percentiles, and scale scores pertain to a single distribution of scores. Oftentimes the teacher desires to know how the scores for the same group are related on two different tests. The commonly reported index of the relationship between two sets of scores made by the same group is referred to as the coefficient of correlation. This coefficient, usually noted as r, expresses the degree to which an individual maintains the same relative position in his group on the two testing occasions.

A MEANINGFUL APPROACH TO STATISTICAL ANALYSIS

Seemingly, the most logical and most desired approach to statistical analysis for the teacher is to begin with the raw scores on a test given to a group and to compute only those statistics essential for putting the test results in a usable, meaningful form. All studies of teacher needs in educational measurement depict that the greatest deterrent of teacher understanding of measurement is the expressed fear of the statistics involved, regardless of how simple they may be. This problem can be averted and fullest understanding of statistical concepts and tools engendered by focusing on simplified computational procedures, organized in an easy stepped fashion, to deal effectively with test scores.

Specifically, the desired approach to statistical analysis is to derive an appropriate scale score for the test scores to facilitate test interpretation and then, when desired, to combine different test scores into a composite score and ultimately into an equitable grade or evaluative scheme. All of this can be accomplished through the computation of two basic statistics—mean and standard deviation. The only other statistical tool that the teacher must be able to apply to be self-sufficient in testing is the coefficient of correlation, so that the relationship can be established between two tests or repeated measurements on the same test. This competency is necessary in the construction of teacher-made tests.

The simplest approach for the teacher in the computation of these essential statistics is through the grouping of the test scores. After explanation of the grouped-data procedure, a description of the normal frequency distribution will facilitate interpretation of test results, and alternative methods of computing without grouping scores will equip the teacher to deal most effectively with statistical analysis.

In essence, the approach to statistical analysis herein will be just as the consumer—the teacher—will apply it, and will entail only those concepts and tools deemed by the author most practical and necessary for the teacher of physical education. The tools and techniques covered through this approach will permit the teacher to analyze test findings and perform related functions that constitute an integral part of teaching and contribute substantially to quality education. Implicit in the ability to analyze test findings are such matters as: interpreting performance of individuals and groups on particular tests; discerning the relationship between scores on different tests; and combining test scores into meaningful composite scores for purposes of interpretation and grading.

AN ILLUSTRATIVE PROBLEM

To indicate the need for the teacher to recognize and understand the essential statistical concepts and to analyze test scores in light of them, an actual test of push-ups administered to 60 entering college freshman males will be considered. The resulting scores follow:

32	34	8	10
23	24	15	29
25	5	1	13
18	60	36	30
10	17	19	22
35	26	25	12
20	35	38	40
45	50	27	16
22	15	25	25
54	44	35	25
28	32	38	42
27	27	25	20
18	25	32	34
26	15	24	25
28	30	30	42

$$N = 60$$

The first concern facing the teacher is the organization of these data in order to obtain the desired information on the push-up test. The teacher will find a test tabulation sheet, such as Fig. 2–1, a valuable guide in organizing data and computing the desired basic statistics.

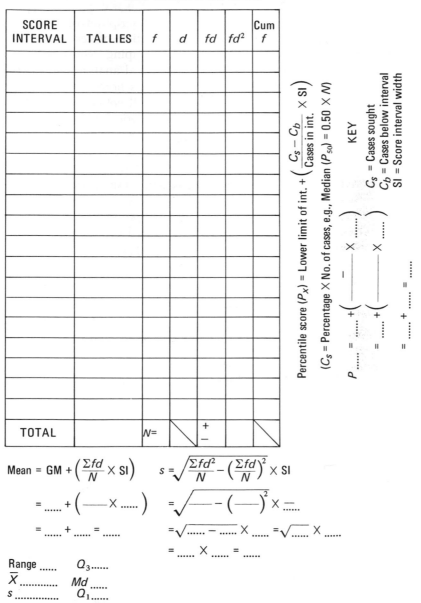

Fig. 2–1. Sample test tabulation sheet.

Such a form can be mimeographed or duplicated in some other practical manner to provide systematic work sheets.

GROUPING TEST SCORES FOR ANALYSIS

The initial task in dealing with the problem according to the proposed approach to statistical analysis consists of grouping the test scores into a frequency distribution, the purpose being to arrange the data in a workable order. If the teacher can work with 12 or 15 or so figures instead of a large number of scores, the statistical analysis becomes much simplified. The four fundamental steps to pursue in arranging data into a frequency table are:

1. *Determine the range of scores.* Find both the lowest score and the highest score achieved on a test. The range consists of the total number of score units contained in the distribution or set of data and represents the difference between the high and low scores plus one. Looking at the illustrative problem, it will be noted that the number of push-ups ranged from a low of 1 to a high of 60, which is a difference of 59 plus 1 or 60. That is, a span of 60 score units is covered by the distribution. Consequently, the range for this set of scores is 60.

2. *Determine the size of the score interval.* In constructing a frequency distribution, data should be grouped into between 10 and 20 score intervals. As a general rule, it is recommended that the teacher strive for between 12 and 15 score intervals with 15 being the most desirable number, inasmuch as it tends to best minimize grouping errors. When working with a small number of scores, the number of score intervals selected tends to be smaller, toward 10, to minimize void intervals in which no score appears. As the total number of scores becomes extremely large, a larger number of intervals—toward 20—becomes preferable. As a basis for ascertaining the desirable interval size, the range is divided by 15. In the sample problem the range of 60 divided by 15 would suggest an interval width of 4. However, in selecting the interval width it is recommended that preference be given, when possible, to an odd number. The use of an odd number results in the midpoint of each unit being a whole integer, which is a desirable feature. An exception to this preference for an odd number is that 10 or multiples of 10 are used considerably because of the relative simplicity of the overall setup. Therefore, when division of the range of 15 gives an even number, except for 10's, the use of the next higher number is preferable, if at least 12 intervals will result. Applying this recommendation to the sample problem, since 5 makes a more convenient interval to deal with, it is selected; making for 13 intervals to cover the range of scores. When in doubt

as to the appropriate number of intervals for a particular distribution of scores, the teacher should err in the direction of too many rather than too few.

3. *Set up the score intervals.* In setting up and recording the score intervals on the tabulation sheet, a rule of thumb that is helpful is to make the lower score limit of the intervals a multiple of the interval width, beginning with the interval that will contain the lowest score and progressing upward to include the highest score. Accordingly, the score intervals for the illustrative problem (see Table 2–1) were constructed to begin

Table 2–1. Frequency Distribution for the Illustrative Problem

Score Interval	Tallies	Frequency
60-64	/	1
55-59		0
50-54	//	2
45-49	/	1
40-44	////	4
35-39	𝅺𝅺𝅺 /	6
30-34	𝅺𝅺𝅺 ///	8
25-29	𝅺𝅺𝅺 𝅺𝅺𝅺 𝅺𝅺𝅺 /	16
20-24	𝅺𝅺𝅺 //	7
15-19	𝅺𝅺𝅺 ///	8
10-14	////	4
5-9	//	2
0-4	/	1
		$N = 60$

with multiples of 5, the interval width. It should be noted that the real limits of each interval extend from 0.5 score units below the lower score to 0.5 units above the upper score, for example, 24.5 to 29.5 for score interval 25–29. The lower divisional point, 0.5 of a score unit below the lower score, is referred to as the lower limit and used in computing the median and percentiles.

4. *Tally the test scores into a frequency distribution.* After the score-intervals have been recorded on the tabulation sheet, the individual scores are tallied in the appropriate score intervals. This procedure is followed until all scores have been tallied, as in Table 2–1. For the illustrative problem, only one score occurs in the first interval, namely, 1. Two scores fall in the interval 5–9, namely, 5 and 8; and four scores in the interval 10–14, namely, 10, 10, 13, and 12, and so on. While it is recommended that the teacher utilize a test tabulation sheet, such as

Fig. 2–1, this and several of the subsequent steps in computing the basic statistics are given in separate tables for the purpose of clarity. The completed tabulation sheet for the illustrative problem will be presented later as part of the discussion of the standard deviation.

5. *Establish the frequency column.* After all individual scores on the test have been tallied, the tallies in each interval are counted; and the number is recorded in the x column. As noted in the illustrative problem (Table 2–1), one score appears in the interval 0–4, two in the interval 5–9, four in the interval 10–14, eight in the interval 15–19, and so on. When the number of scores in each interval has been determined, the numbers are added together. This sum should equal the total number (N) of scores in the data with which the tester is working, and in the case of the sample problem it is 60. The teacher is now ready to compute the desired statistics.

COMPUTING THE TWO BASIC STATISTICS

Two statistics—the mean and the standard deviation—afford the basis for teacher analysis of test results. As stated at the outset of this chapter, if an individual has performed 25 push-ups on a test, that score means very little in itself as far as revealing anything about his standing in the group as a whole. Furthermore, 25 push-ups cannot be added to raw scores on other test items to obtain a composite score, when appropriate, to reflect a quality such as motor fitness. When the mean and the standard deviation for the test group become known, the score of 25 will take on meaning and can be readily transformed to a combinable yet expressive form.

The Mean

Simply stated, the mean (often referred to as the arithmetic average) of a group of scores represents the sum of the scores divided by the number of scores in the data. As such, it is a measure of central tendency of a distribution of scores, serving as a representative score for performance of a group on the measure in question. If five individuals take a chinning test and do 5, 3, 8, 10, and 4 chins, respectively, then 6 chins is the mean score for these five subjects (30 divided by 5). Since such a procedure is not so simple with large numbers of scores, the frequency distribution as set up in Table 2–1 is used. When the data have been grouped into a frequency distribution, the identity of individual scores is lost; and for the purpose of computing the mean, all the scores in an interval are presumed to fall at the midpoint of that particular score interval.

Once the frequency distribution is established as described above, three additional steps are necessary to compute the mean as shown in Table 2–2.

1. *Guess the mean of the distribution.* This implies that the interval selected as containing the guessed mean (GM) will be about in the middle of the distribution and will likely represent the interval with the greatest number of cases. For the sample problem, the interval most likely to include the mean appears to be 25–29 and the GM is the mid-point of the interval selected, or 27. Parallel lines drawn on the tabulation sheet serve to set off the interval containing the GM.

2. *Determine the deviation of each interval from the GM.* This is done by placing in the d column the number of intervals that each interval mid-point deviates from the GM. Numbers above the GM are assigned positive deviations, while those below are negative. In the example it will be seen that the interval 30–34 deviates ONE, the interval 35–39 deviates TWO, and so on. These deviations are above the GM and are therefore positive. Similarly, the interval 20–24 is assigned a minus ONE, and so forth.

3. *Multiply the frequency of each interval by its deviation.* When the deviation column is completed, the figures in the f and d columns for each interval are multipled to form the fd column. All positive figures in the fd column are totaled, as are the negative figures; and the difference is recorded as either a plus or a minus number beneath the fd column.

Now the mean is computed by the formula:

$$\overline{X} = GM + \left(\frac{\Sigma fd}{N} \times SI\right)$$

where the symbol Σ means "sum of," and SI is the size or width of the score intervals. Substituting the figures from the illustrative problem, as shown in Table 2–2, the mean is computed to be 27.4.

In light of the mean of 27.4, the aforementioned score of 25 push-ups takes on some meaning by affording an indication of where a score of 25 stands in relation to the other scores on the test; namely, just below the mean. However, some description of the distribution of scores within the group is needed to impart a clearer interpretation of the score, 25. To obtain this the teacher needs to compute the second basic statistic and companion statistic of the mean, the standard deviation.

Before turning to the standard deviation, one further word is in order relative to interpreting the mean, which is the most widely used measure of central tendency of a score distribution. The teacher should realize

Table 2–2. Computing the Mean for the Illustrative Problem

Score Interval	f	d	fd	cum f
60–64	1	7	7	60
55–59	0	6	0	59
50–54	2	5	10	59
45–49	1	4	4	57
40–44	4	3	12	56
35–39	6	2	12	52
30–34	8	1	8 (53)	46
25–29	16	0		38
20–24	7	–1	– 7	22
15–19	8	–2	–16	15
10–14	4	–3	–12	7
5– 9	2	–4	– 8	3
0– 4	1	–5	– 5 (–48)	1
	$N = 60$		+ 5	

$$\text{Mean} = \text{GM} + \left(\frac{\Sigma fd}{N} \times \text{SI}\right) = 27 + \left(\frac{5}{60} \times 5\right) = 27 + \left(\frac{25}{60}\right)$$

$$= 27 + 0.4 = 27.4$$

that in essence the mean represents the balancing point of all scores appearing in the distribution and changing one score will change the mean. The further from the mean a score is moved or added, the more the mean will change in the same direction. Accordingly, extreme scores in a distribution tend to give a distorted picture. This is readily discernible from the deviation column of Table 2–2, wherein it will be noted that the further a score deviates from the GM, the greater the number of deviation units. Awareness of this characteristic of the mean will alert the teacher to the possibility that an alternative measure of central tendency—the median—which will be described later, may be more desirable when unusual score distributions are encountered.

The Standard Deviation

The standard deviation (s or σ) is the most commonly used measure of variability or dispersion of scores in physical education measurement and research. Use of another measure of variability—the range—was made previously as the basis for setting up the frequency distribution. Although the range describes only the limits of scores and no pattern of their distribution, it does afford an excellent illustration of the importance of knowing something about the scatter or spread of the scores (that is, variability) of a group. For example, suppose the teacher tested a second comparable group of 60 subjects on the push-ups exactly as for the illustrative problem and the mean was identical, 27.4, but the scores ranged from 21 to 35, a range of 15, as contrasted to 60 on the illustrative problem. While the mean scores suggest no difference between groups, the measure of variability reveals that these two groups would not be considered to be the same in their ability to perform push-ups. Furthermore, it would appear that a score of 25 in the group for the illustrative problem would be closer to the mean and have a better standing in relation to the group than the identical score in the second group. However, the range does not provide the necessary evidence for the latter interpretation, since it is actually only a measure of external variability that tells nothing about the way in which the scores between the extreme scores are distributed or what constitutes internal variability.

Hence, in addition to knowing the limits of the spread of scores, as disclosed by the range, it becomes necessary to know how the scores are distributed within that range and about the mean to get the complete picture as a basis for score interpretation. The standard deviation provides this information.

Generally, the standard deviation is best conceived as a special kind of average of the deviations (distances) of the individual scores from the mean. It is expressed in the original units of measurement, for example, push-ups, and thus is compatible with the mean. In instances when the scores constitute a normal distribution, as will be described later, the points that occur one standard deviation above and below the mean will include the middle 68.26 per cent (approximately two-thirds) of the cases. Like the mean, it is affected by extreme scores.

To calculate the standard deviation by what is termed "the short method," that is, using the guessed mean, the frequency table is utilized as developed for computation of the mean. The sample tabulation sheet has been completed (see Fig. 2–2), embodying the steps discussed previously along with the remaining steps to derive the standard deviation. To avoid confusion, the reader should ignore the formula computations on Fig. 2–2 other than that for s, since these are not to be regarded as part of the procedure for computing the standard deviation.

The only new step involved in arranging the frequency table, beyond what has been described previously, is to include the fd^2 column. This column is derived by multiplying each fd value by its corresponding d factor, and all signs will now be positive. The resulting values are then totaled. The formula for the standard deviation is:

$$s = \sqrt{\frac{\Sigma fd^2}{N} - \left(\frac{\Sigma fd}{N}\right)^2} \times \text{SI}$$

TEST TABULATION SHEET

SCORE INTERVAL	TALLIES	f	d	fd	fd^2	Cum f
60-64	/	1	7	7	49	
55-59		0	6	0	0	
50-54	//	2	5	10	50	
45-49	/	1	4	4	16	
40-44	////	4	3	12	36	
35-39	##/	6	2	12	24	
30-34	## ///	8	1	8	8	
25-29	## ## ## /	16	0	0	0	
20-24	## //	7	-1	-7	7	
15-19	## ///	8	-2	-16	32	
10-14	////	4	-3	-12	36	
5-9	//	2	-4	-8	32	
0-4	/	1	-5	-5	25	
TOTAL		$N=60$		+53 −48 $\Sigma+5$	$\Sigma315$	

Percentile score (P_x) = Lower limit of int. + $\left(\dfrac{C_s - C_b}{\text{Cases in int.}} \times SI\right)$

$(C_s$ = Percentage × No. of cases e.g., Median $[P_{50}] = 0.50 \times N)$

$P \underset{......}{=} \underset{......}{......} + \left(\underset{......}{......} \underset{......}{\underbrace{\dfrac{\quad}{\quad}}} \times \underset{......}{......}\right)$

$\underset{......}{=} \underset{......}{......} + \left(\underset{......}{......} \underset{......}{\underbrace{\dfrac{\quad}{\quad}}} \times \underset{......}{......}\right)$

$\underset{......}{=} \underset{......}{......} + \underset{......}{......}$

KEY

C_s = Cases sought
C_b = Cases below interval
SI Score interval width

$$\text{Mean} = GM + \left(\frac{\Sigma fd}{N} \times SI\right)$$

$$s = \sqrt{\frac{\Sigma fd^2}{N} - \left(\frac{\Sigma fd}{N}\right)^2} \times SI$$

$$= \underline{27} + \left(\frac{5}{60} \times \underline{5}\right)$$

$$= \sqrt{\frac{315}{60} - \left(\frac{5}{60}\right)^2} \times \underline{5}$$

$$= \underline{27} + \underline{0.4} = \underline{27.4}$$

$$= \sqrt{\underline{5.25} - \underline{0.0069}} \times \underline{....} = \sqrt{\underline{5.24}} \times \underline{5}$$

$$= \underline{2.28} \times \underline{5} = \underline{11.4}$$

Range <u>60</u> Q_3 <u>34</u>

$\overline{X}$ <u>27.4</u>   Md <u>27</u>

s <u>11.4</u> Q_1 <u>19.5</u>

Fig. 2–2. Test tabulation sheet for the illustrative problem.

Substituting the figures from the problem, as shown in Fig. 2–2, the standard deviation value is computed to be 11.4.

When dealing with a small number of scores, the standard deviation may be determined by taking the actual deviation of each score from the computed mean and applying the formula: $s = \sqrt{\Sigma d^2 / N}$.

With the standard deviation value and the mean the teacher possesses the essential statistics to analyze a test score distribution and the basis for derivation of a meaningful interpretative scale score. To illustrate, it is now possible to compare in a meaningful manner a raw score of 25 obtained both in the illustrative problem group (mean = 27.4, $s = 11.4$) and in the second group, for which a mean of 27.4 and s of 3.1 were given. For the former the score of 25 falls below the mean by 2.4 (27.4 − 25) divided by 11.4 or −0.22 standard deviation units. In the second group the same raw score deviates 2.4/3.1 or −0.77 standard deviations from the mean. Accordingly, a score of 25 in the illustrative problem group is closer to the mean than the same score in the second group, despite identical means, and reflects the better standing in relation to the group as well as the obvious dissimilarity between groups that is attributable to the difference in variability of the distribution as measured by the standard deviation.

This way of expressing scores in ratio form as described above, for comparison in terms of score units of deviation from the means divided by the standard deviation, constitutes conversion of raw scores to standard scores (z-scores). These z-scores indicate the distance of a score from the mean expressed as fractions of standard deviation units with (+) or (−) sign to give direction above or below the mean, respectively. The z-score transformation equates the means and variabilities of different distributions. And it may be that the term *standard score* originally came from the fact that any distribution of scores can thus be "standardized," so that as a distribution of z-scores it has a mean of 0 and a standard deviation of 1. Further clarification of standard deviation as a statistical concept and of standard scores will be gained through the section on normal frequency distribution and through examination of the normal curve table (Table 2–6), where the standard deviation distance from the mean accounts for a precise percentage of cases in the distribution.

It should now be apparent that the importance of the standard deviation for the teacher resides not only in its use to describe the dispersion of scores relative to the mean, but also in that it serves as the basis for standard scores and transformation to a practical normative score, which is of immense value as a tool for the teacher.

DERIVING A NORMATIVE SCORE—T-SCORE

Upon computation of the mean and standard deviation for a set of scores the teacher can readily calculate a normative score, specifically the T-score, to interpret test results and to facilitate combining test scores to get a composite score or for grading purposes. Of the different normative scores commonly used in educational measurement the T-score is most ideally suited to physical education measurement. There are many reasons for this, as will become evident in the ensuing discussion, ranging from ease of calculation to definitiveness and inclusiveness of the scale. The T-score is derived from the standard score (z-score) and represents a linear (straight line) transformation of the raw scores. Such a transformation preserves the original ranking of scores and retains the shape of the distribution. To avoid confusion the T-score should be differentiated from the concept of the T-scale originated by McCall which represents an area transformation and which normalizes the distribution, thus entailing a more involved computational procedure, as will be described briefly in the discussion of other normative scores.[2]

In essence the T-score constitutes an adaptation of the standard score that renders it more feasible for teacher use.[3] Calculation of the standard score is represented by the formula: $z = (X - \overline{X})/s$, where X is the raw score, and $\overline{X}$ is the mean.

By substituting in this formula for a score of 16 push-ups in the problem, $z = (16 - 27.4)/11.4 = -11.4/11.4 = -1.0$. Coincidentally, the z-score for 16 push-ups is indicative of exactly one standard deviation below the mean. As was the case for z-score of -0.22 derived for 25 push-ups in the problem, most z-scores will be reported as decimals to the nearest hundredth which, together with the fact that half of the standard scores are negative, renders this score form somewhat inconvenient for the teacher to work with. The T-score eliminates these undesirable features but retains the principle of expressing individual scores in terms of standard deviation units from the mean. With T-scores, the mean is arbitrarily assigned a T-score of 50 and one standard deviation is accorded 10 scale points. That is, the T-score is a transformed standard score with mean of 50 and standard deviation of 10, in contrast to the standard score with mean of 0 and standard deviation of 1. A score occurring one standard deviation below the mean ($z = -1.0$) for the T-scores, such as 16 push-ups in the problem, becomes a T-score of

[2] "T-score" may be considered as an acronym for *transformed score* to differentiate this score from the normalized or McCall's T-scale. P. R. Lohnes and W. W. Cooley, *Introduction to Statistical Procedures: with Computer Exercises* (New York: John Wiley & Sons, 1968), p. 44.

[3] Some authors designate this adaptation as Z-*score*, rather than *T-score*, to indicate its derivation and to reserve the designation, *T-score*, for normalized (McCall) scales.

40, that is, 10 points below the mean of 50. A score occurring two standard deviations above the mean ($z = +2.0$) is assigned a T-score of 70. In practice T-scores usually range from about 15–20 to 80–85 for large groups and have a narrower range for small groups. T-scores can accommodate extreme scores outside the conventional range, a feature that other scale scores do not possess and is of especial importance in physical education, since extreme scores tend to be less uncommon in physical performance.

To determine T-scores, a specially prepared form is helpful, such as Fig. 2–3, on which partial computations are recorded for the push-up problem. Using Fig. 2–3 as a guide, the steps to convert raw scores to T-scores can be enumerated as:

1. *Enter the mean of the raw scores opposite T-score 50.*

2. *Add one standard deviation to the raw score mean to get T-score 60; add one standard deviation to the raw score for T-score 60 to obtain T-score 70; and derive T-score 80 similarly.*

3. *Subtract one standard deviation from the raw score mean to get T-score 40; subtract one standard deviation from the raw score for T-score 40 to obtain T-score 30; and derive T-score 20 similarly.* For the problem it will be noted that T-score 20 cannot be completed for this distribution, since it would be a negative raw score.

4. *Begin at T-score 20* (or lowest multiple of 10 for which a raw score is recorded, that is, 30 in Fig. 2–3) *and add one-tenth of a standard deviation (0.1s), carried to the nearest hundredth, to the raw score for T-score 20 to get T-score 21; add 0.1s to this latter raw score to get T-score 22; and so on.* For the problem, 0.1s or 1.14 is added to 4.6, the raw score for T-score 30, giving a raw score of 5.74, which is entered for T-score 31. T-score 32 is determined by adding 1.14 to 5.74, making its raw score 6.88.

5. *Complete the T-scores in this manner to accommodate the highest raw score, which will generally be about T-score 80, and then subtract 0.1s from the raw score for T-score 20* (or lowest multiple of 10 for which a raw score is recorded, that is, 30 in Fig. 2–3) *to get the raw score for T-score 19, and repeat this procedure until the lowest raw score is included in the T-scores.* For the problem, T-score 79 is assigned to the highest push-up score, 60, and T-score 27 is derived for the lowest raw score, 1.

As step 4 is carried out, the accuracy of the cumulative raw score total can be checked at the intervals of 10 (30, 40, etc.). The totals obtained by the addition of 0.1s should agree with the figures recorded in steps 2 and 3. In the event a slight discrepancy occurs without any

T-SCORE COMPUTATION TABLE

				SCORES					
T	Raw	T	Raw	T	Raw	T	Raw	T	Raw
100		80	61.60	60	38.80	40	16.00	20	
		79	60.46	59		39	14.86	19	
		78	59.32	58		38	13.72	18	
		77	58.18	57		37	12.58	17	
		76	57.04	56		36	11.44	16	
95		75	55.90	55		35	10.3	15	
		74	54.76	54		34	9.16		
		73	53.62	53		33	8.02		
		72	52.48	52		32	6.88		
		71	51.34	51		31	5.74		
90		70	50.20	50	27.40	30	4.60	10	
		69		49	26.26	29	3.46		
		68		48	25.12	28	2.32		
		67		47	23.98	27	1.18		
		66		46	22.84	26			
85		65		45	21.70	25		5	
84		64		44	20.56	24			
83		63		43	19.42	23			
82		62		42	18.28	22			
81		61		41	17.14	21		1	

Fig. 2–3. Table for T-score computation.

apparent error in addition, the process of addition for the next 10 T-scores should begin with the figure recorded in step 2 or step 3, as appropriate. It is possible that rounding errors might cause a slight discrepancy, although the addition of fractional standard deviation expressed to the nearest hundredth makes this rather unlikely.

Utilizing this procedure the teacher can readily and accurately convert raw scores to T-scores. While the teacher will use this derivation scheme largely for analysis and interpretation of test results, the resultant T-scores constitute a normative score, when appropriate conditions obtain, for teacher-made tests and for comparison of the performance of the same or different individuals on the same measure. Using this method of constructing T-scores the teacher can develop the norms for any test, given the mean and standard deviation. The section on other common normative scores explains the relatively simple conversion of T-scores to other scales for comparative purposes when results for other tests are not given as T-scores.

In the event only a few selected raw scores are to be transformed to T-scores, the calculation can be easily made from the formula: $T = 50 + 10 (X - \overline{X})/s$. If standard scores are available, the formula becomes: $T = 50 + 10z$. From the standard score of -0.22 previously reported for a score of 25 push-ups in the sample problem, the T-score transformation would result in a T-score of $50 + 10(-0.22) = 47.8$, or 48. The T-score obtained through this transformation can be checked with that derived by the T-score computation table in Fig. 2–3.

It should be noted that the derivation of T-scores, as described in detail, results in whole T-score units but fractional raw scores. This represents but a small inconvenience in light of the computational time saved, and the teacher need merely interpolate to obtain the proper T-score for the raw score in question. To illustrate, in Fig. 2–3, 60 push-ups would be a T-score of 79, since 60 lies closer to 60.46 than to 59.32, which are the raw score equivalents for T-scores of 79 and 78, respectively.

An alternative method of constructing T-scores by graphic means warrants mention for teacher consideration, inasmuch as it is a time-saver and yet reasonably accurate. In this alternative procedure a straight line is plotted on a graph, from which the corresponding T-score can be read for each raw score. To set up the graph the T-scores are placed along the abscissa (horizontal axis) of the graph, and the raw scores are entered on the ordinate (vertical axis). The appropriate entries for the illustrative problem are shown on both axes in Fig. 2–4. The reference line is ploted on the graph by placing a dot at the juncture of a vertical line through T-score 50 and the horizontal line through the mean score, 27.4 push-ups in this case. Two additional points should be used to plot the reference line. A second point is necessary to establish the line, and the third is included as a check on the accuracy of the plot. T-scores of 30 and 70 serve as good reference points since they are equidistant from the mean, they fall toward opposite ends of the scale, and they are readily determined from the two basic statistics by subtracting and adding two standard deviations from the mean, respectively. For the problem mean of 27.4 and standard deviation of 11.4, the T-scores of 30 and 70 have raw score values of 4.6 and 50.2. Plotting these values vertically above the respective T-score gives a total of three

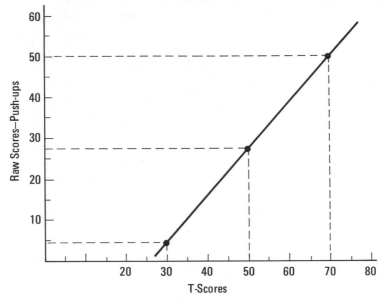

Fig. 2–4. T-score plotting graph for the illustartive problem.

reference points through which the line is drawn sufficiently beyond the end points to accommodate the extreme raw scores. All three points will fall on the line, unless an error is involved.

Once this graph is established, the T-score for a given raw score can be readily found by tracing a horizontal line through the raw score on the ordinate axis to the reference line. The value vertically beneath the intercept point on the reference line is the desired T-score.

An indication of the accuracy of this alternative method can be gained by comparing results obtained in Fig. 2–4 with calculated values in Fig. 2–3. The reader is invited to determine the T-score in Fig. 2–4 for 25 push-ups. It should be realized that proper scale size engenders accuracy in this graphic method; that is, a small scale will necessitate greater approximation and a larger scale will bring more accurate results.

INTERPRETING AND COMBINING T-SCORES

It has been demonstrated that the teacher can relatively simply turn raw scores into the preferred normative scale, as T-scores, after computing the two basic statistics—mean and standard deviation. Once the T-scores have been derived for a set of raw scores, the teacher's interest is directed toward interpreting test performance as expressed by T-scores and combining scores to gain a composite picture of skill and knowledge.

As the basis for interpretation, T-score 50 represents the mean raw score for the group involved, and each T-score unit above and below the mean accounts for one-tenth of a standard deviation in raw score units. Consequently, each original score is expressed in a form that facilitates meaningful comparison with other scores in the same or comparable distributions and combination with scores in like form for other measures. The further a score deviates from the mean, the worse or better the performance relative to the mean for the group, depending upon the direction of deviation. Exceptional scores are those approaching or beyond T-scores 80 and 20 on the high and low ends of the scale, respectively. Fuller understanding of the T-score to facilitate its interpretation will be engendered through the description of the normal frequency distribution, including indication of the percentage of cases in a normal distribution that are found at various points on the T-scale.

The T-score is analogous to a thermometer in the sense that it has no precise limits, top or bottom. This infers that no student possesses maximum skill or knowledge, no student has none whatsoever, and there is no arbitrary limit of what can be achieved. This, of course, is in complete contrast to the earlier, conventional practice in education of grading on a scale of 100 with a passing mark at some arbitrary value, such as 60. This latter convention implies an absolute standard of skill or knowledge and a ceiling upon it. As absurd as this implication is today, reluctance to depart from this inappropriate scoring scale continues.

The prime advantages of the T-score reside in the ease and meaningfulness of interpretation when scores are compared from different tests and in the "combinability" of scores for an individual on different tests. Two conditions should be met in order for the T-score (or any normative scale) to be applicable. First, when scores or relative position in one group are compared to those of another group, the groups must be the same or very similar for the two tests. Second, it should be recognized that comparisons must be made in terms of where the student stands in the group, his "relative position," rather than on the basis of some absolute standard. If one of the students who performed 25 push-ups in the example problem achieved 33 on the sit-up test ($\overline{X} = 45$, $s = 8$), as part of the same group, there is really no way of ascertaining on which test he did better. But it can be calculated that for the sit-ups his T-score is: $T = 50 + 10([33 - 45]/8) = 35$. Comparison of this with the previously determined T-score of 48 for 25 push-ups reveals that, in terms of this individual's relative position in the same group, he performed considerably better on push-ups than on sit-ups.

The T-score affords the teacher the answer to resolving the need for a means of combining scores in a most equitable manner. It is sometimes useful to combine the scores from several tests into a total performance score, for example, a total score on a fitness battery. Also, for grading it generally becomes necessary for the teacher to combine a number of scores. Unknowingly some teachers attempt to add different scores together that are as incompatible as oil and water. To illustrate, raw scores on push-ups and sit-ups should not be added, nor should raw scores on the standing long jump in inches and the 50-yard dash in seconds. In the latter instance the measuring units are entirely different. For push-ups and sit-ups, although the measure is in number of repetitions, the actual size of the numbers are not compatible. The disparity in size of numbers is shown by data on sit-ups ($\bar{X} = 45$, score range = 25–65, $s = 8$) for the group on which push-up data ($\bar{X} = 27.4$, score range = 1–60, $s = 11.4$) was obtained in the illustrative problem.

While the two discrepancies—size of numbers and different measuring units—are readily apparent and afford ample justification for utilization of T-scores to facilitate equitable combination of scores, the inequities caused by the disparity between standard deviations of the scores being combined also warrants recognition. When raw scores are used, such as the number of repetitions on push-ups and sit-ups or scores on knowledge tests, the test with the largest standard deviation is accorded the greatest weighting in the combining process as well as in comparing the relative position of an individual on two tests in the same group. Using the data cited above, an individual's score on push-ups ($s = 11.4$) will contribute more to the relative position of that student on the total score than will the score on sit-ups ($s = 8$). This weighting effect attributable to differences in standard deviations can cause grave injustices, particularly in instances when different weightings are assigned to component parts of a composite score. For example, in determining a grade for associated learning—knowledge and understanding—the teacher may choose to weight each unit test as one and the final test as two. Conceivably, the standard deviations might vary so that the unit tests are not weighted the same and the intended weighting of two for the final test cannot be assured. It is entirely possible that the final test might carry less actual weighting than one or more of the unit tests.

These possible discrepancies are of no concern when T-scores are used. Since the T-score is a transformation of the standard score, raw scores expressed as T-scores are comparable and combinable. A given T-score, for example, 40, means the same thing on test of push-ups, sit-ups, standing long jump, and 50-yard dash; namely, a point one standard deviation below the mean irrespective of the size of the standard deviation. Hence, the T-scores for a student on these different tests can be totaled and divided by four (the number of tests involved, to compute the mean T-score, or can be left as a composite total, as deemed appropriate. As a specific illustration of combining scores, the previously derived T-scores of 48 and 33 for 25 push-ups and 33 sit-ups, respectively, when added and divided by 2 give a mean T-score of 40.5. This combined score represents performance somewhat below average. Such combined T-scores become meaningful in the context of the group of which they are a part or to which they are comparable and, as mentioned earlier, in light of the characteristics of the normal frequency distribution.

THE NORMAL FREQUENCY DISTRIBUTION

Although the normal frequency distribution is actually a mathematical abstraction, it may best be thought of as a picture of the way in which measurements that happen purely by chance will occur. As might be expected, these measures tend to pile up around some central value and taper off toward extreme values, giving the picture of a bell-shaped curve.

For example, assume that a large member of students are given a standard IBM answer sheet designed for 300 true–false items. Each student is then asked to make his response to each item by flipping a coin and marking *true* if a head appears and *false* if a tail comes up. Each student's score would then be the number of *true* responses made. If scores obtained in this manner were plotted as a frequency distribution, they would fall into a shape closely approximating the normal distribution (see Fig. 2–5). For this particular situation, the mean score would be about 150, and very few scores would fall below 124 or above 176. Approximately two-thirds of the scores would fall between 141 and 159, and 95 per cent of them between 133 and 167. The actual derivation of these numbers will be shown later.

A variety of physical measurements, such as height and weight, have been shown to be normally distributed for large, unselected groups, for example, all sixth-grade boys. This result appears reasonable, considering that these physical characteristics are determined by chance hereditary and environmental factors. For the same reasons, we tend to *assume* that many other characteristics (for example, skills, knowledge, and intelligence) are normally distributed. However, this cannot be demonstrated, since the same kind of measuring instruments are not available for these characteristics. No doubt exists that a person who is 6 feet tall is twice as tall as a child 3 feet tall. Nevertheless, it seems unreasonable to conclude that a boy who can do 20 push-ups is twice as strong as a boy who can do only 10, inasmuch as the second boy may equal or exceed the first on some other measure of strength. In other words, no assurance exists that the "inches" of the measuring instruments are the same size all along the scale in which they occur.

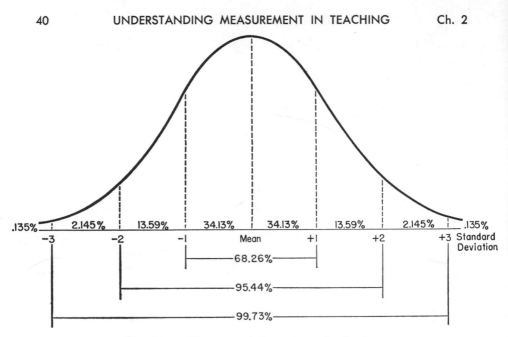

Fig. 2–5. The normal frequency distribution.

Tests are often deliberately constructed so that the results will follow the normal distribution—based on the assumption that if the tests possess units or "inches" that are equal along the scale, the distribution of scores will be normal. That is, the fact that many tests of skills, aptitudes, and knowledge produce normal distributions of scores for large groups cannot be taken as proof that these characteristics are truly normally distributed, since the tests are arbitrarily constructed to produce such results. On the other hand, if the *assumption* of normal distribution seems reasonable, as it often does (and indeed generally is in properly applied measurement in physical education), and the test produces a normal distribution of scores, confidence may be expressed that the units of measurement ("inches") are approximately equal over an entire scale.

Since the normal curve is based on a mathematical formula, a table can be established to give the area between any two points on the base line. It should be realized that the concept "normal distribution" refers only to the *shape* of the distribution, and sets of scores with any mean and standard deviation can be normal. Therefore, the normal distribution is not really one specific distribution but a whole family of distributions having the same basic shape but different means and standard deviations. In order to avoid the necessity of having a great number of tables of areas, that is, one for each specific combination of mean and standard deviation, these are all related to one curve called the "unit normal distribution." The scores from any normal distribution may be easily related to this basic distribution by expressing them as standard scores, since the base line of the unit normal curve is measured in terms of standard scores.

The area between the mean of this distribution and any specific standard score can be found in Table 2–3. For example, between the mean and a standard score of +1.50, there is 43.32 per cent of the total area under the curve. Another way of saying this is that 43.32 per cent of the area under the normal curve lies between the mean and a point one and one-half standard deviations away. To find the area between two points whose corresponding standard scores are −1.5 and +1.5, the 43.32 per cent is doubled, giving 86.64 per cent, because an equal portion of the area occurs on each side of the mean. Subtracting this 86.64 per cent from 100 per cent gives 13.36 per cent, which is the area under the curve that lies in the "tails" of the distribution beyond −1.5 and +1.5.

Another relevant question is what part of the area lies to the left of the point +1.5. Since the normal curve is symmetrical about the mean, exactly half or 50 per cent of the area is to the left of the mean; and this must be added to the 43.32 per cent from the mean up to +1.5, giving 93.32 per cent. To determine the area to the left of a point 1.5 standard deviations below the mean, the area between the mean and −1.5 (43.32 per cent) is taken from the total area to the left of the mean (50 per cent). This subtraction (50 − 43.32 per cent) gives 6.68 per cent as the total area falling to the left of the standard score −1.5. In order to decide whether to add or subtract in problems of this type, the teacher will find drawing a rough diagram helpful until he is able to visualize these in his mind.

Problems of the type outlined above may seem like pointless exercises until the area is given some meaning. There are two useful interpretations of these areas, that is, applications of the normal distribution. First, the area between any two points is directly related to the number of scores (individuals) that fall between those two points. For example, in a set of 200 scores that are normally distributed, 43.32 per cent or 87 cases would be expected to fall between the mean and a standard score of +1.5. Similarly, 173 cases (86.64 per cent of 200) would be expected to fall between standard scores of −1.5 and +1.5.

Referring to the situation previously described in which students responded to a true–false test by flipping coins, it can be shown that the mean and standard deviations expected would be 150 and 8.7, respectively. Table 2–3 discloses that a very small proportion of the scores in a normal curve fall more than three standard deviations from the mean. For the distribution in question, the points three standard deviations from 150 are approximately 124 and 176. Very few, actually less than 3

Table 2–3. Percentage Parts of the Total Area under the Normal Probability Curve Corresponding to Distances on the Base Line Between the Mean and Successive Points fom the Mean in Standard Score Units

Example: Between the mean and a point 1.57 sigma is found 44.18 per cent of the entire area under the curve.

Units	.00	.01	.02	.03	.04	.05	.06	.07	.08	.09
0.0	00.00	00.40	00.80	01.20	01.60	01.99	02.39	02.79	03.19	03.59
0.1	03.98	04.38	04.78	05.17	05.57	05.96	06.36	06.75	07.14	07.53
0.2	07.93	08.32	08.71	09.10	09.48	09.87	10.26	10.64	11.03	11.41
0.3	11.79	12.17	12.55	12.93	13.31	13.68	14.06	14.43	14.80	15.17
0.4	15.54	15.91	16.28	16.64	17.00	17.36	17.72	18.08	18.44	18.79
0.5	19.15	19.50	19.85	20.19	20.54	20.88	21.23	21.57	21.90	22.24
0.6	22.57	22.91	23.24	23.57	23.89	24.22	24.54	24.86	25.17	25.49
0.7	25.80	26.11	26.42	26.73	27.04	27.34	27.64	27.94	28.23	28.52
0.8	28.81	29.10	29.39	29.67	29.95	30.23	30.51	30.78	31.06	31.33
0.9	31.59	31.86	32.12	32.38	32.64	32.90	33.15	33.40	33.65	33.89
1.0	34.13	34.38	34.61	34.85	35.08	35.31	35.54	35.77	35.99	36.21
1.1	36.43	36.65	36.86	37.08	37.29	37.49	37.70	37.90	38.10	38.30
1.2	38.49	38.69	38.88	39.07	39.25	39.44	39.62	39.80	39.97	40.15
1.3	40.32	40.49	40.66	40.82	40.99	41.15	41.31	41.47	41.62	41.77
1.4	41.92	42.07	42.22	42.36	42.51	42.65	42.79	42.92	43.06	43.19
1.5	43.32	43.45	43.57	43.70	43.83	43.94	44.06	44.18	44.29	44.41
1.6	44.52	44.63	44.74	44.84	44.95	45.05	45.15	45.25	45.35	45.45
1.7	45.54	45.64	45.73	45.82	45.91	45.99	46.08	46.16	46.25	46.33
1.8	46.41	46.49	46.56	46.64	46.71	46.78	46.86	46.93	46.99	47.06
1.9	47.13	47.19	47.26	47.32	47.38	47.44	47.50	47.56	47.61	47.67
2.0	47.72	47.78	47.83	47.88	47.93	47.98	48.03	48.08	48.12	48.17
2.1	48.21	48.26	48.30	48.34	48.38	48.42	48.46	48.50	48.54	48.57
2.2	48.61	48.64	48.68	48.71	48.75	48.78	48.81	48.84	48.87	48.90
2.3	48.93	48.96	48.98	49.01	49.04	49.06	49.09	49.11	49.13	49.16
2.4	49.18	49.20	49.22	49.25	49.27	49.29	49.31	49.32	49.34	49.36
2.5	49.38	49.40	49.41	49.43	49.45	49.46	49.48	49.49	49.51	49.52
2.6	49.53	49.55	49.56	49.57	49.59	49.60	49.61	49.62	49.63	49.64
2.7	49.65	49.66	49.67	49.68	49.69	49.70	49.71	49.72	49.73	49.74
2.8	49.74	49.75	49.76	49.77	49.77	49.78	49.79	49.79	49.80	49.81
2.9	49.81	49.82	49.82	49.83	49.84	49.84	49.85	49.85	49.86	49.86
3.0	49.865									
3.1	49.903									
3.2	49.93129									
3.3	49.95166									
3.4	49.96631									
3.5	49.97674									
3.6	49.98409									
3.7	49.98922									
3.8	49.99277									
3.9	49.99519									

Adapted from Karl Pearson, *Tables for Statisticians and Biometricians* (Cambridge: Cambridge University Press, 1924).

in 1,000, of the scores will fall beyond these limits. Likewise, the table reveals that approximately two-thirds of the cases will fall within a range of one standard deviation either side of the mean. Since the scores 141 and 159 approximate that position, it is expected that two-thirds of the cases will fall between these two scores. The justification of the other pair of scores (133 and 167) is left to the reader.

Based on the same relationship between proportion of area and proportion of cases, the relationship can be determined between standard scores and percentiles, which will be described later in discussing other normative scales. It was demonstrated above that 93.32 per cent of the area of the normal distribution lies to the left of a standard score of +1.5. Since this percentage is equal to the percentage of the cases that would fall to the left of (below) that point, and since the percentile is defined as that score below which a specified percentage of the cases fall, it follows that in a normal distribution a standard score of +1.5 is at the 93rd percentile. The raw score that has a standard score of −1.5 will fall at the 6th percentile (actually 6.68 rounded down).

The second application of the normal distribution deals with the likelihood that a single score, selected by chance, will fall within certain limits. Since 86.64 per cent of the cases will fall between standard scores of +1.5 and −1.5, there is an 87-out-of-100 chance that a score picked at random from the set of scores will be somewhere within that range. Similarly, there is about a $\frac{7}{100}$ chance that the score selected will be above +1.5. This notion of likelihood or probability based on the normal distribution is very important in many of the statistical techniques used in physical education research. Many other such tools are based on distributions other than the normal curve but still utilize the same concepts regarding likelihood and area under the curve.

HOW TO TELL IF TEST RESULTS APPROXIMATE A NORMAL CURVE

In analyzing test results the teacher may be interested in determining whether a normal distribution is approximated. The process actually involves two steps. Inasmuch as the normal curve is symmetrical, the first step is a relatively simple procedure to confirm the symmetry of the score distribution.

This can be accomplished in one of several ways, perhaps the most revealing of which is simply to examine the frequency distribution, preferably by plotting it. When the scores are tallied as in Table 2–1, the shape of the distribution can be estimated. However, when the scores are tallied on a tabulation sheet as in Fig. 2–2, which is generally more practical in the long run, it becomes necessary to represent the distribution graphically in order to analyze its shape. A frequency polygon has been constructed in Fig. 2–6 from the push-up data in Table 2–1. The number of scores are placed along the ordinate, and the mid-points of the score intervals are recorded along the abscissa. A critical look at Fig. 2–6 discloses some semblance of symmetry, although slightly more cases appear to the low side of the mean than to the right. This observed disparity might be attributable to the manner in which the scores were grouped, so that it would appear justifiable to proceed with the second step for these data.

However, before describing the next step, mention should be made of two alternative ways of revealing symmetry. For a distribution in which

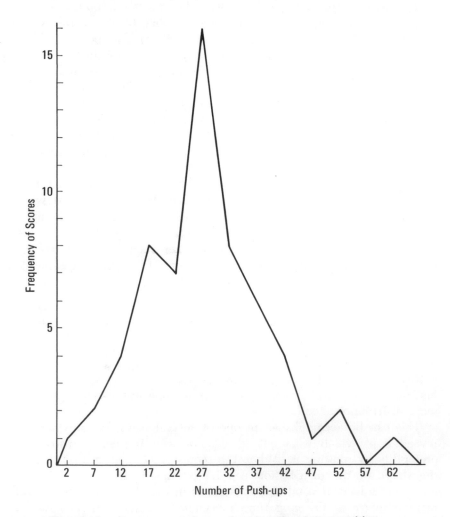

Fig. 2–6. Frequency polygon for the illustrative problem.

the mean, median and mode are determined, these points will be identical in a symmetrical distribution, although symmetry is not necessarily assured when they coincide. The mode is the midpoint of the interval with the most scores in a frequency distribution (27 in the problem) or the score appearing most often in ungrouped data. The median is the midpoint of a distribution, above and below which lie 50 per cent of the scores, and is calculated as 27 for the push-up problem in the section describing other normative scores. For the problem these three points are identical, if the mean is rounded to the nearest whole number. The other alternative indicant of symmetry involves the quartile deviation and will be described as part of the discussion of other normative scores.

Once symmetry of scores in a distribution, or a reasonable semblance of it, can be confirmed, then the second step in ascertaining whether a score distribution approximates a normal curve can be executed. This step entails determining the number of cases, through use of Table 2–3, that fall within one and two standard deviations from the mean in a normal curve, which are 34.13 and 47.72 per cent, respectively. For $N = 60$, in the problem approximately 20 (60×0.3413) cases will fall between the mean and plus-one standard deviation, if the curve approximates a normal distribution. For the problem, 17 scores fall within one standard deviation above the mean (38.8 push-ups) or T-score 60, and 25 scores occur within one standard deviation below the mean (16 push-ups) or T-score 40. The reader can refer ahead to Table 2–7, where these scores are arranged in rank order, to follow the actual determination of the number of scores falling within the stipulated limits. As a further check, approximately 20 (60×0.4772) cases will fall within two standard deviations on either side of the mean, if normal distribution prevails. Actually only 23 cases are contained within two standard deviations above the mean and 34 fall within the same distance below the mean on the push-ups. Thus, the push-up scores do not approximate a normal distribution even though the first two of the methods described in step one alluded to possible symmetry. The final step disproved both symmetry and normal distribution.

Step two divulged asymmetry in the illustrative problem, in which 17 and 25 scores, respectively, fell in the above and below the mean one-standard-deviation groups. It should be noted that both groups might have been equal (for example, either both 17 or 25), hence symmetrical, and still not have reflected the normal distribution for which 20 (60×0.3413) would be needed. The same relationship might obtain at a distance of two standard deviations from the mean; symmetry might exist but not the proportional characteristics of a normal distribution.

This procedure in step two for ascertaining whether a normal distribution is approximated affords the teacher a relatively simple check. The teacher can obtain a clearer picture by plotting the points of the normal curve on the frequency polygon (Fig. 2–6). Also, the addition of ½-standard-deviation units will afford more definitude to the analysis, if desired. It should be explained that this procedure is described because of its practicality for teacher use and is not proposed as a substitute for more refined statistical analysis as presented in statistical texts.

In instances when the distribution is noticeably asymmetrical careful analysis can prove meaningful to the teacher. When the scores tend to pile up toward the low end and the curve is skewed, so that scores are more extreme at the positive end, the distribution is termed *positively skewed*. In a positively skewed distribution, as illustrated in Fig. 2–7,

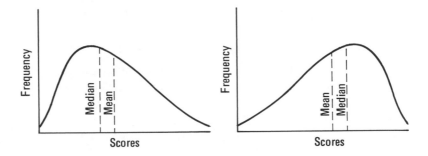

Fig. 2–7. *(Left)* Positively, and *(right)* negatively skewed distributions.

the median (the point below which 50 per cent of scores fall) is to the left or low side of the mean. A positive skew commonly occurs with physical measurements and with scores reflecting physical performance, and for knowledge tests it indicates that the test is too difficult for the group. The reader will note that the distribution for the push-up problem tended toward a positive skew. A negatively skewed distribution occurs when the score are concentrated toward the high end and the extreme scores form a tail extending in the negative direction (see Fig. 2–7). Negative skewness is characteristic of a test that is too easy for the group.

OTHER COMMON NORMATIVE SCORES

Although the need for a normative scale for the teacher of physical education is best met by the T-score, familiarity with two other normative scales should help the teacher to be able to understand the more common scales likely to be encountered and their relationship to the

T-score. As an end result, a fuller appreciation of the appropriateness of the T-score for physical education measurement will be fostered.

The two normative scales that warrant description are the percentile scale and the C-scale. Percentiles describe a distribution in terms of the percentage of cases occurring below a given point (percentile rank). C-scores are derived from the mean and standard deviation and consist of eleven bands that are 0.5 standard deviation in width with the middle band centered on the mean.

Percentiles

Succintly stated, the percentile [4] scale divides a distribution of scores into 100 parts, with each point on the scale, or percentile rank, being assigned the numerical value indicative of the percentage of cases falling below the point in question in the distribution. Percentiles constitute definite points in a score distribution that indicate the location of an individual's score in relation to others who performed the test. Thus, for example, the point below which 50 per cent of the scores occur in a distribution is the 50th percentile, commonly referred to as the median [5] and providing the measure of central tendency for the percentile scale. The raw score that falls at the 50th percentile (or any other percentile in question) is assigned the percentile rank of 50 (or the appropriate rank for other percentiles). The percentile scale is further divided into four equal parts by quartiles, and into 10 parts by deciles. The 1st or lower quartile, Q_1, is the 25 percentile, meaning that 25 per cent or one-quarter of the scores occur below it. Likewise, the 3rd or upper quartile, Q_3, is the 75th percentile, below which are 75 per cent of the scores. The 2nd quartile, Q_2 is the 50th percentile, also called the median (Md), and as such represents the midpoint in a distribution. Similarly, the 1st decile is the 10th percentile, below which occur 10 per cent of the scores; the 2nd, 3rd and 4th deciles are the 20th, 30th and 40th percentiles, respectively, and so on up to the 9th decile.

To calculate percentiles for grouped scores, the frequency distribution is established as in Table 2–1. The only information needed in addition to the columns for score intervals and frequency is a cumulative frequency column, which facilitates locating the interval that contains a desired score. This column is computed by adding the cases in the f column consecutively from the bottom up as they appear in the frequency distribution. The completed cumulative f column for the illustrative problem is shown in Table 2–4.

---

[4] Some authorities in educational measurement advocate use of "centile" instead of percentile to avoid confusion of the percentile concept with a percentage grading scheme.

[5] Basic clarification of the median as a concept is contained in the next section.

Table 2–4. Computing Percentiles and Quartiles for the Illustrative Problem

Score Interval	f	cum f		Percentiles	
60–64	1	60	P_{90}	$.90(60) = 54$	$39.5 + \left(\dfrac{2}{4} \times 5\right) = 42$
55–59	0	59			
50–54	2	59	P_{80}	$.80(60) = 48$	$34.5 + \left(\dfrac{2}{6} \times 5\right) = 36$
45–49	1	57			
40–44	4	56			
35–39	6	52	P_{70}	$.70(60) = 42$	$29.5 + \left(\dfrac{4}{8} \times 5\right) = 32$
30–34	8	46			
25–29	16	38	P_{60}	$.60(60) = 36$	$24.5 + \left(\dfrac{14}{16} \times 5\right) = 29$
20–24	7	22			
15–19	8	15			
10–14	4	7	$P_{50}(Md)$	$.50(60) = 30$	$24.5 + \left(\dfrac{8}{16} \times 5\right) = 27$
5– 9	2	3			
0– 4	1	1	P_{40}	$.40(60) = 24$	$24.5 + \left(\dfrac{2}{16} \times 5\right) = 25$
$N = 60$					
			P_{30}	$.30(60) = 18$	$19.5 + \left(\dfrac{3}{7} \times 5\right) = 22$
			P_{20}	$.20(60) = 12$	$14.5 + \left(\dfrac{5}{8} \times 5\right) = 18$
			P_{10}	$.10(60) = \ \ 6$	$9.5 + \left(\dfrac{3}{4} \times 5\right) = 13$

Quartiles

$Q_3(P_{75})$ $.75(60) = 45$

$= 29.5 + \left(\dfrac{7}{8} \times 5\right) = 34$

$Q_2(Md)$ $.50(60) = 30$

$= 24.5 + \left(\dfrac{8}{16} \times 5\right) = 27$

$Q_1(P_{25})$ $.25(60) = 15$

$= 14.5 + \left(\dfrac{8}{8} \times 5\right) = 19.5$

$C_s = \text{Percentage} \times N$

$P_s = \text{Low lim. of int.} + \left(\dfrac{C_s - C_b}{\text{Cases in int.}} \times \text{SI}\right)$

Using the median to explain the computation of percentiles, first it is necessary to find the number of cases sought (C_s) by the formula: $C_s = \text{percentage} \times N$. For the median (50th percentile) in the example problem, with $N = 60$, this becomes: $C_s = 0.50(60) = 30$. Looking at the data in Table 2–4, the score interval in which the 30th score falls is found by counting the scores from the bottom of the distribution. In the cumulative f column it will be noticed that 22 cases occur up to and including interval 20–24. Or stated differently, 22 cases extend to 24.5— the lower limit of interval 25–29. In order to obtain the other 8 cases to make 30, it becomes necessary to go into the interval 25–29, containing 16 cases, and interpolate to derive the median. At this point it should be noted that in dealing with percentiles the scores in each interval are regarded as being equally dispersed throughout the interval from the lower limit to the upper limit. They are not grouped at the midpoint of the interval as for the mean and standard deviation. The process of interpolation, as well as the figures needed, can be best explained by the formula:

$$\text{Percentile score } (P_x) = \text{Lower limit of int.} + \left(\frac{C_s - C_b}{\text{Cases in int.}} \times \text{SI} \right)$$

where

C_s = the number of cases sought
C_b = the number of cases below the interval containing C_s
SI = the score interval width

Substituting in the formula to compute the median:

$$Md(P_{50}) = 24.5 + \left(\frac{30 - 22}{16} \times 5 \right) = 24.5 + 2.5 = 27$$

To further illustrate this computational process, $Q_1(P_{25})$ can be determined. The cases sought for Q_1 are: $C_s = 0.25(60) = 15$. Referring to the cumulative f column in Table 2–4, it is noted that the 15th case occurs within the interval 15–19. Substitution in the formula gives: $Q_1 = 14.5 + \{([15 - 7]/8) \times 5\} = 19.5$. By coincidence in this instance, simple observation would indicate that since exactly 15 cases occur below the lower limit of the interval 20–24, this limit (19.5) becomes Q_1. Table 2–4 contains computations for the quartiles and for every 10th percentile from P_{10} to P_{90}, that is, deciles, for the illustrative problem.

Table 2–4 constitutes a *percentile table*, one type of norm chart. It can be rendered more definitive by computing additional percentiles as desired. Such a table provides a means of readily and meaningfully interpreting individual scores relative to the group. To illustrate, a student scoring 25 push-ups, is assigned a percentile rank of 40 in Table 2–4, meaning that 40 per cent of the group fell below his score while 60 per cent scored higher. Percentile norms have enjoyed considerable popularity largely due to their ease of interpretation. Notwithstanding, it behooves the teacher to recognize the basic limitations of percentile tables. Each percentile represents a point below which a certain percentage of individuals scored, regardless of the dispersion of scores. Consequently, the percentile table does not possess scale units of equal length, as does the T-score. This inequity in scale-unit length is exemplified by the percentile table for the illustrative problem (Table 2–4) wherein a difference of 2 push-ups occurs between P_{40} and P_{50} and also between P_{50} and P_{60}. However, to increase one's standing, 10 percentile points at either end of the scale requires a disproportionate increase in push-ups; 5 to change from P_{10} to P_{20}, and 4 to change from P_{70} to P_{80}. This discrepancy occurs inasmuch as neither the mean nor the variability of the distribution are taken into consideration, as is the case with T-scores and standard scores. Figure 2–8 shows this characteristic of percentiles as applied to the normal curve and compared to other normative scores. Therefore, data expressed in percentiles cannot be averaged or combined. As a further limitation, percentile values in one group are not directly comparable with those in another. Application of percentile tables should be made in light of these limitations.

As for T-score construction, an alternative method of constructing a percentile scale by graphic means can save teacher time yet still be quite accurate if carefully done. This is particularly important, since computation of percentiles is a tedious process. This alternative proce-

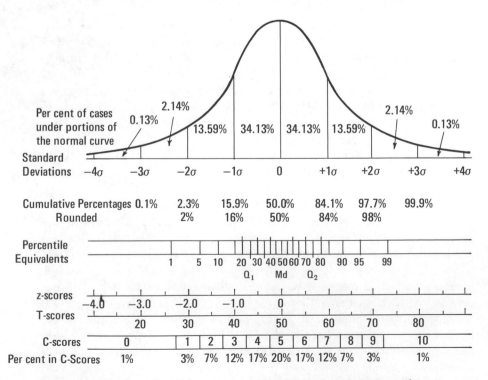

Fig. 2–8. The normal curve with selected normative scales.

dure consists of plotting the data from the first and third columns in Table 2–4 as a cumulative frequency polygon or ogive curve from which the corresponding raw score can be read for a particular percentile or from which the percentile rank can be obtained for a given raw score. To set up the frequency polygon the score intervals for the number of push-ups are arranged along the abscissa with each interval identified by its midpoint and the dividing lines between intervals representing the real limits. Consequently, the line to the left of each figure represents the lower limit of that score interval. Along the left-hand ordinate axis the scale for cumulative frequency of scores is recorded. The right-hand ordinate contains the cumulative percentage scale 0–100 corresponding to the cumulative frequency of scores directly opposite it. The appropriate entries for the illustrative problem are shown on the different axes in Fig. 2–9.

To plot the ogive curve, the cumulative frequency for each score interval is indicated by a dot directly above the upper limit of that interval or the lower limit of the next interval. For example, a dot is

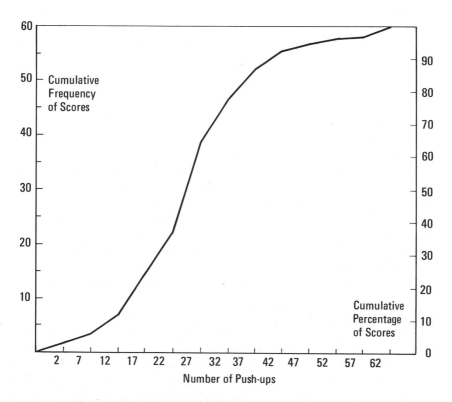

Fig. 2–9. Ogive curve for the illustrative problem.

placed over the line to the right of midpoint 2 for interval 0–4 for a frequency of 1, a dot to indicate a cumulative f for 3 is placed vertically above the upper limit line for midpoint 7, and so forth. The graph is completed by drawing a smoothed curve in such a fashion that an approximately equal number of points fall on either side of the curve. To locate the percentile rank for a particular score a line is traced vertically to the curve from that score and from the point of intercept horizontally to the right-hand margin where the corresponding percentile rank is read. To obtain the various percentiles the process is simply reversed so that, to illustrate, for Q_1 or P_{25} a line is traced horizontally from 25 in the right-hand margin to the curve and then vertically to the abscissa value, which is the division between intervals 15–19 and 20–24, or 19.5. To insure reasonable accuracy in this graph it should be plotted to a suitable scale on appropriately lined and sized paper.

Descriptive Statistics for Percentiles (Median and Quartile Deviation). Whereas the mean and standard deviation represent the two basic statistics for the T-score, the median and quartile deviation serve the same function for the percentile scale. The median constitutes the measure of central tendency for the distribution and the quartile deviation is the corresponding measure of variability.

While the computation of the median has been explained for grouped data, the concept warrants further clarification. The median represents the midpoint of a distribution, and with an odd number of cases it coincides with the middle score. Considering the chinning scores referred to in explaining the mean, 3, 4, 5, 8, and 10, the number 5 represents the exact middle and is the median. (The reader may recall that the mean is 6.) If an even number of scores, such as six, were involved, for example, 3, 4, 5, 8, 10 and 12, then the median would lie halfway between 5 and 8 at 6.5. With a frequency distribution the process is somewhat different and, consequently, the concept may not be as readily apparent. The teacher will find the median of value as a measure of central tendency which is devoid of the influence of extreme scores. Since it divides a distribution of scores into two parts equal in number of scores, when a few scores deviate grossly from the cluster of scores, the median more accurately represents the typical score.

The quartile deviation (Q) is used in conjunction with the median to indicate the variability or dispersion of scores about the midpoint of the distribution. And like the median, it is not influenced by extreme scores. By definition, Q is one-half of the score difference for the middle 50 per cent of the scores in a distribution. To fiind Q the distance between Q_1 and Q_3 (known as the *interquartile range*) is divided by 2: $Q = (Q_3 - Q_1)/2$. Substituting in the formula from the computations in Table 2–4, the value of Q for the problem becomes: $(34 - 19.5)/ 2 = 7.25$; Q expresses the variability of the group, and its interpretation, like that for other measures of variability, becomes a relative matter. Whether a Q of 7.25 is considered great or small depends upon the magnitude of comparable measures for other groups performing the same test.

The value Q affords an alternative indicant of symmetry as referred to in the earlier discussion of how to determine whether a distribution is normal. Only in symmetrical distributions, will the limits determined by the distance of Q taken to each side of the median coincide with Q_1 and Q_3, and, accordingly, actually include the middle 50 per cent of the scores. In a non-symmetrical distribution the clustering of the middle 50 per cent of the scores will be such that Q_1 and Q_3 will not be equally distant from the median. This suggests the feasibility of reporting Q_1 and Q_3, instead of Q, along with the median to present a clear picture for non-symmetrical distributions. The illustrative problem exemplifies this, wherein $Md \pm Q$ gives the limits of the middle 50 per cent as 19.75 and 34.25. However, examination of Q_1 and Q_3 discloses that the limits really are 19.5 and 34; whereby the 25 per cent below the median covers 7.5 score points (27–19.5), while the 25 per cent above the median covers 7 points (34–27). This examination serves to confirm the apparent asymmetry that was observed in the original discussion concerned with determining whether a curve approximates a normal distribution.

Conversion to Percentiles from T-Scores. In following the statistical analysis that is advocated in this book the teacher will not compute percentiles. Upon occasion the teacher may wish to compare results with those for other comparable groups or with norms of a particular test, such as the AAHPER Youth Fitness Test. If these other test results or norms are expressed in percentiles, the direct comparison cannot be made. In such instances when the teacher's results approximate a normal distribution, percentiles can be easily determined directly from the T-scores by use of the conversion chart in Table 2–5. This chart is derived from the area under the normal curve (Table 2–3) and can be readily checked by the comparison of T-scores and percentiles in Fig. 2–8. Because of the rounding factor in computing T-scores, some interpolation may be desirable in deriving the percentiles. This conversion from T-score to percentile rank can be expected to give a good approximation, assuming a distribution of raw scores that is approximately normal, when at least 100 students are involved and, for knowledge tests, at least 30 test items are included.[6] When the above

---

[6] Jum C. Nunnally, *Educational Measurement and Evaluation* (New York: McGraw-Hill Book Co., 1964), p. 49.

Table 2–5. Conversion Table of T-Scores into Percentile Ranks—Assuming a problem.* (Cases 26–57 omitted due to space limitation.)

T-Score	Percentile	T-Score	Percentile	T-Score	Percentile	T-Score	Percentile
80	99.9	64	91.9	49	46.0	34	5.5
79	99.8	63	90.3	48	42.1	33	4.5
78	99.7	62	88.5	47	38.2	32	3.6
77	99.6	61	86.4	46	34.5	31	2.9
76	99.5	60	84.1	45	30.8	30	2.3
75	99.4	59	81.6	44	27.4	29	1.8
74	99.2	58	78.8	43	24.2	28	1.4
73	98.9	57	75.8	42	21.2	27	1.1
72	98.6	56	72.6	41	18.4	26	0.8
71	98.2	55	69.2	40	15.9	25	0.6
70	97.7	54	65.5	39	13.6	24	0.5
69	97.1	53	61.8	38	11.5	23	0.4
68	96.4	52	57.9	37	9.7	22	0.3
67	95.5	51	54.0	36	8.1	21	0.2
66	94.5	50	50.0	35	6.7	20	0.1
65	93.3						

prerequisites do not pertain, and particularly if the distribution cannot be considered approximately normal, the percentiles must be computed directly from the data.

To illustrate the use of this conversion scheme for determining percentiles, data from the sample problem will be utilized, although it should be recognized that it is not truly applicable, inasmuch as the distribution was deemed not to be normal. The raw score of 16 push-ups was assigned a T-score of 40 (see Fig. 2–3). Reference to Table 2–5 shows the percentile equivalent of T-score 40 to be (15.9) in a normal distribution. Conversion of 25 push-ups, a T-score of 48, gives a percentile rank of 42.

Earlier in the discussion of derivation of the T-score it was mentioned that the procedure to establish a normalized T-scale would be briefly described in this section dealing with other normative scores. It appears appropriate to direct attention to this procedure at this point, since the conversion process just depicted is essentially reversed if one desires to set up a normalized T-scale. This means that the raw scores are first changed into percentile ranks. Then a T-score and percentile conversion chart, such as Table 2–5, is used to convert the percentile ranks into T-scores. This computation of raw scores into percentile ranks and thence into normal curve equivalent T-scores changes the shape of the original distribution to a normal curve, assuming that it was not normal originally. This can be illustrated by using the sample problem data which were previously shown not to approximate a normal curve. For example, a raw score of 25 is computed to be a percentile rank of 40 in Table 2–4, which is converted to a normalized T-score of 47 by interpolation in Table 2–5. For a raw score of 25 the linear or transformed (non-normalized) T-score was earlier computed to be 48 (see Fig. 2–3). This discrepancy between the T-scores after the distribution is normalized and the T-scores computed directly from the original distribution further corroborates the non-normality of the push-up scores.

If the teacher plans to follow this procedure, the accuracy of the conversion can be improved by setting up a table appropriate for the direction of the conversion, from percentile ranks into T-scores. By so doing each percentile rank would be listed with the fractional T-score opposite it, thus minimizing the interpolation needed. Such a table, as in the case of Table 2–5, can be easily developed from Table 2–3. To illustrate the process, for P_{40} the body of the table is entered to locate 10 per cent of the area under the normal curve, since the 40th percentile accounts for 10 per cent of the cases below the median (coinciding with the mean in a normal curve). The reader will note that in Table 2–3 10.0 per cent falls between 9.87 and 10.26, which are the values for 0.25 and 0.26 of a standard deviation, or standard score unit, from the mean. Interpolation fixes the actual value at 0.253 unit. Remembering that 1 standard deviation unit equals 10 T-score points, 2.53 T-score units are subtracted from the mean T-score of 50 to give the desired value—T-score of 47.47 rounded to 47. Repetition of this procedure for each percentile rank would result in a complete conversion table. Table 2–5 was established to account for every T-score, thus necessitating interpolation for this normalizing procedure and rendering it somewhat inconvenient if a complete set of scores is to be converted.

Thus, in summary, if for any reason the teacher should desire to normalize a set of scores, after the percentile ranks are computed from the raw scores, they are simply converted by an appropriate table, such as Table 2–5, into T-scores. This description of the derivation of a normalized T-scale is not intended to imply that it should be used by the teacher but is included merely to explain the process of obtaining normalized T-scores and to illustrate the concept of normalizing a distribution. The T-score or transformed T-score, as previously described and derived directly from raw scores, is advocated for teacher use.

C-Scale

The C-scale (or sta-eleven scale), the final normative scale to be described, is included because it represents a different type of scale than either T-scores or percentiles and has seen some application in physical education measurement. The C-scale, together with its sister scale, the stanine, in essence constitutes an adaptation of the standard score that is characterized by score bands of 0.5 standard deviation in width. The middle band of the scale is assigned a numerical value of 5 and is centered on the mean of the distribution, extending from z-scores -0.25 to $+0.25$ or T-scores 47.5 to 52.5. Figure 2–8 shows the C-scale and affords comparison with other scales. The only difference between the C-scale, as developed by Guilford, and the stanine scale is the inclusion of two extreme bands, numbered 0 and 11 on the C-scale. It is addition of a band at either end of the stanine scale that makes the C-scale the more practical of the two for physical education measurement, since differentiation of scores occurring in the tails of the distribution is important in physical education. As it is, the C-scale assigns the same value to all scores occurring 2.25 or more standard deviation units from the mean, or for T-scores of 27.5 or less and 72.5 or more.

The disadvantages associated with the C-scale are that these extreme scores, which are important in physical education, are not accorded a just differentiation, and the scale lacks the refinement of a small unit and consequently does not possess the desired accuracy of discrimination, as for T-scores. As noted above, five T-scores are encompassed within the band that constitutes each C-score, so that raw scores differing by as few as one, or as many as four, T-score points may fall within the same score band. The T-scores of 47 and 48 fall in different bands —4 and 5; yet T-scores 48–52 are all within band 5. The score of 25 push-ups (T-score 48) falls with the band for C-scores 5, as do all scores from 25 to 30 push-ups (T-score 52). This lack of discrimination becomes of special concern when scores for different tests are added to determine a battery score. Since C-scores are derived from the mean and standard deviation they are combinable, but the grossness of the band tends to lose much of the desired discrimination. As a hypothetical example, raw scores leading to T-scores 42, 43 and 44 for subject A, and T-scores 46, 47 and 48 for subject B, would be assigned C-scores of 3, 4 and 4, and 4, 4 and 5, respectively. The composite or total C-scores are 11 for A, and 13 for B, leading to identical rounded mean C-scores of 4. The composite T-scores are 129 for A, and 141 for B, with means of 43 and 47. While this example is intended to illustrate the loss of discrimination attributable to the grouping error with the C-scale in comparison to T-scores, the reader should also be alert to consider the desirability of using composite scores rather than mean scores when appropriate in an endeavor to preserve a differential effect when combining scores.

The C-scale and stanines have seen considerable application in psychology and educational measurement, but because of the significant grouping error possess limited value in educational research generally and in physical education measurement. The use of 0 in the C-scale has met with objections, but these difficulties may be averted by using 1 to 11, if deemed necessary, although this would lose the basic compatibility with stanines.

In summary, the two normative scales that are accorded most use in physical education measurement in addition to the T-score have been described, namely, percentiles and C-scales. This description, by the very nature of the characteristics of these two scales, has afforded substantiating evidence of the suitability and versatility of the T-score for physical education measurement. Percentiles are effective as a means of interpreting test scores, rendering them comparable for like groups, but their utility ends there inasmuch as they cannot be combined. The C-scale permits both comparison and combination but does not afford a desirable definititude of scale points, to say nothing of the implicit grouping error. There may be occasions when for some reason the teacher will want to express the data in one of these other score forms or convert T-scores to compare performance with norms expressed in another form. An accurately drawn comparison of scales of appropriate size based on Fig. 2–8 will afford the teacher an expedient yet efficient means of comparing or converting T-scores to percentiles or C-scores. It should be stated again, however, that converting T-scores to percentiles, or the reverse, necessitates a distribution that approximates the normal curve. This condition is not a concern when T-score and C-score are compared, since both are derived from the two basic statistics—mean and standard deviation.

DETERMINING CORRELATION BETWEEN TESTS

Correlation, expressed in terms of a coefficient r, indicates the linear relationship existing between two variables—the degrees of "going-togetherness" of, or agreement between variables. The degree of relationship may range from a perfect positive ($+1.00$) through zero (0.00) to a perfect negative (-1.00). Thus, from the point of no relationship (0.00), correlation will vary in terms of both direction and size. In the perfect positive relationship, if a large amount of one variable exists, so does a large amount of the other variable. Likewise, when a small amount of the first variable is present, there is a small amount of the second, and so on, in direct proportion. When these variables are exactly related in an inverse manner so that a large amount of one accompanies a small amount of the other, this is expressed as a perfect negative correlation, −1.00. In the event that absolutely no relationship exists between the two variables, the coefficient is expressed as 0.00.

The application of the process of correlation may be illustrated by the two factors of height and weight. When in a group of 100 boys the tallest boy is the heaviest, the next tallest is the next heaviest, and so on right down the line, then a correlation of +1.00 would obtain. Similarly, if the tallest boy is the lightest, the next tallest is the next lightest, and so on, the correlation would be −1.00. With absolutely no relationship between the height and weight, the correlation would be 0.00.

To give purpose to determining correlation for the illustrative problem, assume that it is desired to consider the possibility of substituting dips on the parallel bars for push-ups as a measure of arm and shoulder girdle strength, inasmuch as dips entail less time for each subject. Accordingly, the scores received in a test of dips were also recorded for each student performing the push-ups. The scores for each individual are grouped below (x = push-ups, and y = dips; N = 60):

x	y	x	y	x	y	x	y
32	13	34	15	8	3	10	4
23	8	24	11	15	5	29	12
25	11	5	2	1	0	13	6
18	8	60	25	36	9	30	8
10	6	17	9	19	9	22	12
35	15	26	10	25	11	12	6
20	8	35	13	38	16	40	17
45	20	50	19	27	10	16	7
22	10	15	6	25	10	25	9
54	18	44	18	35	14	25	10
28	11	32	12	38	17	42	20
27	11	27	9	25	10	20	8
18	8	25	10	32	13	34	15
26	10	15	7	24	10	25	7
28	13	30	12	30	14	42	16

The most common means of computing linear relationship statistically, especially if a large number of cases are involved, is the Pearson product-moment method. The steps in finding the coefficient of correlation by this method follow:

1. Set up a scattergram, as in Table 2–6. This is done in the same way that previous frequency tables have been arranged, except that two variables are considered instead of one. Consequently, the size of the score interval for each variable must be determined. These may be any size, depending on the range of scores in the data, and need not be the same. In fact, in the sample problem the data for the push-up test (x data) is arranged in intervals of five; and for the dip test (y data), in intervals of two. The x variable should run from low scores at the left

to high at the right, while the y variable runs from low scores at the bottom to high at the top.

2. Tally a mark in the proper box or cell to represent the pair of scores that the individual received on the two tests. In case number 1, for instance, 32 push-ups and 13 dips were scored. On the scattergram, a tally is marked in the proper cell (this has been heavily outlined for illustration)—the one that lies in the x-score interval 30–34 and the y-score interval 12–13. The second individual scored 23 push-ups and 8 dips. A mark is tallied to represent these scores in the cell that corresponds to the 20–24 interval for x data and the 8–9 interval for y data. Tallying is continued until all cases have been tallied in the proper cells, marking them in the upper left-hand corner as shown in the illustration.

3. Put the frequency column f_y (for the y data) on the righthand side of the scattergram and the f_x frequency column (for the x data) across the bottom.

4. Guess the mean for both x and the y variables, following the same procedure used in Table 2–2. This guessed mean (GM) is the midpoint of the interval selected.

5. Complete the d, fd and fd^2 columns for each variable, and then compute the correction ($C = \Sigma fd/N$) for each in terms of deviation units (do not multiply by the score interval). The standard deviation is also computed. It should be noted that the standard deviation of each variable, s_x and s_y, is also expressed in terms of deviation units without multiplying by the interval size. In the sample problem, C_x is 0.08 and C_y is 0.25. The standard deviation for the x and y data is 2.29 and 2.31, respectively.

6. Complete the scattergram by forming the " $+$ " and " $-$ " columns. It will be noted that the lines drawn for the two guesed means divide the scattergram into four quadrants—upper left, upper right, lower left, and lower right. All of the cells in the upper left and lower right quadrants are negative, while those in the upper right and lower left are positive.

a. Determine the moment ($d_x d_y$) for each cell of the scattergram. This is accomplished by multiplying the number of steps (rows) that the cell deviates from the Y guessed mean, by the number of steps (columns) that the cell deviates from the X guessed mean. Place this number in the lower right-hand corner of the cell. (This has been done for every cell in the lower left quadrant to illustrate the total picture. The upper right quadrant shows suggested use, whereby $d_x d_y$'s are computed only to include the cells needed.) The number of cases in each cell, which is already tallied in the upper left-hand corner, is then multiplied by this number to give the product-moment of that cell. For example, in the heavily outlined cell (case number 1), there are four scores, and the cell deviates one step from each of the two guessed means. This gives a moment of $1 \times 1 = 1$. Therefore, the product-moment for that cell is 4 (4×1). The product-moment for each cell is obtained in a similar manner.

b. For each row of the scattergram, add the positive product-moments and enter the sum in the "+" column. In the same manner, add the negative product-moments and enter the sum in the "−" column.

c. Add all the product-moments in the "+" column and subtract from this amount the sum of the "−" product-moments. The resulting amount is the sum of $fd_x d_y$ for all the cells ($\Sigma fd_x d_y$).

7. Use the following formula to compute the coefficient of correlation.

$$r = \frac{(\Sigma fd_x d_y / N) - C_x C_y}{s_x s_y}$$

As computed in Table 2–6, the correlation between push-up and dip scores for the illustrative problem is expressed as an r of 0.93.

In interpreting correlation coefficients, they should not be confused with percentages or proportions. Several observations may serve to clarify their interpretation for the teacher. The increase in the amount of relationship is not evenly spread out from $r = 0.0$ to $r = 1.0$. Consequently, a coefficient of 0.50 does not signify half of perfect correlation, suggesting that it is half as useful. Similarly, $r = 0.80$ does not imply that the relationship is twice as great as $r = 0.40$; in reality this would be four times. The difference in correlation betwen 0.80 and 0.90 is much greater than that between 0.20 and 0.30. Desirable values of correlation coefficients pertaining to test validity, reliability, and objectivity are presented in Chapters 3, 4, and 5.

To avert misunderstanding it should be made explicit that the correlation coefficient is a measure of linear relationship and is not an indication of cause and effect. It merely expresses the extent to which two variables tend to go together.

In interpreting correlation the teacher should be cautious in the amount of confidence placed on the resultant coefficient, unless a relatively large number of students are involved. Data for at least 100 students should be included, otherwise considerable sampling error may occur. Accordingly, $r = 0.93$ for the illustrative problem appears to suggest a meaningful relationship and that the two items may be measuring the same thing nearly enough that dips could be substituted for push-ups if desirable. However, an effort should be made to involve a larger N before the evidence is regarded as at all certain.

Table 2–6. Calculating Coefficient of Correlation for the Illustrative Problem by the Pearson-r Method

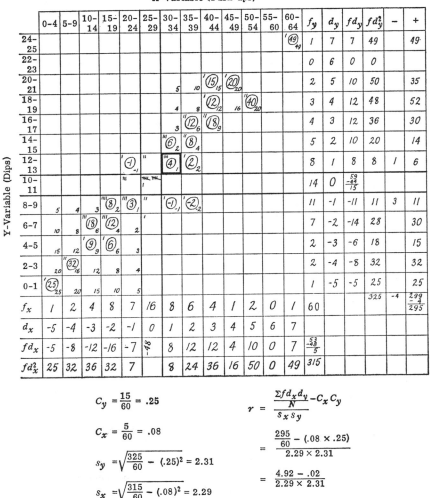

X-Variable (Push-ups)

Y-Variable (Dips)

$$C_y = \frac{15}{60} = .25$$

$$C_x = \frac{5}{60} = .08$$

$$s_y = \sqrt{\frac{325}{60} - (.25)^2} = 2.31$$

$$s_x = \sqrt{\frac{315}{60} - (.08)^2} = 2.29$$

$$r = \frac{\frac{\Sigma f d_x d_y}{N} - C_x C_y}{s_x s_y}$$

$$= \frac{\frac{295}{60} - (.08 \times .25)}{2.29 \times 2.31}$$

$$= \frac{4.92 - .02}{2.29 \times 2.31}$$

$$= \frac{4.90}{5.28} = .93$$

As a final word in interpreting correlation, another statistical concept can be introduced to more clearly disclose the degree of relationship in a correlation coefficient. This concept, called the *coefficient of determination,* expresses the percentage of "common variance" shared by two variables and is found by squaring the correlation coefficient. Hence for the illustrative problem ($r = 0.93$) the coefficient of determination (r^2) is 86 per cent, indicating that the ability to perform push-ups probably contributes about 86 per cent to the ability to do dips. This leaves only 14 per cent of the variance unaccounted for in this correlation.

VISUAL ANALYSIS OF RELATIONSHIP

Conceivably, the teacher may on occasion desire to obtain an approximation of the relationship between two variables (for example, push-ups and dips) without going through the detailed computation procedure. This may be readily accomplished by setting up a scattergram and tallying the scores as described previously for the first two steps of the computation procedure. Then the pattern of tally marks on the scattergram can be examined visually to estimate the amount of relationship involved, according to the following suggested guides:

1. The line of direction proceeds from the lower left to the upper right corners of the scattergram for positive correlation, from upper left to lower right for negative correlation.
2. A perfect correlation exists when a straight line is formed.
3. No relationship is shown by a general scattering of tallies without direction—circle-like.
4. Varying degrees of relationship are revealed by a general trend of marks toward a straight line.

Figure 2–10 illustrates some patterns of relationship to serve as a basis for making approximations. The reader may also refer to the

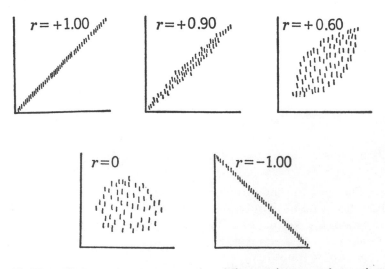

Fig. 2–10. Illustrative scattergrams for different degrees of correlation.

scattergram in Table 2–6 as an example of 0.93 correlation. Reasonable consistency and accuracy in estimating correlation coefficients can be developed through practice in visual analysis of scattergrams appearing with sample problems in measurement and statistics texts or those that the teacher has computed previously.

Actually, in addition to affording an estimate of r the scattergram also represents a visual means of discovering whether a linear relationship exists and, therefore, whether use of the procedure for determining coefficient of correlation as described is justified. In some situations as one variable increases, the other variable also increases for a part of the range. Then after a certain point is reached, a reverse relationship begins, so that as the first variable continues to increase, the second begins to decrease. This type of relationship is referred to as *curvilinear*. The correlation of running ability with age serves as an example of a curvilinear relationship. As a child grows older, he runs faster up to a certain point in his development and then, as he continues to grow older, his speed declines. While a number of situations in education exist in which curvilinear relationships prevail, in most typical measurement circumstances the physical education teacher will not often note curvilinearity. However, the teacher should be alert to this possibility, and if evidence discloses that the relationship between two variables is not linear, then the technique discussed for linear relationships should not be used. In such an instance a book in educational statistics should be consulted and the *correlation ratio* applied.[7] Accordingly, when no marked tendency toward curvilinearity is revealed upon inspection of the scattergram, the procedure for computing r discussed in this book is applicable.

ANALYSIS OF UNGROUPED SCORES

Occasionally it may prove advantageous in computing the desired statistics for the teacher to work directly with ungrouped scores, such as when the number of scores is small or a calculator is available. With a small number of scores, not only is the computational process simplified but also the grouping procedure becomes inappropriate because of the grouping errors that usually occur. The use of a calculator facilitates direct computation from raw scores and generally renders the grouping procedure impractical.

Ranking

The simplest interpretative score reflecting the performance of each individual within a group can be obtained by ranking the raw scores in

[7] Such as: N. M. Downie and R. W. Heath, *Basic Statistical Methods*, 2nd ed. (New York: Harper & Row, Publishers, 1965).

a distribution. Ranking leads to other meaningful interpretative information and affords the basis for correlating test scores with judges' ranking or tournament standings to estabish test validity.

To determine the rank order of a distribution the scores are arranged from best (or highest, except for time measurement) to poorest. Then the ranking is assigned, beginning with 1 for the top score to the nth score for the bottom. For the illustrative problem (see Table 2–7) the top score ranks 1, and the last or 60th score, 60. When two or more scores are identical, a rank number is reserved for each score, and then these numbers are summed and divided by the number of scores that are identical. The mean ranking so derived is assigned to each score that is involved. For example in Table 2–7, two scores of 42 were

Table 2–7. Ranking for the Illustrative Problem

Score	Rank	Score	Rank	Score	Rank	Score	Rank
60	1	34	15.5	25	34.5	19	46
54	2	32	18	25	34.5	18	47.5
50	3	32	18	25	34.5	18	47.5
45	4	32	18	25	34.5	17	49
44	5	30	21	25	34.5	16	50
42	6.5	30	21	25	34.5	15	52
42	6.5	30	21	25	34.5	15	52
40	8	29	23	25	34.5	15	52
38	9.5	28	24.5	24	39.5	13	54
38	9.5	28	24.5	24	39.5	12	55
36	11	27	27	23	41	10	56.5
35	13	27	27	22	42.5	10	56.5
35	13	27	27	22	42.5	8	58
35	13	26	29.5	20	44.5	5	59
34	15.5	26	29.5	20	44.5	1	60
						$N = 60$	

recorded for which ranks 6 and 7 are applicable. Thus, the mean ranking of $13/2 = 6.5$ is assigned to the score of 42. The reader can test his understanding of this process by confirming the rank numbers noted in Table 2–7. By the ranking of raw scores an individual is able to easily perceive his standing relative to his group, for example, 25 pushups in the sample problem ranks 34.5 in a group of 60, or just below the middle score.

From the rank order arrangement of raw scores the percentile rank (PR) can be readily determined as a means of interpreting the test scores on a percentile scale, that is, the percentage of scores falling below that score in the distribution. From the rank for a given score the percentile rank can be determined by the formula: $PR = 100 - ([100R - 50]/N)$, where R is the rank. Substituting in the formula for 25 push-ups, with $R = 34.5$, the percentile rank becomes: $PR = 100 - ([100(34.5) - 50]/60) = 100 - (3,400/60) = 43.3$, or 43.

In the event percentile ranks are to be computed for ungrouped scores without first determining rank order, a frequency distribution is set up as shown for the push-up scores in Table 2–8. The f and cumulative f columns are determined as for grouped data. The entries for p column are derived by taking ½ of the f entry for a given score and adding the figure to the cumulative f for the score immediately below. For example, p for 25 push-ups is ½ of 8, or 4, plus the next lower cumulative f of 22, giving a value of 26. The percentile rank is found by the formula: $PR = p/N \times 100$. Substituting, the PR of 25 push-ups is: $PR = 26/60 \times 100 = 43.3$, or 43. Complete computation of percentile ranks for the sample problem is contained in Table 2–8.

Basic Computations

The mean is computed directly from ungrouped scores by adding the scores and dividing the total by the number of scores, as expressed by the formulas: $\overline{X} = \Sigma X/N$. Table 2–9 shows the suggested scheme or organization of scores to compute the mean and standard deviation. It contains only part of the scores but has correct totals and formula computations for push-ups in the sample problem. All of the scores for push-ups are presented in Table 2–10 along with those for dips as arranged for the correlation computation. The reader may wish to check this table in studying the computation of the mean and standard deviation. The mean for push-ups is computed to be 26.9 as shown in Table 2–9.

To calculate the standard deviation in addition to the column for raw scores, a second column is formed for the square of each raw score. With the sum of these squared scores and the mean, the standard deviation is found by the formula: $s = \sqrt{(\Sigma X^2/N) - \overline{X}^2}$. The tabular computation is $s = 11.4$. When compared to the grouped data calculations of 27.4 and 11.4 for mean and standard deviation, respectively, the values for ungrouped scores exemplify the slight error attributable to grouping the scores for analysis. As another comparison of results for grouped and ungrouped data, the mean and standard deviation for grouped dip scores can be found from Table 2–6 to be 11.0 and 4.6, respectively. The respective values for ungrouped dip scores are computed in Table 2–10 as 10.9 and 4.7.

Table 2–8.   Computing Percentile Ranks for Ungrouped Push-up Scores

Score	f	cum f	P	PR
60	1	60	59.5	99
54	1	59	58.5	97.5
50	1	58	57.5	96
45	1	57	56.5	94
44	1	56	55.5	92.5
42	2	55	54	90
40	1	53	52.5	87.5
38	2	52	51	85
36	1	50	49.5	82.5
35	3	49	47.5	79
34	2	46	45	75
32	3	44	42.5	71
30	3	41	39.5	66
29	1	38	37.5	62.5
28	2	37	36	60
27	3	35	32.5	54
26	2	32	31	52
25	8	30	26	43
24	2	22	21	35
23	1	20	19.5	32.5
22	2	19	18	30
20	2	17	16	27
19	1	15	14.5	24
18	2	14	13	22
17	1	12	11.5	19
16	1	11	10.5	17.5
15	3	10	8.5	14
13	1	7	6.5	11
12	1	6	5.5	9
10	2	5	4	7
8	1	3	2.5	4
5	1	2	1.5	2.5
1	1	1	0.5	1
	$N = 60$			

The reader may note an apparent discrepancy in the formulas cited with some statistics books in that $(N - 1)$ is used instead of N in computing s. For measurement purposes the formulas utilized pertain to descriptive statistics. The value $(N - 1)$ is used for inferential statistics, wherein the interest is in obtaining an unbiased estimate of the population parameter in question from a sample statistic; $(N - 1)$ tends to correct for an underestimation from sample to population.

Table 2–9. Partial Table Showing Direct Computation of Mean and Standard Deviation for Push-ups

Student	X	X^2
1	32	1,024
2	23	529
3	25	625
4	18	324
5	10	100
6	35	1,225
7	20	400
.		
.		
.		
58	34	1,156
59	25	625
60	42	1,764
	$\Sigma X = 1,613$	$\Sigma X^2 = 51,277$

$$\overline{X} = \frac{\Sigma X}{N} = \frac{1,613}{60} = 26.9$$

$$s = \sqrt{\frac{\Sigma X^2}{N} - \overline{X}^2} = \sqrt{\frac{51,277}{60} - (26.9)^2}$$

$$= \sqrt{854.62 - 723.61} = \sqrt{131.01}$$

$$= 11.4$$

Correlation

To compute the Pearson product-moment coefficient of correlation (r) for ungrouped scores the score columns and squared score columns are organized on a tabulation sheet along with a column for the product of both scores for each student. This procedure is shown in Table 2–10 for the illustrative problem (X = push-ups; Y = dips). After the mean and standard deviation are computed for both sets of scores and the product column is totaled, r is computed by substituting the appropriate figures as shown for the example problem in Table 2–10 in the formula:

$$r = \frac{N\Sigma XY - (\Sigma X)(\Sigma Y)}{N^2 s_x s_y}$$

For the push-up and dip data, $r = 0.95$. The reader will note that this shows a slight increase in the coefficient when compared with $r = 0.93$ for grouped data as computed earlier. Again this merely reflects the grouping error that generally occurs when scores are grouped for analysis.

Rank-Order Coefficient of Correlation

Upon occasion the teacher may desire to correlate the performance of a group on two different items, when one or both items are ranked. One example would be in establishing the validity of a teacher-made test by using a criterion measure for which students are ranked by experts according to ability. In order to determine the relationship be-

Table 2–10. Table for Direct Calculation of Pearson-r for the Illustrative Problem

Student	X	X^2	Y	Y^2	XY
1	32	1,024	13	169	416
2	23	529	8	64	184
3	25	625	11	121	275
4	18	324	8	64	144
5	10	100	6	36	60
6	35	1,225	15	225	525
7	20	400	8	64	160
8	45	2,025	20	400	900
9	22	484	10	100	220
10	54	2,916	18	324	972
11	28	784	11	121	308
12	27	729	11	121	297
13	18	324	8	64	144
14	26	676	10	100	260
15	28	784	13	169	364
16	34	1,156	15	225	510
17	24	576	11	121	264
18	5	25	2	4	10
19	60	3,600	25	625	1,500
20	17	289	9	81	153
21	26	676	10	100	260
22	35	1,225	13	169	455
23	50	2,500	19	361	950
24	15	225	6	36	90
25	44	1,936	18	324	792
26	32	1,024	12	144	384
27	27	729	9	81	243
28	25	625	10	100	250
29	15	225	7	49	105
30	30	900	12	144	360
31	8	14	3	9	24
32	15	225	5	25	75
33	1	1	0	0	0
34	36	1,296	9	81	324
35	19	361	9	81	171
36	25	625	11	121	275
37	38	1,444	16	256	608
38	27	729	10	100	270
39	25	625	10	100	250
40	35	1,225	14	196	490
41	38	1,444	17	289	646
42	25	625	10	100	250
43	32	1,024	13	169	416
44	24	576	10	100	240
45	30	900	14	196	420

Table 2–10 (Cont.).

Student	X	X^2	Y	Y^2	XY
46	10	100	4	16	40
47	29	841	12	144	348
48	13	169	6	36	78
49	30	900	8	64	240
50	22	484	12	144	264
51	12	144	6	36	72
52	40	1,600	17	289	680
53	16	256	7	49	112
54	25	625	9	81	225
55	25	625	10	100	250
56	42	1,764	20	400	840
57	20	400	8	64	160
58	34	1,156	15	225	510
59	25	625	7	49	175
60	42	1,764	16	256	672
	$\Sigma X = 1{,}613$	$\Sigma X^2 = 51{,}277$	$\Sigma Y = 656$	$\Sigma Y^2 = 8{,}482$	$\Sigma XY = 20{,}680$

$$\bar{X} = \frac{\Sigma X}{N} = \frac{1{,}613}{60} = 26.88 = 26.9 \qquad \bar{Y} = \frac{\Sigma Y}{N} = \frac{656}{60} = 10.93 = 10.9$$

$$s_x = \sqrt{\frac{\Sigma X^2}{N} - \bar{X}^2} = \sqrt{\frac{51{,}277}{60} - (26.9)^2} \qquad s_y = \sqrt{\frac{\Sigma Y^2}{N} - \bar{Y}^2} = \sqrt{\frac{8{,}482}{60} - (10.9)^2}$$

$$= \sqrt{854.62 - 723.61} = \sqrt{131.01} = 11.4 \qquad = \sqrt{141.37 - 118.81} = \sqrt{22.56} = 4.7$$

$$r = \frac{N\Sigma XY - (\Sigma X)(\Sigma Y)}{N^2 s_x s_y} = \frac{(60)(20{,}680) - (1{,}613)(656)}{(60)^2(11.4)(4.7)} = \frac{1{,}240{,}800 - 1{,}058{,}128}{(3{,}600)(53.58)}$$

$$= \frac{182{,}672}{192{,}888} = 0.95$$

tween the two tests the results must be arranged in rank order for both tests, and the ensuing computation leads to a rank-order coefficient of correlation, *rho*, more properly referred to as the Spearman rank-difference coefficient of correlation.

Although unnecessary and accordingly inappropriate for the illustrative problem, since specific score values were determined for each test rather than mere ranking, the push-up and dip scores are ranked (see Table 2–7 for push-up scores) to illustrate the computational process and compare the resultant *rho* with the previously determined *r*. In the interest of obtaining some legitimacy for this comparison, it can be assumed that the dip scores were listed as judges' ranking of dipping ability. To compute *rho*, the rankings are arranged as shown in Table 2–11 for the sample problem.

Table 2–11. Computation of *rho* for Push-ups and Dip Ability

Student	Push-up Scores	Push-up Rank	Dip Rank	Rank Difference (D)	D^2
1	32	18	17.5	0.5	0.25
2	23	41	45.5	4.5	20.25
3	25	34.5	26	8.5	72.25
4	18	47.5	45.5	2	4
5	10	56.5	53.5	3	9
6	35	13	12	1	1
7	20	44.5	45.5	1	1
8	45	4	2.5	1.5	2.25
9	22	42.5	33	9.5	90.25
10	54	2	5.5	3.5	12.25
11	28	24.5	26	1.5	2.25
12	27	27	26	1	1
13	18	47.5	45.5	2	4
14	26	29.5	33	3.5	12.25
15	28	24.5	17.5	7	49
16	34	15.5	12	3.5	12.25
17	24	39.5	26	13.5	182.25
18	5	59	59	0	—
19	60	1	1	0	—
20	17	49	40	9	81
21	26	29.5	33	3.5	12.25
22	35	13	17.5	4.5	20.25
23	50	3	4	1	1
24	15	52	53.5	1.5	2.25
25	44	5	5.5	0.5	0.25
26	32	18	21.5	3.5	12.25
27	27	27	40	13	169
28	25	34.5	33	1.5	2.25
29	15	52	50	2	4
30	30	21	21.5	0.5	0.25
31	8	58	58	0	—
32	15	52	56	4	16
33	1	60	60	0	—
34	36	11	40	29	841
35	19	46	40	6	36
36	25	34.5	26	8.5	72.25
37	38	9.5	9.5	0	—
38	27	27	33	6	36
39	25	34.5	33	1.5	2.25
40	35	13	14.5	1.5	2.25
41	38	9.5	7.5	2	4
42	25	34.5	33	1.5	2.25
43	32	18	17.5	1.5	2.25
44	24	39.5	33	6.5	42.25

Table 2–11 (Cont.).

Student	Push-up Scores	Push-up Rank	Dip Rank	Rank Difference (D)	D^2
45	30	21	14.5	7.5	56.25
46	10	56.5	57	0.5	0.25
47	29	23	21.5	1.5	2.25
48	13	54	53.5	0.5	0.25
49	30	21	45.5	24.5	600.25
50	22	42.5	21.5	21	441
51	12	55	53.5	1.5	2.25
52	40	8	7.5	0.5	0.25
53	16	50	50	0	—
54	25	34.5	40	5.5	30.25
55	25	34.5	33	1.5	2.25
56	42	65	2.5	4	16
57	20	44.5	45.5	1	1
58	34	15.5	12	3.5	12.25
59	25	34.5	50	15.5	240.25
60	42	6.5	9.5	3	9
				ΣD^2 =	3,250.50

$$rho = 1 - \frac{6\Sigma D^2}{N(N^2-1)} = 1 - \frac{6(3,250.50)}{60(3,600\text{-}1)} = 1 - \frac{19.50}{215.94} = 1 - 0.09$$

$$= 0.91$$

Once the ranking for each student on both tests is entered on the tabulation sheet, the difference between ranks is determined and recorded in the D column without any attention to the direction of the difference, plus or minus. For instance, for student 1 the difference between rankings is 0.5 in favor of the push-up score and the difference for student 2 is 4.5 in the opposite direction. Only the magnitude of this difference is recorded in the D column, 0.5 and 4.5. After the D column is completed and summed, each entry is squared and entered in the D^2 column. Upon totaling the D^2 column, the appropriate figures are substituted in the formula to calculate rho: $rho = 1 - (6\Sigma D^2/N[N^2 - 1])$. As shown in Table 2–11, $rho = 0.91$ for the sample problem.

It should be stressed that the calculation of rho for $N = 60$ would be rather unusual in practice, since comparative ranking of this many cases presents considerably difficulty. This correlation method is useful when the number of pairs is small, less than 30, making ranking more feasible. Again, the sample problem data were only utilized for convenience and comparability. The reader will note that $rho = 0.91$ is somewhat less in strength of relationship than $r = 0.95$ for the same data when ungrouped and slightly less than $r = 0.93$ with the scores grouped. This comparison of rho and r for the same data confirms the fact that, while rho does compare quite favorably, it is a less sensitive statistic than *r*, reflecting the difference in the levels of measurement involved in the two techniques.

The teacher may find it expedient to compute *rho* in instances when *N* is small and ranking is feasible. However, such use should be made with realization of the limitations of correlation analysis when applied to small numbers and that this technique is not as powerful in the statistical sense as *r*.

USE OF ELECTRONIC DATA PROCESSING FOR STATISTICAL ANALYSIS

The application of electronic data processing (EDP), as discussed in Chapter 6, has tremendous implications for measurement programs in physical education. Of particular interest at this point is the implication for computation of test results, wherein not only is the task reduced appreciably when large numbers of scores are involved, but also the accuracy of the computation is virtually assured. The application of EDP to analysis of test scores can be made in two ways: (1) as a pre-planned routine in which test scores for each subject are recorded on a special mark–sense card or answer sheet for data processing, leading to a printout of results including the performance of individual subjects in terms of raw and normative scores; and (2) to make specific computations for any set of scores for which no such pre-planned routine has been developed. This latter concern is relevant here, and the application of EDP will be explained as it pertains to the illustrative problem.

It is not to be implied that the teacher will be conversant with the details of EDP, but rather that access will be available for the teacher to personnel and equipment requisite to utilization of data processing. For the illustrative problem, the teacher would submit the push-up scores for processing on a digital computer along with a statement of the computations that are requested. In order to justify the utilization of a computer for a problem already handled by the teacher computation discussed, the request will include computation of percentiles, along with the mean, standard deviation, and T-scores. The percentile rank for each raw score will facilitate comparison with norms on push-ups for other groups which are expressed only as percentiles.

The computer programmer responsible for the analysis will select or write an appropriate program for the analysis desired and process the push-up scores. For presentation to the computer the test scores are usually recorded on punch cards and arranged behind another deck of cards containing the particular computer program to be run and specific instructions for the computer. Figure 2–11 shows the deck arranged

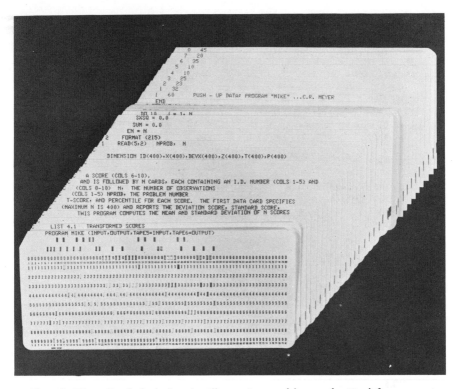

Fig. 2–11. Card deck for the illustrative problem, submitted for computer compilation and execution.

for the illustrative problem with the FORTRAN [8] program in the front portion and the data deck containing the test scores behind. Figure 2–12 contains the listing for the particular FORTRAN program used to obtain the desired statistics. Comparison with cards in the front part of the deck in Fig. 2–11 shows that the program listing itself is presented on cards and is part of the print-out produced by the computer.

Figure 2–13 lists in part the computational information provided on the computer print-out.[9] Because of space limitation only 28 of the 60 individual listings are shown. Close examination of Fig. 2–13 reveals that two columns are printed in addition to the T-scores and percentiles. Column DEV represents deviation in score units of each raw score from the mean. Column Z lists each z-score as derived from the deviation

---

[8] Standing for *for*mula *trans*lation language, a commonly used computer language.

[9] For fuller explanation of computer application to statistical analysis the reader is referred to: Paul R. Lohnes and Wiliam W. Cooley, *Introduction to Statistical Procedures: with Computer Exercises* (New York: John Wiley & Sons, 1968).

```
      PROGRAM MIKE (INPUT,OUTPUT,TAPE5=INPUT,TAPE6=OUTPUT)
C     LIST 4.1   TRANSFORMED SCORES
C
C          THIS PROGRAM COMPUTES THE MEAN AND STANDARD DEVIATION OF N SCORES
C     (MAXIMUM N IS 400) AND REPORTS THE DEVIATION SCORE, STANDARD SCORE,
C     T-SCORE, AND PERCENTILE FOR EACH SCORE. THE FIRST DATA CARD SPECIFIES
C     (COLS 1-5) NPROB, THE PROBLEM NUMBER
C     (COLS 8-10) N, THE NUMBER OF OBSERVATIONS
C     AND IS FOLLOWED BY N CARDS, EACH CONTAINING AN I.D. NUMBER (COLS 1-5) AND
C     A SCORE (COLS 6-10).
C
C
      DIMENSION ID(400),X(400),DEVX(400),Z(400),T(400),P(400)
C
  1   READ(5,2)   NPROB,   N
  2   FORMAT (215)
      EN = N
      SUM = 0.0
      SXSQ = 0.0
      DO 10    J = 1, N
 10   READ(5.3) ID(J), X(J)
  3 FORMAT(I5,F5.0)
C    THIS IS THE MODIFIABLE FORMAT FOR INPUT SCORES.
C
      DO 11 K=1,N
      NBNT=0
      DO 12 J =1,N
 12 IF(X(J).LE.X(K)) NBNT =NBNT+1
      ENBNT=NBNT
 11 P(K) = (ENBNT*100.0)/EN
      DO 4 J = 1, N
  4   SXSQ = SXSQ + X(J) * X(J)
C    STATEMENT 4 ENDS THE ACCUMULATIONS (SUMS AND SUMS OF SQUARES) LOOP.
      XM = SUM / EN
      VARX = (SXSQ - SUM * SUM / EN) / (EN - 1.0)
      SDX = SQRT (VARX)
      WRITE(6,5) NPROB, N
  5   FORMAT (30H1TRANSFORMED SCORES. PROB. NO. I6, 6H. N = I6)
      WRITE(6,6)    XM,    SDX,    VARX
  6   FORMAT (8HOMEAN = F10.5,10H    S.D. = F10.5, 13H VARIANCE = F10.5)
      DO 7 J = 1, N
C
      DEVX(J) = X(J) − XM
      Z(J) = DEVX(J) / SDX
  7   T(J) = 10.0 * Z(J) + 50.0
      WRITE(6,8)
  8 FORMAT(58HO    I.D.    SCORE    DEV    Z    T    PERCENTI
 1 LE)
      DO50 J = 1,N
 50 WRITE(6,9) ID(J),X(J),DEVX(J),Z(J),T(J),P(J)
  9 FORMAT(I6,4X,F6.0,4X,F6.1,4X,F6.3,4X,F6.2,4X,F6.1)
      CALL EXIT
      END
```

Fig. 2–12. Program listing for transformed scores. Modified by addition of percentiles to program listing in: Lohnes and Cooley, op. cit., p. 74.

TRANSFORMED SCORES. PROB. NO. 1. $N = 60$
MEAN = 26.88333   S.D. = 11.58183   VARIANCE = 134.13870

I.D.	SCORE	DEV	Z	T	PERCENTILE
1	32	5.1	0.442	54.42	73.3
2	23	−3.9	−0.335	46.65	33.3
3	25	−1.9	−0.163	48.37	50.0
4	18	−8.9	−0.767	42.33	23.3
5	10	−16.9	−1.458	35.42	8.3
6	35	8.1	0.701	57.01	81.7
7	20	−6.9	−0.594	44.06	28.3
8	45	18.1	1.564	65.64	95.0
9	22	−4.9	−0.422	45.78	31.7
10	54	27.1	2.341	73.41	98.3
11	28	1.1	0.096	50.96	61.7
12	27	0.1	0.010	50.10	58.3
13	18	−8.9	−0.767	42.33	23.3
14	26	−0.9	−0.076	49.24	53.3
15	28	1.1	0.096	50.96	61.7
16	34	7.1	0.614	56.14	76.7
17	24	−2.9	−0.249	47.51	36.7
18	5	−21.9	−1.889	31.11	3.3
19	60	33.1	2.859	78.59	100.0
20	17	−9.9	−0.853	41.47	20.0
21	26	−0.9	−0.076	49.24	53.3
22	35	8.1	0.701	57.01	81.7
23	50	23.1	1.996	69.96	96.7
24	15	−11.9	−1.026	39.74	16.7
25	44	17.1	1.478	64.78	93.3
.					
.					
.					
58	34	7.1	0.614	56.14	76.7
59	25	−1.9	−0.163	48.37	50.0
60	42	15.1	1.305	63.05	91.7

Fig. 2–13. Information contained on computer print-out for illustrative problem.* (Cases 26–57 omitted due to space limitation.)

units and from which the T-score is obtained. The values for mean and standard deviation represent accurate determinations which are rounded for reporting to 26.9 and 11.6, respectively. When compared with the values previously determined by hand computation for ungrouped score (26.9 and 11.4 for mean and standard deviation) a slight difference in the standard deviation value is noted, which is attributable to the fact that the computer program carried multiplication to five places to the right of the decimal.

In summary of computer application for statistical analysis, when the services of the ever-increasing number of data processing units become available to the teacher, the raw scores for push-ups can be submitted for processing, and the teacher will receive a print-out showing the z-scores, T-scores, and percentiles, along with the mean and standard deviation. Obviously, computer programs are available for calculating correlation coefficients and other statistics that may be desired, but are deemed beyond the purpose of this chapter. It should be obvious that computer application for statistical analysis will not eliminate the need for teacher proficiency in calculating selected basic statistics. In instances when a relatively small number of students and one or two sets of scores are involved, the preliminary steps to prepare material for data processing may take more time than the hand computation and, accordingly, not be practical.

RESEARCH METHODS AND INTERPRETATION IN PHYSICAL EDUCATION

An understanding of the statistical tools and concepts utilized in measurement and their application equips the teacher to comprehend the application and interpretation of these same and related tools and concepts to research. The basic difference that the teacher should recognize is that in measurement, *descriptive statistics* are used to present the results for a particular group in and of itself. In research, attention is directed to statistical analysis for a selected, representative group so constituted that the results can be interpreted on a larger scale through inference, hence *inferential statistics.*

Population and Samples

Research in physical education, such as reported in the *Research Quarterly,* and the kinds of questions leading to this research are based on the desire to discover some general principle applicable to a group much larger than one with which it is possible to conduct an experiment. This large group, generally called a *population,* or a *universe,* does not usually include all people but is most often restricted to a group defined by specific requirements. To illustrate, a population might include all persons who have the characteristics of being females in the seventh grade in the United States, or all college freshman males enrolled in a physical education program in colleges with more than 2,000 undergraduates enrolled. Even though these populations are specifically defined and may be only a small proportion of the general population, it would be quite impractical to try to test every member of either of these populations.

Fortunately, procedures have been discovered through which questions about populations can be answered adequately by conducting experiments on a subgroup of the population called a *sample*. Most of the techniques derive from the assumption that a sample can be selected at *random*, which means technically that each member of the defined population has an equal chance of being chosen for the sample. In actuality this again becomes both difficult and impractical inasmuch as a sample of 50 college freshman males chosen on this basis would probably include students from close to 50 different colleges. Usual sampling procedures involve some compromise with this ideal sampling plan, but this should be done with an awareness that results based on the sample can be generalized to the population only to the extent that the sample approximates the ideal of random sampling.

Questions Asked in Physical Education Research

Before discussing the basis on which it is possible to infer conclusions about populations from sample data, it appears desirable to look briefly at the kinds of questions asked in physical education research. These will be stated in terms of the push-up test data from the illustrative problem. The general procedures suggested are applicable only if this sample is considered a *random* sample from the population of male college freshmen. The following questions represent typical research problems.

1. What is the mean score on this test for the population?
2. Does the mean of this population differ from the *known* mean of some other population, for example, senior male college students?
3. Does the mean of this population differ from the mean of some other specified population from which a second sample may be drawn?
4. For the population defined, is the relationship between scores on the push-up test and scores on some other measure, such as dips or sit-ups, different from zero?

It is important to notice that these questions are stated in terms of means or measures of relationship based on the *entire defined population*. Summary numbers, such as the mean or correlation coefficient, based on the entire population are often called *parameters*, to distinguish them from the same kind of summary numbers based on samples and termed *statistics*. Looking at the first question above, the value of a parameter (for example, the mean of the population) would be estimated from the corresponding sample statistic (for example, the mean of the sample).

Careful analysis will show that the first question is of a different type from the other three. It asks, "What is the value of?" a particular parameter. The other three questions only require a "yes" or "no" decision as to the existence of *any* difference (questions 2 and 3 or *any* relationship (question 4), rather than a statement about the size of the difference or the degree of relationship.

The Approach to Making Inferences

The approach to making inferences about population values from sample statistics is based on the logical assumption that the statistic represents an estimate of the parameter, but that it would be very unusual for them to be exactly equal. Some difference between them is expected because the specific group (sample) chosen at random will undoubtedly *not* be exactly representative of the population as a whole. This difference between a parameter and the corresponding statistic used as an estimate is called a *sampling error*.

Fortunately it is possible to show mathematically that for certain common statistics (e.g., the mean), the sampling errors from many estimates of the same parameter fall into a distribution that is normal in shape, where (1) the average of the errors is zero; and (2) the dispersion of the errors, that is, about how large they tend to get, can be determined. The term usually applied to the index of the size of the errors is the standard error of the statistic in question, the mean in this instance. This index is nothing more than the standard deviation of the distribution of errors.

The general procedure for applying this knowledge to questions of the type, "What is the value of the population mean?" is to establish *two* values based on the sample data and conclude that the population mean lies somewhere between these two values. Then a statement must be added as to the certainty of this conclusion; for example, "There is a 95 per cent chance that this conclusion is correct." This percentage, called the *level of confidence*, is set arbitrarily by the investigator at the beginning of the study. Then the information about the distribution of possible sampling errors is applied in a way so as to produce the desired limits. They are established so that for the 95 per cent confidence level there is (1) only a 2½ per cent chance that the obtained sample mean would occur if the population mean were smaller than the lesser of the two limits, and (2) only a 2½ per cent chance that the obtained mean would occur if the population mean were larger than the greater of the two units. Therefore, a total chance of error (in either direction) of 5 per cent exists, and the investigator may conclude that he has a 95 per cent chance of being correct in saying that the population mean lies somewhere between the two values calculated. These two values are commonly called *confidence limits*. The 95 per cent and 99 per cent levels of confidence are commonly used in this procedure. Other things being equal, the larger the sample, the narrower the confidence interval will be.

The types of questions previously illustrated by 2, 3, and 4 ask that a determination be made as to whether some difference exists. As in establishing confidence limits, the investigator must first determine how much risk of making an incorrect decision he wishes to take. More specifically, he must state as a percentage the risk he is willing to take *of concluding that there is a difference when in reality there is no difference,* as shown in Fig. 2–14. This percentage is called the *level of sig-*

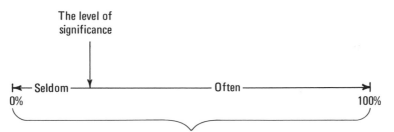

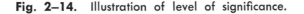

The probability that chance alone could produce the observed result, as a percentage

Fig. 2–14.   Illustration of level of significance.

nificance, and the most commonly used values are 5 per cent and 1 per cent. The basic reasoning for this type of inference follows. Suppose that the observed sample difference is large enough that the likelihood of its occurring as a result of sampling error when in reality no difference exists is less than, say, 5 per cent. Then the conclusion may be drawn that a real difference exists with only a 5 per cent chance of being wrong. In other words, an investigator may conclude that a difference is significant at the 5 per cent level of significance between the number of push-ups that can be performed by entering college freshman males and senior males (question 3). This indicates that he has found a difference between his sample means so large that it would occurs as a result of sampling error less than 5 per cent of the time, if there were no difference in the means of the two populations.

Attention should be drawn to the fact that the investigator using these techniques states the risk he takes of making a specific kind of error *but does not state the risk he is taking of concluding that no difference exists when in reality there is a difference.* This risk is *not* equal to the risk of making the other type of error and is often considerably larger. Most commonly used techniques do not adequately provide a measure of the degree of risk the investigator would be taking if he were to conclude that no difference exists. Therefore, when the careful researcher finds that he is unable to conclude that a difference does exist, he will conclude that he has "not shown any difference" rather than that "no difference exists."

There are a wide variety of specific techniques designed to handle many questions that are asked in physical education research. Whether the symbol reported is a CR, t, X^2, F, or still another, the reader may be confident that the reasoning process followed is basically similar to the one outlined above.

RESOLVING THE ILLUSTRATIVE PROBLEM

The illustrative problem has indicated the need and provided the focus for presenting what the teacher of physical education and the reader and consumer of research needs to know about statistical tools and analysis. The meaning and value of the different statistical concepts can now be realized. With an understanding of these concepts, the teacher is equipped to analyze test results effectively by describing:

1. The representative score for a group, such as the mean, median, or mode.
2. The variability of a group utilizing an appropriate index, such as standard deviation, range, or quartile deviation.
3. The relative position of individuals in groups, using T-scores, standard scores, or percentiles.
4. The relationship between two sets of scores for the same group, using an appropriate coefficient of correlation.

The advocated approach to statistical analysis as used for the illustrative problem is primarily concerned with the two basic statistics (mean and standard deviation) for the teacher to use in analyzing test results, and with a simplified, straight-forward procedure to obtain these desired statistics and the interpretative score (T-scores) derived from them. Additional methods of statistical computation of these basic statistics, and alternative and supplemental statistical tools, were described with relevance to the illustrative problem so as to equip the teacher to more fully comprehend the peculiarities or special circumstances that may be encountered in the analysis and interpretation of the results of measurement. Strong emphasis is placed upon the utilization of the T-score for physical education measurement, since it is a discriminating scale that affords meaningful comparison of scores for an individual or between individuals, as well as a means of equitable combination of an individual's performance on different tests into a composite score, when desired.

Comparative results for the sample problem illustrated the grouping error that is likely to occur when data are grouped for computation in contrast to direct computation from ungrouped scores. This error is deemed to be of no particular consequence for teacher use and, therefore, should not deter utilization of the grouping procedure as described when computational assistance is unavailable.

An awareness of the normal frequency distribution, its meaning and implications, sheds further light upon analysis of test results and provides a basis for developing a realization of the kind of information derived from the application of advanced statistical procedures for research procedures. The latter should serve to engender the teacher's conception of research methodology and interpreting results as expressed in research studies. A working knowledge of the basic statistical concepts and analysis presented herein becomes essential if the physical education teacher is to be not only prepared to, but also more likely to, utilize measurement effectively and to comprehend and use research reports more fully.

SELECTED REFERENCES

1. MEYERS, CARLTON R. *Basic Computations for Measurement in Physical Education.* Manchester, England: Technical Services Centre, Didsbury College of Education, 1971.
2. MEYERS, CARLTON R. *Essential Statistics for the Physical Education Teacher,* rev. ed. Buffalo: University Publication Services, State University of New York at Buffalo, 1973.
3. MONTOYE, HENRY J., ed. *Laboratory Manual of Exercises* (*An Introduction to Measurement in Physical Education,* Vol. 5). Indianapolis: Phi Epsilon Kappa Fraternity, 1970.
4. POPHAM, W., and SIROTNIK, K. A. *Educational Statistics: Use and Interpretation,* 2nd ed., New York: Harper & Row, Publishers, 1973.
5. REMMERS, H. H., GAGE, N. L., and RUMMEL, J. F. *A Practical Introduction to Measurement and Evaluation,* 2nd ed. New York: Harper & Row, Publishers, 1965.
6. SAFRIT, MARGARET J. *Evaluation in Physical Education.* Englewood Cliffs, N.J.: Prentice-Hall, Inc., 1973.

3

Selecting Tests

As pointed out earlier in describing the approach to measurement, in his quest to become more effective in teaching, the teacher should understand the many factors and considerations involved in test selection as well as in constructing tests scientifically—be they concerned with technical, associated, or concomitant learnings (that is, relating to educational objectives in the psychomotor, cognitive or affective domains). In order to utilize measurement efficiently and effectively, the teacher must be competent in selecting measurement tools and, where available tests do not meet teacher needs as desired, be able to devise an appropriate test scientifically. All of the competencies of a teacher in the field of tests and measurement are to no avail unless they include test selection and construction. The challenge to be met in this chapter lies in a meaningful depiction of the important concerns dealing with test selection, such as those posed in the illustrative problem, so as to engender teacher proficiency in this regard.

AN ILLUSTRATIVE PROBLEM

As an illustrative case in point, take the teacher who is responsible for fifth- and sixth-grade physical education for boys and girls and feels the need for an appropriate motor fitness test in view of national, state, and local interest and attention to the fitness of children and youth. Some tests are available for consideration by the teacher, including tests of national, state, and local scope. Do any of these tests meet the particular need for the teacher? If so, how effective are they in doing the job intended? Just how does the teacher determine the efficacy and appropriateness of a given test? These questions pose a simulated problem to provide the focus for presentation of factors and considerations involved in the selection of physical education tests.

BASIC TYPES OF TESTS

Tests may be classified in several different ways, irrespective of the type of learning involved—technical, associated, or concomitant. Classification may be according to: (1) purpose, into two types—*teaching* and *research;* (2) reference or basis for interpreting results, two types—*norm-referenced* and *criterion-referenced;* and (3) mode of construction, two types—*published tests* and *teacher-made tests.* For the types of tests derived from classification by purpose, the first group, teaching tests, consists of tests that characteristically possess practical value as teaching devices in the physical education program. The prime purpose behind their use resides in complementing and supplementing other teaching methods and materials to render learning most effective and comprehensive. This group constitutes the concern of the author herein—familiarity with available teaching tests in addition to an understanding of the desired procedure in devising one's own teaching tests.

The second group, research tests, is designed for research purposes, not for teaching. Accordingly, such tests serve to compile data and contribute to better understanding pertaining to the many and varied facets with which physical education and its teaching are concerned. Research, and the tests that comprise it, are fundamental to progress in any profession or aspect of living; hence the significance of this group of tests. The main difference between these two types of tests lies in the detailed, thorough, and time consuming format of the research test that by itself renders this test almost devoid of interest, let alone practicality, for routine teaching use. It should not be inferred that these two types of tests are in no way related, for actually they are. A teaching test may quite naturally and logically evolve from a research test. Certain items, sections, or complete tests of the research type may be adapted or modified for use as a teaching test. The reverse applies as well; in that the data and accompanying information derived from teaching tests may make a definite contribution to research. So while each of these test groups has a specific purpose, each in turn renders an important contribution to the other's purpose.

The second classification, according to the reference for interpretation, has evolved relatively recently from the distinguishing by measurement and instructional specialists between norm-referenced and criterion-referenced approaches to measurement. The more common and traditional norm-referenced test is used to identify an individual's performance with respect to the performance of others on the same measure. Thus it affords a picture of the spectrum of total performance of a particular group on a test or series of tasks. A criterion-referenced test is used to identify an individual's status relative to an established standard of performance. The American Red Cross swimming and life saving tests serve as examples of this "check list" approach of criterion-referenced tests, wherein the individual must perform certain skills or tasks satisfactorily to pass, irrespective of how well others perform on the test; a strict pass/fail distinction based on essentiality of the tasks that constitute a minimal satisfactory performance level. The reader will recognize that this approach to measurement is implicit in programmed learning and computer assisted instruction, where students complete a task correctly before proceeding to the next. Inasmuch as the norm-referenced approach is more appropriate in total perspective for teaching tests, which constitute the concern of this book, as well as affording the basis for and being readily adaptable to criterion—referenced measurement, focus is accorded to it. If the teacher should wish to select or develop a criterion-referenced test, the only modification involves the considerations for scientific authenticity, and then primarily for knowledge tests. However this presents no problem, since any special considerations will be readily apparent to the teacher who is conversant with norm-referenced tests.[1]

The last classification of tests, according to mode of construction, is not intended to imply a differential in quality between the two types—published and teacher-made—for quality should be sought regardless of the type. The mere fact of professional dissemination by publication is the differentiating characteristic. This classification by construction leads directly to the concern of this chapter—how to select good and appropriate tests—and then how to construct good and appropriate tests when none is available to meet a particular need or purpose. "Published tests" will be used to refer to all published tests, standardized or not. It should be recognized that, while most published tests are standardized, publication of a test does not predicate standardization.

In essence, standardization refers to the process of deriving comparative norms or achievement levels so that the scores of anyone taking the test can be compared with the attainments of the standard group to which the test was administered. The scores on a carefully prepared standardized test have more meaning and can be interpreted more objectively than those obtained on an ordinary informal teacher-made test. As now interpreted, however, test standardization means much more than the mere derivation of norms, although the existence of norms remains as the most distinctive feature of the standardized test. Briefly

---

[1] W. J. Popham and T. R. Husek. "Implications of Criterion-Referenced Measurement." *Journal of Educational Measurement,* 6, No. 1 (Spring, 1969), 1.

described, a standardized test reflects careful formulation of test content in light of specific test objectives, critical study of test items and their orderly arrangement, and rigid statistical analysis of results of administration to a specific group of testees (standard group).

A standardized test differs from a test in its original form or the usual teacher-made test in four essential aspects:

1. The content has been standardized; each item has survived the most careful scrutiny.
2. The method of test administration has been standardized, involving such matters as definite directions, appropriate time limits, and others.
3. The method of scoring has been standardized, which includes the preparation of scoring keys and instructions for marking and determining final scores.
4. The process of interpretation has been standardized; that is, tables of norms or the basic statistics to develop them are available for interpreting various scores made on the tests.[2]

Teacher-made tests can be readily developed into standardized tests, when appropriate, through provision of these four aspects.

The same careful thought and deliberation given to the construction of tests must be accorded to their use. Unfortunately, oftentimes a teacher succumbs to certain pitfalls regarding utilization of standardized tests, such as: (1) assuming that the test objectives are identical to his objectives, (2) being impressed with the appearance of a published test and assuming that the test measures something significant even if he cannot identify it, and (3) attempting to interpret scores without fully understanding the outcomes the test is designed to measure. When objectives of the test, content of material covered, and constituency of testees are in accord, then the standardized test is appropriate for the particular situation. Pertaining to the illustrative problem, the American Association for Health, Physical Education, and Recreation (AAHPER) Youth Fitness Tests exemplifies a standardized test on the national level, whereas the New York State Physical Fitness Test serves as an example of a state level standardized test appropriate for New York State.[3] The appropriateness of these or similar tests depends upon the aforementioned characteristics of the local situation.

When a test is desired but no available published tests meet the peculiarities involved, it will be necessary to devise a teacher-made test. In reality, this constitutes the source of many standardized tests—tests

[2] Adapted from C. C. Ross, *Measurement in Today's Schools* (2nd ed.; Englewood Cliffs, N.J.: Prentice-Hall, Inc., 1947), p. 282.

[3] The reader is referred to Chapter 8 for information regarding motor fitness tests published by other states.

designed for a particular situation, proven effective, subjected to thorough statistical analysis, and published for the information and use of teachers when suitable.

APPRAISING TEST VALUE

The key to effective utilization of measurement might well be concisely described as the ability to appraise the value of available tests and, when none of desired value is available, to construct appropriate tests scientifically. Certainly, an understanding of considerations involved in appraising test value is basic to test construction. Therefore, it seems only logical to discuss these factors first. The reader should continually view the ensuing discussion in light of the illustrative problem, which entails examining specifically the national, state, and local motor fitness tests as each test characteristic is presented. The fundamental considerations in appraising test value may be expressed as desirable test characteristics and arbitrarily categorized under the topical headings of scientific analysis, administrative feasibility, and teaching utility.

Scientific Analysis

In appraising the value of a test, attention is generally focused first upon an analysis to ascertain the extent to which the test has been devised scientifically. Unless a test is satisfactory in this aspect, no need exists to consider it further. This scientific analysis involves those desirable test characterisitcs dealing with validity, reliability, and norms.

Validity.   Does the motor fitness test, or any other test under deliberation, actually "tell the truth"? If the test measures motor fitness, or whatever it is intended to measure, then the test is telling the truth and possesses *validity*. That is, validity constitutes the degree to which the test fulfills its purpose. In considering validity, it should be recognized that validity is always specific in relation to some definite situation; that is, it must possess relevance. Such a thing as general validity does not exist. Tests can be described as valid only in terms of their intended use, including taking into account the ability level of students. Validity is specific also in that a test may be valid for use with one group (or age) of students but not valid for use with a different group of students. A sundial type of time measurement may be quite satisfactory for a camper, whereas a split-second watch is essential for officials of athletic events. It would appear almost as ridiculous to attempt to use a sundial to time an athletic event as it would to measure temperature or atmospheric pressure with it.

Validity constitutes the most important characteristic of a good test. Unless a test is valid, it serves no useful function. A test of motor fitness serves no useful function as a measure of motor fitness, unless it measures motor fitness. That is why extreme care should be exercised by teachers to assure the validity of tests used. In other words, to measure a particular quality the appropriate measuring device must be used; a ruler is not expected to measure time.

Validity, then, indicates the degree to which measurement represents the quality or characteristics being considered or to which the test is capable of achieving a certain purpose. Validity is classified into three types—criterion-related, content, and construct—on the basis of a joint report of the American Psychological Association, American Educational Research Association, and National Council on Measurement in Education.[4] The physical education teacher is primarily concerned with the first two types of test validity; criterion-related or empirical validity, and content or curricular validity.

Criterion-related validity refers to the amount of relationship that exists between the test in question and a criterion measure which is selected as being representative of the quality to be measured. For example, to what extent does a test of motor fitness that may be under consideration measure that quality, in comparison to a previously validated and generally accepted test of motor fitness chosen to constitute the criterion measure? This is criterion-related validity. As an illustration of the concept of validity in technical learning, and specifically criterion-related validity, a valid test of skill in tennis would correlate well with the criterion measure consisting of the final ranking of a ladder tournament conducted among the "test group." Those individuals who scored well on the tennis test would be among the leaders in the tournament ranking, if the test actually measures tennis ability. Contrariwise, in the event individuals scoring well on the tennis test were comparatively low in tournament ranking, the test would appear not to be valid; it does not measure tennis ability as revealed by competitive play. In instances when one known measure is not available, a composite of a number of specific factors that comprise the quality in question or the rating of expert judges afford a criterion measure. For instance, the rating of two or three teachers of the tennis ability for the classes in a particular school may prove more feasible as a criterion measure under certain conditions than either an existing test or tournament rankings. Accordingly, if none of the available motor fitness tests is deemed desirable as a criterion measure for the test in question, a composite of

[4] *Standards for Educational and Psychological Tests and Manuals* (Washington, D.C.: American Psychological Association, Inc., 1966).

items representing the various factors that seemingly comprise physical fitness as identified by Fleishman [5] would constitute a desirable criterion.

In interpreting criterion-related validity, heed should be paid to the fact that the comparison is between the test in question and the criterion measure, which serves as an indicant of validity. The amount of this relatedness between the test and the criterion is expressed statistically by a coefficient of correlation.[6] It should be realized that in essence the problem is not to determine which test is more valid, but rather how valid is a particular test in relation to the criterion measure used as the indicant of validity. Actually, the expression of statistical relationship discloses the degree to which a test measures the same quality or qualities as the criterion measure. In reality, therefore, a test can be proven no more valid than the test or measure used as the criterion.

Strictly interpreted, it should be recognized that two types of criterion-oriented validity can be identified, namely, concurrent and predictive. For *concurrent validity* the criterion data represent status on that measure at the same time the results on the test in question are given. The previously described illustrations of motor fitness and tennis represent the concurrent type of criterion-oriented validity. For *predictive validity* the criterion data are obtained at a later time than the results on the test in question. Presently the use of predictive validity is limited in physical education, although tests of motor capacity or athletic potential reflect this feature wherein a test is used to predict the subsequent performance of individuals on the criterion.

Content validity, as suggested by its title, expresses the relationship of the test to: an analysis of a course or unit of study or of performance in a particular skill; recommendations of test specialists; or local determination of objectives and outcomes. This relationship is expressed by describing the criterion and stating the relative degree of relationship deemed to exist, such as, high, satisfactory, or low. Succinctly stated, content validity entails showing how well the test samples the performance or subject matter about which conclusions are to be drawn. Although used rather extensively for written tests, content validity is not restricted to tests of associated learning. It is used for concomitant learning measures as well as for tests of technical learning. In the area of technical learning the terms face validity, logical validity, or descriptive validity are sometimes used to describe what is actually content validity. For example, validation of the 50-yard dash as a test of speed would be accepted on the basis of its content or face validity. Another

---

[5] Edwin A. Fleishman, *The Structure and Measurement of Physical Fitness* (Englewood Cliffs: Prentice-Hall, Inc., 1964).

[6] Because of this and in contrast to content and construct validity, this type of validity is sometimes referred to as *statistical validity*.

example would be the development of a test of softball throwing ability based on analysis of the skill as utilized in the game itself.

Construct validity is concerned with determining what qualities a test measures by demonstrating that certain explanatory concepts or constructs account for performance on the test. This type of validity is of little practical consequence for the physical education teacher. In the main, studies of construct validity check on the theory underlying the test and are inferential rather than conclusive. Construct validity is ordinarily used when the tester has no definitive criterion, and when he wishes to study the psychological qualities being measured by the test.

When validity is expressed as a correlation coefficient, the following chart will serve as a guide in interpreting the meaning of the coefficient:

A Validity Coefficient of:	Indicates a Correlation That Is:
.85 or above	High
.80–.84	Very good
.70–.79	Fair to good
.60–.69	Poor
.59 and below	Illustrative of a generally unuseful test

A later discussion of validity determination relating to test construction will be more definitive in fostering a clear conception of validity.

Reliability. Can the motor fitness test, or any other test, under consideration, be relied upon? Is it trustworthy? If the test measures motor fitness, or whatever it may measure, consistently, it can be regarded as trustworthy and possesses *reliability*. Reliability, then, refers to the degree of consistency of results obtained by a measuring instrument—the extent to which a test agrees with itself or to which the measuring instrument gives a constant score for a constant degree of that which it measures. Depending upon the quality being measured, this test characteristic may be expressed as the extent to which (a) a test gives the same results when repeated, (b) a test is internally consistent, or (c) two or more forms of a test can be relied upon to give the same results. In essence a highly reliable test should yield basically the same score when administered twice to the same individual, provided that no learning occurs while the test is being taken or that no learning or forgetting occurs in the interim between tests.

A simple measuring tape serves as an instrument to illustrate reliability. Consistent results can be obtained through use of a steel tape, whereas a cloth tape is apt to yield inconsistent results due to its tendency to stretch in varying amounts under strain. To apply the previously used illustrations to reliability, a reliable motor fitness or tennis skill test administered to a particular group by a given instructor would yield consistent results when repeated by the same instructor a week later. Ideally, in the case of a tennis skill test, such a test would be administered at a time when testees would not be likely to have an opportunity to play tennis between tests. Further considerations pertaining to reliability will be discussed in relation to test construction.

Reliability may be regarded as an aspect of validity in the sense that a test must be reliable in order to be valid, that is, measure accurately the thing it was intended to measure. This relationship of reliability to validity is one-way so that, while reliability is not only essential to but sets limits on validity, satisfactory reliability is no guarantee of validity. A test can be highly reliable without being valid. The mere fact that an instrument measures something accurately does not mean that it is necessarily measuring what it is intended to measure. For instance, the aforementioned tennis test may give consistent results, but its high-scoring individiuals may be low in the tournament ranking. The test would then be reliable but not valid. The test measures what it measures consistently (reliability) but does not measure competitive tennis ability as intended (validity).

Because of this one-way relationship, it is practical to consider reliability before validity. Actually the reliability of an instrument determines the ceiling of maximum validity that can be attained. If the reliability is low, it must be increased before the test can possibly attain the desired validity. Only when the reliability coeffcient is above 0.80, and preferably above 0.90, can the test be a highly valid assessment of performance. The maximum potential validity of an instrument can be estimated from the square root of the reliability coefficient, that is, Validity limit prediction $= \sqrt{r_t}$. Thus, a test with a reliability coefficient of 0.80 would possess potential validity up to 0.90 ($\sqrt{0.80} = 0.90$); for a reliability coefficient of 0.50 it would be 0.70. It must be emphasized that this formula affords only an *estimate* of the *maximum possible* validity and should not be misconstrued as predicting test validity *per se*.

The following key is applicable in interpreting the reliability and objectivity coefficients.

0.90–0.99	High correlation. Most physical education tests involving such variables as strength, explosive speed, jumping, and throwing for distance are objective and as such should lend themselves to consistent measurement.
0.80–0.89	Good correlation. Satisfactory for individual measurement.
0.70–0.79	Fair correlation. Satisfactory for group measurement but generally unsatisfactory for individual measurement.

0.69 and below   Poor correlation. Satisfactory for school surveys and
group comparisons.

As a rule of thumb, when possible, it is desirable to have the coefficient
reach at least 0.75 for group use or 0.85 for individual use.

Standard Error of Measurement. Another concept that is used to
express reliability of a test and discloses pertinent information for the
teacher in test selection is characterized by the statistical tool known as
the *standard error of measurement* (*SE*).[7] Succinctly described, the
standard error of measurement indicates the amount of error to allow
for when interpreting individual test scores or, strictly speaking, the accuracy of a test score. To clearly differentiate the standard error of
measurement from reliability coefficients, the latter describes the relative
accuracy with which groups of individuals are ranked by a test; whereas,
the standard error of measurement expresses in test units the absolute
accuracy or amount of fluctuation that could be expected in repeated
testing of an individual. Since any test reflects but a sample of a subject's performance, it can be expected to include some error and, therefore, constitutes an estimate of an individual's true score. A multitude
of factors (such as the testee's physical and emotional state, and environmental setting) may influence the test performance and tend to
make an individual's score higher or lower than the true score. If the subject is given a retest or another equivalent test, other factors or a different combination of factors may be present and affect the score. The
results of these many factors and their interaction are not reproducible,
since they may not always be present or exert the same effect, but taken
together these factors comprise the error component of an individual's
score. In essence then, all obtained scores consist of two parts—one
associated with error factors, and the other a true score component.

If the same individual were to be tested many times over with the
same test, which obviously is not practical, a distribution of scores would
be obtained. The mean of this distribution of scores would be an estimate of the individual's true score, and the standard deviation of these
scores would be the standard error of measurement. That is, the standard
error of measurement is the standard deviation that is expected in a
given subject's scores when the same test is administered several times.
Because of the impracticality of repeating the same test for a person, the
standard error of measurement for a test is estimated from group data.

[7] It is included here rather than in Chapter 2, because the concern is to describe
the concept of standard error of measurement as an aspect of test selection rather
than a statistic for teacher computation. To clarify the relationship between reliability, standard error of measurement and objectivity, reliability can be viewed as
test reliability per se, standard error of measurement as testee reliability, and objectivity as tester reliability.

It is determined by the formula: $SE = s\sqrt{1 - r_t}$, where s and r_t are standard deviation and reliability of the test.

From this formula it can be seen that the standard error of measurement will approximate 0 as the test reliability approaches being perfect, and as the reliability coefficient decreases in magnitude the standard error of measurement increases. This relationship can be illustrated by assuming the same standard deviation of scores (for example, 10) for different forms of a test that have reliability coefficients of 0.91, 0.84 and 0.75, respectively. The following standard errors show that the more reliable the test, the less the standard error of measurement:

$$\text{For } r = 0.91 \quad SE = 10\sqrt{1 - 0.91} = 3$$
$$r = 0.84 \quad SE = 10\sqrt{1 - 0.84} = 4$$
$$r = 0.75 \quad SE = 10\sqrt{1 - 0.75} = 5$$

It should be evident that the standard error of measurement is actually a special kind of standard deviation which indicates the amount of error in a test attributable to unreliability.

The standard error of measurement is interpreted as any standard deviation, so that the standard error taken on either side of the mean accounts for 68 per cent of the cases. Thus, for a score of 45 on a test for which $SE = 3$, the chances are 2 out of 3 that the obtained score is no more than 3 score units from the true score, that is, within the range 42–48. In other words, the standards error of a score tells the range within which scores on the same test would be expected to fall approximately two-thirds of the time if a large number of the tests, equivalent in all respects, were given to the same students. By further application of the normal curve model it can be expected that a 95 per cent probability exists that the true score will lie within 2 standard errors of the score, or within 6 score units of a score of 45 with $SE = 3$, or within the range 39–51.

The limitation imposed on a test with a large standard error of measurement should be apparent, since the precision with which the test can be used for any purpose is materially reduced. In summation, in interpreting the standard error of measurrement the smaller its size, the more confidence that can be placed in the obtained score.

Objectivity. Can consistent results be obtained from the use of the same means of measurement by different individuals? If so, the test possesses *objectivity*. Whereas reliability is concerned with the consistency of the test itself, objectivity entails consistency of test results obtained by different test administrators. Included in analyzing the ability of different examiners to get the same results are matters pertaining to the actual administration of the test as well as concerns in scoring the test performances. Thus, it becomes apparent that objectivity (referred to as tester or examiner reliability by some authors) depends upon clarity of directions, standardized procedure for using the particular means of measurement, and standardized procedure for scoring the results of this particular measuring instrument.

As shown previously, the steel tape is a reliable measuring instrument. Given standardized directions for its use, different officials at a track meet could measure the same broad jump performance with this tape and secure consistent results—thus reflecting satisfactory objectivity. While reliability and objectivity are closely related, satisfactory reliability does not guarantee objectivity. Only when proper considerations are taken and factors are such as to insure similar test administration can objectivity be anticipated. To illustrate objectivity, a motor fitness or a tennis skill test of satisfactory objectivity would yield consistent results when given to the same group by different individuals, other factors being equal, such as no influential learning experiences between tests, and the like.

In summarizing the description of this test characteristic, it can be broadly stated that the degree to which all qualified observers can agree on the description of a performance determines its degree of objectivity.

Norms and Directions. Is a set of norms or achievement levels available for the test under consideration? This desirable test characteristic, the last of those included under scientific analysis, is concerned with a prepared description of test performance made by a defined group—regarded as typical for the purposes involved—for use in interpreting and analyzing the results of a test. Simply stated, a norm represents the achievement level of a particular group to which an obtained score may be compared. Therefore, unless the norms accompanying a test reflect an accurate picture of typical accomplishment, they are not only useless but in reality deceitful.

A clear conception of norms may be enhanced by describing the derivation of norms for a particular test. The factors to be considered in establishing norms include the following:

1. *The sampling procedures should be based on a wide distribution of the population.* Regardless of the test level—national, regional, state, or local—the sample should include the length and breadth of the population distribution involved.

2. *The sampling should entail a relaitvely large number of cases.*

3. *The testing sample should be representative of the population for which the test is intended and should be selected on a random basis.*

A test should have representation of the various areas of the geographical region for which it is designed, including rural and urban, and should reflect approximately the same proportion as actually exists. Using a national sampling for illustration purposes, a certain percentage of high school students in this country are found in cities over 500,000, and a certain percentage are found in cities from 100,000 to 500,000 population. Also, a certain percentage of elementary school pupils receive their education in small rurals schools. The testing sample should represent these three illustrative groups to approximately the same extent as is found in the entire national population, thus constituting a proportionate stratified sample. Also, selection of the actual groups to be tested should be made at random in an endeavor to insure realistic representation within each group and the population as a whole.

Thus, in evaluating norms, attention should be directed to insure several provisions, namely: (1) that a sufficient number of subjects are included for the comparison group to guarantee desirable accuracy of normed scores; (2) that the data reflect a representative and random sampling of the population involved; and (3) that the norms were intended for use with the specific group involved, that is, care must be exercised to prevent the application of norms to groups for which they were not intended.

This would mean that to evaluate the norms of the AAHPER Youth Fitness Test, as a case in point, consideration must be given to the number, age or grade level, and appropriate geographical distribution of subjects involved, as well as whether the sample was selected on an appropriate random basis. In light of these factors, the decision is made regarding the suitability of the norms for a particular situation. Norms for a state-level fitness test would be evaluated similarly in light of the aforementioned factors for consideration. However, it should be readily discernible that norms on a state level should be more meaningful, since many of the divergences resulting from geographical location are eliminated and the test is specifically designed for use with a comparatively more homogeneous group. This serves to indicate that the more specific the norm, the more useful it becomes. Local norms would be more meaningful than those at state or national level. And for the individual the norms pertaining to a particular school or school district become even more meaningful. That is to say, the closer to the individual the normative group is, the greater the comparability and significance; particularly in physical education measurement where differences in the characteristics and experiences of students and in testing variables tend to increase and render comparison less meaningful the further removed from the individual the standard group becomes. This then explains the axiom that should permeate use of norms, namely, *the individual*

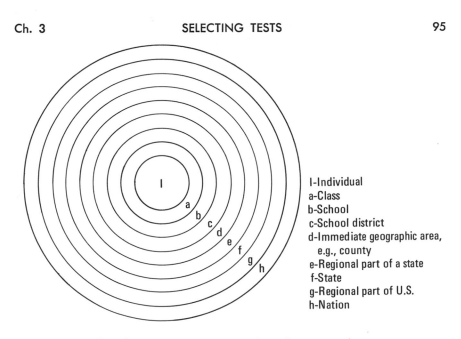

I-Individual
a-Class
b-School
c-School district
d-Immediate geographic area,
   e.g., county
e-Regional part of a state
f-State
g-Regional part of U.S.
h-Nation

Fig. 3–1. Normative groupings in perspective.

represents his own best norm. Figure 3–1 illustrates the relevance of norms in concentric circle format where the individual represents the center and the most meaningful norm groups for the individual are those immediately surrounding him, namely, class, school, and school district. Succinctly, the meaningfulness of norms is inversely related to the proximity to the individual.

While not related to norm construction as such, another factor of importance to be considered in evaluating norms is how old are the norms. Caution should be exercised to insure that the norms are still applicable after passage of time. Obviously, no arbitrary maximum time limit can be stipulated for the applicability of norms, since this is a function of the changing nature of the quality involved. For instance, norms for the national and selected state motor fitness tests were revised several years after their inception, because students then at the various grade levels had been exposed to concerted attention to motor fitness and improved physical education programs which the original comparison or standard group had not experienced. As a result the original norms were rendered inappropriate; students taking a particular test were no longer comparable to the standard group. Thus, there was a need to up-date the norms by administering the test to another group for standardization.

One further concern that is easily overlooked in evaluating norms warrants consideration. In many instances the time of year or period of time during which the normed test was administered is an important factor relative to the appropriateness of the norms. Therefore, attention should be directed to insuring that the norms for a test under consideration were gathered during the time of year that coincides with the teacher's plans for use of the test. For instance, the meaningfulness of norms on a motor fitness test given near the end of a school year is speculative and certainly questionable, if the teacher plans to give the test in the fall of the year. Obviously, the students comprising the normed group would have experienced almost a school year in physical education at the grade or age level involved, whereas the students constituting the fall test administration would be about eight months behind, developmentally and in terms of experience in physical education. In this instance if comparability with the norms for the standard group is deemed important, the teacher would need to find a test with norms developed in the fall or delay administration of this test until the spring. If this comparability with the standard group is not particularly important, the test may be used in the fall but, since the norms would be inappropriate, the teacher would be restricted to the data obtained in the local administration of the test in interpreting the scores.

As an admonitory note it warrants mention that an overzealous and unjustified regard for norms has been a deterrent to testing progress and enhanced test validity. Specific reference is to the apparent reluctance in physical education measurement to make necessary changes for improvement of test items because of the uncomparability with previous noms, which in many instances are actually inappropriate for one or more reasons. This attitude prevents the incorporation of better test items and perpetuates unsatisfactory ones. Furthermore, it reflects a serious misconception regarding norms and reliance upon them at levels most remote to the individual and his immediate group. In proper perspective these desirable test changes will result in tangible benefits such as increased test value and administrative feasibility, as well as important intangible ones such as minimizing the legitimacy of "anti-testing" attitudes. The accruing benefits thus become more important in the long run than norms per se, which can be readily developed.

Upon what are norms based? Generally, norms are based upon age or grade, physical characteristics such as height and weight, or various combinations of age and physical characteristics that may be expressed as an index of some kind. The national AAHPER Youth Fitness Test contains two sets of norms tables. The first set is based upon age, whereas the other tables are based on the Neilson–Cozens Classification Index, which combines age, height, and weight. Hence, the performance of a group or a particular student can be compared to these national norms by using either age or classification index. The comparison should then be interpreted to reveal the group or individual performance in light of the standard national group from which norms were derived. For example, a teacher has administered the AAHPER Youth Fitness Test to a class group and compares the class performance to the appropriate table for the average age of the students. This comparison informs the teacher how the performance of this class stands in relation to the national standard group upon which norm tables are based. Entering the appropriate table for a particular test event with a particular student's score will afford a means of ascertaining an individual student's performance in relation to the national norms. It might be pointed out that subsequent retests take on added significance by making possible appraisal of individual and group performance in terms of past performance as well as national norms.

In summary, norms serve to furnish a reliable and useful basis for interpretation and application of test results to the extent that the sampling is truly representative and conditions affecting the administration of the test are rigidly replicated. The latter stipulation necessitates clear and definite directions concerning both administering and scoring the test. Are clear and concise directions available for administering and scoring the test under consideration? Are there any unanswered questions pertaining to administering and scoring it? A response of yes and no, respectively, should be elicited by these two questions to indicate a desirable test. Without carefully devised instructions, a number of variables may exercise different influences on the scores attained and, consequently, render the norms relatively meaningless. Only when caution is observed to insure that any administration of a given test duplicates as closely as possible the initial administration to the group upon which the norms are based, can reasonable assurance be held for the reliability and usefulness of the norms.

Consequently, the test should be accompanied by a detailed set of directions that fully delineates the procedures to be followed in administering the test. The directions should include considerations specifically for the teacher or test administrator and those to be read to the testees. The directions should be inclusive and readily comprehensible in all aspects, leaving no room for teacher interpretation, and no need for supplemental instructions for the testees. If the standardized directions are not sufficiently clear and thorough, the likelihood of variation in the manner in which the test is given increases and the comparability with norms for the standard group becomes not only reduced but also inappropriate.

Administrative Feasibility

After critical analysis of a test to determine whether it possesses scientific authenticity, the next step in appraising test value is an examination of the factors that constitute the administrative feasibility of utilizing the test in question in a particular situation. Is it practical to use the test under deliberation? The factors comprising administrative feasibility, or what may be descriptively termed "usability," may be enumerated as (1) ease of administration and scoring, (2) justifiable cost, and (3) adaptability to purpose. That is, the question of administraitve feasibility resolves itself to the fact that the test should be easy to use, while the cost of its use is within reason, and the objective the test is intended to serve conforms to its designed purpose.

Ease of Administering and Scoring. Is the test under consideration easy to use? This question should be interpreted to infer ease of administration and scoring *relative to the value accrued.* How easy is the test to use in light of the benefits derived from such usage? Actually, the desired test in this regard would be one that provides the best possible results while still possessing a desirable degree of ease in usage.

Basically, this particular consideration involves demands made by a test upon students and school personnel alike. Such demands entail both time and effort. A desired test would not make unjustifiable demands upon the time required by, and effort necessitated on the part of students and testers, but rather would be designed to facilitate administration of the test. In a motor fitness test or any physical performance test, as in ordinary physical education class activity, the emphasis should be upon maximum activity by participants in a given period of time. The physical education teacher organizes each class session with a view to providing the maximum participation possible for students. Likewise, a test should lend itself to administration whereby the greatest possible activity of testees is maintained, so as to minimize the time and effort needed to carry out the test.

Duplicate or equilavent forms of a test are a consideration that contributes appreciably to the case of administering tests, particularly tests of associated learning—knowledge and understanding. Presently, the availability of equivalent forms of skill tests is limited, and the contribution to ease of administration is not as significant as in the case of tests of associated learning. A number of tests of knowledge and understanding are available in equivalent forms, which makes administering to large groups and retesting an easier matter.

While a physical performance test is being administered, the various test items must be scored; and upon completion of the test, the total score must be computed. Regardless of the type of test—technical, associated, or concomitant learning—the ease of scoring a test depends largely upon the objective nature of the test items, adequate measuring and recording devices or scoring keys, and complete yet concise directions for scoring. Including test items of an objective nature facilitates scoring by providing for a definitive, relatively precise recording of performance, thus endeavoring to minimize subjective judgment in rating performance and the requisite training of raters generally entailed. To illustrate provision for such objectivity, the scores on the AAHPER Youth Fitness are recorded as either number of repetitions of an activity, as for pull-ups; distance covered, as in the standing broad jump; or elapsed time, as in the 50-yard dash.

The availability of adequate measuring and recording devices for test items notably affects the ease of scoring. In the foregoing illustration of test items, all that is required for basic equipment consists of a steel measuring tape and one or more stop watches, both of which are easy to use. The physical setup or layout of sheets for recording scores, ratings or answers plays an important part in facilitating scoring. When test scores are conducive to such handling, machine scoring contributes greatly to the case of scoring tests.

Complete scoring directions do much to facilitate scoring as well as to contribute to the objectivity of the test and applicability of the norms. Even in objective measurement involving the standing broad jump with a measuring tape or the 50-yard dash with the stop watch, specificity in directions becomes necessary to indicate clearly to what particular unit of distance or time measurement the performance should be recorded —to the nearest inch or foot, tenth of a second or second.

Justifiable Cost. Is the cost entailed in the test justified in light of the value derived from its use? Cost involves not only the test itself but also the equipment required. The cost of the test itself, scoring sheets, and the like is of greater concern for written tests and rating scales than for physical performance tests. But the reverse is true regarding equipment for the test; in which case considerable expense may be necessary for the physical activity tests. Analysis of the AAHPER Youth Fitness Test in terms of necessary equipment reveals that nothing is required that is not generally found in the physical education equipment inventory. Certain other tests require special equipment that is largely, if not entirely, of use only for the specific test in question, such as the Rogers Strength Test to cite an example. Justification for such expenditures lies in the contribution of the test to the program objectives. If the cost of the test and equipment does not present financial demands disproportionate to the potential educational contribution of the information provided by the test, then the expenditure would appear warranted. Where the cost appears to make unreasonable financial demands and would thereby necessitate unwarranted limitation of other aspects of the physical education program, the cost cannot be justified.

Adaptability of Purpose. A final concern to be expressed under administrative feasibility may be contained in the following questions. Are the test objectives and the teacher objectives for the test in accord? Is the test appropriate? Does purpose of the test conform to the teacher need for a test? Does it provide the information that is desired to meet a definite teaching objective? Is the purpose and value of the content of a test compatible with the purpose for which a test is needed?

In considering a motor fitness test, such as the AAHPER Test for purposes of illustration, it should educe performance compatible with the type of physical education program offered, which is determined by such factors as the particular school educational objectives; the school organizational pattern; and characteristics of students, facilities, and climate. For instance, the climatic conditions affecting a given program may be such as to limit seriously the opportunity for outdoor activity in running and throwing. Testing results obtained in such events would be comparatively poor and meaningless on a national test for such a physical education program.

All justifiable testing is purposeful. So a test that appears to serve satisfactorily a definite need in the situation in which it is used and fits naturally into it, in terms of suitability to program, locality, and students, may be described as possessing this characteristic—adaptability of purpose.

Teaching Utility

After a test is analyzed and known to be satisfactory in terms of having scientific authenticity and being administratively feasible, the practicability of the test as a teaching device must still be determined. Granted, considerations included under these two topical headings influence its value as a teaching device. However, attention is now directed to additional desirable characteristics of a test that have not been specifically covered and yet determine markedly the teaching usability. The particular concern of the following test characteristics then lies in the question: Does the test under consideration reflect effective and efficient teaching methodology? As conceived herein, teaching utility encompasses such considerations as:

1. Entailing important abilities performed under conditions similar to actual use.
2. Eliciting skillful performance of one individual.
3. Possessing interest, meaning, and appropriate difficulty for performers.
4. Providing accurate and adequate record of performance.

Important Abilities in Actual Use. Does the test entail important abilities performed under conditions similar to actual use? The vital issue in this consideration is that the performance elicited be significant to the activity (in sport skills) or characteristic (in traits or general qualities) with which the test deals and represents actuality as nearly as possible. In the case of a motor fitness test, the various items included should all involve qualities regarded as important to motor fitness so as to reflect a realistic level of motor fitness in light of emphases characterizing American educational and recreational programs. For sport skill tests, the items accorded prime consideration should be those involving skills that are basic to the fundamental purpose of the game or otherwise present vital concern. This consideration implies that teachers should compile a list of important skills comprising each activity or general quality for use as a ready reference in test selection and construction. Knowing what abilities are deemed important provides the basis for selecting and constructing appropriate tests.

Mere inclusion of important abilities alone, however, does not fully satisfy this test characteristic. Care should be taken that the skill is not completely out of context but is performed under conditions simulating, as nearly as possible, the actual performance situation. A test in throwing as part of a softball ability test affords a classic example. Nowhere in a game situation does a fielder have undue time to make a throw to a baseman or other player. Yet oftentimes a softball test can be found to include a throwing test of unhurried and, thereby, unrealistic throws. A gamelike test should more properly consist of actually receiving the ball and then throwing at a target with some provision or design feature to include the pressure of time. Satisfying the requirements of this test characteristic will insure that a test measures important abilities under actual or nearly actual conditions.

Skillful Performance of One Individual. Does the test elicit skillful performance of one individual? This stipulates that good form be required in executing the activity and that only a single testee be involved at one time. Heed should be paid to insure that testees using poor form cannot score as well or better than individuals displaying good form. For example, a test on the short serve in badminton should differentiate between the expert server who drops each service into the high-point area with the bird flight close to the net and the less proficient server who also hits the high-point area but with a high arcing flight well above the net. Reference is also made to averting test situations in which testees might adopt special peculiarities of technique to score better on a test than may be possible by precise execution of the particular skill involved. Certain volley tests in tennis and volleyball with the stress on time may tend to encourage unorthodox technique, which is not only in poor form but also is not "gamelike."

The items of a motor fitness test likewise warrant attention to call for skillful performance, as well as consideration of the second aspect of this test characteristic; namely, that the performance of one individual is not influenced by the activity of another. In other words, each test should involve one performer only so that an individual's performance is not affected by the variability of the performance of a second individual who serves to cooperate or compete in the testing situation. A test of ability in the tennis forehand drive using an assistant or aid to put the ball into play illustrates such a variable. A poorly thrown or stroked ball from the assistant will markedy influence the caiber of the forehand drive executed. A series of well-placed balls for poorly skilled testees might conceivably result in better scores for these testees than comparable scores of skilled players who were forced to play poorly thrown balls. Utilization of a ball-tossing machine in this situation removes the objectional element.

A desirable test, then, will encourage the skillful performance of an individual; and the results will be solely attributable to the testee and not to the variable and fluctuating cooperative or competitive performance of another individual.

An Appropriate Challenge for Performers. Does the test possess interest, meaning, and appropriate difficulty for performers? A desirable teaching device certainly should afford a challenge to students that is appropriate in terms of provoking interest, possessing meaning, and displaying compatible (but demanding) difficulty. Interest and meaning do accrue from the previously mentioned characteristics of teaching utility, but specific attention is directed to them inasmuch as their presence is vital to test value as a teaching device and should not be left to chance or concomitant provision. Interest and meaning are necessary to foster attainment of the best effort by students in test performance. Motivating interest and enhancing meaningfulness can be fostered by test design and the content itself, as well as suitable means of interpreting and applying the results. Intimately connected with interest and meaning is the matter of appropriate difficulty. Some tests are too hard, or too easy, or fail to discriminate adequately between slightly different levels of ability. Since such tests do not present suitable difficulty for the individuals being tested, interest and meaning cannot prevail. Interest and meaningfulness are both nurtured and maintained by a comprehendible scoring system and means of interpretation of results through which it is possible to advise students of their performance and its significance without undue delay.

Considering the illustrative chapter problem, school children throughout the nation, as well as the populace in general, are certainly more aware of the concern for youth fitness today than ever before in history; which fact can be utilized to develop interest and meaning. An analysis of the AAHPER Test or other motor fitness tests being appraised must be made to determine whether the test items are conducive to develop interest and meaning along with scoring techniques, achievement awards, and other supplementary material. The question of the appropriateness of difficulty of the test must also be resolved. By fulfilling this test characteristic, a test furthers substantially its case as a desirable teaching test.

A Suitable Record of Performance. Does the test provide an accurate and adequate record of performance? Generally, a test that cannot be scored accurately possesses poor reliability and objectivity. But more important from the standpoint of teaching usability, since reliability and objectivity are considered separately under scientific analysis, is the matter of testee morale. Accurate scoring of a test engenders a feeling of satisfaction among students in contrast to a test in which results cannot be measured accurately.

The softball thrown at a target of concentric circles leaves some question (without elaborate electric light zone indicators or the like) regarding balls hitting on or nearly on lines. A softball thrown at a hole in the target area gives more definitive results. At this point it should be recognized that a compromise between accuracy and the number of trials to secure an adequate record may be made. Ideally, it may be desirable to have a softball thrown at a precise hole target for a great number of times. However, because of time limitations, it may be deemed advisable to sacrifice accuracy somewhat with the use of concentric circles and reduce the number of trials sufficiently to be within the realm of practicality. The number of trials permitted in each test item warrants serious thought. Generally speaking, the number of trials necessary to provide a truly representative score is derived empirically. The number of trials allowed should suffice to minimize chance variations. The greater the element of chance found, the greater should be the number of trials given. Tests involving maximum effort, where control plays no significant role, may be measured in one to three trials. The number of trials must be increased when performance is based upon accuracy. That is, if a high degree of accuracy typifies skilled performance, then the number of trials must be greater. As previously described, the type of scoring affects the number of trials. Success or failure tests necessitate more trials than tests in which each attempt is scored for relative accuracy, as illustrated by concentric circle targets. Furthermore, the number of trials is related to the ability level of performers. Less trials are quite often needed for advanced or skilled performers than for less proficient individuals on the same test. The purpose served by a test also influences the number of trials. For example, fewer trials would be necessary for diagnostic or classification purposes.

In considering the accuracy and adequacy of the record of performance, a point of no return should be recognized by the teacher. This is the point below which it is undesirable to reduce the number of trials in an event to save testing time. Rather, the selection of tests should be limited to the most important qualities to preserve the accuracy and adequacy of those items recorded. It should be recognized in evaluating a test that the test authors have carefully scrutinized the test in this regard and any modification a teacher chooses to make in the number of trials will render the norms invalid.

Review of the suitability of the record of performance afforded by a test completes the analysis to ascertain the practicability of the test as a teaching device. And this in turn completes the analysis of the fundamental considerations involved in appraising test value, be it either for purposes of test selection or as the basis for test construction.

PROCEDURE IN TEST SELECTION

After the foregoing presentation of the desirable characteristics of a test that comprise test value and thus afford the basis for test selection, it would appear appropriate to describe briefly the procedure to follow in selecting a test. Simply stated, the procedure consists of defining the need, appraising the value of a test to determine if it satisfactorily meets the desired value, and then selecting the best one of the tests appraised as desirable. The steps in the suggested selection procedure can be depicted most vividly in the form of questions to be resolved.

1. *What is needed?* Basic to test selection, the teacher should define the purpose for which a test is needed; that is, delineate the objectives for the test. What is to be measured and the intended use of test results should be indicated.

2. *By its characteristics of design, does the test meet this need?* The purpose and content value of the test being considered should be examined to insure that the characteristics and purpose of the test are in accord with the purpose for testing. Also entailed for achievement tests is the consideration that the test content distribution should coincide with emphases in the course; the same proportionate emphasis given to various phases of activity during instruction is reflected in test content. Succinctly stated, the test should elicit the type of performance that is desired.

3. *Is the test appropriate for the particular physical education program concerned?* The test should be compatible with the type of program offered and program emphases as determined by characteristics of the local situation, such as educational philosophy, location, facilities, and the nature of the students.

4. *Is it a good test in terms of scientific consideration?* A critical scientific analysis provides information regarding the validity, reliability, objectivity, and norms and directions for the test. Unless a test possesses the desired technical aspects of a measuring instrument, its selection cannot be justified. In analyzing the various scientific considerations attention should be directed beyond the statistics and other summary findings to the procedure followed in deriving these findings. This is important, because appraisal of quality of a test rests upon a careful examination of the procedures used in constructing the test and on a judgment regarding the adequacy of those procedures. For example, a highly satisfactory validity coefficient is meaningless if the criterion is inappropriate; consequently the manner in which the reported facts are derived is a necessary aspect of this question. And an implicit concern not to be overlooked is to insure that the scientific authenticity is relevant to the intended age group. A test may be reliable or valid at one grade level and unreliable or invalid at another.

5. *Is the test administratively feasible?* This includes administering and scoring the test and its cost in addition to the consideration regarding the adaptability of purpose as covered by questions 2 and 3 above. The realm of practicality may pose restrictions that will need to be reconciled in choosing a test, given satisfactory answers to the aforementioned questions.

6. *Does the test possess teaching utility?* The test should possess the desirable characteristics that comprise usability as a teaching device. The meaningfulness and appropriateness of a test for a particular group or educational setting is controlled by the factors comprising teaching utility.

7. *On the basis of the overall appraisal of value, questions 1 to 6, does the test satisfactorily realize the value desired; and, if so, how does it compare with other desirable tests?* This step constitutes the actual selection of the test deemed most desirable of those tests that are available. As described, the consideration in this final step is twofold: (a) to determine whether the test possesses the value desired in a test on a relative basis, and (b) to select the best test available from among those regarded as desirable in terms of value. Realistically it should be recognized that the appraisal of overall value of a test will sometimes not be a clear-cut

acceptable or unacceptable. But rather, the decision may be to judge the test acceptable for use in the intended context, while recognizing certain limiting factors or conditions. Perhaps the test can be organized to obviate these limitations, or maybe the results will have to be interpreted in light of them. It is anticipated that such qualified acceptance will be the exception. Furthermore, in such instances it is recommended that the teacher give first consideration to the construction of a satisfactory test. In some instances norms may be unavailable, out-of-date, or otherwise inappropriate. Nevertheless the teacher may select such a test if it is satisfactory in all other aspects, with the realization that test interpretation will be limited to locally developed norms.

The questions entailed in the selection process make it apparent that certain basic information about each test is needed. In order to be able to appraise a test accurately and render the test sound, the teacher should obtain as complete descriptive information about the test as possible. This descriptive information is generally contained in the test manual but, if not, can be obtained from the authors or publishers of a particular test. The information should include such items as:

1. Purpose of the test.
2. For whom intended—sex and age level.
3. Description of test items.
4. Equipment needed.
5. Leadership needed.
6. Time requirements, including number that can be tested.
7. Adequate instructions.
8. Testing organization and procedure.
9. Scoring and recording plan.
10. Description of procedures of construction, including:
    a. Number and representativeness of test group.
    b. Validity.
    c. Reliability and standard error of measurement.
    d. Objectivity.
    e. Norms.
11. Limitations.
12. Rating of test by experts.

As is readily discernible, these items that constitute a description of the test encompass the *way, what, where,* and *how* of the test. That is, *why* use this test, respecting its purpose and intended use; *what* is included in the test as to content, and *what* is the evidence concerning scientific test design; *where* conduct the test, with referenec to facility and equipment considerations; and *how* best to organize, administer and score the test and utilize the results, realizing its limitations and its rating by test experts. This material should lead to a thorough understanding of the test in question, and in turn to a more accurate determination of test value, and hence favorably contribute to the process of test selection.

To exemplify this aforementioned approach in test selection, reference can be made to the illustrative problem in which the concern is to fiind an appropriate test of motor fitness for boys and girls on the fifth-and sixth-grade levels, be it of national, regional, state, or local scope. The teacher must first carefully delineate the purpose for which this test is desired—for example, to serve as a measure of motor fitness of boys and girls—and then set out to ascertain whether any of the available tests meet this need and to what extent. Then, the appropriateness of the test for the particular teaching situation concerned must be carefully considered. Do the test items reflect skills or qualities that are characteristic of the teaching situation for which it is intended? Earlier in this chapter, the example was presented of a test giving undue stress to running as being inappropriate for a climate which seriously limits the amount of time available for outdoor activity and less restricted running than can be done indoors. Test appropriateness may be described as being life-like, encompassing items that reflect needs, habits, and skills of the usual life of the student and stressed to the approximate degree or extent that is reality.

If the test meets the stipulations embodied in questions 2 and 3, it must next be determined to be scientifically authentic, administratively feasible, and possess teaching utility. Assuming that a teacher finds that a national level test and a state level test both display desired value on the basis of this overall appraisal, a comparison must then be made to ascertain which test appears more satisfactory for the particular situation. On the other hand, should the evaluation of available tests indicate that none is desirable in terms of an overall appraisal of its value, then the teacher must undertake to construct a test designed to serve the intended purpose with the desired characteristics.

Upon completion of this discussion of test selection, the teacher should realize that not all of the essential information for selecting a test of a particular quality or trait has been covered. Basic to implementation of the procedure for test selection the teacher should be fully conversant with the desired characteristics of a test of the quality or trait in question as described in later chapters dealing with the construction, organization and administration of tests, and with considerations peculiar to tests of that particular quality.

SELECTED REFERENCES

1. AHMANN, J. S., and GLOCK, M. D. *Evaluating Pupil Growth,* 4th ed. Boston: Allyn and Bacon, Inc., 1971.

2. DOWNIE, N. M. *Fundamentals of Measurement: Techniques and Practices,* 2nd ed. New York: Oxford University Press, 1967.
3. KATZ, MARTIN. *Selecting an Achievement Test: Principles and Procedures* (ETS T&M Kit). Princeton: Educational Testing Service, 1973.
4. MEHRENS, W. A., and LEHMANN, I. J. *Measurement and Evaluation in Education and Psychology.* New York: Holt, Rinehart and Winston, Inc., 1973.
5. MONTOYE, HENRY J., ed. *Principles and Operational Practices (An Introduction to Measurement in Physical Education,* Vol. 1). Indianapolis: Phi Epsilon Kappa Fraternity, 1970.
6. POPHAM, W. JAMES, ed. *Criterion-Referenced Measurement: An Introduction.* Englewood Cliffs, N.J.: Educational Technology Publications, 1971.
7. THORNDIKE, ROBERT L., ed. *Educational Measurement,* 2nd ed. Washington: American Council on Education, 1971.

4

Constructing Tests

AN ILLUSTRATIVE PROBLEM

In reality an unresolved problem in test selection poses a problem for test construction. Carrying on with the problem presented in Chapter 3, in the event that none of the available tests of motor fitness proves satisfactory for fifth- and sixth-grade chidren, how does the teacher proceed to construct an appropriate test scientifically? And if the teacher desires to devise tests of knowledge and of attitudes and behavior relating to fitness, what considerations are entailed in tests pertaining to associated and concomitant learnings? While the construction of an appropriate test by no means presents an insurmountable task, it is nevertheless a distinct challenge that necessitates a thorough understanding of, and careful attention to the basic principles and procedures in constructing a teacher-made test.

GENERAL CONSIDERATIONS

Construction of satisfactory measuring instruments presents one of the most difficult duties the teacher has to perform, but without which teaching cannot realize its fullest potential in a purposeful manner. Devising a test is a creative task, assuming skill and knowledge of techniques. The ability to construct tests efficiently and adequately is to be greatly desired, inasmuch as the number of available published tests that are satisfactory on the basis of value appraisal for a given local situation can be expected to be rather limited. Published tests are often found to be unrelated to and inappropriate for the local situation in such important elements as content and points of emphasis, length and organization, norms, and difficulty. Also, tests may not be attuned to students in matters such as their experience in the quality to be measured, their attitude toward various aspects of the tests, as well as their rate and caliber of performance.

These likely pitfalls of available tests in their application to local situations suggest some of the factors involved in test construction. On many occasions the teacher desires to ascertain to what extent the students have learned the material presented as well as that stressed; or the amount of improvement manifested by students in technical, associated, or concomitant learnings; or to compare student's achievement with others and diagnose difficulty in terms of local course content. Hence, the local or teacher-made test constitutes an invaluable tool for instructional purposes. Because of its specific, appropriate content and application, the teacher-made test finds use as a basis for individual motivation and meaningful grading in addition to the values mentioned above.

The three types of learning involved in physical education—technical, associated, and concomitant—relate to objectives in the psychomotor, cognitive, and affective domains, respectively, and are grossly different in nature. In the main they necessitate different types of measuring instruments that possess relatively little similarity in the way they are constructed. Therefore, the discussion of procedure in developing tests in the various areas of learning must of necessity be largely in terms of the specific area concerned. Nowithstanding, regardless of the learning area involved, the process of test construction can be characterized as calm, deliberate, time consuming, and consisting of four steps, namely:

1. Planning the test.
2. Formulating the test.
3. Using the test.
4. Appraising the test.[1]

PLANNING. In the first step, planning the test, heed is paid to assure that the factors comprising test value, as described previously, are adequately provided for. The need to conform to desirable test characteristics should govern the planning of the test, as well as affording direction to the ensuing steps in test construction. The test objectives are established in light of the physical education program objectives, and the test is planned so as to utilize those test techniques deemed most appropriate for each particular objective. Thereby an attempt is made to determine the best means of measuring those outcomes that analysis reveals as warranting measurement. The test should reflect the approximate proportion of emphasis given to instructional contents as well as a design that lends itself to practicality in administration. A desirable

---

[1] These four steps of test construction are in reality applicable not only to the test as a whole, as mainly referred to here, but also to analysis of each particular test item as the test is planned and formulated.

perspective for the planning phase can be derived from recognition that: "The real ends of instruction are the lasting concepts, attitudes, skills, abilities and habits of thought and materials of instruction—the specific factual content—are to a large extent only a means toward these ends." [2]

FORMULATING. The formulation of the test, the second step, should predicate the completion of a carefully devised plan. Basically, the nature of the learning involved—technical, associated, or concomitant— together with the purpose of the test (for example, diagnostic as compared to achievement) will dictate the specific things to consider in formulating a test. Some factors that have general applicability, irrespective of the type of learning involved, are: (1) the general desirability of including more test items in the first draft of the test than will actually be needed; (2) the advisability of a time lapse after which the test is subjected to critical revision; (3) arranging items in logical and psychological order; (4) providing for a convenient and appropriate written record of performance; and (5) furnishing directions for students and for the test administrator that are as clear, complete, and concise as possible. As a word of clarification for factor 3 above, it is generally recommended that test items be arranged in ascending order of difficulty, which possesses justification in the psychological sense, and in logical order relative to content and item interrelationship. The implications of this will be mentioned in the subsequent discussion of tests for the different types of learning. Heed should be directed in this stage of test construction to the different considerations implicit in providing for satisfactory reliability, as discussed following this brief description for the four steps in test construction. In test formulation care should be taken to insure that the test is prepared according to the plan provided and, consequently, in light of the desired test characteristics. Any substitution or revision that may be necessitated by unforeseen circumstances should not be attempted without reconsidering the plan as a whole and the relationship of the item or question to the whole test and the interrelationships with the other constituent parts of the test.

USING. Once the test is formulated as planned, the third step ensues, namely, using the test, that is, what may be described as a trial administration of the test. Attention is directed specifically to providing conditions for performance of the test as intended in the planning and preparation of the test. The test should be tried out under conditions that typify its intended use as stipulated by the test instructions. Ample time should be allotted for this initial administration. Simplicity should

---

[2] E. F. Lindquist, "The Use of Tests in the Accreditation of Military Experience and in the Educational Placement of War Veterans," *Educational Record*, XXV (October, 1944), 366.

characterize the scoring procedure for the test to the greatest practical extent. Specific directions for scoring and necessary scoring keys, computers, and the like should be available.

APPRAISING. After the test has been used and scored, the key to its future is determined by the fourth step in the process of test construction—appraising the test. This consists of determining the overall test value as indicated by the fundamental concerns dealing with scientific authenticity, administrative feasibility, and teaching utility. In other words, the value of the test is appraised in light of the desirable test characteristics that were utilized as the guide in constructing the test. This appraisal will disclose how effectively the test meets the fundamental considerations it was designed to meet.

Actually, the questions resolve themselves to: *Did the test do what was intended and, if so, how effectively did it do this?* The major effort in appraisal is directed to the scientific analysis of the test in an effort to discern how effectively the test reveals the qualities of a scientifically devised test. Certainly, no attempt is made to belittle the appraisal of test value in terms of administrative feasibility and teaching utility in favor of scientific authenticity. In the main, however, a test planned and formulated in light of these considerations for test construction will generally closely approximate the desired qualities and, consequently, not entail the time and concern necessitated by the scientific analysis. In appraising a test, the teacher should not lose sight of the fact that the value of a test is contingent upon its ability to measure a trait or skill closely enough to differentiate between levels of the quality in question in different individuals, whether the variation be large or small. It should be noted in passing that the process of establishing norms, as included under the discussion of scientific analysis and later in this chapter, would take place, if norms are desired, only after a satisfactory test has been devised. The test must be in finished form before appropriate norms can be determined.

Invaluable information pertaining to the test and its application can be derived by eliciting a frank expression of criticism, suggestions, and constructive comment from testees after completion of the testing process, which should be conceived to include availability and use of the test results. This query concerning opinion about the test should be preceded by a succinct yet adequate statement describing the process of test evaluation and the reasons for obtaining their reaction. This brief statement should not be included in the usual pre-test remarks and instructions that are intended for everyone taking the test. To do so might tend to motivate student effort and lead to unusual, distorted results; that is, normal conditions would not prevail since future testees would not be contributing to the construction of a test in a like manner and therefore would not have this added incentive. The inquiry regarding student opinion should be made after the customary interpretation of test results has been completed. Some of the essentials inherent in teaching utility are best determined by a statement from students coupled with observation of student reaction. Such constructive criticism from testees along with opinion emanating from the individuals who administered the test serve to provide pertinent information for a valid and meaningful evaluation of the test.

If upon completion of the evaluative step in the process of test construction a test is deemed unsatisfactory, it must be subjected to a repetition of the process of test construction. The unsatisfactory test must be revised in the matter of planning and formulating and then be used and appraised in its new form. It may be necessary to repeat these four steps one or more times before the test reaches the desirable finished form.

It can be readily seen that test construction is a laborious process, if properly done to guarantee a satisfactory product. Once the value of the test has been established and the norms developed for it, the critical examination of its use should continue. The teacher-made test, like any published test, should be continually subjected to appraisal to assure test efficacy in the situation in which it is used, as indicated by the objectives the test is to serve. Changing the program emphases, approaches, and content, no matter how slight, necessitates alertness to preserve the suitability of the test and all the items comprising it. This admonition possesses especial importance in view of the fact that good, sound physical education programs are not typically static or unchanging. Thus, this fluid and ever-adapting nature of good programs further substantiates the need for viewing test development and appraisal as an on-going process, wherein continual feedback is obtained and analyzed, and needed change instituted.

The need for continued vigilance to appropriateness of a test and its items in view of purposes served suggested a technique for compiling pertinent test items as a resource not only for test revision but also for initial test construction. This technique, which serves admirably as a ready source of test items, consists simply of a card file arranged in a manner deemed most accessible. The cards are generally arranged either according to specific objectives concerned, such as particular qualities looked for in a motor fitness test and specific skills on a speed-ball test, or according to the type of test item, such as multiple-choice and completion for knowledge tests. As indicated, the card file can serve as an excellent source of pertinent test items for all tests dealing with technical, associated, or concomitant learning in addition to greatly facilitating the process of arranging items in progressive order of difficulty. Either 3- by 5- or 4- by 6-inch cards, depending upon personal preference, are usually most appropriate, since each card should contain only a single test item. Space is also needed on each card to make notations as to the effectiveness of the item as well as a record of the test or tests on which the item has been used. This latter information is useful when constructing an alternate form of a particular test or with similar problems. While long test items may necessitate two or more cards, this seems more advisable in terms of the economy of card cost and storage space rather than using the 5- by 8-inch size and needing but a small portion of each card for the vast majority of items.

Each test item included in the file should be carefully devised so that it represents a potentially desirable test item as recorded without necessitating extensive revision upon selection. On occasion, good test items will come to a teacher's mind but will long be forgotten by the time he devises a particular test, unless they are recorded. Also, unless these ideas are recorded systematically in a particular place, they may not be readily available at the time of test construction. Building a card file of desirable test items is a deliberate, continuing process that guarantees a carefully conceived, extensive collection from which to select items in constructing a test. To illustrate in light of the chapter problem, the teacher could consult such a file under appropriate headings of arm strength, explosive power, agility, or the like in an endeavor to find satisfactory test items for use in a battery as a test of motor fitness. If this file was the result of careful scrutiny of test items over a period of time, the chance of finding more suitable items in less time is certainly much greater than approaching the problem of motor fitness test construction with little organized resource material.

Test items that prove ineffective and unsatisfactory should be removed from the file, thereby maintaining a file of items of proven effectiveness or potential value. The time and effort expended in the preparation of such a card file is more than repaid, since test construction and revision is greatly facilitated by this definitive compilation of pertinent test items that can be readily subjected to critical evaluation for selection purposes. Consideration might well be given to putting all discarded items in a separate file as a resource of test items previously used and found ineffective. Conceivably, unless some record is kept of "failures" as a check-scheme, these items may be unknowingly re-tried at a later date, needlessly wasting time and effort.

Special Attention to Reliability

The importance of reliability as a test characteristic was stressed in an earlier discussion relating to test selection. The relationship of reliability to validity was epitomized by citing a formula for predicting the maximum validity limits as the coefficient derived from $\sqrt{r_t}$, the square root of the test reliability coefficient. Particular attention is now drawn to factors and considerations to be kept in mind during test construction to insure maximum reliability.

1. *Length of the test.* The general axiom is that, other things being equal, increasing the length of a test increases the reliability or, stated in another way, a long test tends to be more reliable than a shorter test. Obviously, there are practical limits to length. Also, the inclusion of poor or redundant test items to increase the test length will not favorably influence the reliability.

2. *Range of ability.* The magnitude of the reliability coefficient tends to be directly related to the range of ability, that is, the variability for the group involved. A wide range (heterogeneity) of ability leads to a high coefficient, whereas a narrow range (homogeneity) results in a low coefficient. This relationship points to the desirability of knowing the variability of the group, usually the standard deviation, when interpreting a coefficient. For instance, conceivably, $r = 0.70$ for a restricted group may be equally as good as $r = 0.90$ for a group with a large range.

3. *Level of ability.* A test that is either too difficult or too easy in terms of the mean level of ability of a group will yield less reliability. This possesses particular relevance for tests intended to encompass a considerable range in age. When a test is appropriate for an older age group, it tends to have a lower reliability for younger groups. This is readily illustrated for tests of associated and concomitant learning, but likewise pertains to measures of technical learning, that is, physical performance.

4. *Conditions for testing.* The more nearly that testing conditions can be replicated for subsequent test administrations, the better the reliability; that is, reliability is relative to the specific conditions that surround the testing. This substantiates the need for explicit test directions and attention to the technical aspects of organization and administration of tests as described in Chapter 6. For example, fluctuations in how motor fitness test items are performed or in motivational technique will affect the reliability.

5. *Scorer reliability.* Unless the test scorer evinces reliability, test reliability suffers. Scorer reliability is a function not only of the personal qualifications of the scorer for the task but also of the scoring scheme and technique itself.

Attention to the aforementioned factors in test construction will serve to derive maximum reliability inherent in a particular test. In the quest to construct reliable instruments the teacher is well advised to be cognizant of the various sources of unreliability in measurement. While the factors affecting reliability and the sources of unreliability are obviously interrelated to a considerable extent, fullest comprehension of reliability necessitates brief recognition of some of the important sources of unreliability, which include: [3]

1. *Errors attributable to day-to-day fluctuations.* The greatest source of measurement error is due to day-to-day variations in the individual which affect the test scores. Such variables as changes in physical and emotional well-being, and the effect of events in one's personal life, literally account for the ups-and-downs in performance and the resultant inconsistencies in test scores on different occasions.

2. *Errors attributable to long-range instability.* The stability of test scores over relatively long periods of time affects reliability. This concern is illustrated by the fact that results on interest inventories of children tend to change as time progresses, as may IQ, although the latter tends to change less quickly.

3. *Errors attributable to the maturational process.* This source of unreliability accounts for changes occurring during the growth and development of individuals. While the normal pattern of growth and development is relatively continuous, it is characterized by fluctuations in constancy and rate both within and between individuals.

4. *Errors attributable to the homogeneity of the group or the nondiscriminatory power of the test.* Reliability errors can be anticipated when the group being tested is quite homogeneous on the quality involved, or when the instrument is not capable of discriminating satisfactorily between different levels of the quality in question.

5. *Errors attributable to the sampling of content.* The longer, more thorough tests tend to be more reliable, basically because more of the content has been sampled.

6. *Errors attributable to test standardization.* This source deals with errors that arise from failure to follow carefully and completely the instructions that pertain to the test and its administration.

7. *Errors in scoring tests.* Both human and mechanical errors in scoring tests must be contended with.

8. *Errors attributable to chance factors.* This source is best illustrated by the factor of guessing in objective written tests, especially on true–

[3] Adapted in part from: Jum C. Nunnally. *Educational Measurement and Evaluation* (New York: McGraw-Hill Book Co., 1964), pp. 77–82.

false items, although astute analysis of physical performance tests also reveals areas in which chance may influence the results.

In light of this emphasis on considerations implicit in test reliability as it relates to test construction, the teacher should be able to: (1) make adequate provision for factors that insure desirable reliability; and (2) recognize factors that adversely affect reliability so as to avoid them or at least control their influence to the extent possible.

Developing Norms

After the actual process of test construction has been completed, resulting in a satisfactory test, the teacher conceivably may wish to establish norms for use in interpreting and analyzing the test results. The basic considerations mentioned in Chapter 3 should characterize the construction of norms. This includes provision that:

1. *A sufficient number of subjects are involved to insure desirable accuracy of normed scores.* An arbitrary minimum number cannot be established because of the difference in variability of results of tests of different qualities. In endeavoring to construct norms for a motor for a fitness test for fifth- and sixth-grade boys and girls of a particular school system, considerably more students should be involved in normed scores than would be the case for a normed chart of height of these students, which will vary considerably less. The sample size should be large enough to be representative of the full range of variance.

2. *The data reflect a random sampling of the population involved.* The purpose of this provision is to represent actuality in sample composition. The sample group should be selected at at random from among the fifth- and sixth-grade children for the illustrative problem. It may often be impractical, if not impossible, to choose the sample group by random sampling in the literal sense. Then meaningful organizational units, such as schools or classes within a school or schools, are randomly selected and all students within each unit are tested.

3. *The standard group involved in establishing the norms for a test should be typical of the group for whom the test is intended.* A variation in the physical-educational and recreational experience of children in subsequent fifth and sixth grades would exemplify a variable that would make the norms inappropriate for the group to be involved. For example, the fifth-grade students beginning next year might experience a much broader, more extensive physical education program and have available much better park and recreational facilities than did the present fifth- and sixth-graders upon whom the norms will be based. If so, the norms will not be completely suitable for use with the new group because of this disparity in background.

4. *In constructing norms, care must be taken that the normality of each test item is assured before test norms are constructed.* Each item included in the motor fitness test for fifth- and sixth-grade students should reflect a normal distribution within the sample group. In other words, the achievement of the standard group in each test item should resemble a normal curve of distribution, as generally typifies the total performance of normed scores.

The actual presentation of the norms may be done in a number of ways, depending upon the purposes to be served. Some of these ways are:

1. Simply listing the basic statistics—mean and standard deviation, and leaving derivation of the type and detailedness of a standard score norm to discretion of the test user.
2. Giving selected points on a normative scale, such as: T–20, T–25, T–30 to T–80 for T-scores; or P_{10}, P_{20} to P_{90}[4] or Q_1, Md, and Q_3 on a percentile scale.
3. Listing the scale score for every raw score that might fall within the range encompassed,[5] or at least the scale score for each raw score occurring in the standard group.

The construction of a definitive scale derived from standard scores that is, based on mean and standard deviation), *and specifically the T-score,* is recommended for norms for all tests in physical education—published and teacher-made. (As a reminder why such scores are preferable to percentiles, percentile rank clearly indicates that one individual's relative position is better than another's but cannot indicate how much better and cannot be treated arithmetically. Whereas, the standard score, or a derivative form, is a relative-position measure that indicates how much better one score is than another and can be handled arithmetically.) The procedure to follow in developing T-scores is delineated in Chapter 2. It is further recommended that these T-score norms be set up so that T-scores are reported for all possible raw score values that might occur within the anticipated range, generally at least T–20 to T–80. The importance of this definitiveness warrants noting, for without it some of the desirable features of the T-score are needlessly lost. To illustrate, some test literature in physical education reports the T-score for a test at intervals of five T-score units, for example, T–20, T–25, etc. And in some instances a range of two or more raw scores is reported for each fifth T-score. The practice of reporting scattered scale points necessitates interpolation for accurate interpretation, but more than likely will

[4] See Table 2–4.
[5] See Fig. 2–3.

result in the use of only the gross T-score unit (nearest multiple of five) for any raw score falling among those listed opposite the particular gross T-score. Obviously, this loses the desirable discrimination that is characteristic of T-scores.

If for any compelling reason the teacher reports a scattered score norm, and this should be avoided whenever possible, precise instructions for interpolation should be given. Unfortunately, the test literature contains T-score norms reported as every fifth T-score with associated raw scores, and no interpolation instructions are included. In such instances the reader must guess whether the reported T-score represents the middle of the range of raw scores listed or whether the raw scores are arranged beginning from the reported T-score to the next higher T-score value. To avert such needless confusion it is strongly advocated that the teacher report the norms in full. If this is impossible, a strong case can be made for reporting only the mean and standard deviation, which would necessitate user construction of T-scores for the raw scores recorded in particular situation, but which would eliminate the problem of misinterpolation and the attendant misinterpretation.

On the basis of the foregoing presentation of considerations applicable to measuring instruments dealing with all three types of learning—technical, associated, and concomitant—attention can now be directed to a discussion of test construction as it pertains directly to physical performance tests, written tests of knowledge and understanding, and rating scales and self-report instruments.

MEASUREMENT OF SKILL AND PHYSICAL QUALITIES—TECHNICAL LEARNING

Physical Performance Tests

Physical performance test is an arbitrary descriptive title given to a test dealing with technical learning (psychomotor domain), including tests of specific sport skills and physical qualities. Such measurement of necessity entails objective evidence of performance or existence of a physical quality as well as subjective evidence. For our purposes, *performance test* will refer to objective measurement of performance, whereas *performance rating* will be used to describe subjective measurement pertaining to physical qualities or skills.

The importance of teacher competence in constructing skill tests and the needed attention to the proper procedure is evinced by the limited number of available standardized tests as well as the restricted appropriateness in many instances of those that are available. The need for this competency can be readily substantiated, such as by the survey of 700 teachers and administrators in the Far-west which revealed that the ability to devise and construct valid and objective skill tests ranked higher than knowledge of standardized skill tests in importance.[6]

Procedure for Developing Physical Performance Tests. The important considerations involved in planning and formulating the physical performance test may be enumerated in a suggested sequential order as: [7]

1. *Clear recognition and delineation of test objectives (that is, what is to be measured) and a definitive analysis of the skill or quality in question.* Looking at the illustrative need for a motor fitness test for fifth- and sixth-grade boys and girls, this might entail such factors as arm strength, abdominal strengh, explosive speed, explosive power, endurance, and agility, to list a few. A definitive analysis of the skills found in a particular sports activity can be accomplished by listing the specific skills included along with a rating of comparative importance. A cursory check of the rating assigned to the importance of the various skills can be obtained by comparison with the teaching time allocated to each skill. Generally speaking, the more important skills will receive more teaching emphasis than that accorded to skills of lesser importance. An illustration of such a skill analysis for beginning badminton, using a 3-point rating scale, is given below:

Skill	Rating (3 high)
Grip	3
Strokes	
Forehand	3
Backhand	3
Overhead	2
Underhand lift	1
Around the head	1
Service	
Short	3
Long	2
Court play	
On-guard stance	3
Proper footwork	2
Singles position play	1
Doubles position play	1

Such an analysis serves to indicate the importance relegated to skills at any particular level, such as beginner in the above example. The skill level and game strategy will influence the importance of the particular

[6] Elmo S. Roundy, "Problem of Competencies Needed by Men Physical Education Teachers at the Secondary Level," *Research Quarterly,* 38, No. 2 (May, 1967), 274.

[7] The reader should realize the inextricable relationship of considerations entailed in constructing a test and in organizing and administering a testing program, because of which common elements are mentioned briefly from different vantage points under both topics.

skills concerned, so such a rating becomes specific for the situation in question. The axiom—things accepted as desirable outcomes and planned for in teaching should be tested—should govern this determination of the quality to be measured. This first consideration in planning and formulating a physical performance test entails a complete analysis of the ability to be measured.

2. *Determine what appears to be a desirable sample performance; in other words, select and arrange test items or situations in accordance with performance objectives.* Seldom, if ever, can a test be so comprehensive as to be all-inclusive. Consequently, selection of representative sample performance is important. Assurance should be made that the previously described characteristics of teaching utility are provided for, namely, important abilities in actual use, skillful performance of one individual, appropriate challenge for performers, and a suitable record of performance. Each test item should be subjected to critical trial administration of a typical group in an endeavor to verify the desirability of the sample performance. It is usually advisable to propose two or more test items for each area of consideration so as to facilitate the process of finding the most appropriate test item. To illustrate, the standing long jump, vertical jump, and high jump might all be used as a test item to measure leg thrust or jumping ability per se on a motor fitness test or general abilities test, as the case may be. The best item for the purpose intended would be selected. However, in selecting test items that are indicative of actual performance, attention must be directed to avoiding items that entail too much time as well as equipment not generally found in school physical education programs. One last admonition at this time concerning item selection is to eliminate those items that limit performance at either end of the scale—too hard or too easy for the group.

When more than one test item is involved, the decision regarding test order should evolve from deliberate analysis of the sample performance so as to reflect logical and psychological justification and not merely happenstance. Particular points of concern implicit in test order are discussed under specific considerations in developing physical performance tests.

3. *Prepare suitable directions, as test items are devised, to standardize the testing procedure with a view to insuring comparable testing conditions for all testees.* This consideration entails clear and concise instructions that explain and govern all aspects of the performance and include, as appropriate, description of necessary equipment and facility specifications, dress of participants, and the like. As an example, a seemingly simple matter of failure to note the specific hand position as forward or reverse grasp in a pull-up test will render results relatively useless, since

the hand position can be expected to influence the results obtained. This preparation of directions should include critical trial administration as previously suggested under number 2 above. The basic purpose in directing deliberate attention to instructions is to prevent the situation from arising in which a number of variables exercise different influences on the scores attained. An attempt is made to foster to the extent possible duplicate testing conditions for the test in question. Particular mention should be made of the influence on validity, reliability, or objectivity, inasmuch as the descriptive level of the quality in question for the test under consideration will prevail only when conditions surrounding the test administration and the characteristics of the group concerned approximate those affecting the tryout group.

4. *Deliberative selection of students to comprise the tryout group, so as to guarantee a typical situation.* The students selected for use in test development should be truly representative of the particular segment of school population for which the test is being designed. This consideration includes attention not only to age and developmental level or fitness of the group, but also to the skill and experience level of students in the particular area in question. Only when heed is paid to these factors can assurance be had that the test is being designed for a certain school population of which the tryout group is typical.

The size of the tryout group depends upon a number of factors. A greater number of students must be included as the range or variability of the ability displayed by the group increases and when the reliability of the measuring instrument is somewhat reduced. To illustrate, a substantially greater number of students would be needed for a tryout group concerning a motor fitness test for fifth- and sixth-grade boys and girls than for a skill or quality of less variability, such as rope jumping or elementary soccer in which basic instruction has been given. The degree of confidence desired in the test results also affects the size of the tryout group. For the most part, 100 students is regarded as the minimum number for a tryout group. It should not be implied by the expression "size of the tryout group" that this gorup participates in a single administration of the test, for example, all at one time. Reference is made solely to the total number comprising the size of the group. This total tryout group size may result from either administering the test to several different groups or just once to a large group.

The criterion measure to be used for validation influences the manner in which the test is administered. When a rating of performance is necessary, the groups must be limited to a smaller number than when a validated test serves as the criterion measure. In essence then, as in the case of norm construction, the concern in tryout group selection is to obtain a group of sufficient number and breadth to represent typically the over-all group for whom the test is intended.

5. *Select a satisfactory criterion measure for determining validity.* In order to determine validity of a physical performance test, it becomes necessary to find a sample for comparison, a criterion measure, that represents the quality to be measured (criterion-related validity), or to afford descriptive justification of content validity. Previously validated tests, tournament rankings or records (or similar measures of ability, for example, game statistics), ratings of expert judges (single and combined), comparison of divergent groups, and a combination or composite of any of these, serve as examples of such measuring rods or criteria against which a test may be judged as to its validity. Content validity may be established by a jury of expert opinion, or logical explanation to disclose the presence of test characteristics similar, if not identical, to qualities the test purports to measure.

The use of previously validated tests as the criterion measure offers perhaps the most expedient means, along with tournament rankings or other performance records, of expressing validity as a correlation co-efficient. However, the test in question may be a refined test through which the author endeavors to achieve greater validity than heretofore attained by any other test. In such an instance, another method of validation must be chosen, since the test in question can only be judged for validity in comparison to the criterion measure and, accordingly, can never be attested to possess any greater validity than that attributed to the criterion measure. When the established test is too lengthy or otherwise undesirable for use, a proposed substitute test can be validated against it and then employed, if the amount of correlation appears satisfactory.

Tournament rankings, or won–loss records, and similar readily available measures of ability such as game statistics (for example, batting and fielding averages, shooting percentage) constitute widely used and satisfactory criterion measures. Care must be taken to be certain that the measure selected is based upon sufficient contests to reflect a valid measure of ability. With this assurance, the results of a skill test in tennis, for example, could be correlated with the tournament rankings to provide a measure of validity.

The ratings of expert judges as a criterion measure may in reality take either of two forms: single rating as rendered in a typical rating scale, or a combined rating of judges as utilized in competitive diving. Actually, the two forms are very closely related and are differentiated only to point out that the single rating generally entails an elaborate and definitive check list type of rating of what often comprises a breakdown of a particular skill or quality. The combined rating usually requires that each judge rate the performance in the particular skill or quality as a whole, and then the ratings of all judges are combined to arrive at a final rating.

Regardless of the form of rating, certain factors must obtain to afford a satisfactory criterion measure. It is essential in securing ratings of performance to define clearly and carefully the ability or quality to be rated. Such definition should include a description of the range of rating desired, which in turn is conditioned by the degree of discrimination possible in the ability in question. The judges selected should be competent, well-trained individuals who are fully informed regarding the particular activity and capable of objective, proficient rating. The actual rating process should permit ample and wholly adequate opportunities to observe participants outside of and apart from the testing situation; failure to provide for this opportunity will be reflected in variation in judges' scores. Judges should be encouraged to avail themselves of a practice period prior to actually rating participants. Making a player-to-player comparison can be effectively utilized to present a picture of various levels of skill and engender better use of the full range of ratings. When combining judges' scores or ratings, it is generally preferable to use the total score accumulated for each performer rather than the mean. If three judges rated a tenis skill on a 5-point scale as 3, 4, and 5, the total of 12 tends to have more meaning in terms of the possible range from 3 to 15 points than would the mean of 4 on a 1- to 5-point basis. Furthermore, this sum of scores provides a range of rating scores that facilitates determining the coefficient of correlation, since it more nearly approximates the range of test scores and avoids computational and rounding errors in finding the mean.

The judges' ratings should be correlated to ascertain the degree of agreement in judgment. In the event that the scores of one judge do not correlate well with scores of the other judges, the ratings of the judge reflecting disagreement would not be used. Usually, a minimum coefficient of 0.80 should be indicative of acceptable agreement. The correlation of judges' rating might suggest further training of the judges selected, refinement of rating instructions and procedure, or other elements concerning the use of judges' rating as the criterion measure for the quality or ability in question. Oftentimes, one of the judges is much more familiar with the performance of a group of students, such as the coach of a sport or teacher of the class concerned, than are any of the other judges. In such a situation, it may appear advisable to give extra consideration to the rating or judgment of this particular individual. This is accomplished by using a constant, such as 1.5 or 2.0, to multiply the given rating by and arrive at a weighted score. It is felt that this procedure gives due recognition to rating based upon more extended observation. Notwithstanding, this practice may be challenged by some individuals who feel that the teacher's or coach's rating may not be as purely an objective rating of performance as other raters but rather may be definitely opinionated due to the personal contact and closer relationship with the particular student. Accordingly, this point of view contends that his rating should certainly be accorded no more than equal consideration as an indicant of performance.

A jury of expert opinion may be utilized as a basis for validation of tests of general qualities or the like to substantiate the content validity [8] where the more specific, aforementioned criterion measures are not appropriate. Validation of a test of motor fitness illustrates the need for such a jury to judge collectively the validity of a test in terms of its avowed purpose. Does the test under consideration reflect those aspects of motor fitness that are necessary and desirable for life in our society? The answer to this question should be based on an analysis of and extensive experience with educational and recreational philosophy and programs coupled with a thorough understanding of the human body and its functioning. This basis for validation can best be provided by a jury of professional leaders who by their interest and qualifications seem best suited for this task. The jury should be selected in view of the particular test area. Test validation through a jury of expert opinion, as for other means of establishing content validity, cannot be expressed statistically but rather in general descriptive terms—high, good, moderate, fair, or poor. The illustration of validating a motor fitness test does not imply that such a test cannot be validated in another way, nor that the use of experts is confined to content validity. On a local level it is entirely feasible and plausible that a group of experts could observe and rate the performance of a group in varied physical education activity relative to the overall fitness of the students in activity. This rating would serve as the criterion measure for a motor fitness test and afford the basis for derivation of a correlation coefficient to express criterion-related validity. A highly regarded and previously validated test, or a composite of test items representative of the various aspects deemed to comprise motor fitness, afford other criterion measures for the validation of a motor or physical fitness test. In this instance, for a motor fitness test, as in any case of selecting a criterion measure, the particular means of test validation is selected that appears to be most practical in the given situation for the results attained.

[8] The reader is reminded that the descriptive and logical derivation of validity (sometimes called face validity) for physical performance tests is defined as a form of content validity.

6. *Determine the reliability of each test item.* The preferential method of ascertaining the consistency with which a test item operates is to administer the test on two successive days or two days within a week with similar conditions prevailing, such as time of day, health status of participants, and other influential factors. Applying this, to determine the reliability of the standing long jump as a motor fitness test item, it would be given on two successive days or with an intervening day to a group of students. This suggested procedure appears to be more desirable than successive repetitions of test items on a single day because of the fatiguing or warmup effect—depending upon the strenuousness of the test item—of the first test administration. The results of this double testing are correlated to express reliability as a coefficient, indicating the degree to which consistent results were obtained for equal amounts of ability. Reliabiilty can be fostered only by provision of testing conditions based upon recognition of the many factors affecting the consistency of results, such as fluctuations in student effort, individual and group reaction, and conditions of administration, including motivational factors. Should the coefficient be relatively low (at least 0.85 is desirable, and 0.90 is preferable), the item can be either eliminated or remodeled in content, or revised as to the number of trials allowed. After any remodeling or revision, the test is administered successively again and the results are correlated. This process is repeated as necessary until the test item yields a satisfactory correlation coefficient of reliability.

In instances where double administration of a test item is impractical and the test consists of a number of trials, a correlation may be computed between alternate trials of the test and stepped up by the Spearman–Brown prophecy formula to estimate the coefficient for actual test length.[9] The sum of the odd-numbered trials is correlated against the sum of the even-numbered trials, resulting in a correlation for half of the actual number of test items. The application of the Spearman–Brown prophecy formula provides an estimate of reliability of the complete test on the basis of split halves. For comparative purposes it is appropriate to note that, based on a definitive study of the applicability of this formula to physical performance tests, Baumgartner[10] concluded that the use of the test–re-test method is more appropriate than the split-half method, regardless of whether the test is administered on two different days or on the same day.

When a test item falls below acceptable reliability but possesses many

---

[9] The reader is referred to page 161 for an example of the application of the Spearman–Brown prophecy formula.

[10] Ted. A. Baumgartner, "The Applicability of the Spearman–Brown Prophecy Formula When Applied to Physical Performance Tests," *Research Quarterly*, 39, No. 4 (December, 1968), 847.

desirable features, the number of trials might be increased in an effort to increase the reliability coefficient. The Spearman–Brown prophecy formula affords an estimate of the likelihood that increasing the number of trials will increase the reliability sufficiently to render it acceptable. This reliability prediction, however, should be considered as the upper limit of the reliability for the specified number of trials.[11] If the formula suggests the desirability of increasing the trials, the test should be administered again as revised and re-subjected to reliability analysis.

Test items failing to meet an acceptable level of reliability should be eliminated from the test. Not only is such an item deficient in terms of reliability, but it should be remembered that a test item must be reliable in order to be valid, even though reliability does not insure validity. A test must measure consistently whatever it measures, if it is to tell the truth or be valid. So an item that is not satisfactorily reliable would detract from the validity of the test.

7. *Ascertain the validity of each test item.* For criterion-related validity, once the criterion measure is established, the test scores can then be correlated with the criterion scores to determine the validity—the extent to which the test measures the ability in question as displayed by the criterion measure. Upon computation of the validity coefficient, it must be interpreted. What does a coefficient of 0.80 mean as derived for a standing long jump, as a case in point? The reader is referred to the interpretation chart for validity coefficients cited in Chapter 3.

Usually a coefficient below 0.80 is deemed unsatisfactory for use as an individual test. Nevertheless, tests ranging in validity from 0.60 to 0.79 might be combined to form a battery of tests reflecting desirable validity. The 0.80 validity coefficient obtained for the illustrated standing long jump would be interpreted as being a useful and meaningful test.

For content validity, evidence relating to each item is an integral part of the overall description of the rationale to justify test validity.

8. *Ascertain the objectivity of each test item.* The consistency with which the same scores are obtained in administration of the test item by different testers is determined by correlating the test scores reported by various scorers. Items that possess a definitive scoring method, supplemented with concise yet thorough instructions, reflect high objectivity. Items involving judgment or rating by the tester characteristically display poor objectivity, although specificity of instructions can favorably influence this quality. A good example of this is afforded by the postural appraisal part of the New York State Physical Fitness Test. Specific directions and an illustrated rating chart are combined to favorably affect

[11] *Ibid.*

the objectivity of this test item. Good objectivity is essential for validity, although it does not assure a satisfactory level of validity.

9. *Compute the intercorrelation between the desired items, when a combination of test items into a battery is wanted.* The purpose of this procedure is to find test items that, while in themselves valid measures of the basic quality or skill in question, do not measure the same specific thing and would then correlate relatively poorly, one with another. This process serves to eliminate test duplication and, accordingly, unnecessary test items. In determining a motor fitness test battery, for instance, consideration may be given to pull-ups and push-ups, both of which were found to possess statistical validity. However, should the intercorrelation suggest that the two tests may be measuring the same thing, for example, a 0.89 correlation, it would not appear necessary to include both in the battery. In such an instance, assuming that the other desirable characteristics are comparable, the decision can be based on the intercorrelation with other test items. The test that reflects the lowest correlations with other items would then be selected.

The basic principle pertaining to combining test items into a battery is that *each test in a battery should possess desirable validity itself but show little relationship to its companion tests in the battery.* This in essence guarantees that each test measures some particular aspect or element of the desired quality that is not measured by the other tests. And, as illustrated above in deciding between two motor fitness test items, the process of intercorrelation plays an important role in bringing about the best possible combinations of the items being considered.

10. *Determine the best combination of tests as a battery.* The aforementioned intercorrelations afford the basis for determining possible test combinations. The multiple correlation of each proposed combination with the criterion measure is then computed.[12] This computation gives an expression of the degree of validity of any given combination of tests. On the basis of this multiple correlation, the best combination is selected. Attention should be directed in the selection process to factors of administrative feasibility, when two proposed batteries have comparable multiple correlations. Again attention is directed to the illustration of a

[12] The intricate statistical computational procedure for multiple correlation, while beyond the scope of this book, presents no problem when computer analysis is available. Herein, the intent is to describe the application of the concept of multiple correlation. The reader interested in computational instructions for the multiple correlation coefficient (R) is referred to a basic statistics book. One computational approach is described as it pertains to test battery construction in: C. H. McCloy and N. D. Young, *Tests and Measurements in Health and Physical Education,* 3rd ed. (New York: Appleton-Century-Crofts, 1954), pp. 442–43; and M. G. Scott and Esther French, *Measurement and Evaluation in Physical Education* (Dubuque: Wm. C. Brown Co., 1959), pp. 90–93.

battery of motor fitness test items containing push-ups and a second battery employing pull-ups in the place of push-ups, other items being the same in both batteries. Given comparable multiple correlations, the combination that necessitates fewer limitations or special provisions in administering the test items should be selected. Assuming a 0.82 and 0.84 multiple correlation for push-up and pull-up batteries, respectively, the former would conceivably warrant selection in view of the greater time and equipment needed for administering pull-ups. Also related to the matter of determining the best test combination, the effect of adding an item to a test battery can be indicated, by multiple correlation. If the validity coefficient shown by multiple correlation is not affected appreciably with the addition of a particular test, the addition would appear unwarranted.

11. *Determine the method to be used in combining the scores on the different tests in the battery.* After the desired test combination for a battery has been selected, it must be decided how the various item scores should be combined or, in other words, the weighting to be assigned each test in the battery. When the tests have approximately equal value in the battery, the appropriate scale scores (for example, T-scores) can be added directly to give the total battery score. When the tests possess different value, using the sum of these scores is not feasible. In such instances a multiple regression equation, based on the multiple correlation of the different tests, is employed.[13] This equation takes into account the variability of raw scores on each test as well as the relative value of each test in the whole battery. The way in which this is done is illustrated by the regression equation formula for a three-test battery.

$$\beta_1 \left(\frac{s_c}{s_1} \right) \text{score test}_1 + \beta_2 \left(\frac{s_c}{s_2} \right) \text{score test}_2 + \beta_3 \left(\frac{s_c}{s_3} \right) \text{score test}_3$$
$$= \text{Battery score}$$

where:　β_1, β_2, and β_3 represent beta values taken from the multiple correlation computation.

s, s_1, s_2, and s_3 are the standard deviations for the criterion measure, and tests 1, 2, and 3, respectively.

Generally speaking, the weightings calculated are rather cumbersome to use. Consequently, it is desirable to compute the relationship between

[13] As for multiple correlation, the intent herein is to describe the application of multiple regression for combining test battery scores. Computer programs are available for the actual computational process. For illustration of the application of a multiple regression equation for test score combination see: McCloy and Young, *op. cit.*, pp. 93–94.

the different weights and substitute the appropriate figures in the formula. To illustrate using three tests, the lesser of the weightings—assumed to involve test $_3$—is reduced to 1.0 and the proportionate changes are made in the weightings for tests $_1$ and test $_2$ by completing the ratio:

$$\frac{\text{wt. test}_1}{x_1} = \frac{\text{wt. test}_3}{1.0} \quad x_1 = \frac{\text{wt. test}_1}{\text{wt. test}_3} \text{ and } x_2 = \frac{\text{wt. test}_2}{\text{wt. test}_3}$$

By proper substitution the formula becomes:

$$x_1 \text{ score test}_1 + x_2 \text{ score test}_2 + 1.0 \text{ score test}_3 = \text{Battery score}$$

12. *Convert battery scores to appropriate derived scores.* To facilitate interpretation and foster meaningfulness of battery results, the battery score should be converted to the desired derived score, such as T-score or percentile scale, as described in Chapter 2. When the different tests have equal value so that the scores are combined directly without consideration of weighting coefficients, the battery score will be in the form of a composite T-score, standard score or another standard score transformation. (It warrants reiteration at this point that raw scores for different tests cannot be added without transformation to standard score form nor as percentiles.) Although it may suffice to convert composites to mean scale scores for interpretative purposes, to be most meaningful the composite score should be re-scaled to remove the regression effect that characterizes combined scores; for example, each composite T-score could be expressed as a mean T-score for the battery but, preferably, T-scores should be computed for the T-score composites to give a singular battery T-score. Likewise when the multiple regression equation is utilized to determine the battery score, this score will need conversion to a derived score to be meaningful.

13. *Determine the reliability and objectivity for the test battery, as appropriate.* If deemed necessary, the battery reliability and objectivity can be computed from either the final scores or the derived scores for the battery. In instances when the test items are initially administered as a battery, the scores used to establish individual test reliability and objectivity can be combined in appropriate form to ascertain these respective coefficients for the battery. Or alternatively, the individual test coefficients can be combined by mathematical formula to express battery reliability and objectivity. When individual tests are not administered as a battery initially, the teacher may wish to establish reliability and objectivity specifically as a battery, perhaps by using a selected sample of the normative group for retesting. However, unless some extenuating circumstances prevail when the particular test items are administered

as a battery, the general axiom can be expected to apply, whereby, increasing the test length tends to increase reliability and objectivity. Accordingly, if satisfactory reliability and objectivity are derived for individual tests, the respective coefficients for the battery can be expected to be satisfactory, when compliance with sound principles of test administration obtains.

14. *Prepare a manual for use in administering the test battery.* To assure the scientific authenticity as well as the overall usability of a test battery, a carefully prepared manual of directions becomes essential. Such a manual should provide all the basic descriptive information requisite to an evaluation of the test battery, which in essence means why use the battery, what it encompasses, and how to administer the battery as intended. The manual should state information under the specific headings (as suggested near the end of Chapter 3) in a clear and concise manner, provocative of understanding. The way in which this material is presented should be such as to encourage use of the battery rather than to lose readers in needless detail and, consequently, engender disinterest in consideration of the test battery.

15. *Establish norms for the battery, when possible.* The preparation of norms in the broad connotation for the test battery is certainly highly desirable. However, preparation of norms must await the administration of the battery to a large number of cases and reflect a random and representative sampling of the population for whom the test is intended. In instances wherein the test is being standardized for a particular and relatively limited population, such as a school district rather than all schools within the state, the entire population would best be included. Strictly interpreted, for a teacher-made test designed for students in a particular situation, the T-scores computed for that group in reality constitute norms for that group or comparable groups for that teacher in that situation. Nevertheless, the typical reference to norms is in the context of a large population, both in scope and numbers. The factors and considerations that should characterize the establishment of norms are discussed earlier in this chapter. The statistical approach in constructing the recommended normative score, T-score, is described in Chapter 2. While it should be reiterated that the mean and standard deviation comprise the basic statistics from which anyone can construct the appropriate norms, the completely developed test materials should include the norm table.

The establishment of norms completes the procedures entailed in developing physical performance tests. Close attention to the fifteen foregoing important aspects of planning and formulating a physical performance test should enhance the efficiency and effectiveness of the construction process as well as result in a desirable physical performance test or battery of tests. Any test worth constructing is worth constructing well.

The following check list is proposed as a guide or blueprint for the teacher in the process of constructing a physical performance test to insure that all steps are covered and in preferred sequential order and, consequently, to virtually guarantee the development of a desirable test. In the event a particular step cannot be carried out satisfactorily the construction process should then cease, inasmuch as an acceptable and desirable test cannot result.

CHECK LIST FOR CONSTRUCTING PHYSICAL PERFORMANCE TESTS

1. *What is to be done and for whom?* Delineate the test objectives (to indicate its purpose) and for whom it is intended.
2. *What is needed?* Definitively analyze the skill or quality involved to divulge illustrative sample performance amenable to testing.
3. *What test items warrant consideration?* Propose possible items and choose the preferable ones.
4. *What is the test description?* Devise suitable prescriptive and detailed directions for each test item, including necessary equipment and facility specifications.
5. *What is the proper test order?* Specify the order in which the different test items should be administered.
6. *What is the testing sample?* Properly select a typical group of sufficient size to represent the intended test population.
7. *What is the basis for validation?* Choose a justifiable criterion measure or describe the content validity, as appropriate.
8. *What is the reliability?* Establish reliability at an acceptable level for each test item.
9. *What is the validity?* Establish the validity for each test item.
10. *What is the objectivity?* For tests proposed for use by others establish the objectivity.
11. *What scoring method is proposed?* Select an appropriate scale score for transformation of raw score; preference recommended for T-scale.
12. *What about combining test items?* When test items are to be combined into a battery:
    a. Determine the intercorrelation between intended items.
    b. Ascertain the best combination of test items as a battery.
    c. Establish the basis for combining test scores into a composite battery score.
    d. Convert battery composite to a meaningful score, such as mean T-score or battery T-score.
    e. Report coefficients or indicate basis for satisfactory reliability and objectivity of the battery.

13. *What are the norms?* Develop norm chart (for example, T-scores) for test items and battery, as appropriate, for the standard group.
14. *What about a test manual?* Prepare a manual containing complete descriptive materials regarding the test, its construction, use and norms.

Specific Considerations. In order for the teacher to be fully knowledgeable in test construction, it becomes necessary to understand the specific factors and concerns relevant to the particular type of test involved in addition to the general considerations pertaining to tests of all types of learning—technical, associated, and concomitant. Accordingly, it is essential to draw particular attention to the specific considerations implicit in constructing physical performance tests to supplement the foregoing presentation of the important aspects entailed in a procedural analysis of planning and formulating such tests. Specifically, then, the teacher should be alert to matters relating to the following concerns:

1. *Test Length.* A feasible limit is necessary for the number of test items (or tests in a battery) to be included. An excessively long test will prove impractical. For the most part, tests of technical learning are scored by observing and immediately recording performance, in contrast to tests of associated and concomitant learning which are usually taken and scored at different times. Analysis of sport skill testing suggests a limit of three items for such tests, inasmuch as additional items generally exert relatively little effort upon the validity.

The number of trials allowed constitutes another important aspect of test length. In tests of speed, strength, and skill other than accuracy, one to three trials appear sufficient, depending upon the nature of the quality being measured. One trial generally suffices for cardiovascular endurance (for example, 12-minute run) and muscular strength and endrance (for example, sit-ups). Two or three trials are usually necessary for distance throws, speed events, jumping, and measures of static strength. Items purporting to measure accuracy usually entail a considerable number of trials, such as from 10 to 20. For accuracy it sometimes is necessary to determine the minimum number of trials requisite for scientific authenticity in an endeavor to establish a length that falls within the limits of administrative feasibility. For example, whereas 15 trials on a softball throwing accuracy test may result in good test reliability, time limitations may render infeasible a test of more than 10 trials. If satisfactory reliability can be obtained with 10 trials, it can be compromised, otherwise this particular accuracy test should not be included.

The relationship of the number of trials to skill performance level warrants mention. Chance variation and extreme variability of unskilled performers influence the number of trials permitted. As noted above, tests involving maximum effort where control plays no appreciable role may be measured in very few trials, whereas accuracy tests necessitate a large enough number of trials to sample adequately the element of chance. Likewise, the erratic, unskilled performance of a novice or poorly trained individual requires a greater number of trials than the consistent skilled level of performance exemplified by an advanced player or well-trained individual.

2. *Scoring.* A test item and scoring scheme that results in a reasonable range and distribution of scores is desirable. If the test item cannot be scored so as to disclose a range of ability in the group for whom it is intended and where differences in performance should be manifested, the test item should not be used. Occasionally the discriminatory power of a test item can be rendered acceptable by increasing the precision of measurement. For example, it may be that measurement of the standing long jump to the nearest half-inch, rather than nearest inch, would make a test satisfactory for a particular group. Again the matter of administrative feasibility warrants consideration, such as in the case of the softball throw for distance. In case measurement to the nearest foot did not result in the desired discriminatory power for this test item, it would almost certainly not be feasible administratively to measure throws to the nearest inch, assuming that this would result in the desired range and distribution of scores.

3. *Test order.* The importance of order in a test battery should be recognized. The meaningfulness of norms on test items for which no test order is prescribed may justifiably be questioned unless careful investigation has actually revealed no ordering effect. Many times test developers have merely assumed no effect of order, which is inconsistent with other scientific controls that are vigorously espoused in test construction. Obviously, in some mass testing situations it may become imperative that testees be divided into groups and spread among the various test stations and then rotated in a sequential fashion. When this is the case, it warrants careful notation so that interpretation of results can be made in light of this fact. It is particularly important to have all testees take the items in the same order, if the performance on one or more of the test items is likely to have a discernible effect on items that follow. This effect can be two-directional, plus or minus, in that it may be facilitative of better performance on subsequent test items (warm-up effect) or detrimental to true performance on later items, such as through fatigue.

A number of factors need to be considered in arranging the order for the performance of test items. The order should proceed in overall perspective from the least strenuous to the most demanding, to the extent feasible with the various items to be included; for example, the 12-minute run would be the last item when included in a physical or motor fitness battery. As a parallel consideration, for test items involving varying degrees of motor coordination the concept of difficulty progression should not be overlooked; from simple to complex. The basic principles of exercise administration should be heeded, whereby the different body parts and muscle groups are varied to permit adequate recovery before repeated involvement. This concern is especially important in motor and physical fitness tests, although it should be followed to the extent that is practical for skill testing as well. For instance, in a softball test it will generally be next to impossible to avoid having some successive tests items involving throwing. The concern regarding test order would be to arrange the items so as to be facilitative and not inhibitive with reference to throwing items. When this is done, it becomes necessary to expose all testees to the same test item sequence, so that they all experience the same facilitative effect. Matters conducive to efficient and expeditious test administration should also be considered in establishing test order, when possible without compromising considerations more directly affecting test value. For instance, a test would best begin with items lending themselves to participation by the total group, either simultaneously or in halves, with subsequent items arranged in an order to minimize delays as determined by availability of multiple stations for different test items.

4. *Test score.* The most appropriate score should be reported for each test item with due consideration given both to reliability and to teacher application. When practical, the mean score for the trials, or the sum of trials, affords the most reliable measure.[14] For example, the sum of two 20-second bouts of wall volleying constitutes a relatively simple item score to derive. However, it becomes impractical from the point of teacher computation and immediate reporting of scores when time in tenths of seconds or distance in fraction of inches are recorded. In such instances, for example—standing long jump, it appears justifiable for the teacher to use the better or best score for the trials attempted, inasmuch as available evidence indicates that the anticipated small loss in reliability is tolerable and more than offset by the practicality in test administration.

5. *Control of testing conditions.* Performance on tests of technical learning is particularly susceptible to and readily influenced by variable elements in the testing situation. Therefore, deliberate effort should be directed to control the testing conditions to the extent deemed practical and plausible through the directions devised for the test. Much of what is entailed in controlling the testing situation is beyond the realistic and logical purview of test directions and pertains to test organization and administration in general. This latter topic presents the focus for Chapter

[14] Franklin M. Henry, "'Best' Versus 'Average' Individual Scores," *Research Quarterly,* 38, No. 2 (May, 1967), 317.

6. However, the teacher should recognize the various concerns involved so as to incorporate relevant admonitions and instructions for administering the test. Essentially, three aspects exist—extraneous factors, equipment and facility specifications, and motivational procedure.

The influence of extraneous factors, although largely a general concern for test administration, may occasionally need particular mention for a given test. Extraneous factors are conceived as including such things as time of day, light intensity, and, for outdoor activity, slope of the field, and weather elements—wind direction and velocity, and temperature. Regarding the second aspect, when the test is developed, appropriate stipulations dealing with equipment and facilities that are involved should be clearly stated. This is imperative not only for test standardization purposes, but also in terms of safe testing practices. Such matters as the kind or specifications of balls, type of running surface, or composition of rebounding targets are illustrative of this aspect.

The final aspect, motivation, warrants especial note because of its tremendous effect upon test results. This concern can best be vivified by the conclusion of one researcher that "the validity of the measures of physical fitness tests is dependent upon the motivating conditions under which the tests are administered." [15] He also observed that "it is conceivable that some tests should be discarded because they measure the strength of the motivating conditions under which the tests were administered, rather than the physical condition of the subject." [16] In test directions the teacher should endeavor to standardize motivational procedure, since many test users seemingly fail to realize the important effect that motivational factors exert on test results. The practice of permitting some subjects to run the 50-yard dash alone, while others run in groups of two or more represents one common error in the motivation category. The clarity and tone of the directions given to testees has a motivational influence and should be standardized. This appears to be most effectively handled by including in the test directions the specific instructions to be read to the testees along with admonitions for the teacher to exercise in administering the test.

6. *Errors in measurement of physical performance.* The teacher should be alert to ways in which errors may be committed in the measurement of physical performance so as to control, if not obviate, them in test construction. Likely errors include the following:

   a. *Observation.* The observation of subjects and instruments necessitates careful control. Of particular concern is parallax, that is, the apparent displacement of an observed object due to a change in the

---

[15] Clinton H. Strong, "Motivation Related to Performance of Physical Fitness Tests," *Research Quarterly,* 34, No. 4 (December, 1963), 497.
[16] *Ibid.*

observer's position. This is a factor in reading instrument dials and in viewing contrivances such as may be utilized in posture appraisal.

b. *Landmarks.* Errors involving landmarks are generally attributable to improper placement of the landmarks. For example, flesh pencil markings to indicate certain bony protuberances should be placed when the subject has assumed the desired position for the purpose at hand. A change in body position will in many instances alter the relationship of markings to their reference points, because of joint movement and resultant changes in skin stress, so that the markings will no longer appear directly over the intended reference points.

c. *Distances.* The method of measuring distance needs to be clearly stipulated and carefully followed. This entails the points of reference for measuring (from where to where), such as for the standing long jump, and whether measurement is made on or parallel to a line of direction, as in the softball throw, or represents actual distance regardless of direction, such as in the shot put.

d. *Timing instruments.* Certainly the basic instructions relating to the use of timing devices is beyond the purview of test specifications and directions. It may be appropriate, however, to describe a recommended procedure for routine checking of the stop watches or other timing instruments. The desirability of retesting students with the same timing device, when practical, should be indicated.

e. *Instrument design.* Attention to the appropriateness of the instrument for the task is an important consideration. Generally instruments have certain limitations in terms of their design. In many instances instruments are suitable for use only for a certain range within the total spectrum of the particular quality that is involved. For example, cable tensiometers are selected according to the range of force in pounds to be encountered in the particular muscular actions being tested. The suitability of the size and contour of instruments, such as a hand manuometer, should be determined in light of the developmental age of the subjects; obviously, the physical characteristics of elementary and secondary school students vary considerably.

The teacher should realize that this brief description of the kinds of possible errors is intended to be suggestive through the illustrations cited and not definitive and all-inclusive; the latter is neither practical nor possible.

7. *Reliability coefficients.* In Chapter 3 the rule of thumb regarding an acceptable level of reliability was cited as a coefficient of at least 0.85 for individual use, and 0.75 for group use. Basic to the development of

tests in selected sports activities, the Sport Skills Project Committee of the Research Council, AAHPER, adopted as the criterion of reliability that correlation coefficients should be no less than 0.80 for events scored on the basis of distance and no less than 0.70 for events scored on the basis of accuracy and form.[17] The complexity of variables involved in a particular physical performance test should be considered in interpreting the reliability coefficient in terms of its acceptability. For instance, the minimum level of satisfactory reliability for a test of cardiovascular endurance would be less than that for a distance-covered skill event, because of the obvious difference in complexity of the variables.

8. *Instrument reliability.* The same concern for test item reliability applies for test instruments used to measure aspects of physical performance, for example, cable tensiometer for static strength, as for performance items such as number of push-ups or wall volleys. Sometimes manufactured test instruments are presumed to be reliable or, once checked and found reliable, assumed to remain so thereafter. The teacher should provide for routine analysis of the calibration of test instruments to verify their reliability. This is necessary to insure that changes or instances of no change that may be recorded upon re-testing at a later time are not due to alteration in instrument readings but rather in the item being measured. If needed, the teacher can obtain advice pertaining to instrument calibration from the manufacturer, college testing personnel, or engineering specialists.

Performance Rating

Performance rating, as previously mentioned, refers to specific instruments designed to measure subjectively certain aspects of, or overall, performance, either when objective measurement of physical performance cannot be obtained for some reason, or as a supplement to available objective measurement. Some of the salient factors of concern in rating were discussed earlier in this chapter in conjunction with the use of rating as a criterion measure for validation of a physical performance test. A description of various forms of rating scales is presented in Chapter 5 under measurement pertaining to concomitant learning. At this point, it would seem appropriate to depict those factors to be considered in devising a rating procedure or scale to evaluate a particular physical quality or skill.

The teacher has innumerable occasions to use an appropriate means of rating. These include rating a player's skill in an activity to supplement, or in lieu of, specific skill test scores, and rating an activity, such

---

[17] *Skills Test Manual: Football* (Washington: AAHPER, 1965), p. 7.

as dance, diving, or posture, for which satisfactory objective measurement may not exist. In some sport skill areas no objective tests exist to measure certain important abilities, for example, the overhead smash in tennis, or rebounding in basketball. Performance ratings are advantageous in several other ways as well. They are sometimes more economical of teacher time, and rating of performance requires the teacher to observe each student carefully on an individual basis, which constitutes a desired but oft-neglected characteristic of teaching. On many occasions ratings afford the only feasible scheme of appraising performance in game situations.

Procedure for Developing Performance Rating Devices. For teacher rating of the desired skill or quality to be valid necessitates careful observance of certain basic considerations in constructing the rating device to be used. The following statements, arranged in desired sequential order, are intended to serve as guides in devising a rating scheme.

1. *Describe definitively what is to be rated.* Specific points of emphasis should be vividly depicted so that a clear conception is fostered of the particular aspects of the quality or skill to be rated. In some instances the teacher may desire to break down a skill, such as the tennis service, into its components for rating—grip, ball setup, and so on. When appropriate, identifying meaningful parts to be rated and then combining the ratings into a composite score tends to enhance reliability and validity. If desired, the ratings given to the component parts of a particular skill can be assigned a weighting based on their importance in overall perspective.

2. *Define the range of rating and the degree of discrimination desired.* In essence, this step consists of determining the number of categories for rating purposes. If the range of rating is relatively small and the degree of discrimination desired is likewise small, a small number of categories will suffice. As an example, a teacher may wish to observe and rate the motor fitness of his fifth-grade class on the basis of their continuous activity throughout a particular class period. The range of this quality is observed, and the degree of discrimination possible might suggest three categories for rating. The degree of discrimination desired should be governed by the purpose for rating. Obviously, needless time and effort can be expended by discriminating between a number of levels of ability when only a rough differentiation is actually necessary. Given a skill in which the range is greater and more discrimination is desired, the number of categories would be increased. An appraisal of standing long jump form or a tumbling stunt would encompass a greater range of ability and be conducive to greater discrimination; five cate-

gories might prove desirable. For fine discrimination, ten categories or scale points can be used, such as those employed in rating competitive diving and gymnastics. However, when more than seven categories are used, the higher degree of discrimination becomes more difficult and, with relatively inexperienced raters, consumes more time.

3. *Describe precisely each category or scale point for rating.* Such a description should be custom-made for the activity or quality involved and should depict the differentiating characteristics of the various levels of ability to be encountered. The use of diagrams, photographs, stick figures, or any suitable aid to present a vivid portrayal of each scale point is suggested. An example of the use of descriptive illustrations in a rating scheme is the New Yok State Posture Rating Chart, as shown in Chaper 10. It may be that a verbal description can be made definitive enough to suffice, such as the following chart devised for appraising form in tennis forehand and backhand strokes.

Rating	Reflects
5 = Superior	Very alert assumption of proper body position (including eye on ball) Strong, proper, and smooth stroke mechanics Well-coordinated effort with easy weight shift and body pivot
4 = Good	Quick proper assumption of body position Proper stroke mechanics with slight weakness in some aspect of swing Good coordination with proper weight shift and body pivot
3 = Average	Deliberate assumption of satisfactory body position Satisfactory stroke mechanics with some weakness in aspects such as: backswing, forward swing, follow-through, arm and wrist action, grip, or point of impact Satisfactory coordination with weight shift and some body pivot
2 = Fair	Hesitancy in footwork in assuming position for stroke; position may be slightly off; eye may not be on the ball Stroke mechanics show considerable weakness in aspects mentioned above Coordination deficient; inadequate weight shift and body pivot
1 = Poor	Improper footwork and position; little focus on ball Unsatisfactory stroke mechanics—inadequate swinging, grip, arm and wrist action, and point of ball impact Coordination lacking; no semblance of weight shift and proper body pivot

4. *Prepare a specific rating procedure.* This primarily entails provision for control of the variable factors involved in administering the rating that affect the actual rating given. This step may be succinctly described as an effort to standardize the rating procedure. Definitive, inclusive

directions contribute greatly to this endeavor by insuring that each administration of the rating scheme will be conducted in the same way and the results will be interpreted in the same manner. When more than one skill or quality is to be rated, that is, multiple rating, all individuals should be rated on one item at a time. To illustrate, for a tennis ability rating comprised of forehand, backhand, and service, all subjects would first be rated on the forehand. Then the ratings of backhand would be completed, before turning to the service.

Prepared forms for rating also contribute greatly toward the goal of fostering accurate, efficient rating. These forms should be designed so as to facilitate the rating process and the recording of scores. Careful design will preclude the likelihood of recording a particular rating in any place but the intended space. Basically, two types of rating forms are used —individual and group. For the individual type, the sheet usually contains the specific points to be noted with their appropriate description and space for the assigned rating. The group form, in general, provides space for recording the assigned rating for each member of the group on the number of items for consideration. The actual descriptive details basic to the rating are not included on the group scoring form, as is done on the individual forms.

5. *Plan adequately for the rating.* While intimately connected with the specific rating procedure, the concern of this guide statement is to provide emphatically for factors that affect the validity of the rating. Adequate planning is conceived as insuring provision for:

a. *Ample time to render the rating desired.* A hurried rating is valueless. This entails sufficient time not only for repeated trials for the subject to display his ability but also for the observer to render sound, considered judgment. If insufficient time is available for the rating as planned, the type of rating must be revised accordingly or eliminated.

b. *Rating to be made during the period of observation and not at some later time.* This likewise implies that rating is based on actual performance during the observation period and not in light of previous performance. This is not in contradiction to the earlier discussion of expert rating for physical performance test validation. Here the concern applies to a specific rating on a specific performance, whereas the earlier concern involved rating overall ability in an activity or skill as a criterion measure for validity.

c. *Assuring reasonable equalization of ability of competing individuals, when ratings are based on performance with others.* If reasonable equalization cannot be arranged, players should be rotated to play against varying levels of ability. A player of average ability creates a very favorable impression against an individual with comparatively poor ability, whereas competition against a good player will result in a poorer showing for the average player.

d. *Conditions conducive to uninhibited observation by raters.* The raters should be positioned so as to have an unobstructed view of the performance, and every effort should be made to elmininate any elements that apepar distracting to the raters.

e. *Using other raters when the teachers needs the services of additional raters.* This provision includes recognition of the basis for selecting raters, instructions necessary to orient the raters, and ways of identifying students (such as numbered jerseys) to other raters who may be unfamiliar with the group.

Rating techniques devised in accordance with the aforementioned guides and, as appropriate, in light of the basic principles concerning the construction of other types of rating scales and measuring instruments will prove to be valuable teaching devices. The use of properly devised rating procedures does much to foster greater reliability in judging skill and overall performance in physical education activities.

To facilitate the construction of acceptable instruments for rating performance, the checklist presented below contains the essential steps for the teacher to follow.

CHECK LIST FOR CONSTRUCTING A DEVICE FOR PERFORMANCE RATING

1. Describe the purpose of the rating.
2. Plan for appropriate validation.
3. Describe definitively the skill or quality to be rated (in terms of its constituent parts).
4. Determine the range and specific scale for rating in light of the stated purpose.
5. Clearly define the rating scale points or categories.
6. Provide for details essential to observation and immediate rating of a typical performance by testees.
7. Stipulate the rating procedure in necessary detail, including provision of a rating form.
8. Describe the process to derive a total score when different components are rated.
9. Establish the validity, reliability, and objectivity.
10. Devise a chart or basis for meaningful interpretation of the total score.
11. Prepare appropriate descriptive materials for the rating scheme as developed.

Specific Considerations.   In constructing a performance rating device the teacher particularly needs to be cognizant of the following concerns:

1. *Factors limiting the accuracy of a rater.* In the accuracy of his ratings a rater is limited by: experience in observing and rating performance; the opportunity to observe the subjects; knowledge of the skill or quality being rated; understanding of the rating instrument; willingness and ability to give an unbiased and objective judgment; and ability to concentrate on the task at hand.

2. *Importance of rater "warm-up."* Before the rating process begins, the rater should observe the performance of the group of subjects to the extent possible and practical. During the observation period the rater should notice the range of talent (from poorest to best) to gain perspective regarding the apparent distribution of ability in the group on the rating device. Continual reference should be made to the details of the rating scale during this period as well as during the actual rating.

3. *Use of other raters.* This concern is comprised of three facets—the benefit of using more than one rater, attention to the orientation of other raters, and rater accuracy. Regarding the first facet, assuming that all raters have an equal chance to observe the subjects being rated, the pooling of independent ratings of two or more judges has essentially the effect of lengthening a test. Consequently, it tends to enhance the reliability of the rating instrument. The prime concern of the orientation of raters is to familiarize them with the rating device and its proper use on the intended subjects. Generally concerted attention to clarification of scale points and their defining characteristics is desirable. The final facet, rater accuracy, refers to a reasonable degree of agreement in judgment of the different raters that are used. To a considerable extent rater accuracy is a function of the qualifications of the raters and the effectiveness of their orientation. As described in the discussion of use of judges for test validation, usually a minimum coefficient of correlation of 0.80 is indicative of acceptable agreement between raters. When a satisfactory agreement of judgment is not reached, the situation needs rectifying by rater removal, replacement, or training, as appropriate. To avert misunderstanding it should be stated that in this discussion of rater accuracy it is presumed that satisfactory objectivity has been established for the rating instrument. Obviously, no attempt to ascertain rater accuracy is warranted unless the instrument evinces acceptable objectivity.

4. *Common errors in rating.* Three common errors appear in rating that have relevance for both construction and use of the instrument involved. These are: (a) *generosity* or *leniency error,* in which the ratings tend to pile up at the high end of the scale; (b) *halo error,* in which the tendency is to rate in terms of overall impression without clearly differentiating the specific aspects encompassed; and (c) *error of central tendency,* in which little spread is accorded to ratings above and below the mid-

point of the scale. In addition, the teacher should be aware of another possible error that may be encountered—*logical error,* wherein similar ratings are given on qualities that to the rater appear logically related. A well-constructed, definitive instrument complete with explicit instructions regarding rater use and orientation will obviate or certainly do much to minimize these errors.

This description of performance rating concludes the general presentation of requisite knowledge for developing measuring instruments for technical learning, that is to say physical performance, including those factors basic to construction of measurement tools for all three types of learning. Prior to initiating the actual test construction procedure for a test of technical learning, the teacher need only become informed of any specific considerations that apply to the development and administration of a test pertaining to the particular performance quality in question. While the teacher can now resolve the illustrative problem in part, by constructing a suitable motor fitness performance test, attention needs to be directed next to the procedure and considerations entailed in the development of instruments to measure associated and concomitant learnings related to motor fitness.

SELECTED REFERENCES

1. McCloy, C. H., and Young, N. D. *Tests and Measurements in Health and Physical Education,* 3d ed. New York: Appleton-Century-Crofts, Inc., 1954.
2. Montoye, Henry J., ed. *Principles and Operational Practices* (*An Introduction to Measurement in Physical Education,* Vol. 1). Indianapolis: Phi Epsilon Kappa Fraternity, 1970.
3. Montoye, Henry J., ed. *Sports Tests and Evaluation in Dance* (*An Introduction to Measurement in Physical Educatiaon,* Vol. 3). Indianapolis: Phi Epsilon Kappa Fraternity, 1970.
4. Research Council. *Research Methods in Health, Physical Education Recreation,* 3d ed. Washington: AAHPER, 1973.
5. Safrit, Margaret J. *Evaluation in Physical Education.* Englewood Cliffs, N.J.: Prentice-Hall, Inc., 1973.
6. Thorndike, Robert L., ed. *Educational Measurement,* 2d ed. Washington: American Council on Education, 1971.

5

Constructing Tests of Associated and Concomitant Learnings

TESTS OF KNOWLEDGE AND UNDERSTANDING—ASSOCIATED LEARNING

Many physical educators have failed to recognize the importance of tests of associated learning (cognitive domain) and have viewed the time devoted to this type of testing as an impingement upon the already limited time available for physical activity within the school program. Now concerted attention is being directed toward the importance of knowledge and understanding in physical education.

Present-day pressures for the re-examination of curriculum and procedures demand that more attention be given the creative use of the intellect in physical education. The intellectual, the verbally expressive content of physical education is as significant as the motor content, and needs to be assessed. In appraising the student's progress in physical education, therefore, evidence should be obtained of the acquisition of knowledges and understandings in addition to the mastering of physical skills.[1]

Knowledge and understanding present different characteristics and qualities than physical performance. Consequently, the construction of appropriate measuring instruments should entail certain special considerations. Attention will be directed to applying the basic factors of test

[1] *Knowledge and Understanding in Physical Education* (Washington: American Association for Health, Physical Education and Recreation, 1969), p. xi.

construction to the area of associated learning, with emphasis upon the special factors that should be heeded. In constructing written tests, a teacher engages in a creative task that necessitates skill and understanding. Many factors enter into the process and influence the quality of the test that results, which reduces to almost nil the possibility of a well-written test occurring by chance. Poorly constructed tests or test items are usually evidenced quite vividly by student questions or statements revealing their misconstruement of the test item. Such embarrassing situations do nothing to foster respect either for the teacher or for the use of measurement.

Procedure for Developing Tests of Associated Learning

The particular concerns in the basic procedure for developing writteen tests may be enumerated as:

1. Clear recognition of test objectives.
2. Have the test reflect content distribution of the learning activity.
3. Determine the type or types of test items compatible with the purpose and content of the test.
4. Prepare appropriate test items and directions for the types selected.
5. Arrange test items by type and evaluate them in the intended context.
6. Administer the test as organized.
7. Analyze test quality.
8. Make changes or revisions as indicated.

CLEAR RECOGNITION OF TEST OBJECTIVES.—Emphasis is placed upon recognizing very distinctly the purpose of the test, as was mentioned initially in the general comments pertaining to the planning step of test construction. Why this test? The answer to this question furnishes direction in construction. Using a tennis test as an example, a teacher may desire to ascertain the knowledge and understanding of tennis reflected by his or her classes after covering a unit devoted to tennis at a particular grade level.

HAVE THE TEST REFLECT CONTENT DISTRIBUTION OF THE LEARNING ACTIVITY.—The intent herein is that the test distribution should be planned to approximate the emphasis given to instructional activity or, succinctly, that content validity be established. The prime concern is not that each area should have identical emphasis but rather to insure that the test constitutes a representative sample of objectives and content, and that all important areas are covered and to a greater extent than any points of considerably lesser importance. A chart showing the distribution of questions according to instructional objectives and content areas can be a very simple, yet effective, way of detecting the proportionate emphasis of the test. Such a chart, generally referred to as a *table of specifications*,[2] should include a descriptive title of the content areas, appropriate objectives, a tally of the questions pertaining to each area, and a column indicating the percentage of emphasis. For a tennis knowledge test, the content areas might be described as: historical development; the court and playing equipment; fundamental skill—position and footwork, basic strokes; court position and strategy; advanced strokes; and rules.

DETERMINE THE TYPE OR TYPES OF TEST ITEMS COMPATIBLE WITH THE PURPOSE AND CONTENT OF THE TEST.—At this point, it seems appropriate to differentiate between knowledge and understanding, inasmuch as some types of test items measure the former while other types serve to reveal understanding. Concisely stated, *knowledge* implies awareness of facts, beliefs, or other information; whereas *understanding* entails, in addition, cognizance of the applicability and significance of this knowledge. Accordingly, an alternative-response type of question, such as true-false, might serve as an appropriate means of ascertaining knowledge but would not be as effective for the purpose of reflecting understanding. For the latter, carefully constructed multiple-choice test items or short-answer recall questions are more desirable. The reader is referred to the later section dealing with types of tests for a description of commonly used types of objective tests as a basis for determining the compatibility of various types of test items.

Focus should be directed to insuring that the form of the item is suited to its content and function. The teacher should avoid forcing objectives or content into items of a specific type into which they do not fit. Illustrating briefly with a tennis test, a rules question such as the legality of service with an underhand motion must of necessity be structured as an alternative-response item. A test item dealing with the point at which the ball should be contacted in the backhand stroke lends itself to a multiple-choice item, since a number of feasible and plausible alternatives can be listed.

Implicit in selecting types of test items compatible with purpose and content of the test, and not to be overlooked, is the concern for appropriateness for the age or grade level involved. For example, the teacher might not deem certain types of items suitable for some elementary grades, such as matching or completion items.

PREPARE APPROPRIATE TEST ITEMS AND DIRECTIONS FOR THE TYPES SELECTED.—While concerted attention is necessary to what type of test

[2] For further relative to table of specifications see: Norman E. Gronlund, *Constructing Achievement Tests* (Englewood Cliffs, N.J.: Prentice-Hall, Inc., 1968), pp. 19–22.

items are included, how well an item is constructed is more important than the type of item it represents. Hence, the teacher should be deliberative and stress quality in item writing. If a card file system of organizing test questions is utilized, as suggested in Chapter 4, the preparation of test items becomes much simplified and in essence consists of selecting and adapting test items on file. With or without this resource file, the preparation of specific test items is a deliberative process in which the intent is to devise items deemed appropriate in light of important considerations in test construction. Each test item should be presented in the manner most conducive to ready comprehension, which in some instances will require the use of diagrams, charts, or the like. As an example, questions pertaining to position play or game strategy can be stated much more clearly through the use of situation-like drawings than by means of verbal description alone.

The importance of using reading vocabulary suitable to the grade level concerned, especially in the elementary school, should be heeded in constructing written tests. Patty [3] provided suggestive considerations in this concern, and a teachers' work reference [4] is available, to cite two resources to guide the process of selecting words compatible with the reading difficulty range for a particular grade level. Perhaps the most feasible resource in this matter is for the physical education teacher to consult with elementary classroom teachers in the particular situation. Obviously, this constitutes a factor that can vary appreciably among schools due to a number of variable influences, such as socio-cultural background. Earnest concern for proper word level will render more likely the probability that student response to test items is indicative of their understanding of the subject matter rather than of their ability to understand the manner in which the items are expressed.

This last concern also constitutes a prime consideration in preparing directions for each type of test item, namely, that the test directions are explicit and readily comprehensible so that the response to the different test items is an indication of the knowledge and understanding possessed rather than a function of ability to understand the directions. When the test item is familiar to the group involved, the directions need merely consist of a brief descriptive statement of procedure. However, when the typical method of response to a type of test item is modified in some way or an unfamiliar or new test item is used, very definitive directions together with one or more sample test items are necessary. If the teacher has any doubt regarding the familiarity of the group with a particular

[3] W. W. Patty, "Reading Difficulty Differences of Health Knowledge Tests," *Research Quarterly*, **16**, No. 3 (October, 1945), 206.

[4] E. L. Thorndike and Irving Lorge, *The Teachers' Word Book of 30,000 Words* (New York: Bureau of Publications, Teachers College, Columbia University, 1944).

type of test item, it becomes imperative that a concise yet definitive description of how to proceed be included with appropriate examples.

ARRANGE TEST ITEMS BY TYPE AND EVALUATING THEM IN THE INTENDED CONTEXT.—After the appropriate items are prepared, they should be arranged by type in a logical, sequential order and in terms of relative progressive difficulty. Then the test items should be appraised in light of the context in which they are to be utilized. Any noted discrepancies regarding the suitability of a test item should result in revision or elimination with necessary substitution, as may be indicated. The following admonitions for constructing tests of associated learning are presented at this point for suggested use as guides in arranging and evaluating test items.[5]

1. Include a large number of items in the test, utilizing varied forms or types of questions.
2. State questions clearly, avoiding ambiguous and "tricky" or "catchy" phraseology.
3. Make the test comprehensive but exclude insignificant and trivial items.
4. Emphasize the functional value of knowledge concerned, not the content objectives.
   This entails that the test situations be suggestive of the actual situations in which the learning will be applied.
5. Make sure that each item is independent of the other items; that is, each item should be complete in and of itself and not reflect a continuation of a previous item.
6. Be certain that no item can be answered by simply referring to other items.
7. Each item should have a definite answer with a real basis for the correct response.
8. Each test item should differentiate between those who know and those who do not.
9. Do not include any item for which the answer appears obvious to a person not familiar with the subject matter.
10. Include items of known value and difficulty.
11. Avoid inclusion of clues, specific determiners (all, never, always), or any artificial source of aid to testees.
12. Exercise caution to avert a pattern being formed by the responses.
13. Make the method of scoring as simple as possible.
   Arranging blanks for recording answers along one side of the

---

[5] Adapted in part from W. J. Micheels and M. R. Karnes, *Measuring Educational Achievement* (New York: McGraw-Hill Book Co., 1950), pp. 132–49.

page is highly desirable. This minimizes the possibility of errors in answering and scoring.

14. Avoid weighting of test items.

Each test item should be assigned one score unit unless, as in the case of a fill-in or short-answer supply type item, several points are elicited. In the latter instance, each point would be accorded one score unit. Although teachers often desire to count some items more than others, for reasons of importance or difficulty, available evidence has shown no increase in reliability or validity when scores are weighted. Weighting merely complicates the scoring task and augments the likelihood of scoring error. If a teacher wishes to increase the relative weight of an area in the total test score, the best way is to construct more items in that area.

Implicit in the concern for arranging test items by type is the need to arrange the different types of test items according to logical and psychological order. Basically, this consists of presenting the types of items in ascending order of difficulty and time-involvement, whereby the true–false section is presented first, then multiple-choice, and so on in the order as described later in this chapter.

ADMINISTERED THE TEST AS ORGANIZED.—The arrangement of suitable test items in the desired form predicates readiness for administering the test to a group typical of that for which the test was designed. This administration provides the data and information upon which to base analysis of test items and of overall test suitability.

ANALYZE TEST QUALITY.—In analyzing test quality the considerations may be categorized as: (1) content validity, that is, external test validity; (2) item analysis to ascertain internal test validity; and (3) test reliability and objectivity.

1. *Content validity.* Sometimes referred to as curricular validity, content validity is provided for by steps 2 and 3 in the procedure for planning and formulating written tests which insure the prime concern involved, namely, that the test be attuned to the objectives and content of the course or instructional unit. Satisfactory content validity will result only when the test truly reflects the content of the learning experiences in light of the purpose for which these experiences were intended. The more directly, completely, and reliably a test measures the attainment of these goals implicit in the content of instruction, the better its content validity. Thus, analysis of content validity at this point serves to affirm the overall compatibility of the test with curricular goals and content, as previously planned.

2. *Item analysis.* The matter of ascertaining internal test validity through item analysis is of especial importance, since the quality of the test as a whole is a function of, or is limited by the quality of the individual items that comprise the test. Item analysis is essentially a study to appraise the value of each item in a test so that undesirable items may be removed or revised as indicated. Item analysis comprises three factors: (1) difficulty rating, (2) functioning of responses, and (3) index of discrimination.

Difficulty rating (*DR*), as one might expect, simply involves expressing the difficulty of a test item in terms of the percentage of correct responses. It is obtained by dividing the number of correct responses on a given test item by the number of individuals who took the test. A low percentage indicates that comparatively few individuals answered the item correctly and, thereby, represents a difficult question. A sample analysis of five selected questions in a tennis knowledge test given to 200 students is presented below.

Question No.	Number of Correct Responses	Difficulty Rating
4	184	92
11	152	76
18	106	53
25	57	29
32	16	8

To illustrate computation of the difficulty rating for question 4, this was determined by:

$$\frac{\text{Number of correct responses}}{\text{Number taking the test}} \times 100 = \frac{184}{200} \times 100 = 92$$

What basis is used to interpret the difficulty rating? Items such as question 4, *DR* = 92, are rather easy and are answered correctly by almost everyone, thus contributing very little to differentiating between students. The same holds true for items such as question 32, which are too difficult and, accordingly, will be answered incorrectly by almost everyone. While limits of acceptability of *DR* may be set at any desired percentage, the practice generally advocated is to establish working limits of 20 to 80 per cent *DR* (absolute limits of 10 to 90 per cent are imperative) with the mean rating being 50 per cent and the scores tending to be concentrated about the mean. A test composed of items that are easy, like question 4, results in high scores with little, if any, gradation between higher levels of achievement, since so many attain the same score. Accordingly, a test composed of items that are predominately very difficult, such as question 32, gives low scores and fails to disclose ability spread between students, except for a few. While the optimum arrangement of difficulty rating may be almost impossible, attention to obtaining a spread of approximately 20 to 80 per cent with a concentration about 50 per cent will provide a test conducive to discerning between levels of test performance. Of the five questions shown above, questions 4 and 32 would be eliminated as they now stand, since they fall outside of the desired spread range of 20 to 80 per cent. Decisions regarding the inclusion of items with DR's that fall slightly outside the working limits should be made on the basis of compensating factors in the other two aspects of item analysis. Other DR spreads are sometimes used, such as 30 to 70 per cent to remove items outside the midrange levels of difficulty in order to maximize the discriminatory function, or 30 to 90 to eliminate the most difficult items. In terms of utility in test construction, difficulty rating affords the basis for arranging test items in order of increasing difficulty.

The second aspect of item analysis, determining the *functioning of responses* (*FR*), serves to reveal those response alternatives or distracters that were selected by very few, if any, testees. If a distracter is never used when the test is administered to a group deemed to be representative of general student ability, such a response should be replaced or revised so that the test item has a satisfactory minimum level of functioning for all response alternatives.

An accurate picture of *FR* is afforded through the use of a response pattern tally sheet, as presented in Fig. 5–1. On such a sheet, the various

RESPONSE PATTERN TALLY SHEET FOR TEST
ITEM ANALYSIS

TEST:

QUESTION	1(R)	2(W)	3	4	5	NO ANSWER	DR	ID	REVISE	DISCARD
1										
2										
3										
4										
5										
6										
7										

Fig. 5–1. Sample response pattern tally sheet.

responses to the different questions can be tallied and then examined to facilitate item analysis not only as to functioning of responses but also in terms of the other two aspects—difficulty rating, and index of discrimination. Such a basic tally sheet, designed for adaptability, may be mimeographed and used for analysis of alternative-response and multiple-choice items. A special revision of this tally sheet can be prepared for matching questions.[6] Also, the basic sheet can be adapted for use with completion questions for purposes of computing difficulty rating and index of discrimination.[7] As shown in Fig. 5–2, questions 1 to 3 were true–false items involving two responses, so the last three columns were crossed out, leaving column 1 (R) for true and column 2 (W) for false answers. Figure 5–2 contains a summarized tabulation of responses to selected questions on a tennis knowledge test given to 200 students.

Examining Fig. 5–2 for FR, it is noted that in question 1, a true–false

RESPONSE PATTERN TALLY SHEET FOR TEST ITEM ANALYSIS

TEST: _Tennis_

QUESTION	1(R)	2(W)	3	4	5	NO ANSWER	DR	ID	REVISE	DISCARD
1	6	194					3			
2	147	53					74			
3	88	112					44			
20	13	163	18	6			82		✓	
21	41	27	102	30			52			
22	44	58	20	39	36	3	18			

Fig. 5–2. Scores tallied on selected questions. Alternative-response correct answer is shown in column 1 (R). Multiple-choice correct response is outlined in black, for example 21–3.

[6] In such a revision, the vertical columns may be reduced in size, so as to permit including the number of columns needed, which is generally no more than 12 to 15. Or the sheet may be so aligned that the vertical columns run across the width (or narrow dimension) of the paper.

[7] for such use with completion questions, only the first two columns are used to indicate right (1) and wrong (2) along with the column indicating no answer given, when appropriate.

item, only 6 of 200 cases (3 per cent) selected true as the response. The decision must then be made as to what constitutes the minimum level of functioning for a response. This is usually expressed as a percentage ranging from 3 to 5 per cent, depending upon type of item (that is, number of distracters) and the number of students in the group. On this basis, a 3 per cent functioning of true response for question 1 might justifiably be considered inadequate, since only two responses were possible. Furthermore, it should be noted that for two-response items inadequate functioning of response will be reflected in an unsatisfactory DR (e.g., $DR = 3$ for question 1). Analysis of question 20, a multiple-choice item, poses a slightly different problem. Distracter No. 4 received 6 choices of 200 cases (3 per cent), while distracter No. 5 was not used at all. Therefore, distracter No. 5 should be revised or discarded; and distracter No. 4 should receive critical analysis to disclose the need for possible revision, inasmuch as it functioned at the minimum level. Thus, the process of analyzing the functioning of responses serves to produce test items in which all distracters are selected as answers to some extent by a typical group. With reference to the effect of group size on the acceptable minimum level of functioning, it may conceivably be proper to retain a multiple-choice distracter that functions at 3 per cent level in a small group (example, 80) with the realization that this might increase to at least 5 per cent in a larger sample.

The third aspect of item analysis, *index of discrimination* (*ID*), in essence constitutes an expression of the capability of a test item to differentiate between levels of ability of different individuals. Index of discrimination appears somewhat related to difficulty rating (*DR*) and confusion between the two might well occur. The *DR* concerns itself with group performance. It expresses the percentage of the group answering a given question correctly. In contrast, *ID* may be described as concerning itself with how well a given test item tells the difference between students who achieved a good total score on the entire test and students who received a poor total score. The relationship between *DR* and *ID* is easily discerned. Any easy item, *DR* of 90, might be expected to possess relatively poor discriminating power, a low *ID*, since almost all students would answer it correctly. However, as examination of Figs. 5–2 and 5–3 will verify, this relationship does not necessarily follow. A test item (question 3 for example) can be reasonably difficult in terms of group response (*DR* = 44) and still fail to discriminate to a comparable degree between student ability (*ID* = 0.22). This means that a number of poor students answered the item correctly and some good students missed it. The best test item from this discriminatory aspect is one that is answered correctly by all the good students and failed by the poor students, that is, *ID* = 1.00.

For further illustration, assume that a teacher is comparing two test items with a *DR* of 50. This means that 50 per cent of the group answered each question correctly, but the students who constituted each 50 per cent group would in all probability not be the same for both tests. A student might answer one right and the other wrong. For one of the assumed test items, suppose that the students who answered it correctly also comprised the top 50 per cent of total scores, while those who missed the item were the lower 50 per cent on total test score. This test item then possesses the best possible discriminatory power, namely, *ID* = 1.00. The second item with a *DR* of 50 might have been missed by half of the better students and answered correctly by a number of the poorer students. This is illustrative of poor capability of a test item to discriminate between levels of ability. The first item exemplifies why test makers should strive to prepare many items at or near the 50 per cent level of difficulty, since only at this level is maximum discrimination possible, that is, all in the upper half of test scores get it right, while none in the lower group do.

Since a test discriminates when the good students answer it correctly while the poor students do not, to determine the *ID* for a test item it becomes necessary to compare the performance of the good students with the poor ones. This process can be readily shown by the most easily derived form of an index of discrimination, referred to as the Upper–Lower (U–L) Index.[8] To derive the U–L index two sub-groups are first formed from the total test group based on total score, namely, the top 27 per cent of the scores on the total test and the bottom 27 per cent. The U–L index is computed for each test item by taking the number of correct responses made on the item by students in the upper group, subtracting the number of correct responses on the item in the lower group, and dividing the remainder by the size of each group (that is, 27 per cent of the total group). By formula this becomes:

U–L Index = $R_U - R_L/0.27N$, where R_U and R_L are the number of correct responses in upper and lower groups, respectively. In determining group size, the teacher rounds the 27 per cent to the nearest whole number. The U–L index of discrimination is interpreted as follows:[9]

+0.4 and above—high
+0.2 to .4—moderate
+0.1 to .2—low and needs revision
less than +0.1—not discriminating

[8] A. Pemberton Johnson, "Notes on a Suggested Index of Item Validity: The U–L Index," *Journal of Educational Psychology*, XLII, No. 8 (December, 1951), 499.

[9] Robert L. Ebel, "Procedures for the Analysis of Classroom Tests," *Educational and Psychological Measurement*, XIV, No. 2 (Summer, 1954), 352.

The U–L index affords the teacher a relatively easily determined measure of discriminatory power.

A more sophisticated measure has been developed by Flanagan[10] which can be readily computed and understood by the teacher. This procedure expresses the relationship of the upper and lower percentages as a correlation coefficient and, as for the U–L index, uses the high and low 27 per cent of test scores as good and poor groups.[11] For the illustrative tennis knowledge test, the groups would consist of 27 per cent of 200, or 54 students.

To compute *ID* the correct responses to each question made by the good group are first tallied on a Response Pattern Tally Sheet (see Fig. 5–3), using the upper portion of each box. After the good group has been recorded, the correct responses of the poor group on each item are recorded in the lower portion of the proper box with a different colored pencil. It should be noted that only the correct responses are needed in this instance. As an aside, it should be explained that the complete data for item analysis (that it, *DR, FR,* and *ID*) can be recorded on a single tally sheet, if desired. To do so, all responses (right and wrong) for good and poor groups are tallied, the *ID* for each item is computed, and then the remaining 46 per cent of responses are tallied so that *DR* and *FR* can be determined. Obviously, the procedure was broken into Fig. 5–2 and 5–3 for simplicity in presentation.

The actual computation of *ID* for each item is done in two steps. First, the percentage of the good group that answered each item correctly is determined and the same is done for the poor group. In question 2, Fig. 5–3, this would be $42/54 = 78$ per cent, and $26/54 = 48$ per cent, for good and poor groups, respectively. At this point it is of interest to observe that computation can be facilitated, when hand-calculation is involved, by using 25, 33, 50 or 100 as the group size whenever 27 per cent of the total group comes within close proximity of any of these figures. For example, using the top and bottom 50 cases, rather than 54,

[10] John C. Flanagan, "General Considerations in the Selection of Test Items and a Short Method of Estimating the Product-Moment Coefficient from Data at the Tails of the Distribution." *Journal of Educational Psychology,* XXX, No. 9 (December, 1939), 674.

[11] A disadvantage of using 27-per cent groups is that the extreme cases at the two ends of the distribution are grouped with others closer to the mean and near the first and third quartiles and, thereby, do not receive the greater weight they deserve. To overcome this, Flanagan subsequently devised tables for upper-lower groups of 29 per cent with the extreme 9 per cent weighted double, and found them to be somewhat better than the 27-per cent groups. (See: John C. Flanagan, "The Effectiveness of Short Methods for Calculating Correlation Coefficients," *Psychological Bulletin,* XLIX, No. 4 (July, 1952), 342. However, in terms of teacher practicality the slight improvement in results is not deemed sufficient to warrant the added computational involvement. The recommended use of 27-per cent tables herein is substantiated by continued use of 27-per cent groupings by authorities in educational measurement.

RESPONSE PATTERN TALLY SHEET FOR TEST
ITEM ANALYSIS

TEST: *Tennis*

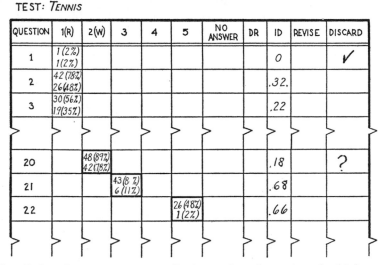

QUESTION	1(R)	2(W)	3	4	5	NO ANSWER	DR	ID	REVISE	DISCARD
1	1 (2%) 1(2%)							0		✓
2	42 (78%) 26(48%)							.32.		
3	30(56%) 19(35%)							.22		
20		48 (89%) 42(78%)						.18		?
21			43(8 %) 6 (11%)					.68		
22					26 (48%) 1(2%)			.66		

Fig. 5–3. Correct responses tallied on selected questions for high and low groups as a basis for computing *ID*.

each case is 2 per cent (1/50 = 2 per cent). Thus, the number of correct responses is multiplied by 2 to obtain the percentage of correct responses, simplifying the calculation considerably with relatively little difference in resultant figures. With 25 cases the multiplier becomes 4, for 33 it is 3, and for 100 it is 1.

After determining the percentage of correct response to each item for each group, good and poor, the second step of the *ID* computation can be done using Flanagan's Table of Indices of Discrimination (see Table 5–1). These percentages for a given item are entered in the table to derive the index. The figures across the top of the table indicate the percentage for the good group. The figures arranged vertically on the left-hand side indicate the percentage of correct responses in the poor group. Entering Table 5–1, with 78 per cent for the good group, find the column headed by 78. Next go down this column until the horizontal row is reached in which the percentage for the poor group, 48, appears at the left side. The figure appearing at the junction of the vertical column and the horizontal row, (32), is the *ID* for the particular item in question 2.

In interpreting the *ID*, as a general rule, all items with an index of 0.20, or above are retained, providing that the item is satisfactory in terms of *DR* and *FR*. Items with an *ID* below 0.15 should be discarded. An

Table 5–1. Flanagan's 27-Per Cent Table of Indices of Discrimination. A Table of the Values of the Product-Moment Coefficient of Correlation in a Normal Bivariate Population Corresponding to Given Proportion of Successes— Prepared by John C. Flanagan and reproduced with his permission.

Proportion of Successes in the 27 Per Cent Scoring Lowest / Proportion of Successes in the

	01	02	04	06	08	10	12	14	16	18	20	22	24	26	28	30	32	34	36	38	40	42	44	46	48	50
01	0	11	23	30	35	40	43	46	48	51	53	55	57	58	60	61	63	64	65	67	68	69	70	71	72	72
02	-11	0	12	20	26	30	34	38	40	43	45	47	49	51	53	54	56	57	58	60	61	63	64	65	66	67
04	-23	-12	0	08	14	19	23	27	30	33	36	38	40	42	44	45	47	49	51	53	54	55	57	58	59	60
06	-30	-20	-08	00	06	11	15	19	23	25	28	31	33	36	38	40	41	43	45	47	48	50	51	53	54	56
08	-35	-26	-14	-06	00	05	09	13	16	20	23	25	28	30	32	34	36	38	40	42	44	45	47	48	50	51
10	-40	-30	-19	-11	-05	00	04	08	12	15	18	21	23	26	28	30	32	34	36	38	40	41	43	45	46	48
12	-43	-34	-23	-15	-09	-04	00	04	07	11	14	16	19	21	24	26	28	30	32	34	36	38	39	41	43	44
14	-46	-38	-27	-19	-13	-08	-04	00	04	07	10	13	15	18	20	22	25	27	29	31	33	34	36	38	40	41
16	-48	-40	-30	-23	-16	-12	-07	-04	00	03	06	09	12	14	17	19	21	23	25	27	29	31	33	35	37	38
18	-51	-43	-33	-25	-20	-15	-11	-07	-03	00	03	06	08	11	14	16	18	20	22	24	26	28	30	32	34	36
20	-53	-45	-36	-28	-23	-18	-14	-10	-06	-03	00	03	06	08	11	13	15	17	19	22	24	26	27	29	31	33
22	-55	-47	-38	-31	-25	-21	-16	-13	-09	-06	-03	00	03	05	08	10	12	15	17	19	21	23	25	27	29	30
24	-57	-49	-40	-33	-28	-23	-19	-15	-12	-08	-06	-03	00	03	05	07	10	12	14	16	18	20	22	24	26	28
26	-58	-51	-42	-36	-30	-26	-21	-18	-14	-11	-08	-05	-03	00	02	05	07	09	12	14	16	18	20	22	24	26
28	-60	-53	-44	-38	-32	-28	-24	-20	-17	-14	-11	-08	-05	-02	00	02	05	07	09	11	13	15	17	19	21	23
30	-61	-54	-45	-40	-34	-30	-26	-22	-19	-16	-13	-10	-07	-05	-02	00	02	04	07	09	11	13	15	17	19	21
32	-63	-56	-47	-41	-36	-32	-28	-25	-21	-18	-15	-12	-10	-07	-05	-02	00	02	04	07	09	11	13	15	17	19
34	-64	-57	-49	-43	-38	-34	-30	-27	-23	-20	-17	-15	-12	-09	-07	-04	-02	00	02	04	06	09	11	13	15	17
36	-65	-58	-51	-45	-40	-36	-32	-29	-25	-22	-19	-17	-14	-12	-09	-07	-04	-02	00	02	04	06	08	10	12	14
38	-67	-60	-53	-47	-42	-38	-34	-31	-27	-24	-22	-19	-16	-14	-11	-09	-07	-04	-02	00	02	04	06	08	10	12
40	-68	-61	-54	-48	-44	-40	-36	-33	-29	-26	-24	-21	-18	-16	-13	-11	-09	-06	-04	-02	00	02	04	06	08	10
42	-69	-63	-55	-50	-45	-41	-38	-34	-31	-28	-26	-23	-20	-18	-15	-13	-11	-09	-06	-04	-02	00	02	04	06	08
44	-70	-64	-57	-51	-47	-43	-39	-36	-33	-30	-27	-25	-22	-20	-17	-15	-13	-11	-08	-06	-04	-02	00	02	04	06
46	-71	-65	-58	-53	-48	-45	-41	-38	-35	-32	-29	-27	-24	-22	-19	-17	-15	-13	-10	-08	-06	-04	-02	00	02	04
48	-72	-66	-59	-54	-50	-46	-43	-40	-37	-34	-31	-29	-26	-24	-21	-19	-17	-15	-12	-10	-08	-06	-04	-02	00	02
50	-72	-67	-60	-56	-51	-48	-44	-41	-38	-36	-33	-30	-28	-26	-23	-21	-19	-17	-14	-12	-10	-08	-06	-04	-02	00
52	-73	-69	-62	-57	-53	-49	-46	-43	-40	-37	-35	-32	-30	-28	-25	-23	-21	-19	-16	-14	-12	-10	-08	-06	-04	-02
54	-74	-70	-63	-58	-54	-51	-48	-45	-42	-39	-37	-34	-32	-29	-27	-25	-23	-21	-18	-16	-14	-12	-10	-08	-06	-04
56	-75	-70	-64	-59	-56	-52	-49	-46	-43	-41	-38	-36	-33	-31	-29	-27	-25	-23	-20	-18	-16	-14	-12	-10	-08	-06
58	-76	-71	-65	-61	-57	-54	-51	-48	-45	-43	-40	-38	-35	-33	-31	-29	-27	-24	-22	-20	-18	-16	-14	-12	-10	-08
60	-77	-72	-66	-62	-58	-55	-52	-49	-47	-44	-42	-39	-37	-35	-33	-31	-28	-26	-24	-22	-20	-18	-16	-14	-12	-10
62	-78	-73	-68	-63	-60	-56	-54	-51	-48	-46	-44	-41	-39	-37	-35	-32	-30	-28	-26	-24	-22	-20	-18	-16	-14	-12
64	-78	-74	-69	-64	-61	-58	-55	-52	-50	-48	-45	-43	-41	-39	-36	-34	-32	-30	-28	-26	-24	-22	-20	-18	-16	-14
66	-79	-75	-69	-66	-62	-59	-57	-54	-51	-49	-47	-45	-43	-40	-38	-36	-34	-32	-30	-28	-26	-24	-23	-21	-19	-17
68	-80	-76	-70	-67	-64	-61	-58	-56	-53	-51	-49	-47	-44	-42	-40	-38	-36	-34	-32	-30	-28	-27	-25	-23	-21	-19
70	-80	-77	-72	-68	-65	-62	-60	-57	-55	-52	-50	-48	-46	-44	-42	-40	-38	-36	-34	-32	-31	-29	-27	-25	-23	-21
72	-81	-78	-73	-69	-66	-64	-61	-59	-56	-54	-52	-50	-48	-46	-44	-42	-40	-38	-36	-35	-33	-31	-29	-27	-25	-23
74	-82	-78	-74	-70	-68	-65	-63	-60	-58	-56	-54	-52	-50	-48	-46	-44	-42	-40	-39	-37	-35	-33	-31	-29	-28	-26
76	-83	-79	-75	-72	-69	-66	-64	-62	-60	-58	-56	-54	-52	-50	-48	-46	-44	-43	-41	-39	-37	-35	-33	-32	-30	-28
78	-84	-80	-76	-73	-70	-68	-65	-63	-61	-59	-57	-56	-54	-52	-50	-48	-47	-45	-43	-41	-39	-38	-36	-34	-32	-30
80	-84	-81	-77	-74	-71	-69	-67	-65	-63	-61	-59	-57	-56	-54	-52	-50	-49	-47	-45	-44	-42	-40	-38	-37	-35	-33
82	-85	-82	-78	-75	-73	-71	-69	-67	-65	-63	-61	-59	-58	-56	-54	-52	-51	-49	-48	-46	-44	-43	-41	-39	-37	-36
84	-86	-83	-79	-77	-74	-72	-70	-68	-66	-65	-63	-61	-60	-58	-56	-55	-53	-51	-50	-48	-47	-45	-43	-42	-40	-38
86	-87	-84	-80	-78	-76	-74	-72	-70	-68	-67	-65	-63	-62	-60	-59	-57	-56	-54	-52	-51	-49	-48	-46	-45	-43	-41
88	-87	-85	-82	-79	-77	-75	-73	-72	-70	-69	-67	-65	-64	-63	-61	-60	-58	-57	-55	-53	-52	-51	-49	-48	-46	-44
90	-88	-86	-83	-81	-79	-77	-75	-74	-72	-71	-69	-68	-66	-65	-64	-62	-61	-59	-58	-56	-55	-54	-52	-51	-49	-48
92	-89	-87	-84	-82	-80	-79	-77	-76	-74	-73	-71	-70	-69	-68	-66	-65	-64	-62	-61	-60	-58	-57	-56	-54	-53	-51
94	-90	-88	-86	-84	-82	-81	-79	-78	-77	-75	-74	-73	-72	-70	-69	-68	-67	-66	-64	-63	-62	-61	-59	-58	-57	-56
96	-91	-89	-87	-86	-84	-83	-82	-80	-79	-78	-77	-76	-75	-74	-73	-72	-70	-69	-69	-68	-66	-65	-64	-63	-62	-60
98	-93	-91	-89	-88	-87	-86	-85	-84	-83	-82	-81	-80	-79	-78	-78	-77	-76	-75	-74	-73	-72	-71	-70	-70	-69	-67
99	-94	-93	-91	-90	-89	-88	-87	-87	-86	-85	-84	-84	-83	-82	-81	-80	-80	-79	-78	-78	-77	-76	-75	-74	-73	-72

item with an *ID* of 0.15 to 0.20 may be retained in instances where it appears to be the best available item of its kind, again providing that the item satisfies the other two aspects of its validity. Interpreting the sample questions in Fig. 5–3, question 1 should be discarded and question 20 needs appraisal in light of *DR* and *FR*. The remaining questions appear satisfactory regarding *ID*.

27 Per Cent Scoring Highest

52	54	56	58	60	62	64	66	68	70	72	74	76	78	80	82	84	86	88	90	92	94	96	98	99
73	74	75	76	77	78	78	79	80	80	81	82	83	84	84	85	86	87	87	88	89	90	91	93	94
69	70	70	71	72	73	74	75	76	77	78	78	79	80	81	82	83	84	85	86	87	88	89	91	93
62	63	64	65	66	68	69	69	70	72	73	74	75	76	77	78	79	80	82	83	84	86	87	89	91
57	58	59	61	62	63	64	66	67	68	69	70	72	73	74	75	77	78	79	81	82	84	86	88	90
53	54	56	57	58	60	61	62	64	65	66	68	69	70	71	73	74	76	77	79	80	82	84	87	89
49	51	52	54	55	56	58	59	61	62	64	65	66	68	69	71	72	74	75	77	79	81	83	86	88
46	48	49	51	52	54	55	57	58	60	61	63	64	65	67	69	70	72	73	75	77	79	82	85	87
43	45	46	48	49	51	52	54	56	57	59	60	62	63	65	67	68	70	72	74	76	78	80	84	87
40	42	43	45	47	48	50	51	53	55	56	58	60	61	63	65	66	68	70	72	74	77	79	83	86
37	39	41	43	44	46	48	49	51	52	54	56	58	59	61	63	65	67	69	71	73	75	78	82	85
35	37	38	40	42	44	45	47	49	50	52	54	56	57	59	61	63	65	67	69	71	74	77	81	84
32	34	36	38	39	41	43	45	47	48	50	52	54	56	57	59	61	63	65	68	70	73	76	80	84
30	32	33	35	37	39	41	43	44	46	48	50	52	54	56	58	60	62	64	66	69	72	75	79	83
28	29	31	33	35	37	39	40	42	44	46	48	50	52	54	56	58	60	63	65	68	70	74	78	82
25	27	29	31	33	35	36	38	40	42	44	46	48	50	52	54	56	59	61	64	66	69	73	78	81
23	25	27	29	31	32	34	36	38	40	42	44	46	48	50	52	55	57	60	62	65	68	72	77	80
21	23	25	27	28	30	32	34	36	38	40	42	44	47	49	51	53	56	58	61	64	67	70	76	80
19	21	23	24	26	28	30	32	34	36	38	40	43	45	47	49	51	54	57	59	62	66	69	75	79
16	18	20	22	24	26	28	30	32	34	36	39	41	43	45	48	50	52	55	58	61	64	69	74	78
14	16	18	20	22	24	26	28	30	32	35	37	39	41	44	46	48	51	54	56	60	63	68	73	78
12	14	16	18	20	22	24	26	28	31	33	35	37	39	42	44	47	49	52	55	58	62	66	72	77
10	12	14	16	18	20	22	24	27	29	31	33	35	38	40	43	45	48	51	54	57	61	65	71	76
08	10	12	14	16	18	20	23	25	27	29	31	33	36	38	41	43	46	49	52	56	59	64	70	75
06	08	10	12	14	16	18	21	23	25	27	29	32	34	37	39	42	45	48	51	54	58	63	70	74
04	06	08	10	12	14	16	19	21	23	25	28	30	32	35	37	40	43	46	49	53	57	62	69	73
02	04	06	08	10	12	14	17	19	21	23	26	28	30	33	36	38	41	44	48	51	56	60	67	72
00	02	04	06	08	10	12	15	17	19	21	24	26	29	31	34	37	40	43	46	50	54	59	66	72
-02	00	02	04	06	08	10	13	15	17	19	22	24	27	29	32	35	38	41	45	48	53	58	65	71
-04	-02	00	02	04	06	08	11	13	15	17	20	22	25	27	30	33	36	39	43	47	51	57	64	70
-06	-04	-02	00	02	04	06	09	11	13	15	18	20	23	26	28	31	34	38	41	45	50	55	63	69
-08	-06	-04	-02	00	02	04	06	09	11	13	16	18	21	24	26	29	33	36	40	44	48	54	61	68
-10	-08	-06	-04	-02	00	02	04	07	·09	11	14	16	19	22	24	27	31	34	38	42	47	53	60	67
-12	-10	-08	-06	-04	-02	00	02	04	07	09	12	14	17	19	22	25	29	32	36	40	45	51	58	66
-15	-13	-11	-09	-06	-04	-02	00	02	04	07	09	12	15	17	20	23	27	30	34	38	43	49	57	64
-17	-15	-13	-11	-09	-07	-04	-02	00	02	05	07	10	12	15	18	21	25	28	32	36	41	47	56	63
-19	-17	-15	-13	-11	-09	-07	-04	-02	00	02	05	07	10	13	16	19	22	26	30	34	40	45	54	61
-21	-19	-17	-15	-13	-11	-09	-07	-05	-02	00	02	05	08	11	14	17	20	24	28	32	38	44	53	60
-24	-22	-20	-18	-16	-14	-12	-09	-07	-05	-02	00	03	05	08	11	14	18	21	26	30	36	42	51	58
-26	-24	-22	-20	-18	-16	-14	-12	-10	-07	-05	-03	00	03	06	08	12	15	19	23	28	33	40	49	57
-29	-27	-25	-23	-21	-19	-17	-15	-12	-10	-08	-05	-03	00	03	06	09	13	16	21	25	31	38	47	55
-31	-29	-27	-26	-24	-22	-19	-17	-15	-13	-11	-08	-06	-03	00	03	06	10	14	18	23	28	35	45	.53
-34	-32	-30	-28	-26	-24	-22	-20	-18	-16	-14	-11	-08	-06	-03	00	03	07	11	15	20	25	33	43	51
-37	-35	-33	-31	-29	-27	-25	-23	-21	-19	-17	-14	-12	-09	-06	-03	00	04	07	12	16	23	30	40	48
-40	-38	-36	-34	-33	-31	-29	-27	-25	-22	-20	-18	-15	-13	-10	-07	-04	00	04	08	13	19	27	38	46
-43	-41	-39	-38	-36	-34	-32	-30	-28	-26	-24	-21	-19	-16	-14	-11	-07	-04	00	04	09	15	23	34	43
-46	-45	-43	-41	-40	-38	-36	-34	-32	-30	-28	-26	-23	-21	-18	-15	-12	-08	-04	00	05	11	19	30	40
-50	-48	-47	-45	-44	-42	-40	-38	-36	-34	-32	-30	-28	-25	-23	-20	-16	-13	-09	-05	00	06	14	26	35
-54	-53	-51	-50	-48	-47	-45	-43	-41	-39	-38	-36	-33	-31	-28	-25	-23	-19	-15	-11	-06	00	08	20	30
-59	-58	-57	-55	-54	-53	-51	-49	-47	-45	-44	-42	-40	-38	-36	-33	-30	-27	-23	-19	-14	-08	00	12	23
-66	-65	-64	-63	-61	-60	-58	-57	-56	-54	-53	-51	-49	-47	-45	-43	-40	-38	-34	-30	-26	-20	-12	00	11
-72	-71	-70	-69	-68	-67	-65	-64	-63	-61	-60	-58	-57	-55	-53	-51	-48	-46	-43	-40	-35	-30	-23	-11	00

Comparing both Fig. 5–2 and Fig. 5–3 to gain a complete picture of item analysis, the reader will note that question 1 should be discarded relative to all three aspects—the DR is outside the desired 20–80 range, FR is unsatisfactory, and ID is not acceptable. All other items appear satisfactory with the exception of questions 20 and 22. Question 20, as mentioned, necessitates some deliberation regarding DR and FR. The item falls within the region of acceptability on ID only if DR and FR are satisfactory and it appears to be important for content validity. All told then, the evidence suggests that the item be discarded, inasmuch as DR exceeds the upper limit of 80 and only three plausible distracters functioned. However, if the situation is such that the content of the question represents a critical learning point and does not lend itself to inclusion as a different type of test item (for example, true–false, or matching), the teacher would be justified in attempting to render the item satisfactory by revision. For question 22, although *DR* is marginally too difficult in terms of the lower limit of 20, retention is warranted in view of the reasonably strong *ID* value along with a satisfactory *FR*.

In the overall context of item analysis the teacher is admonished to be cognizant of the specificity of the results of the particular test administration upon which the analysis is based and to make decisions in that light. The three aspects of item analysis can be expected to vary from one group to another. This has obvious implications for interpretation of marginal indices of discrimination which in reality reflect small differences in magnitude.

The existence of alternative methods of item analysis warrants mention, a comprehensive overview of which is afforded by Downie.[12] Fan[13] has developed a table based on the high–low-27-per cent group method that provides estimates of item difficulty as well as item discrimination. Simplified schemes for use by classroom teachers have been described by Diederich[14] and Gronlund.[15] A new approach to item analysis has been afforded by the use of electronic data processing (EDP).[16] A general discussion of the application of EDP to physical education measurement appears in Chapter 6, and its application for computation of test scores was described in Chapter 2. For item analysis the mark-sense answer sheets or cards, on which students place their responses with electrographic pencil, provide the initial input.[17] The computer print-out contains the three elements of item analysis (*DR, FR, ID*) and may also include the test mean and standard deviation and, with some programs, reliability (coefficient of internal consistency) and standard error of measurement. The actual form of item analysis reports may vary, depending on the EDP installation. Item analysis becomes more practical for teacher-made tests in terms of time and effort as test scoring and analysis by EDP becomes increasingly available in the schools, leaving the teacher virtually no excuse for continued use of poor test items.

---

[12] N. M. Downie, *Fundamentals of Measurement: Techniques and Practices* (New York: Oxford University Press, 1967), Chap. 10: "Item Analysis."

[13] Chung-Teh Fan, *Item Analysis Table* (Princeton: Educational Testing Service, 1952).

[14] Paul B. Diederich, *Short-Cut Statistics for Teacher-Made Tests* (ETS T&M Kit). (Princeton: Educational Testing Service, 1973), pp. 1–3.

[15] Gronlund, *op. cit.*, pp. 85–88.

[16] For background information on EDP the reader is referred to: Howard W. Stoker, *Automated Data Processing in Testing* (Guidance Monograph Series III: Testing) (Boston: Houghton Mifflin Co., 1968). Chap. 3: "Processing Test Results."

[17] An illustrative appliaction is described in: Downie, *op. cit.*, pp. 221–23.

3. *Test reliability and objectivity.* The last consideration in analyzing the quality of the written test being constructed directs attention to the matters of test reliability and objectiviy. Reliability and objectivity do not necessitate the especial attention for written tests that is characteristic of physical performance tests. In general, satisfactory reliability and objectivity follow quite consistently when items are objective in type, sufficient number of items are included, item validity is acceptable, as disclosed by item analysis, and conditions governing test administration and scoring are definitively described by explicit instructions. Some facets of interest relevant to reliability that warrant noting are:

1. A long test is almost always more reliable than a shorter test.
2. Items high in *ID* lead to high reliability.
3. Items of moderate difficulty are most reliable.
4. The smaller the range of difficulty of items, the higher is test reliability. (Taken with No. 3, above, this gives rise to the concern that *DR*'s should be centered around 50, with mean being about 50.)

For written tests three methods of ascertaining reliability are used. These may be listed in order of probable teacher-use as: (1) split halves, (2) repeat same test, and (3) equivalent forms.

The split-halves method, briefly described under physical performance tests, actually finds far greater use for written tests, since a considerable number of items is necessary to be effective, which poses no appreciable restriction for written tests as compared to physical performance tests. The reliability coefficient for the split halves is computed by correlating the scores for the odd-numbered test items with those for the even-numbered items. For the illustrative tennis knowledge test given to 200 students, the split-halves reliability coefficent was 0.80. To estimate the reliability coefficient for the actual test length the Spearman–Brown prophecy formula is used. Accordingly, the split-halves correlation of 0.80 is substituted in the formula:

$$r_D = \frac{Nr_{12}}{1 + (N-1)\,r_{12}}$$

$$= \frac{2(0.80)}{1 + (2-1)\,0.80} = \frac{1.60}{1.80} = 0.889 = 0.89$$

where: r_D is the coefficient to be estimated.

r_{12} is the split-halves correlation.

N is the proportion of increase in length (which is 2 for split halves)

The estimated reliability coefficient of 0.89, as computed for the tennis test, is referred to as a *coefficient of internal consistency*, inasmuch as it is derived from analysis of performance on a single test administration.

Table 5–2 contains the estimated reliability coefficient for split-halves

Table 5–2.   Correlation Coefficients Stepped Up by the Spearman–Brown Prophecy Formula as an Estimate for Twice the Number of Trials.

Odd-Even	S-B	Odd-Even	S-B	Odd-Even	S-B	Odd-Even	S-B
0.60	0.75	0.70	0.82	0.80	0.89	0.90	0.95
0.61	0.76	0.71	0.83	0.81	0.90	0.91	0.95
0.62	0.77	0.72	0.84	0.82	0.90	0.92	0.96
0.63	0.78	0.73	0.84	0.83	0.91	0.93	0.96
0.64	0.78	0.74	0.85	0.84	0.91	0.94	0.97
0.65	0.79	0.75	0.86	0.85	0.92	0.95	0.97
0.66	0.80	0.76	0.86	0.86	0.93	0.96	0.98
0.67	0.80	0.77	0.87	0.87	0.93	0.97	0.98
0.68	0.81	0.78	0.88	0.88	0.94	0.98	0.99
0.69	0.82	0.79	0.88	0.89	0.94	0.99	0.99

correlation coefficients ranging from 0.60 to 0.99, as derived by use of the Spearman–Brown prophecy formula. To check the above computations, entering the odd–even column in this table with the split-halves coefficient of 0.80 gives the corresponding estimated reliability of 0.89 for the total test.

Another measure of internal consistency, Kuder-Richardson Formula 20 (KR20), is sometimes reported for published tests. In essence the KR20 method yields a coefficient equal to the mean of all possible split-half correlations of the test, as contrasted to one specific type of split described above. This method is particularly useful when an item analysis has ben made and item difficulty values (DR) are available. The KR20 formula is:

$$r_{KR20} = \frac{k}{k-1}\left(1 - \frac{\Sigma pq}{s^2}\right),$$

where k = number of items, p = item DR, $q = 1 - p$, and s^2 = standard deviation squared or variance of the total test scores. Using the DR values from Fig. 5–2 for selected questions on a tennis test, the computation of Σpq is illustrated below.

Question	p	q	pq
1	.03	.09	.0027
2	.74	.26	.1924
3	.44	.56	.2464
20	.82	.18	.1476
21	.52	.48	.2496
22	.18	.82	.1476

$$\Sigma pq =$$

The test variance is derived through the computational procedure for standard deviation described in Chapter 2.

A second formula, KR21, was developed to provide an estimate of internal consistency without difficulty values.

$$r_{\text{KR21}} = \frac{k}{k-1}\left(1 - \frac{\overline{X}(k - \overline{X})}{ks^2}\right),$$

where $\overline{X}$ = mean, as computed in Chapter 2. This short-cut procedure is appropriate only with objective tests in which items are scored +1 and 0 and only one type of item is used. It is based on the assumption that all items possess the same difficulty, and variations in difficulty lead to underestimation of results. Within its limitations, KR21 affords a quick estimate of test reliability with minimum computation. If KR20 or KR21 is applied to tests containing items answered either correctly or incorrectly by all testees, the resultant coefficient is attenuated. As a final note on internal consistency, none of the three measures described is appropriate for use with speed tests, that is, in which the purpose is to ascertain how many items (usually of low difficulty) can be answered in the allotted time.

The second method of determining reliability—repeated administration of the same test—presumes that the interim between tests is of sufficient length that students will have forgotten the details, and no learning experiences occurring in conjunction with the first testing or since then would likely influence the test results appreciably. A reliability coefficient derived by this test–re-test method is termed a *coefficient of stability* .

The third method of ascertaining reliability consists of adminstering two equivalent forms of the test to the same group of students under the same conditions and with little or no time elapsing between tests. These equivalent forms of the test are designed to serve the same purpose and cover identical content but use different test items. Not many teachers initially construct equivalent or duplicate forms. These forms generally evolve from careful critical test construction and in many instances may be a split half of a thorough, comprehensive test. This type of reliability coefficient is referred to as a *coefficient of equivalence.*

Turning specifically to the objectivity of written tests this becomes largely a function of thorough, concise instructions for administering the test coupled with a definitive explanation of the scoring procedure. A poor objectivity coefficient, assuming satisfactory reliability, would suggest attention to refinement of directions and scoring.

MAKE CHANGES OR REVISIONS AS INDICATED.—Upon careful scrutinization of the important factors indicative of test quality, the necessary changes or revisions should be made. Thus, any undesirable characteristics that may filter through the construction process, despite stringent observance of the recommended procedural concerns, can be rectified. This then constitutes the last step in developing tests of associated learning, and the test can be prepared in final form for use.

CHECK LIST.—The check list presented below is intended as a guide for the teacher to follow sequentially in constructing a written test. For a "one-shot" test the teacher would execute at least the first eight steps and, hopefully, would proceed through step 11 to ascertain the quality of the test items individually and in the total test context. Execution of all steps in the check list will result in a completely developed test for future use, when appropriate.

CHECK LIST FOR CONSTRUCTING WRITTEN TESTS

1. Clearly identify the purpose and objectives of test.
2. Provide for content validity by preparing a plan for proportionate test content distribution, such as a table of specifications, paralleling course experience or other basic frames of reference.
3. Select appropriate types of test items in terms of test purpose and content, as well as test-taking experience of students.
4. Carefully devise thoughtful test items covering content best suited to each type of item included and in accordance with the test blueprint or table of specifications.
5. Arrange items properly within each type, according to recommended considerations, and place different types in the desired order.
6. Carefully appraise the relationship of items within and among types in the overall context of the test with particular reference to duplication or omission of content areas, and make needed changes that become evident.
7. Prepare clear and concise directions for each type of test item, including sample questions for types of items that may be unfamiliar to the test group.

8. As the basis for test analysis, administer the test to a suitable group under controlled conditions with respect to appropriate time limitations and supervision of test setting.
9. Determine test reliability, expressed as a coefficient of internal consistency.
10. Ascertain internal test validity by item analysis—*DR*, *FR*, and *ID*.
11. Appraise test quality, in terms of the implications of the item analysis, in particular for reliability and content validity.
12. If test quality warrants, make necessary changes, such as by revision, deletion, and addition of·items, to render the test acceptable in all its aspects.
13. Administer the revised test to other typical groups for whom the test is appropriate, to establish meaningful norms, and where the test will be used by other teachers, to provide evidence of objectivity.
14. Prepare a test manual describing test development, characteristics, use, and norms.

Specific Considerations

As is readily discernible from the description of the basic procedure in developing tests of associated learning, certain factors and concerns peculiar to tests of this type of learning are entailed. Accordingly, the teacher should be cognizant of the following matters with particular reference to written tests in order to supplement the general considerations in constructing tests regardless of type of learning, as discussed in Chapter 4.

1. *Establishing validity.* The simplest and most direct evidence of content validity can be obtained from examination of the test itself by a competent judge. However, the teacher or any test developer can aid potential test users to judge both content and internal validity of the test by clearly and succinctly:
   a. Stating the criteria and principles which served as guides in choosing item topics and in writing items.
   b. Presenting an outline of the achievements covered by the test.
   c. Indicating which items are intended to measure each achievement.
   d. Giving detailed data for the internal analysis of the test items, recognizing that this will tend to be somewhat specific to the population tested.
2. *Test emphasis.* It warrants specific mention that, to rank a selected group of students in order of their achievement, test items should entail the "critical" points of learning. They are critical in the sense that it becomes necessary to understand them for truly high level achievement; they go beyond the obvious and super-

ficial. Questions on critical points often require understanding, implications, applying information, and reorganizing data.

3. *Time allowance.* In tests designed to measure achievement the time allocation should be generous enough to afford 80 to 90 per cent of the students the opportunity to finish.

4. *Test item review.* When feasible, it is a good practice to have the different test items interpreted and criticized by persons who have taken the test. The prime concern is to permit students to identity any items which appear ambiguous or which were misconstrued by them.

5. *Test difficulty.* For evaluative purposes the difficulty of a test serves as a useful, albeit rough, indicator of its adequacy. The difficulty index (DI) can be calculated from the formula: $DI = \overline{X}/n$, where $\overline{X}$ is the mean score on the test, and n is the number of test items.

6. *Group size for item analysis.* A minimum of 80 to 100 students is necessary for item analysis. Little credence should be given to item analysis performed on smaller groups.

7. *Test item revision.* The teacher must remain cognizant of the basic test blueprint encompassing the balance among types of items, overall length, relatedness of factors in item validity, and of the fact that any contemplated change should be considered in light of the effect on other aspects involved in the quality of the test. Available evidence suggests that revising poor items may be a more economical process for obtaining good items for a test, or for future tests, than discarding items that need revision and replacing them with new items. One study disclosed that the construction of new items took approximately five times as long per item as the revisions did.[18] In analyzing responses to each item, the teacher should be alert to revise the responses which the upper group chooses more often or nearly as often as the lower group, excepting, of course, the correct response.

8. *The factor of guessing.* Guessing on objective tests when there is no penalty will always maximize test score. Guessing without penalty has a prize but no stake, whereas guessing with a penalty (risk taking) has both a prize and a stake.[19] Use of the correction formula serves to emphasize the range of knowledge within the group tested. Just as the use of the correction-for-guessing formula penalizes the risk taker, through the accompanying DNG (do not guess) directions, the use of this formula also tends to penalize the non-risk taker.[20] The standard correction formula is:

[18] A. Lange, I. J. Lehmann, and W. A. Mehrens, "Using Item Analysis to Improve Tests, *Journal of Educational Measurement*, IV, No. 2 (Summer, 1967), 65.

[19] Malcolm J. Slakter, "Risk Taking on Objective Examinations," *American Educational Research Journal*, IV, No. 1 (January, 1967), 31.

[20] Malcolm J. Slakter, "The Penalty for Not Guessing," *Journal of Educational Measurement*, V, No. 2 (Summer, 1968), 141.

Test score $= R - (W/[O-1])$, where R is the number right, W is the number wrong, and O is the number of test item options. For true–false items this becomes: $R - (W/[2-1]) = R - W$.

9. *Prevalent criticisms.* Close scrutiny of knowledge tests in use in physical education reveals a number of obvious shortcomings, as substantiated by Ley.[21] These include:

   a. Tests tend to contain a disproportionate number of factual items, to the neglect of items entailing generalization, understanding, application, and interpretation.
   b. Tests tend to contain a great overemphasis on rules of play.
   c. Relevance of test item content often appears neglected, if not overlooked.
   d. Although identification items or illustrations are invaluable in imparting descriptive material for test item content, often little use is made of them.

Types of Test Items

In light of this description of the suggested procedure for developing tests of associated learning, discussion can now be directed to the different types of objective tests that are used along with their salient features, advantages, limitations, and suggestions pertinent to construction. Actually, fullest comprehension of the planning procedure as described can accrue only from an understanding of the different types of test items. However, the author deemed it advisable to keep the construction process in proper perspective by first describing the "how to proceed" or overall approach before depicting the "specific wherewithal" or actual tools to be employed. The ensuing discussion of test items is intended to engender the degree of understanding especially requisite for several important considerations of test planning that were enumerated previously, namely, determining the types of test items compatible with test purpose and content, preparing appropriate items of different types, and evaluating items in the intended context.

The different types of objective test items may be categorized into two basic groups: *selection* and *supply*, which formerly were commonly referred to as recognition and recall. The selection group includes alternative-response, multiple-choice, matching, identification, analogy, and arrangement types of test items. Simple-recall or completion, and short-answer or free response items comprise the supply category.

As a basis for enhancing understanding of the place of the various types of test items, it seems plausible to refer to the hierarchical arrange-

[21] Katherine L. Ley, "Constructing Objective Test Items to Measure High Levels of Achievement in Selected Physical Education Activities" (Microcard Doctoral Dissertation, University of Iowa, 1960).

ment of cognitive behaviors proposed by Bloom and associates for the classification of educational objectives in the cognitive domain. that is, those related to the recall or recognition of knowledge and the development of intellectual abilities and skills.[22] The main organizing principle implicit in this structure is the degree of complexity of the cognitive process involved in each category, moving from simple to complex and from concrete to abstract. The six major categories of this taxonomy include:

1. *Knowledge.* Remembering material learned previously.
2. *Comprehension.* Grasp the meaning of material; represents the lowest level of understanding.
3. *Application.* Use of material in new and concrete situations.
4. *Analysis.* Break down material into its constituent parts so that its organizational structure and relationships may be understood.
5. *Synthesis.* Put parts together to form a new whole.
6. *Evaluation.* Judge the value of material for a given purpose according to specified criteria.

A word of caution seems indicated in interpreting this hierarchy of cognitive processes as it pertains to the selection and supply categories of test items. It should not be implied that the selection kind of item is limited to the lower levels and the supply test category to higher levels. The use of selection and supply to describe a category of different types of test items is based on the response elicited by the question and may not necessarily deal with the level of cognitive function involved. For example, as will be made evident in a later discussion, the multiple-choice type of test item is categorized as a selection item but as such may not deal wtih mere knowledge of facts but with ability to think through a problem involving a higher level function and choose the likely solution from a list of several alternatives. The challenge presented in written test construction is to devise test items to elicit response involving the level of cognition desired. Some types of items have limiting factors that confine their use to the lower levels of this hierarchy more so than other types of items. To foster a better understanding of written tests, it is best to turn to a description of the various types of test items.

The selection group of objective test items comprises the greater proportion of test items used in written tests, and on that basis warrants discussion first. The different types of items are described in the recommended order of arrangement within a test, that is, in ascending level of difficulty.

[22] Benjamin S. Bloom (ed.) *Taxonomy of Educational Objectives, Handbook I: Cognitive Domain* (New York: David McKay Co., Inc., 1956).

Alternative-Response. This type of test item is characterized by only two possible responses—true or false, yes or no, right or wrong. Of the variations, the true–false has seen most extensive use and, it might deservedly be added, misuse. One of the advantages of the alternative-response test item is the apparent ease of construction. This in itself has proved a menace since, as the saying goes, "It's not as easy as it looks." As a result, much of the resistance to objective-type written tests is attributable to poorly constructed alternative-response tests.

Illustrative alternative-response questions from the proposed tennis knowledge test, as given below, afford focus for discussion of the characteristics of this type of test item.

DIRECTIONS: *True and False.* Encircle T if statement is true, or F is false in whole or part. *Do not guess.* Graded right minus wrong.

T F 1. Imparting top spin to the ball on a forehand drive causes the ball to stay in the air for a longer time.

T F 2. Both feet should be parallel to the net in executing the forehand drive.

DIRECTIONS: *Yes or No.* Encircle Y if statement is correct, or N if incorrect. *Do not guess.* Graded right minus wrong.

Y N 1. Is the score love–15 when the server has won the first point?

Y N 2. In a doubles contest with your partner serving, may you position yourself in the center of the court to obstruct the view of the receiver?

Since this type of question has seen common usage, what are some of the reasons for it? Several advantages may be noted for the alternative-response test:

1. Covers more items in the same time than any other test.
2. Applicable to a wide range of subject matter.
3. Conducive to complete objectivity in scoring.

Recently the alternative-response, particularly the true–false, test items have been held in low esteem by test experts as as evidenced by the little use of these items in new standardizd achievement tests. The limitations of alternative-response tests consist of the following:

1. Difficulty encountered in constructing good test items.
2. Tend to be conducive to overemphasis of trivial, less important material.
3. Guessing factor.
4. In instances where real understanding of the subject matter is involved, this is not truly measured by the alternative-response type of test, due to the guessing factor.
5. In instances of using true-false items with young pupils, there exists a negative-suggestion effect. This refers to the tendency of young pupils to interpret the definitive false statement as reality.

Such an effect is eliminated through use of a yes–no test item, which puts the same material in the form of a question.

6. A serious disadvantage exists in the likelihood of this item type being influenced by response sets, that is, individual differences in in tendencies to respond to all items in a constant fashion that is unrelated to the purpose of the test. To illustrate, some students tend to answer affirmatively to alternative-response items about which they feel uncertain.

In addition to the general guides suggested on page 149, the following specific hints are proffered for alternative-response test item construction.

1. Make the test relatively long and prepare it carefully. At least 75 items is desirable, with 60 considered the bare minimum to restrict the measurement error due to guessing. In instances where a test is devised solely for instructional purposes, or where it covers a very narrow range of material, a lesser number of items is acceptable.
2. Restrict the use of the alternative-response test to situations in which the other test forms are not applicable, and then exercise caution in the wording of the items.
3. Let the content, not the form, of the statement determine the response.
4. Have each item contain only one significant idea, and highlight the central point by placing it in a prominent position in the statement.
5. Make approximately half of the item *true*, or *yes*.
6. An item can be constructed as a factual question or as a thought question that requires reasoning and knowledge application as desired. Nevertheless, the guessing factor is still present.
7. Avoid statements that are negative or ambiguous, or use specific determiners and textbook phraseology, as well as those that are long and complex.
8. Make statements unequivocally *true* or *false*, without qualifications or exceptions.

A number of variations of the true–false type of item are prevalent; however, suffice it for purposes herein to give an example with two variations.

DIRECTIONS: *True and False.* Encircle T if statement is true, or F if false in whole or part. Explain why the statement is true or false in the blank space below the statement.

T   F   1. Imparting top spin to the ball on a forehand drive causes the ball to stay in the air for a longer time.
Why? _____

_____

One variation might be to explain only false statements. Another variation of this type of item would be to have testees underline the word or words that are incorrect or otherwise render the statement false.

Scoring the alternative-response test brings up the controversial point of whether testees should be penalized for guessing, that is, in the application of a correction formula, as discussed briefly under specific considerations. Certain studies have indicated that the validity of a standardized test tends to increase when a guessing correction factor is applied. Presently, there appears little evidence to suggest that the informal teacher-made test is significantly improved by correction for guessing. Evidence indicates that students do relatively little blind guessing. In longer alternative-response tests, the guessing factor becomes a minor concern in achieving a passing grade. It should be recognized that instructing students not to guess will reduce the test reliability to the extent that items are omitted. Use of the correction factor has the further limitation of adding to scoring difficulty somewhat. This decision regarding the application of a correction factor for guessing remains arbitrary. If guessing is to be corrected, it should be so stated in the directions, along with how it is to be done, for example, right minus wrong. The author encourages use of the correction factor only to be in conformity with procedure deemed appropriate in standardized tests. Seemingly, considerations that are important in standardized test construction should, when practical, guide all test construction, since well-constructed teacher-tests can present a valuable source of standardized tests.

Multiple-Choice. As indicated by its title, this type of test item consists of either a question or an incomplete statement, commonly called the stem, followed by several possible responses. These responses include the desired answer and several plausible wrong answers, called distracters. Variations of multiple-choice may call for selecting the correct answer, the best answer, or the wrong answer from the alternatives. The multiple-choice item is generally regarded as the most valuable and most widely applicable of all test forms. Unless there are especial reasons to the contrary, "it is strongly recommended that the multiple-choice item be employed for most objective tests." [23] This test item can be devised to determine more effectively than any other type of objective item the student's ability to interpret, discriminate, select, and apply information learned. Furthermore, multiple-choice items can measure a variety of learning outcomes, ranging from simple to complex. [24] The

[23] Jum C. Nunnally, *Educational Measurement and Evaluation* (New York: McGraw-Hill Book Co., 1964), p. 121.
[24] For an illustrative discussion of twenty-two questions reflecting imaginative use of m-c items the reader is referred to: *Multiple-Choice Questions: A Close Look* (ETS T&M Kit). (Princeton: Educational Testing Service, 1973.)

scoring of this item can be made entirely objective without concern for the guessing factor.

Illustrative multiple-choice questions from the proposed tennis knowledge test follow:

DIRECTIONS: *Multiple-Choice.* For each item below, choose the alternative that answers the question or completes the statement correctly (or when appropriate, best answers the question or completes the statement). Place the identifying letter of your answer in the blank at the left of the item number.

_____ 1. In relation to one's body, the ball is hit for the volley at a point
    (A) well in front
    (B) slightly in front
    (C) in line with the body
    (D) slightly behind
    (E) dependent upon player preference

_____ 2. The overhead volley involves similar movement as the smash with
    (A) more spin imparted
    (B) less spin imparted
    (C) more wrist action
    (D) more speed
    (E) less speed

While the value of multiple-choice items is clearly recognized, it does not accrue automatically but rather depends upon careful, deliberate construction. Despite the fact that the multiple-choice item requires considerable time to construct and considerable space to present, the potential value seems to warrant doing so. An important determinant of the value of the multiple-choice item lies in skillful selection of plausible incorrect choices (distracters) presented in the items. To effect fullest realization of the potential value of multiple-choice items, the following hints for construction are suggested.

1. Do not use multiple-choice if a simpler type of item will suffice.
2. The stem of the item should present a basic problem, stated vividly and succinctly, and should include any words that would otherwise need to be repeated in each alternative.
3. The incomplete statement form is preferred for the stem by most item writers, since it saves space and permits a smooth transition from the problem to correct response. However, usually students below sixth grade level more easily comprehend items expressed as questions rather than as incomplete sentences.
4. The answer and distracters should be grammatically consistent with the stem and parallel with one another in form and arranged in logical order, if one exists.
5. The correct or best answer should be unquestionably so.
6. Avoid consistent tendency to have correct answer generally longer or shorter, more specific or more abstract, more or less technical, as compared to the distracters.

7. Offer at least four, preferably five, possible answers. An equal number of alternatives for all items is of concern only when the correction factor will be applied in their scoring (not recommended for teacher-made tests).
8. Eliminate irrelevant or superficial clues and obvious incorrect distracters.
9. The distracters should be plausible, so that students who do not possess the achievement being tested will tend to select them rather than the correct answer. Good distracters are those selected more frequently by members of the low scoring group.
10. Use the "none of the above" distracter sparingly, if at all, and with caution.
11. Correct responses should be distributed reasonably equally among the possible answer positions.

Matching. This type of item is suited to learning that involves the association of two things in the mind of the student. It is particularly applicable for determining student's ability to recognize relationships and make associations, for naming and identifying things learned, and for answering problem questions using proposed alternatives. The student is required to match each item in one list with the most closely related item in another list. In reality, the matching item consists of a variation of the multiple-choice type in which the same choices are applicable in answering each of the items.

An illustrative matching exercise dealing with scoring for tennis on a knowledge test follows:

DIRECTIONS: *Matching.* For each item in the left-hand column, select that item from the right-hand column that is best identified from the alternatives listed. Place the proper identifying letter in the blank to the left of the item in the left-hand column. Do not use a letter more than once.

_____ 1. First point after deuce	(A)	Advantage
_____ 2. Receiver at game point	(B)	Deuce
_____ 3. Each side has won 3 points	(C)	Game
_____ 4. Server wins 2 consecutive points after love–30	(D)	Love-all
_____ 5. Second consecutive point after deuce	(E)	15–all
_____ 6. Each side has won 1 point	(F)	30–30
	(G)	30–40
	(H)	40–30

A variation of this type of exercise can be made by changing the last sentence of the directions to read: "You may use a letter as many times as necessary. All of the letters need not be used." Such a variation tends to minimize the elimination-guessing aspect of the exercise. Another variation is to give a few matching items for a list of situational items, such as the following interpretation questions.

_____ 7. Stepping on the line when serving before con-   (A) Fault
          tacting the ball   (B) Let
_____ 8. When a ball hits the net on serves, otherwise   (C) Point
          good
_____ 9. First serve hits service line, is not returned
_____10. Good serve underhand, not returned

Actually, this variation consists of a series of multiple-choice stems for which the same alternatives are possible. Another illustration of this variation would be the use of the responses (A) chop, (B) drive, (C) lob, (D) smash, (E) volley, for a series of situational premises dealing with the most appropriate tennis stroke, such as: *The most effective stroke for a drop shot.*

The matching item is relatively easy to devise and makes possible the inclusion of a large number of items in a small space with a single set of directions. The matching item can be made to facilitate quick and objective scoring, and with proper construction, the guessing factor presents no concern. However, the questions provide a poor measure of complete understanding and interpretation and tend to overemphasize the recognition of facts. A further limitation lies in the fact that, unless skillfully constructed, the matching item may contain irrelevant clues and also may be time consuming for the student.

In constructing matching items the following hints should be heeded.

1. For the common type of matching exercise, as a general rule have at least 5, and no more than 10, premises or stem statements. (The length of a matching exercise should afford no particular concern, if the principle of homogeneity of content is applied as stated in 3 below.)
2. Include at least two extra choices from which responses are selected *with* at least two plausible choices for each premise. Some authorities advocate that the list of responses should be at least 50 per cent longer than the list of premises.
3. Include only similar or related material in a matching exercise, arranged on one page. All entries in both lists should relate to the same central theme. Attention to homogeneous nature of items is important to prevent students from using heterogeneity as the basis for matching rather than knowledge.
4. Arrange the responses in the right-hand column in a logical order to facilitate selection, such as alphabetically or numerically.
5. Explain in the directions the basis for matching and the procedure to be followed.

Identification. This test item should find increasingly greater use in physical education measurement, inasmuch as it appears admirably suited to much test content. It consists simply of presenting an illustration containing numerical or letter indicators of the item to be identified. The identification item presents material in a more concise and lucid manner than can be done through written description and, accordingly, proves to save test time and item space. Countless variations and adaptations of this method are possible; all of which embody the fundamental principle of identifying certain features, parts, or relationships in a given illustration.

Examples of identification items on a tennis knowledge test follow:

DIRECTIONS: *Identification.* For the items below, select the identifying letter on the illustration that answers the question and place this letter in the blank by the item number.

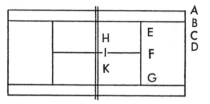

_____ 1. The server should stand
_____ 2. After playing the ball in singles, a player should
_____ 3. go to either of two positions to await return

Court position

DIRECTIONS: *Identification.* Each question below involves the identification of some part of the illustration that appears alongside it. Find the symbol for each question on the illustration and name or describe, as appropriate, what the symbol indicates in the space provided between the item number and the symbol.

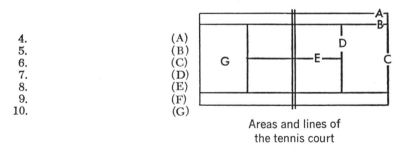

4.   (A)
5.   (B)
6.   (C)
7.   (D)
8.   (E)
9.   (F)
10.   (G)

Areas and lines of
the tennis court

The court-position diagram represents a selection type of test item where the correct response for each item is identified from a key-list, which in essence is a matching exercise. The reader should immediately realize that the second illustration goes outside the realm of selection or recognition and in reality elicits a supply or recall response. While arbitrarily included in the selection group, this identification item can be designed for either purpose very effectively. In reality, the identification item basically consists of the utilization of illustrations to identify points of reference for material organized in one of several test item types, such as multiple-choice, matching, and fill-in.

While both of the aforementioned illustrations are designed to afford the basis for several responses, in some instances one illustration may be furnished for a single fill-in response. Another variation is to describe or name an item and to have the response to it made by checking (X) or using designated letters on the particular part or spot on the illustration that is entailed.

The identification item provides a means of testing response to game situations to reveal basic understanding of game fundamentals, rules, and strategy. Its potentiality seems to warrant greater utilization in physical education measurement than has been the case heretofore.

In addition to the general suggestions pertaining to all objective tests, several hints for constructing identification items are:

1. Design items to be completely objective by having illustrations simple and making directions clear and specific as to the response desired.
2. Use one illustration to serve two or more questions when possible.
3. Use an identification item only when it appears to be the most feasible and plausible type.

Analogy. Like the identification item, the analogy does not represent a distinct form of objective test item, as alternative-response, multiple-choice, matching and completion do, but constitutes a means of expressing questions to be answered utilizing one of these other basic formats. The two most popular forms of analogy are multiple-choice and completion, although analogies are also adaptable to matching and alternative response. The analogy item is particularly suited to measure the ability to associate meanings and to infer relationships. This item presents three terms or facts, the first two of which are related in some manner. The item task is to select or supply, as appropriate, the fourth term whose association to the third term reflects the same relationship inferred between the first pair of terms.

Examples of analogies on a tennis knowledge test follow:

DIRECTIONS: *Analogy.* For each item below, determine in what ways the first pair of terms is related and then supply the proper term in the blank at the left of the item to make a similar relationship with the third term.
Sample Question.
(racket)   1. Golf : club : : tennis : _____
In the first pair, the club is used to hit the ball in golf, just as the answer, *racket*, is in tennis.
_____   1. Chop : backspin : : slice : _____
_____   2. "Deuce" is to "advantage in" as "30–30" is to _____

Question 2 is expressed in an alternative form for illustrative purposes only. Whichever form is used should be maintained throughout. The use of the analogy item has been limited in physical education. The teacher should always remain alert to utilize the best item type in terms of the nature of the material and the grade level involved. If relationships constitute an important aspect of test content, then the analogy item may be appropriate.

Analogies should be constructed in light of the following suggestions.

1. Directions should be explicit with easily comprehensible example(s).
2. Students should be familiar with this type of item to obviate any sense of artificiality and so that the item can actually measure those aspects for which it is most appropriate.
3. Follow specific suggestions for constructing basic item format that is used, such as the considerations for multiple-choice or completion items.

Arrangement. In the arrangement item the student is required to put a series of randomly presented material into some specified order. The basis for the ordering is determined by the nature of the material involved and may consist of one of the following: difficulty, importance, chronology, size, logic, and the like. This type of item places more emphasis on the relationship of things or ideas rather than on specific facts.

Illustrative arrangement items for a tennis knowledge test follow.

> DIRECTIONS: *Arrangement.* For each item-group below, arrange the parts in order of progression on the specified factor, so that the number (1) is placed in the blank in front of the part that should appear first, (2) for the second, and so on.
>
> 1. The difficulty order of tennis grips, with the easiest assigned the number (1).
>
> _____ Continental
> _____ Eastern
> _____ Western
>
> 2. The preferred order in which strokes should be learned.
>
> _____ Backhand drive
> _____ Chop
> _____ Forehand drive
> _____ Lob
> _____ Serve
> _____ Smash
> _____ Volley

The arrangement item poses some difficulty in scoring, which tends to discourage its use. Nevertheless, for some aspects of knowledge and understanding it may represent the best testing approach. This item is most easily scored by giving one or two points for the correct arrangement of each group or set and no partial credit. This practice can be followed for items consisting of less than five parts, such as question 1 above. For items with five or more parts the scoring becomes more difficult. Cureton[25] has reported a method that appears preferable for scoring the arrangement item regardless of the number of parts. But of particular concern is that this method constitutes the most practical equitable scheme available for scoring items consisting of five or more points, wherein consideration for partial credit becomes imperative. This scoring scheme entails adding the differences in ranking (ignoring minus signs) for each part between the key and the student's response. It is illustrated below using the order assigned by a student in response to question 2 above, a seven part item.

Correct order:	2	7	1	5	3	6	4
Student's order:	1	7	3	6	2	5	4
Differences:	1	0	2	1	1	1	0
Total: 6							

The sum of the differences occurring between the student's order and the keyed order, 6, is entered in Table 5–3 by locating the column for 7 items ranked and following the directions given below the table proper. The total of 6 falls between 5 and 9 listed in the column for 7 items, and the score corresponding to it is found by following the line separating 5 and 9 to the left-hand margin, giving the answer—4. Thus, the student's response to seven-part question 2 is assigned a score of 4 out of 7. The score derived by Cureton's table reflects the correlation between the keyed order and that assigned by the student. While this procedure is somewhat involved, it represents the most satisfactory means so far developed to accord partial credit on arrangement items.

The use of arrangement items would appear limited for the physical education teacher, particularly for items of more than four parts wherein hand-scoring becomes more tedious. Nevertheless, the teacher should be aware of this type of item which, like in the case of analogy, may prove to be the most appropriate type for certain aspects of the content area for a test.

In addition to the general suggestions concerning all objective test items, some specific considerations for constructing arrangement items are:

1. Preference should be given to use of this item with less than five parts. It is recommended that four represent the maximum num-

[25] E. E. Cureton, "The Rearrangement Item," *Educational and Psychological Measurement*, XX, No. 1 (Spring, 1960), 31.

Table 5–3. Scoring Table for the Rearrangement Test [26]

Score	Number of Items Ranked																		Score
	3	4	5	6	7	8	9	10	11	12	13	14	15	16	17	18	19	20	
20																		3	20
19																	3	9	19
18																3	9	17	18
17															3	9	15	23	17
16														3	9	15	23	29	16
15													3	7	15	21	29	37	15
14												3	7	13	19	27	35	43	14
13											3	7	13	19	25	33	41	49	13
12										1	7	11	17	23	31	39	47	57	12
11									1	5	11	17	23	29	37	45	53	63	11
10								1	'5	9	15	21	27	35	43	51	61	69	10
9							1	5	9	13	19	25	33	39	49	57	67	77	9
8						1	5	9	13	17	23	31	37	45	53	63	73	83	8
7					1	3	7	11	17	21	29	35	43	51	59	69	79	89	7
6				1	3	7	11	15	21	25	33	39	47	55	65	75	85	97	6
5			1	3	5	9	13	19	23	29	37	45	53	61	71	81	91	103	5
4		1	3	5	9	11	17	21	27	33	41	49	57	67	77	87	97	109	4
3	1	1	5	7	11	15	19	25	31	37	45	53	63	71	81	93	105	117	3
2	1	3	5	9	13	17	23	29	35	41	49	59	67	77	87	99	111	123	2
1	3	5	7	11	15	19	25	31	39	45	53	63	73	83	93	105	117	129	1
0																			0

Directions: 1. Match the key against the examinee's answers. For each item write the difference (without regard to sign) between the key rank and the examinee's rank. Add the difference and record the sum. Every such sum must be 0 or an *even* number.

2. In the column headed by the number of items ranked, find a horizontal line with a number smaller than the sum above it and a number larger than the sum below it. (The table contains only *odd* numbers, so no tabled number can *equal* a sum.) The number at the end of the line, at left or right, is the score.

3. If the sum is less than the figure at the top of the column (0 for columns 4-12; 0 or 2 for columns 13-20), the score is the number of items ranked. If the sum is greater than the figure at the bottom of the column, the score is 0.

ber of parts in a set for the elementary level and that a maximum of ten parts be applied at the higher grade levels.
2. Directions should clearly explain the item task and stipulate the direction of the order to be assigned.
3. The difficulty of the item is a function of the degree of discrimination required within the set and by the number of parts it contains. Generally, the finer the discrimination required and the greater number of parts, the more difficult the item becomes.

Supply.   In essence, the identification and analogy items, while categorized as selection, actually serve to bridge the gap between selection and supply groups of objective test items; they may be presented in either format. The basic difference between these two main groups lies

[26] Reproduced from: Cureton, *op. cit.*

in the fact that no proposed answers are given in supply items, only the basic question or problem. The level of intellectual activity thus involved enables supply test items to obviate some of the objectionable aspects of selection test items. While differentiation between kinds of supply items is difficult, for discussion purposes, the author arbitrarily distinguishes two types on the basis of the response elicited—simple recall and free response. The simple recall form can either ask the student to furnish a word or figure to answer a direct question or to complete a statement by recalling the proper key word(s) or figure. In either instance, the basic statement and response should result in a complete, meaningful and correct combination. Question 1 below illustrates the former, while question 2 requires recalling equivalent information to complete a statement.

> DIRECTIONS: *Supply.* In the blank at the left of or below each statement, as appropriate, insert the key words or figures that appear to be the best answer to a question or best complete the sentence.
>
> _____ 1. How many inches in height should the tennis net be at the center?
> _____ 2. The height of the tennis net at the sides should be ____ inches.
> _____ 3. When both players have won 3 points, the score is _____.
> 4–7. List the four basic tennis strokes in the order they should be learned.
> 4. _____
> 5. _____
> 6. _____
> 7. _____
> 8–10. What are the three most important considerations to keep in mind when executing a serve?
> 8. _____
> 9. _____
> 10. _____

The free-response items encompass concerns ranging from computing the solution to situational problems, such as question 3 above, to listing or enumerating statements of fact or generalizations. Items 4 to 7 represent a listing of specific things. Items 8 to 10 serve as an example of a free-response question designed to reveal a higher level of understanding of tennis. The reader will note that the supply items, as illustrated above, may also be classified by the item format, such as simple question (question 1), simple fill-in or completion (questions 2 and 3), and short-answer expressed as an incomplete statement (questions 4–7) or a question (questions 8–10).

From the examples above, it is obvious that supply items are used to measure the retention of specific points or the application of these points. As such, accurate information is needed that stimulates desirable study habits and almost completely eliminates guessing. While the supply items comprise one of the most familiar test types and one of the easiest to construct, the challenge lies in phrasing the test situations so that responses of a higher intellectual level than rote memory will be elicited and that scoring can be done with relatively little time and effort. While it is acknowledged that scoring of supply items is not as objective as for selection items, unless particular caution is taken, the scoring may prove to be quite laborious and not always objective. Previously, supply items have been used excessively with a resulting overemphasis on verbal facility and memorization of facts and isolated bits of information, and, consequently, have proven time-consuming for the students.

The supply items introduce a scoring consideration that does not apply to the selection type, namely, the problem of spelling. Obviously, this concern also applies to essay tests. If the teacher gives credit only when the answer is spelled correctly, the poor spellers cannot manifest their true level of achievement. The test then becomes an uninterpretable mixture of knowledge and spelling ability, and the validity of the test as a measure of associated learning in the particular subject area is lowered. However, the practice of ignoring spelling interjects the element of sub-jectivity as to whether the word is the intended answer and tends to reduce the dependability of scores as measures of knoweldge and under-standing. One solution to this concern is to render two grades, one for mastery of test content and the second for ability to spell special terms. In general, the author suggests that the teacher of physical education stress spelling as appropriate in presenting material to the students but overlook it in scoring tests, always assuming that the misspelled word can be clearly interpreted as the correct answer.

As the basis for constructing supply test items, in addition to the general guides enumerated earlier for all tests of associated learning, the teacher will find it helpful to peruse the specific considerations delineated for the various selection-type test items for applicable hints. Some specific suggestions for constructing supply items follow.

1. Be alert to phrase the statement to indicate the type of response desired and to have only one correct answer without embodying unwarranted clues, e.g., *a* or *an*. If synonymous answers are acceptable, they should be keyed and counted as correct.
2. Use direct questions to the extent possible. The desired approach is to start with a direct question and change to an incomplete statement only when greater conciseness is gained.
3. Ask for the most important information and make certain that the item contains the key words for the student to recognize what is required in the answer.
4. Pay especial heed to avoid textbook phraseology.
5. For completion statements omit only significant words, and these

words to be supplied by the student should relate to the main point of the statement.

6. Standardize the length of blanks as appropriate for each type of supply item—simple recall and free response—so as to accommodate all responses but not suggest length of response. Allow enough space to permit legible writing. Have the blank appear at the end of the statement, whenever possible.

7. Have enumeration items elicit specific facts or points of information and be limited to no more than eight parts per item. When enumeration in order is asked for, determine the specific scoring method. (Refer to hints for arrangement items.)

8. To the extent feasible in terms of test content, arrange supply items so that those of like format are grouped together—simple questions, fill-ins, and short-answers.

ESSAY TESTS.—It seems appropriate as a conclusion to the discussion of objective test forms, and particularly of supply forms, to recognize the gradual transition from the supply type of objective test to essay tests. Whereas identification and analogy items seem to tie together the selection and supply test forms, the free-response objective test item (such as questions 8 to 10 on page 180) leads quite naturally from supply to essay test items. The supply form differs from the essay test primarily on the basis of length of response required. Properly conceived, the essay-type item should require students to make a comparison, write a description, or explain certain points. The student should be permitted freedom of expression in analyzing, comparing, describing, explaining, or reasoning. Justifiable criticism that has been leveled at essay tests deals with their construction and scoring, not the test type per se. Carefully constructed and scored essay tests can furnish very desirable and useful information concerning a student's achievement or development. The use of essay questions should be limited to measuring the attainment of objectives that cannot be measured more effectively by objective test items. While the utilization of essay tests in physical education appears limited, the teacher should be apprised of its characteristics in the event appraisal is desired of learning outcomes best measured by essay items.

Since the freedom of response permitted by essay questions varies considerably, essay questions are generally categorized into two types— restricted response, and extended response. In the *restricted response* form the student is required to give a brief and precisely defined answer. This form is useful for measuring learning outcomes indicative of comprehension, application, and analysis. The *extended response* form accords the student great freedom in determining the nature and scope of the answer and, accordingly, permits measuring learning outcomes entailing synthesis and evaluation which cannot be measured by the restricted response form or any other type of test item.

The desirable features of essay tests can be engendered and the dis-advantages minimized by paying heed to the following suggestions in construction.

1. Determine specifically what objective or learning outcome is to be measured by the test and the suitability of essay forms for this purpose, recognizing that essay questions should be used only for complex learning outcomes.
2. Relate the questions as directly as possible to the learning out-comes being measured, and carefully word each question and the directions to the student so as to require a specific answer. The main problem in constructing essay tests is stating questions that are neither too general nor too specific.
3. Construct questions of such a range of difficulty as will allow all students to demonstrate their level of competence.
4. Elicit the desired type of response by directing the student to *compare, contrast, criticize, describe, explain, justify, prove,* and *tell how,* rather than merely to list or enumerate.
5. As a general rule, employ a relatively large number of restricted response items, rather than a relatively smaller number of extended response items. This permits eliciting more directive responses, provides a better sampling of test content, and limits the advantage accorded on extended response items to highly verbal students who may not be particularly knowledgable.
6. Provide ample time for answering and suggested time limits for each question. Do not require so much writing for the time avail-able that the test becomes a speed writing contest. Also, do not use both essay and objective questions in the same test if the time for testing is limited.
7. Do not permit a choice of questions. While allowing some student choice may tend to reduce unfairness attributable to content sampl-ing, test performance and the resultant scores are not comparable unless all students are required to answer the same questions.

The matter of how to score essay tests effectively and efficiently war-rants especial attention and differs slightly between restricted and ex-tended response forms. For restricted response questions a scoring model should be prepared by delineating the specific points to be expected for each question. Each significant point should be given 1 score point, with the sum to determine the total item score, rather than assume the value or importance to be accorded the item. Scoring then is done by allowing 1 score point for each point covered in the answer. By the very nature of the learning outcomes they are designed to measure, extended response questions do not lend themselves to such a scoring system. The quality of the answer for this form is judged partly on organization and presentation of thought and ideas rather than solely on delineation of particular points of information. Accordingly, the answer to the extended response form is graded by the rating method using clearly defined criteria as a guide. The term "grade" is used rather than "score" for extended response questions to denote that the quality of the answer is interpreted somewhat subjectively in terms of the defined criteria.

In addition, careful attention to two other practices in scoring or grading can favorably influence the validity and reliability of essay tests, namely: concealing student names on the test papers or some other means of preventing identification during the scoring process, and scoring or grading one essay item on all papers before proceeding to the next. This latter procedure makes it possible to maintain a more uniform standard for judging the answer to each question and also helps to offset the halo effect in grading. Finally, when appropriate and feasible, the teacher should compile a cummulative score from several essay tests, since such total scores are likely to provide satisfactorily high reliability.

To conclude presentation of the considerations involved in constructing written tests, it should be pointed out that, like the work of a reputable chef, an understanding of the effects realized by a certain combination of specific ingredients, blended together into a masterful recipe, constitute a good teacher-made test. Awareness of the various purposes served within recognized limitations of the different test items is imperative for the most effective utilization and arrangement of items. Diligent adherence to the procedural approach and pertinent considerations as described herein will virtually assure the development of a quality written test. In addition the teacher will find critical review of test items, contained in available published knowledge tests given in Chapter 14, a valuable idea resource in constructing tests of associated learning.

MEASUREMENT OF ATTITUDES AND BEHAVIOR— CONCOMITANT LEARNING

Whereas the construction of measuring instruments for associated learning differed somewhat from that of tests for technical learning, the area of concomitant learning (affective domain) presents still another type of characteristics that necessitates especial consideration. The attitudes and behavior that comprise concomitant learning vary basically in nature from physical qualities as well as from the particular constituency of knowledge and understanding. By its very makeup concomitant learning is difficult to appraise and, accordingly, mistakenly labeled intangible and avoided or ignored entirely by many teachers. Inasmuch as this type of learning constitutes the most influential aspect in shaping an individual's pattern of living, this area should receive due emphasis and not be ignored. Further discussion of rating and appraising concomitant learning is included in Chapters 6, 7 and 15. Presently, the concern is to depict the specific points to heed in constructing such measuring instruments.

Teachers will vary in the extent to which they wish to devise and utilize devices for appraising attitudes and behavior. However, the basic considerations in constructing measuring instruments in this area should be understood by all teachers. Progress in the refinement of such measurement will not be enhanced without concerted effort to design practical tools to do the teacher's job. Most of the rating scales presently in use are prepared by teachers and are relied upon as an important part in evaluation and grading plans.

Appraisal of attitudes and behavior in physical education can best be accomplished through two types of tools: rating scales, and self-report scales and inventories. Discussion of two other techniques relevant to concomitant learning—sociometry and anecdotal records—will be covered in Chapter 15. *Rating scales* refer to a device designed to describe overt behavior as observed by a judge. *Self-report scales and inventories* encompass expression of student reaction or behavior in certain situations as indicated by response to written statements or questions, and in the case of some inventories may be given in interview format.

Procedure for Developing Measures of Concomitant Learning

In light of the general concerns for test construction applicable to measures of all types of learning as presented in Chapter 4, it becomes essential to recognize the particular factors deemed important in developing measures of concomitant learning, either of observer or self-report variety. These factors to be considered are enumerated in a suggested procedural sequence below.

1. *Delineate the purpose to be served by the instrument.* A definitive statement of purpose affords the basis for validation of the instrument. In essence such a statement constitutes the criterion for establishing either content or construct validity, as applicable, by clearly indicating what is desired. Within the realm of concomitant learning the teaching may purport to (a) rate the behavior of students in physical education activity, (b) determine their attitude toward physical education, or (c) assess selected personality traits or interests with particular relevance to physical education. A vital aspect of the purpose in terms of instrument design is the nature of the intended population with which it will be used, including such concerns as sex, age, and ability level. This initial step of stating the purpose of the instrument gives precise direction and limitations to the actual construction process that ensues.

2. *Clearly define the characteristics on which rating or response is desired.* This definition of each characteristic should involve but a single trait or quality at a time and should include a description listing the elements of such a trait, that is, what to look for. As a case in point assume that an inventory is being designed, one purpose of which is to disclose self-confidence manifested through physical education experiences. This step, then, necessitates recognition of the elements deemed to be indicative of self-confidence or "faith in oneself."

3. *Determine the appropriate rating or response scheme.* The range and defiintiveness of the rating by observers or response on self-report devices should be based upon a number of factors. These considerations include (a) the purpose of the instrument, (b) the nature of the quality to be measured, (c) characteristics of the group involved, such as age, sex, and ability or trait level and range, and (d) administrative limits of the particular situation. The rating scale points, or differentiating responses, should be descriptive of identifiable behavior or basic elements of the trait concerned. The number of scale points or response provided is related to the accuracy with which such rating or response can be made. The descriptive phrases at the ends of the contniuum or categorical arrangement should not be so extreme as to be avoided by raters or respondents. The meaning of the intermediate levels of the scale should be closer to the average or neutral phrase than to the extreme phrases, so as to induce raters or respondents to use a wider range of the line or available categories, and to help counteract the tendency to concentrate ratings around the middle of the line or categories.

4. *Design suitable questions or statements dealing with each trait, including, as appropriate, the specific elements comprising a given trait.* Each topic or question area selected should involve a single trait or quality; no multiple-trait questions. It is essential that enough questions involving the various aspects related to each trait be included to provide sufficient evidence to represent the ability or trait level of the student, while at the same time avoiding any redundancy. Referrring again to an inventory concerned with self-confidence in physical education activity, the question should encompass ·those aspects of an individual's experience that will disclose faith in oneself. For example, a general question might be, "Can you play your best in contests against very superior opponents?" A specific question might be, "Would you like to represent your school in tennis matches against students from other schools who are either about your ability or slightly better?" In designing statements care should be taken to insure that they are compatible with the type and definitiveness of response desired. Stress should be placed on de-

veloping well-constructed statements geared to the understanding level of the rater or respondent and containing words as precise in meaning as possible. In general it is desirable to avoid such words as *very, some, average,* and *large,* which have different meanings for different people. Colloquial expressions and slang sometimes prove helpful. Succinctly, each question or statement should mean the same thing to everyone concerned.

5. *Arrange the questions or items in a logical and psychological order.* Thus, the simpler, more fundamental concepts should be presented before response to more complex situations and those entailing more skillful performance. Using a personality inventory format to illustrate, a question dealing with handling one's weight in an emergency would precede a query pertaining to body contact in a competitive sport situation. This concern about item arrangement refers not only to all questions pertaining to a particular trait, but also in the overall context to the order in which the various traits are presented in the scale or inventory. In both instances—among and within different traits—the order should reflect deliberative organization based upon relevant logical and psychological considerations. While this admonition was expressed as a general concern in formulating tests of all types of learning, it is emphasized here to avoid omission or being judged as inapplicable to concomitant learning. In reality attention to the order of presentation may be justifiably regarded as most vital in measures of this type of learning, where maintenance of desirable rapport is essential to obtain candid and reliable response.

6. *Stipulate the conditions for administering and scoring the instrument.* As with other measuring instruments, it is important to insure that similar conditions will prevail whenever the scale or inventory is used. Further, by their very nature, attitudes and behavior afford a challenge for reliable assessment. Consequently, careful attention to provision of an atmosphere for measurement conducive to valid response is most essential. Particular reference is directed to establishing proper rapport involving the rater or the self-report device and the student; not to overlook the actual environmental setting in which the assessment is made.

7. *Provide for external verification of validity.* The instrument should be subjected to critical analysis by two or more individuals authoritative in the content area to verify satisfactory realization of the avowed purpose of the instrument and, further, that the rating or response scheme is suitable. Although attention to this concern is drawn at this point near the end of the procedural description, this aspect may well consist of

consultation with selected resource personnel to develop the blueprint for design of the instrument at the beginning and a rather cursory examination of the instrument prior to its trial administration to confirm satisfactory compliance with the basic plan. Ideally, the teacher will obtain such authoritative opinion as necessary at the outset and throughout the planning and formulating stages of the instrument to assure development of a good instrument with a minimum of wasted effort.

The nature of the qualifications of people to serve as judges for validation purposes will vary somewhat with the type and purpose of the instrument. While it would be most desirable to have each judge competent in both physical education and the measurement of attitudes and behavior, the rather limited availability of such combined competence may necessitate use of people who are qualified in one area and possess limited understanding of the other. Both aspects should be competently represented. In practice the teacher will be able to obtain the necessary assistance to confirm either the content or the construct validity of the instrument, as appropriate, from other teachers in the school or from a nearby college or university.

8. *Subject the instrument to trial application as the basis for determining its final form.* This trial administration affords evidence of the effectiveness of the instrument in producing valid and reliable assessment within practical limits of size and design. Needed adjustments can then be made to produce a final form of the instrument that is satisfactory in all aspects, including length and content. A word of admonition regarding instrument length appears in order to avert the tendency to include too many traits or characteristics for assessment. Should a decrease in the length of an instrument be imperative, the teacher should recognize that it may be necessary to reduce the number of traits assessed by the instrument rather than to sample any traits inadequately in an effort to preserve the number of traits included. As is typical of tests of any quality, sampling of content that is representative of each trait must be adequate for reliable appraisal to be possible.

As a guide to follow in constructing measures of concomitant learning, a definitive enumeration of the procedure involved is presented below in the form of a check list. Careful adherence to satisfactory execution of each step will assure development of a desirable instrument for appraisal of attitudes or behavior. Although some slight procedural variations may occur between measures for use by a rater and those based on student response, the check list is designed for application to both types. Details peculiar to either rating scales or self-report devices will be covered in the discussion of each type.

CHECK LIST FOR CONSTRUCTING MEASURES OF CONCOMITANT LEARNING

1. Describe the purpose for which the instrument is intended.
2. Provide for validation by instrument design to conform to its purpose.
3. Indicate the traits or qualities to be measured, and identify the important topical areas or aspects constituting each trait or quality.
4. Define the method of rating or response to be used.
5. Carefully devise questions that cover all pertinent aspects of the traits or qualities concerned and are compatible with the rating or response scheme.
6. Arrange the questions properly both within and among the different traits or qualities.
7. Deliberatively review the questions in the overall context, with reference primarily to omissions, needless overlap or duplication, and desirable content relationship, and then effect necessary changes to assure validity as planned.
8. Prepare explicit, concise directions for use of the instrument by rater or respondent, including provision for suitable rater orientation.
9. Describe how the instrument should be scored.
10. Administer the instrument to an appropriate trial group to analyze quality (including suitability) of questions individually and collectively, and make revisions as may be indicated.
11. Establish satisfactory reliability of the instrument and also, for scales and self-report instruments for use by others, acceptable objectivity.
12. Administer the instrument again to analyze quality, if the nature of the revision warrants it, with all self-report devices to be given in final form to other typical groups to establish norms.
13. Plan a scheme to afford meaningful interpretation of scores on the instrument.
14. Prepare a suitable manual describing the construction, characteristics, use, and interpretation of the instrument.

Rating Scales

As the basis for discussing the construction of rating scales, the reader is referred to the description of this device as a criterion measure in test validation (see page 123) as well as to the presentation on rating scales for physical performance appraisal (see page 139). By so doing, one can be apprised of the general concerns of rating scales that are applicable to concomitant learning. Rating scales are primarily devices for recording observations, although it is comomn for some rating scales to require the rater to interpret what is observed. In reality, it should be noted that no precise line exists between observation and interpretation. In applying rating scales to concomitant learning, the effectiveness of rating scales will obviously depend upon the degree to which the category of behavior to be recorded is accurately defined and the extent to which the rater can observe the kinds of behavior to be recorded.

Three distinct types of rating scales can be identified, namely, descriptive, numerical, and graphic. *Descriptive rating scales* are comprised of a series of usually three to seven words or phrases which express different degrees of the trait or quality in question in behavioral tems. The rater merely selects from the listing the word or phrase that appears most applicable to the person being rated. Illustrations might also be used instead of verbal descriptions, but this format is generally more appropriate for performance rating, such as posture appraisal. An example of a descriptive rating scale follows:

DIRECTIONS: Place a check in the blank preceding the phrase that appears most appropriate.
1. To what extent does he (she) seem at ease?
_____ At ease in all situations?
_____ Usually at ease and rarely tense
_____ At ease often by tense occasionally
_____ Usually tense
_____ Tense in all situations

In *numerical rating scales* numbers are assigned to the various levels or categories of each trait, from the least to the most, and the rater indicates that number representing the degree to which the student possesses the trait in question. For example:

DIRECTIONS: Indicate the degree to which the individual displays the characteristic in question by encircling the appropriate number, whereby: 1—minimum, 3—average, 5—maximum, with intermediary points 2 (below average), and 4 (above average).
1 2 3 4 5   1. How does he (she) get along with others?

Graphic rating scales consist of horizontal lines, defined at each end, and generally at intermediary points, on which the rater checks the student's standing with reference to each trait or quality. This type of scale permits flexibility in assigning a rating anywhere along a continuum in contrast to the more rigid categorical scheme utilized in the two other scale types. Graphic rating scales may take one of two forms, using either constant alternatives or changing alternatives. The former uses either the same descriptive words for each trait, such as always, often, sometimes, seldom, and never, or a numerical scale, for example, 1–5. In the changing alternatives form separate distinguishing descriptions are provided for each trait. The general behavior rating questions below [27] are expressed in the changing alternatives form of graphic rating scales and are arranged to show the procedure of varying the direction of the response continuum from favorable to unfavorable and vice versa.

DIRECTIONS: Put a check anywhere on the horizontal line for each item to indicate the degree to which the characteristic in question is reflected.

1. What about his (her) temperament?

Generally very even tempered	Happy or depressed as conditions warrant	Rarely changes mood—impassive	Strong and frequent changes of mood	Has periods of elations or depressions

2. Does he (she) persevere?

Wilts before slight obstacles or objections	Obstinate—never gives in	Gives up before adequate trial	Persists until convinced of mistake	Gives everything a fair trial

As a point of interest it can be readily observed that, if these graphic point descriptions were arranged as categories in a listing, they would then constitute a descriptive type of rating scale, thereby eliminating the "in-between categories" rating. This is mentioned only to illustrate the similarity between the scales and not to imply that descriptive scales possess limited value, for although graphic scales are very popular, in some instances a continuum format is neither appropriate nor practical. In the main these two general behavior rating questions, and the previous examples for descriptive and numerical rating scales, are applicable to all behavioral settings. If a teacher desires to rate behavior or similar characteristics peculiar to physical education or a particular activity, specific appropriate questions may be devised.

While not a scale in the usual sense of the word, another technique that is sometimes used in behavior rating is the *forced-choice* or paired-comparison method.[28] In this method the rater is confronted with pairs of items from which the one deemed to be more closely characteristic of the subject for each pair is selected. An illustrative forced-choice item for rating general behavior is:

Could reflect more enthusiasm.

Displays need for more complacency.

[27] Adapted from M. E. Haggerty, W. C. Olson, and E. K. Wickman, *Haggerty–Olson–Wickham Behavior Rating Schedules* (Yonkers, N.Y.: World Book Co., 1930).

[28] For a comprehensive presentation of this method, as well as an authoritative resource for rating scales, the reader is referred to: J. P. Guilford, *Psychometric Methods,* 2nd ed. (New York: McGraw-Hill Book Co., 1954), pp. 274–278.

This approach was conceived as a means of controlling the effects of various rater response sets, such as leniency, halo, and acquiescence.

Before beginning to construct a rating scale for concomitant learning, several stipulations should prevail, namely, that:

1. The ability or trait in question can be described or defined and also can be differentiated from similar characteristics so as to permit rating.
2. Each individual can demonstrate this characteristic to an observer.
3. Different individuals vary significantly in the characteristic in question so that levels of existence can be differentiated.
4. The individuals who are to be rated display, and can demonstrate, this characteristic relatively consistently.

If the characteristic of behavior to be rated lends itself to rating as stipulated by the foregoing points, the construction of the rating scale may proceed.

Specific Considerations. When applying the procedural approach described earlier for developing measures of concomitant learning in constructing rating scales, in addition to matters pertaining to rating in general, concerns peculiar to behavioral rating need to be recognized. Specifically, these considerations include the following:

1. *Scale simplicity.* Simplicity in the scale should be stressed, not only to enhance validity and reliability, but also to avoid placing undue demands upon raters. The number of scale points used should be related to the accuracy with which rating of the trait in question can be made. Rating scales utilizing general class (A,B,C,D,E,) or numerical points (1,2,3,4,5) should include verbal description of the elements to be present for each class or point. This practice fosters thorough understanding while at the same time serves to prevent misunderstanding.

2. *Trait questions.* Each scale should be introduced by an explicit question about a trait or quality to which the rater gives an answer. To enhance reliability those traits to which the rater can respond objectively should be included and not those that require interpretation or subjective evaluation.

3. *Frame of reference.* As appropriate, the frame of reference in which the rating is to be made should be clearly identified, since this may well influence the rating. For example, teacher and mother view the child in different frames of reference.

4. *Scale directionality.* When rating involves a number of scales, they should be set up so that the desirable ends of the scales occur either at the right or left side in random fashion, rather than being consistently

at one side. This consideration, as shown by the example of graphic scales for temperament and perseverence, prevents an observer from perfunctorily checking a subject the same on each trait; thus obviating a response set. It is obviously important to instruct the rater to read each rating description carefully inasmuch as the directionality of the scales varies.

5. *Graphic scale marking.* Graphic scales should contain either a great many or no segments on the line in order to emphasize the continuity of the trait and to encourage the rater to put a check mark at any place on the line deemed representative for the individual being rated.

6. *Rating sheets.* Standardized or especially prepared rating sheets, preferably the graphic type when suitable, should be used to promote uniformity and administrative facility.

7. *Factors affecting rating.* To insure the proper setting, the conditions and procedure for administering the rating should be precisely described in the directions to provide for "sameness of circumstances" and to avoid conditions that may be conducive to overrating or underrating. The setting for rating should be such as to minimize distractions for both ratee and rater. It is imperative to provide ample time for rating as part of the observation, not at a later time. The teacher should be cognizant of relevant concerns about rating that have implications for scale construction, such as those discussed under specific considerations for performance rating (see page 143) and categorized as: factors limiting accuracy of a rating; importance of rater "warm-up"; use of other raters; and common errors in rating.

Self-Report Scales and Inventories

In some instances a rating scale cannot be used to advantage, because of the unavailability of rating time or the relative inapplicability of the rating technique to the characteristic in question. Such circumstances would suggest consideration of the self-report technique as a means of ascertaining attitudes and behavior. This approach involves student response to questions pertaining to an individual's reaction or typical behavior in specific situations. Two variations of the self-report are identified to facilitate meaningful description, namely, scales and inventories. The self-report scale is in reality a form of inventory but is identified separately to refer to attitude scales, in contrast to inventories designed to assess personality characteristics, interests, and other purposes except for attitude measurement. Attitude scales can be used by the teacher to determine the extent to which each student possesses favorable or unfavorable feelings about physical activity, the school physical education program, selected aspects of physical education, or the teacher, to cite some of the more probable instances. Inventories afford a means of assessing selected personality characteristics and interests of students that have particular relevance in physical education.

In constructing self-report instruments the teacher should not overlook the fact that the general characteristics of a good test item should apply. This entails concerns such as including a relatively large number of items, stating the questions clearly and precisely, insuring that a real basis for correct response exists for each question, and averting a definite pattern of response. The teacher should also be certain that no item suggests the appropriate response to another item, and should avoid including clues for response and omit the unavoidably obvious response questions. When designing questions, it should be realized that behavior and attitude assessment is more effective when the characteristics being looked for are expressed as undesirable behavior.[29] That is to say, individuals are more prone to express their undesirable behavior in the form of positive statements than to note their failure to display the desired form of behavior. As an illustration, the following two statements endeavor to express the same behavior.

I am a good loser.

I have a tendency to be a poor loser.

The second statement is easier for a poor loser to answer accurately, since a negative answer to the first statement acknowledges obvious failure to reflect the desired behavior. The forced-choice method of presenting sets of statements from which respondents select the most descriptive of their behavior also embodies this "save face" approach which facilitates more valid response by circumventing the creditability aspect.

Much valuable assistance in the construction of self-report scales and inventories can be derived from consulting sample instruments cited in Chapter 15 (general behavior as well as specific to physical education) to note the type of questions involved and the relation of question type and design to the trait or characteristic concerned. Such consultation will serve to guide the development of appropriate questions.

Edwards has summarized the various informal criteria for editing statements to be used in the construction of attitude scales, as suggested by Wang, Thurstone and Chave, Likert, Bird, and Edwards and Kilpatrick, as follows:

1. Avoid statements that refer to the past rather than to the present.
2. Avoid statements that are factual or capable of being interpreted as factual.

[29] For a definitive analysis of points to consider in constructing measures of attitudes, the reader is referred to R. M. W. Travers, *Educational Measurement* (New York: The Macmillan Co., 1955), Chap. 10.

3. Avoid statements that may be interpreted in more than one way.
4. Avoid statements that are irrelevant to the psychological object under consideration.
5. Avoid statements that are likely to be endorsed by almost everyone or by almost no one.
6. Select statements that are believed to cover the entire range of the affective scale of interest.
7. Keep the language of the statements simple, clear, and direct.
8. Statements should be short, rarely exceeding 20 words.
9. Each statement should contain only one complete thought.
10. Statements containing universals, such as *all, always, none,* and *never,* often introduce ambiguity and should be avoided.
11. Such words as *only, just, merely,* and others of a similar nature should be used with care and moderation in writing statements.
12. Whenever possible, statements should be in the form of simple sentences rather than in the form of compound or complex sentences.
13. Avoid the use of words that may not be understood by those who are to be given the completed scale.
14. Avoid the use of double negatives.[30]

Inventories may be developed in either written or oral format. Generally speaking, the written or questionnaire form of the inventory will be utilized since it demands much less time to administer than the oral version. Where adequate time is available, however, the interview technique can be expected to provide more definitive results because of the personal approach.[31]

Recently, considerable need and interest has been evinced by physical education teachers in devising appropriate self-report scales to determine the attitude of students toward physical education or physical activity. Of the available methods for developing attitude scales, only the Likert method [32] of scale construction, often descriptively referred to as the method of summated ratings, can be deemed practical for teacher construction. Another type of scale, as developed by Thurstone,[33] has been utilized in the construction of some instruments for use in physical education. However, the Likert procedure is considerably less laborious and results in scales that are simple to score, yet correlate well with

[30] Allen L. Edwards, *Techniques of Attitude Scale Construction* (New York: Appleton-Century-Crofts, Inc., 1957), pp. 13–14.

[31] An applicaton of this technique is described in Carlton R. Meyers, "Determination of the Effects of Sports Activities on Personality Development," *The Educational Forum,* XXVIII, No. 4 (May, 1954), 411.

[32] R. A. Likert, "A technique for the measurement of attitudes," *Archives of Psychology,* No. 140 (1932). A definitive description of this technique is contained in: Edwards, *op. cit.,* Chap. 6.

[33] L. L. Thurstone, and E. J. Chave, *The Measurement of Attitude* (Chicago: University of Chicago Press, 1929).

Thurstone scales. Consequently, the Likert-type scale appears to be more widely used than the Thurstone variety.

Concisely stated, in constructing a Likert-type attitude scale the basic intent is to produce a set of usually 20 to 25 statements that will differentiate between high and low groups based on total scale score. To construct such a scale a comprehensive list of statements is drawn up that reflects both clearly favorable and clearly unfavorable attitudes about that which is to be measured. The initial scale, consisting of a greater number of items than desired for the final scale, is administered to a large number of examinees, who respond to each statement on a five-point scale: strongly agree (SA), agree (A), no opinion or undecided (U), disagree (D), and strongly disagree (SD). Illustrative statements for a Likert-type scale are:

SA   A   U   D   SD   1. Physical education is exciting.
SA   A   U   D   SD   2. Physical education is a waste of time.

In scoring favorable statements, such as the first example, the alternatives are assigned values of 4,3,2,1,0, from SA to SD, respectively.[34] The scoring weights are reversed for unfavorable statements, such as the second example above. Thus, a student with a highly favorable attitude toward physical education would score a total of 8 points on the above two statements, whereas the responses of a very unfavorably disposed student would sum to 0.

Selection of statements for the final scale is based upon an item analysis of the trial statements. The total summated ratings are compiled and equal-sized groups of high and low scores are selected, consisting of at least 25 subjects each. As for written tests, the upper and lower 27 percent might be used. The mean scores for each statement are determined for each group, and the statements are then arranged in rank order on the basis of the magnitude of the difference between the means of the two groups. The desired number of scale statements is then selected from this ranking, assuming that a distinct differential exists between means. Murphy and Likert[35] suggested use of this procedure upon noting that it resulted in very close agreement with the ordering obtained using the correlations between item responses and total score.

The final scale should contain an approximately equal number of favorable and unfavorable statements. Such a balance minimizes possible response sets by subjects that might be generated if only favorable or unfavorable statements were included. Reliability of the scale is

---

[34] Some authors suggest a 1–5 point scale, but the 0–4 scale is reported herein as developed by Likert from the normal deviate system of weights.

[35] G. Murphy, and R. Likert, *Public Opinion and the Individual* (New York: Harper & Row, 1937).

readily determined by the split-half method. Reliability coefficients reported for scales constructed by this method of summated ratings are typically above 0.85, even when less than 20 items comprise the scale.

Interpretation of an attitude score on a Likert-type scale cannot be made independently of the distribution of scores of some defined group. There is no evidence that the 'neutral" point on a summated rating scale will necessarily correspond to the mid-point of the possible range of scores, such as the score of 40 on a 20-item scale. However, this is of no consequence when, as for the physical education teacher, the scale is used for noting change of attitude over a period of time or analysis of a subject's attitude relative to that of others. The conversion of scale scores to T-scores affords a basis for meaningful interpretation of these attitude scores.

Specific Considerations. In following the general procedure for developing measures of concomitant learning it is essential to be cognizant of certain concerns peculiar to self-report instruments that warrant attention, as described below. In addition to these specific considerations, the teacher should review those discussed earlier under behavior rating scales as applied by observers for possible implications relating to the construction of self-report instruments.

1. *Establishing rapport.* Care must be exercised both in instructions given and in the design of questions to establish proper rapport as the basis for obtaining candid, honest responses. The validity of this self-report technique is greatly influenced by success in eliciting accurate responses. In this regard, special mention should be made of the importance of writing explicit instructions for the student to describe in what vein the questions should be answered and why it is necessary to do so. In other words, the student is encouraged to answer as he actually would respond and not as he thinks he should to reflect the desired or correct behavior. Only when this is done can the results indicate what really exists. When applicable, achieving accurate response is facilitated by assuring students that their responses will in no way affect their grades.

2. *Question specificity.* The study of attitudes is complicated by the fact that a person may reveal different attitudes when exposed to different situations. Therefore, it is esential that attitude- and behavior-searching questions be specific for the desired situation and should be interpreted in like manner.

3. *Response variations for inventories.* Questions should be designed in light of the definitiveness of response desired, based on factors discussed in the procedural description for concomitant learning. In some in-

stances a yes–no response will suffice; whereas a shading of response can be obtained through always–sometimes–never or always–frequently–sometimes–rarely–never behavior response, or the equivalent. When question content permits, the use of yes–no or a three-response pattern may be preferable to make interpretation of results somewhat easier. Sometimes the forced-choice pattern of response may be utilized, whereby the inventory item contains two or more specific statements from which the student selects the proper response. In such instances this same consideration holds regarding the suitability of response alternatives.

4. *External verification of validity.* Behavior observation affords an indication of validity for self-report devices in addition to the external validation described in the general procedure for measures of concomitant learning. A suitable record of behavior observation can be provided by the application of relevant rating scales or anecdotal record forms as discussed in Chapter 15. For example, if an individual's overt behavior reflects a lack of self-confidence in a certain physical education activity as compared to his positive answers pertaining to such situations on the inventory, obviously the response on the inventory is not representing reality. An analysis should then be made to determine whether the design of questions is to blame or the lack of integrity of the responding student.

This completes the discussion of the construction of both kinds of devices to measure concomitant learning—rating scales and self-report instruments. With it the teacher should now be familiar with the fundamental concerns entailed in constructing measures appropriate for all three types of learning—technical, associated, and concomitant—as well as the specific considerations for each type. For measures of technical learning this information may need to be supplemented by certain considerations peculiar to the particular physical performance quality in question, as contained in subsequent chapters. Thus, the teacher should be prepared to resolve in an effective and competent manner all aspects of test development tasks that may be encountered, such as that posed by the illustrative problem cited at the outset of the presentation on test construction in Chapter 4. That is, in light of the material presented and specific considerations for motor fitness performance items, the teacher can now construct suitable tests or measures of performance, knowledge and understanding, and attitude pertaining to motor and physical fitness for fifth- and sixth-grade children, as may be desired.

SELECTED REFERENCES

1. GRONLUND, NORMAN E. *Constructing Achievement Tests.* Englewood Cliffs, N. J.: Prentice-Hall, Inc., 1968.

2. *Making the Classroom Test: A Guide for Teachers* (ETS T&M Kit). Princeton: Educational Testing Service, 1973.
3. MARSHALL, J. C., and HALES, L. W. *Classroom Test Construction*. Reading, Mass.: Addison-Wesley Publishing Co., 1971.
4 MEHRENS, W. A., and LEHMANN, I. J. *Measurement and Evaluation in Education and Psychology*. New York: Holt, Rinehart nad Winston, Inc., 1973.
5. OPPENHEIM, A. N. *Questionnaire Design and Attitude Measurement*. London: Heinemann (New York: Basic Books), 1966.
6. RESEARCH COUNCIL. *Research Methods in Health, Physical Education, Recreation*, 3rd ed. Washington: AAHPER, 1973.
7. SAFRIT, MARGARET J. *Evaluation in Physical Education*. Englewood Cliffs, N. J.: Prentice-Hall, Inc., 1973.
8 SHEEHAN, THOMAS J. *An Introduction to the Evaluation of Measurement Data in Education*. Reading, Mass.: Addison-Wesley Publishing Co., 1971.
6. THORNDIKE, ROBERT L., ed. *Educational Measurement*, 2nd ed. Washington: American Council on Education, 1971.

6

Organizing and Administering the Testing Program

The desired approach to measurement, which comprises the first part of this book, would not be complete without a discussion of the planning and organization of the testing program and the administration of it. An effort has been made through the preceding chapters to develop an understanding of the place of measurement, the basic statistical concepts, and proper selection and construction of measuring instruments. Fullest realization of the potential value of measurement cannot be assured, despite this background information, unless careful attention is given to organizing and administering the testing program. While the reader should now comprehend how to select or construct an appropriate test for a given area and type of learning, a description should be made of the procedure and considerations in organizing this and other tests as part of a purposeful testing program. How can a testing program and the tests that comprise it be organized and administered in a most effective and efficient manner? The attempt to answer this question will be made by a discussion of the steps embodied in the testing program, namely:

1. Defining the problem
2. Selecting the tests for use
3. Resolving the organizational details
4. Administering the tests

5. Scoring the tests
6. Presenting the results
7. Interpreting the results

As a guide in organizing and administering tests, the teacher will find pertinent details largely included in steps 4 (administering the tests) and 5 (scoring the tests). Additional comments relevant to a particular type of test are contained under specific considerations in the chapters devoted to the different areas of measurement. Thus, as for test selection and construction, the teacher should supplement the general factors discussed in this chapter with specific considerations for the particular measurement area concerned to be fully apprised of all aspects pertaining to efficient test organization and administration. Also the teacher should pay close heed to these administrative concerns, inasmuch as many aspects have relevance for test construction—primarily details for inclusion in test directions and organizational procedure. And basic to organizing and administering tests, the teacher should remain cognizant of the factors under administrative feasibility and teaching utility as aspects of the process of appraising test value in Chapter 3.

Returning to the testing program as a whole, in order to focus clearly upon the many and varied factors involved, a description of an illustrative problem appears in order, with the hope that it will pose the incentive and challenge to facilitate a meaningful depiction of the organization and administration of a testing program.

AN ILLUSTRATIVE PROBLEM

To pose an illustrative problem, consider the teacher of boys' physical education in a junior high school who desires to establish a testing program in his teaching situation. Where does he begin? What and how much should he include? Who can help him? The crux of the problem is to establish a testing program that is effective and appropriate in light of the physical education program—its content and objectives.

To resolve this simulated problem the teacher should attack it systematically by recognizing the steps in the testing program and proceeding in accordance with them.

STEPS IN THE TESTING PROGRAM

In an effort to organize a testing program effectively and efficiently, it becomes necessary to delineate a desirable approach—a step-by-step procedure arranged in logical order. As previously mentioned, the factors involved in organizing and administering a testing program are many and varied. Thus, only through a carefully defined procedure can as-

surance be had that all factors are included and given proper consideration. A good testing program demands careful planning, beginning well
in advance, to insure desired ends. All the advantages of having appropriate tests are to little or no avail, if they cannot be administered
so as to derive their potential and intended value. Much of the criticism
leveled by school administrators against measurement in physical education stems from misuse and otherwise poor administration of physical
education tests. Thorough and thoughtful consideration of each step in
the testing program not only will eradicate this criticism but also should
serve to engender respect and support of school administrators and other
critics.

Defining the Problem

Describe accurately the job to be done. What does the problem encompass? It should be stated in a clear-cut manner. In reality the definition of the problem will constitute the purposes of the tests or the testing
program being envisaged within the framework of the particular situation. The testing program will obviously vary with the structure and
objectives of each school program. Likewise, in defining the problem,
it will be necessary to pay heed to the attitude of the community and
school administrators toward the particular tests involved and the testing
program as a whole. A clear definition of the problem will permit the
testing program to be more limited in extent and more intensive.

Definition of the problem should reflect recognition of a complete
description of the situation and the circumstances surrounding it, be it
for a particular test or for the testing program as a whole. This entails
consideration of such matters as: the students, their needs and characteristics, recognition of program objectives, what information is desired,
the facilities and equipment available, time and leadership available,
and other factors that may comprise the situation being faced.

In the illustrative problem, the teacher desires to establish a testing
program. First, a description of the situation is necessary as the basis for
determining what information should be sought. Assume that in view
of an analysis of all factors, the teacher concludes that finding a test of
motor fitness and a skill and knowledge test each season, involving either
soccer, tumbling, or tennis as appropriate, comprises the problem. The
teacher will use the information derived from the fitness test as a basis
for classifying students for class activity; providing an indication of effectiveness of the program in promoting motor fitness; and providing a
measure of student status, progress, and needs in motor fitness. Similar
information will be derived from use of the skill and knowledge tests in
soccer, tumbling, and tennis. Hence, the definition of the problem results

in recognition of certain purposes or testing areas to be served and leads quite naturally to the next step—selecting the tests for use.

Selecting the Tests for Use

In light of the knowledge of the job to be done, the tools to do the job can be selected. Certainly, only acceptable tests should warrant consideration. The basic factors and procedure governing the selection of a test or tests apply as presented in Chapter 3. It is desirable to be completely cognizant of the application and implications of the many considerations pertinent to test selection, so that this second step in testing program organization can be accomplished most effectively.

In selecting a test for use, the teacher should remain alert to consider the test value on one hand and the requirements to administer it satisfactorily on the other. The basic information disclosed in defining the problem will be of use in test selection. Particular attention should be directed to the adequacy and availability of the facilities and equipment, the teacher's preparation for the jobs planned, and the teacher's knowledge of the students to be tested. Tests that are not selected in light of these factors may be incongruous in terms of the planned testing program.

The matter of selecting tests for use in the illustrative problem consists of determining the best of the desirable tests in the quality or skill involved for this particular boys' junior high school physical education program. In the event that no test proves satisfactory in a particular area, an appropriate test should be constructed.

Selection of the tests for use should reflect realization that the student should benefit from every test in as many ways as the characteristics of the test permit. Reference here is to the concomitant values found in some tests, such as the physical activity and enjoyment provided, development of interest and incentive, and skill learning. These values are in addition to the purposes of the test and the uses to be made of the results. It should be emphasized that a test should not be used if the same information can be obtained in a more economical, yet feasible, manner.

Although matters relating to organizational details and actual administration of a test follow selection of the test itself, the ensuing discussion of these matters will suggest further things of importance for consideration in selecting tests for use.

Resolving the Organizational Details

In essence, resolving the organizational details of the testing program consists of arranging for best utilization of the tools selected. The teacher should keep in mind that the organization and administration of a testing program should strive to provide conditions that will meet test specifications to the best degree possible. Accordingly, the organization of the testing program should be such as to facilitate the efficient administration and realization of full potential value of the test. This step implies deliberative, purposeful planning regarding all organizational matters, rather than attempting to meet situations as they might arise from a basic structure or framework which represents the only prior planning.

Referring to the illustrative problem, many questions must be answered relative to the organization of the testing program as a whole as well as for the particular tests included in the program. Not only must the best testing organization be arranged for the motor fitness test but also for the tests of soccer, tumbling, and tennis skill and knowledge. A systematic approach to resolving the organizational details should include consideration of factors pertaining to such concerns as: extent of the testing program, time allotted to testing, the testing schedule, necessary testing assistance, availability of adequate facilities and equipment, and publicity.

Extent of the Testing Program.   This concern, as used herein, refers to the grade levels and number of classes and students to be included in the testing program at the outset, in addition to any plans for expansion. The prime admonition pertaining to the extent of the program is to involve only the number of students that can be handled efficiently and conveniently, and no more. By so doing a number of advantages accrue, such as:

1. Time is available for more thorough study of testing results and their implications, as well as for follow-up of students as need is indicated.
2. The efficacy of testing procedures can be determined and the desirable approach can be standardized without the confusion created by large numbers of students.
3. The teacher will be more inclined to undertake a testing program on a limited basis and, accordingly, will approach it with greater confidence.
4. The successful accomplishment of a testing program involving a limited number of students can be used to show more effectively and convincingly the purpose served by such a program than is the case with less successful, mediocre results with a greater number of students.
5. Meager but successful beginnings will engender effective programs of physical education and the development of desirable testing programs.

In light of this, it certainly behooves the teacher not to "bite off more than he can chew" in terms of the number of students involved in the testing program, but rather to limit the number within the realm of practicality. Then the results will be more indicative of reality. In the illustrative problem, the situation might suggest that the teacher include all seventh-grade boys in all classes during the first year, with a view to adding the eighth grade when the present seventh grade has moved up and adding the ninth grade the following year. The testing program would then consist of two grade levels the second year and three grade levels the third year and thereafter. Or alternatively, for various reasons, the extent of the program may be limited to the seventh grade annually.

To properly depict the extent of a testing program in total perspective it becomes necessary to go beyond the limited range of the illustrative problem and encompass the complete range of grade levels concerned, for example, K–12 or 4–12. The planning thus takes on a longitudinal nature extending well beyond the horizontal dimension of a particular grade level (for example, 7) or horizontal and vertical dimensions within a school level (for example, junior high, grades 7–9). To illustrate, it may be decided to give a physical or motor fitness test yearly from grade 4 to grade 12, a motor ability test at two-year intervals from grade 5, an attitude scale at three-year intervals from grade 4, and a body mechanics appraisal at grades 6, 9, and 12. In addition, sport skill and knowledge tests may be incorporated in conjunction with instructional units for grades 7–12, and skill and knowledge proficiency examinations may be employed in grades 9–12 as part of an exemption–elective physical education program. Obviously, this example is merely intended to be suggestive of the varied patterns of testing possible, depending upon situational needs.

Time Allotted to Testing.   Over the years a general consensus among authorities has held that as a rule of thumb the time devoted to testing should not exceed 10 per cent of the physical education program. When viewed from the fact that "the mere taking of certain kinds of examinations results in genuine learning, perhaps as much per unit of time, as any other kind of activity," [1] along with the generally conceded fact that the best practice for a skill or activity is actual participation in that activity, it becomes apparent that time devoted to testing is not spent in activity separate from learning experience, but rather is an integral part of the learning experience in itself. That is to say, careful analysis suggests that the physical education program stands to gain more from the time (up to a justifiable limit) spent in a good testing program than from any other utilization of the physical education program time.

[1] J. B. Stroud, "Experiments on Learning in School Situations," *Psychological Bulletin,* 37 (1940), 777.

The teacher should consider the proportion of time to be spent in testing just as he must determine the amount of time to be devoted to each teaching unit; the proportion of emphasis on practice of fundamentals and actual participation in the activity; and the amount of time allocated to discussion, verbal description, and instructional aids. Certainly, all the aforementioned aspects of the program are important, but their emphasis must be ascertained in light of the recognized program objectives. Testing, then, should be regarded as a teaching device as well as an integral part of teaching. Thus, while a specified percentage of the program time can serve as the maximum time to be devoted to testing, it should be realized that testing and the time spent on it should be justified on the basis of its contribution to the physical education program and not as a matter of time taken from the program itself.

While the traditional maximum of 10 per cent of program time for testing might be useful as a guide, it should be pointed out that this guideline was formulated in the early years of tests and measurement. At that time testing was largely conceived as a service function performed to a great extent on a mass or large scale basis apart from the class program itself. Both the approach to and the conception of measurement and evaluation has changed considerably since these beginnings, and measurement has come to be recognized as an on-going process entailing many aspects and affording the basis for continual evaluation of students and the physical education program. Today certain teaching–learning practices, such as teacher rating of skill during class participation and performance of selected learning tasks (for example, number of successful basketball free throws in 25 attempts), would properly be classified as measurement time in the broad connotation. In the earlier and traditional sense of testing time these practices would have been identified merely as part of teaching with no recognition of their contribution to the testing program in the broad sense. Suffice it to say, the evolvement of learning theory with reliance on feedback and knowledge of results, and other products of measurement, renders archaic the stipulation of a testing maximum in the traditional sense. Thus, the determining factor in the amount of time allotted to testing is the most purposeful use of physical education program time rather than an arbitrary maximum.

Within any limits that may be specified, only the time actually needed for the specific testing program should be allotted. This also suggests the feasibility of a gradual beginning in testing so that whatever is undertaken can be handled expeditiously yet suitably. As the testing program is expanded, more time within the desired limits can be allocated. The ubiquitous challenge is to so organize and administer the testing program as to provide for greatest utilization of the allotted time. For each test, the teacher must ask himself: "How can this test be organized and administered so as to minimize the time involved without adversely affecting its value?" Tests vary as to their requirements and characteristics; and, consequently, this necessitates specific attention to the manner in which each is administered.

Testing Schedule.   Knowing the tests to be used, the extent of the testing, and the time allotted to it, the next consideration consists of scheduling the testing to afford the best possible provision for the many important factors involved. The schedule should actually represent the best consideration of all these factors. Such questions as when the information is needed and the availability of assistance and facilities relative to this time serve as examples of concerns in making a schedule. Since testing comprises an integral phase of teaching, the same careful planning should pertain to the testing schedule as characterizes the other aspects of teaching.

The testing schedule will not only provide for the order in which different tests will be given during the school year but also for the timing of the particular tests within the established order. For instance, the order in the illustrative problem might be to have the motor fitness test administered in the spring, some time prior to the tennis skill test; while the soccer and tumbling tests would be given during the fall and winter, respectively. Obviously, the timing of the motor fitness test and tennis tests are important. They should not be scheduled so closely that any learning or test aftermaths in terms of physical discomfort from the motor fitness test may affect the results of the tennis test. Yet it may be desirable to have the motor fitness test administered as close to the end of the spring semester as possible, in order to reflect the fullest influence of the year's growth and development and serve as a basis for classification of students for physical education in the fall. A satisfactory resolution of this problem affords a challenge for scheduling.

The matter of the timing of particular tests also enters into skill and knowledge tests, when these tests are given to indicate achievement in the unit of which they are a part, for example, soccer. Likewise, when skill and knowledge tests are used for classification purposes, this timing matter is important. In programs with a great number of tests, the concern of proper scheduling becomes more difficult than in instances, such as the illustrative problem, where the program is just beginning to develop or for other reasons is comparatively meager. Also inherent in the timing factor is the question as to when the information is needed. The schedule for a test should allow for administration and availability of test results by the time these results are to be used, and at the same time not provide such a time lapse that the results may no longer be truly representative.

Annual tests are often scheduled for the spring to afford a means for appraisal of the year's progress as well as, when appropriate, to make results available for classifying students for all class participation. The motor fitness test in the illustrative problem was scheduled in the spring for these reasons. One admonition warrants recognition at this point because of its obvious implications; the concern is the annual medical examination. This health appraisal should precede the administration of any strenuous physical tests. Consequently, it is best given in the fall, thereby making it impractical if not impossible to administer the motor fitness test in situations like the illustrative problem at the outset of the fall semester as the basis for classification of students.

A final consideration that should not be overlooked in testing scheduling is the importance of long-range planning. Scheduling should not be done solely on the basis of the tests presently included in the testing program. Rather, the scheduling should reflect an awareness of the planned or anticipated expansion of the testing program. When testing is scheduled in view of long-range plans, the flexibility of the testing program is engendered, and desirable balance and coordination of the future testing program is more likely to occur.

Necessary Testing Assistance. Like the aforementioned concerns inherent in an effort to resolve the organizational details of a testing program, the matter of needed assistance warrants careful thought. The assistance needed varies with the type of test, the extent of testing, and related factors. However, the purpose of the discussion herein is to familiarize the teacher with the available resources. Necessary testing assistance is comprised of both human and material resources. Human resources are needed for a number of responsibilities, which again vary with the type of test and related factors, ranging from clerical help to duties more closely associated with supervision of the test itself. The necessary material resources consist of devices, equipment, signs, printed instructions, and the like that are not part of the test itself but serve to facilitate the test administration and its efficacy.

Turning first to human resources for help with the testing program in its different facets, they may be categorized into two groups: those available from within the school itself, and individuals from outside the particular school. The physical education staff, selected students, and other interested faculty constitute the school-source people. Physical education personnel at other schools, students from teacher education institutions, and test experts constitute valuable sources of help outside a particular school. Students from teacher education institutions may assist in the testing program either as part of their student teaching responsibility in the school to which they are assigned, or as members of a testing team assigned to one or more schools to help with phases of the testing program as part of their field experience or in conjunction with a course in physical education tests and measurement.

Resolving the matter of personnel to assist in testing does not end with determination of the number of assistants needed and their selection. It also concerns the proper orientation of these individuals to assure best results. Needless to say, the training should be specifically related to the duties involved. When at all possible, individuals assisting with actual test administration (be they student squad leaders, faculty members, or others) should actually perform the test item or events with which they will be working. An analysis of the features of good and poor performance, in light of their experience with the test item, should serve to enrich their understanding of it and enhance their value as assistants. Certainly, it is not necessary for a clerical recorder to perform the test items as above. However, each individual should have specific instructions and necessary training in the duties to be performed. If scoring of a test item is involved, the assistant should have specific training for the item concerned. This should include: explanation of written instructions prepared for assistants; instruction and practice in the various measurement tools and equipment to be used, such as stop watches; and a sample test demonstration; all of which should preferably precede the previously mentioned actual performance of the test items by the assistants. The special orientation for testing assistants should encompass at least one organizational meeting to stress the standardization of procedure as well as the individual and collective responsibilities. For the illustrative problem, the teacher can handle the skill and knowledge tests as part of the class activity, either without assistance or with help from student leaders, and may plan to conduct the motor fitness test as part of the regular class, utilizing assistance from a student teacher or substitute teacher and squad leaders. Alternatively, the motor fitness test could be administered as a large-scale endeavor using a cadre of assistants as available from the aforementioned sources.

Included as an aspect of standardizing the testing procedure should be the matter of motivating student participation. Specific, constructive suggestions for use by assistants in creating desirable student rapport for testing and encouraging student performance become imperative in an attempt not only to elicit the desired effort but, equally important, to minimize if not eliminate the variability in effectiveness of the approach to motivation by different individuals. A reasonable similarity in the interest shown, pleasure derived, and encouragement offered by the different assistants will assure comparable influence on the performance of all testees and, consequently, foster satisfactory test objectivity.

Material resources provide not only necessary but valuable assistance. This category of assistance encompasses everything from written instructions for assistants and test directions for testees, to devices for scoring events efficiently and accurately, that is, those things that are essential for effective administration of the test outside of the equipment required in the test performance. For instance, the stop watch and tape measure are required to measure performance in the 50-yard dash and standing broad jump, respectively, and thus do not represent items of concern in this regard. However, signs and markings to facilitate such measurement or the flow of testing traffic and to separate floor areas illustrate the material assistance to which reference is made. Clear and concise instructions, an appropriate display on the bulletin board to explain the test or its organization, and a chalkboard diagram of rotation procedure for various test item stations tend to clarify and speed up test administration. Another common practice to facilitate measurement and save testing time is the use of masking tape and quick-drying water-soluble paints for marking lines, targets, and the like. Additional specific examples of material assistance are discussed as part of the remaining steps in the testing procedure.

Availability of Adequate Facilities and Equipment. Closely related to the necessary testing assistance is the concern regarding the availability of adequate facilities and equipment. This concern resolves itself into two aspects: actual determination of what is available, and arranging for the best utilization of satisfactory items that are available.

Determining the adequacy of facilities and equipment presents a matter that should be considered in terms of the content of the testing program. The facilities and equipment in a given situation may be adequate for one testing program yet fail to be satisfactory for other tests. The safety and overall adequacy of the facilities and equipment should be analyzed in light of the job to be done and the tools to be employed in doing it. Basically, this matter entails the amount and condition of floor, field, and wall space, and the equipment needed as part of, or adjunctive to the test. In the illustrative problem, the adequacy of the facilities and equipment needs to be appraised in terms of the intended tests—skill, knowledge, and motor fitness.

Once the adequacy of the facilities and equipment available for testing in accordance with the testing schedule has been established, the challenge of organizing to foster best and maximum use of the facilities and equipment presents itself. Careful thought and continual appraisal, which should characterize the planning, are essential to insure that the facilities and equipment will be used in the most effective and efficient manner.

Publicity. The final concern involved in resolving the organizational details of the testing program is publicity about the testing program. Publicity, as used herein, is not intended to connote the attention-getting, "look at what we have done" approach for mere recognition and ego satisfaction. Rather, the intended connotation is to provide information about, present interpretation of, and foster understanding of the testing program that will serve to enhance the significance of the tests, testing program, and the physical education program as a whole. Prevalent opinion suggests that physical educators direct attention to engendering the development of a favorable attitude of community and educational administrators toward physical education tests and the testing program. It should be realized that the common resistive, indifferent attitude often encountered in physical education measurement does not apply to all areas of the school curriculum. The people of the community accept and recognize testing in the form of quizzes, tests, and final examinations as an integral part of various subject matter areas, such as social studies and mathematics, to use but two examples. Hence, this non-supportive attitude toward physical education testing is implicit in the prevalent misunderstanding and misconception of physical education and is not attributable to any general condemnation of testing. It logically follows that any success in fostering the development of a more desirable attitude toward physical education testing will contribute appreciably to promoting better public understanding of physical education.

In endeavoring to influence favorably public attitude toward physical education measurement, the publicity should relate the purposes to be served by a test or the testing program and the use to be made of the results. The publicity should depict how the student and the physical education program will benefit from the testing or, broadly stated, the contribution that will be made to the total educational program. Furthermore, the publicity should be deliberatively planned and definitively purposeful to accomplish desired ends and not merely left to spontaneous, impulsive thought. Situation-like demonstrations of tests at school open house and PTA meetings afford an excellent means of presenting the testing program in desired perspective for parents, administrators, and other teachers. When practical, participation by interested and able parents in selected tests as part of test demonstrations can prove very beneficial in enhancing understanding of, and favorable disposition toward the testing program.

Administering the Tests

After the organizational details have been resolved, attention is directed to matters dealing more directly with administering the tests, that is, actually doing the job for which tools have been selected and arrangements made for their best utilization. While the reader may feel that some of the matters covered are primarily concerned with testing organization, these aspects were deemed to be intricately involved in administering the testing program and best described in that context. Permeating all concern for test administration should be the desire to administer the test with dispatch and efficiency in order to make time available for other learning experiences or testing procedures. Focus should be on administration of tests as a well-organized endeavor according to prescribed directions and recognized guiding principles. As suggested earlier, in addition to this presentation the teacher should consult later chapters for specific considerations in administering and scoring that may be peculiar to tests of a particular quality, for example, cardiovascular function or body mechanics. As part of this attention to specificity in planning for test administration it is imperative that each test item be analyzed carefully to determine what is necessary for the most effective and economical administration of it.

Pre-Testing Orientation. Before the actual testing process can begin, the need for orientation of students and testing assistants should be apparent, not only to facilitate test-taking but to insure truly representative results. Certainly, the authenticity of test findings becomes quesionable when testees do not fully comprehend what is expected of them and why it is necessary, and when testers do not administer the test properly.

The orientation of testing assistants has been discussed under organizational details in the section dealing with necessary testing assistance. In the main it consists of two phases: familiarity with performance and scoring of the particular test items for which the tester will be responsible, as well as the relevant principles of test administration; and understanding of the fundamental considerations in effecting desired testing rapport and consistent motivation, in addition to specific suggestions for eliciting candid response and maximum performance, as appropriate. Preferably the testing assistants should receive their training and instruction before the orientation session for testees. Also, they should participate in the orientation for testees, when feasible, for further experience and to assist as necessary in effecting a thorough and meaningful indoctrination of students to the testing purpose and procedure.

The importance of providing for orientation of students to testing and the particular tests which they will take cannot be overemphasized. It is necessary to (1) instill a favorable mind-set or predisposition on the part of the testees to perform to the best of their ability, and (2) clearly describe the task involved so that the test represents their best possible performance and is not limited by inadequate understanding of the test. This pre-test orientation should be designed to:

1. Explain the purpose of the test or testing and the intended use for the results.
2. Describe what will be measured, why it is of value, and the importance of all-out effort.
3. Acquaint testees with the equipment, nature of the test items, and correct procedure in performing them.
4. Describe the organizational pattern and procedure to be followed from the time of reporting for the test until completion of the testing session.
5. Provide other relevant information as appropriate to effect desired testing rapport and motivation of performance.

This orientation may be undertaken either on a day prior to the test day or as part of the testing session itself. The latter is possible when the test is rather brief in terms of time commitment, so that it can be administered to a group and still leave adequate time for pre-test orientation within the time allocated to the testing session. More commonly, however, the time requirements for both the test and adequate orientation will necessitate providing the test indoctrination on a day prior to the actual test. It is essential that each test item and other aspects of the testing procedure be clearly demonstrated, supplemented as feasible with film strips, loop films, diagrams, and other visual aids. When the pre-testing session is held at a prior time, it is generally advisable to present a brief review explanation–demonstration of the test at the outset of the testing session, and as consistent with test directions. Wherever appropriate, such as in most physical performance tests, the testees should be afforded the opportunity to practice the test items. This is especially true of items with which the student may not be familiar, so the the test performance represents actual ability level rather than initial learning trials. Obviously, the teacher should be alert to schedule this pre-testing session so as to allow for several intervening days before the test in the event that some muscular discomfort may result from the practice session.

Despite careful attention to these procedural concerns in test administration, meaningful results still may not be obtained unless desirable rapport and consistent motivation characterize the testing situation. For meaningful results it becomes necessary for students to apply themselves to the task presented by the test arduously and to the best of their ability. If this is to occur, they will have to be impressed with the importance of the testing and experience a testing environment conducive to such all-out effort. The role of pre-testing orientation in setting the stage in this regard should become readily apparent.

Preliminary Considerations.   Before the students arrive on the testing scene it is important to ascertain the readiness of all facets of the test situation. Because of the magnitude of the various aspects of test administration, many of the details that constitute the requisite preliminary considerations are discussed in the ensuing sections. The concern at this point is primarily to admonish the teacher to insure that all features of the testing set-up are present, operative, and properly arranged. This encompasses both human and material resources—testing assistants, measuring instruments, equipment used in test performance, organizational aids, and scoring materials. The best contrived testing plans may be to no avail unless their implementation is thoroughly scrutinized beforehand.

Prior to the testing day the required measuring devices should be checked for accuracy, when appropriate, such as for scales, stop watches, and cable tensiometers. Also the suitability of equipment used in the tests should be carefully checked in advance, both in terms of conformity with test specifications and state of repair, so that needed repairs or replacement can be made. Just prior to the testing session a check should be made to determine that: testing assistants are prepared for their roles; equipment for the various test items is serviceable and properly arranged; required markings and directions for the different items and test routing instructions are in order; an adequate number of record forms are available; and extraneous variables fall within tolerable limits regarding their effect upon test results. These extraneous variables include light intensity, temperature, and humidity for indoor activity, in addition to wind and weather conditions for outdoor testing. The time demanded by such prior checks is well spent in relation to the inconvenience, confusion, and "test contamination" which they can obviate. In some instances the teacher may choose to administer the test initially to a small sample group (that is, 10 to 15 students) before beginning a large-scale administration. This approach is particularly useful when some doubt exists as to how the actual testing will work out.

Reporting for the Test. As the students report for the test, either as part of class activity or as a special occasion, they should be in readiness, including punctuality, and directed to stations in a continuous process to provide full utilization of all testing stations, when applicable. This suggests that in instances where more than a scheduled physical education class is taking a test, such as having students report to the gymnasium directly from a study hall, effort should be made to insure a steady, continuous flow of students.

Deliberate control of the numbers reporting for a test is desirable to assure a manageable backlog for each station rather than permitting an oversupply where inactivity will prevail and result in needless noise, confusion, general distraction, and delays. Along this vein it becomes important to consider the behavior of testees during the testing period and to plan the test administration so as to minimize situations that might contribute to behavior problems. All students reporting for the test should be kept active by using multiple stations for the same test item, as well as stations for other test items, and through provision of specific areas to practice or warm up for a particular test item. In situations such as a soccer skill test or a motor fitness test, when, because of limitations of facilities and assistance only a portion of the class can be accommodated at one time, a volleyball game or similar organized activity can be used to keep active those who are awaiting or have finished the test. The involvement of students in a test may vary. In some tests all students will be tested simultaneously, while for other tests the group will be divided into halves so that two consecutive administrations will take care of the class. Still other tests will require using the squad system with the availability of either more than one testing station or some other activity for rotation purposes, be it a test practice area, game play, or both. And for some tests students may be processed individually or in pairs.

As students report to the testing scene, it is prudent to arrange them in a fashion conducive to expeditious organization for the intended testing pattern. For example, the students can sit in a double line on the floor as they arrive. After preliminary explanation in this arrangement, the double line can be divided into squads of paired testees or processed in another manner more suitable for the planned testing pattern. The practice of dividing students into pairs for physical performance testing is a noteworthy organizational scheme which many teachers find advantageous. In effect this provides a testing assistant for each testee. While one student is performing a test, the partner assists as required, in manually supporting the performer (for example, for sit-ups) or controlling performance infractions (for example, any swinging in pull-ups), and in scoring and recording test results. Test-scoring may take a number of forms, namely: counting the number of correct executions of a task; sighting zones for the distance run over a set time; noting elapsed time as announced for a distance run; and spotting contact points in target and distance throws.

Administering a test entails selection of the most effective organizational scheme for the particular test consistent with test directions and, accordingly, should be based upon careful analysis of the factors affecting the organization as previously discussed. A definite order in which to take the tests should be established, if not already specified by directions or set for prior administration, to indicate the organizational relationship of the testing stations. This will not only serve to systematize the administration of the test but also will insure that the results are obtained under comparable circumstances, eliminating variability attributable to the order in which test items are performed. When not prescribed by the test directions, the rotational sequence of testing stations (referring to a different station for each test item, unless otherwise stated) should be set up in accordance with recognized guidelines to the extent that they are applicable and plausible. Such considerations include proceeding in the overall context from the simple to the complex and from the relatively less strenuous to the most demanding. The prime concern in the latter is to conclude with the most demanding item (for example, an endurance item such as the treadmill exercise on the New York State test, or the 12-minute run) rather than have other items following it. Also, when two test items involve the same muscle groups or body regions, it would appear imprudent to arrange them consecutively. In such cases the order should be arranged to permit a desirable time lapse between events by having at least one item intervening, even a less strenuous item. In matters relating to the timing of events it is advisable to have test instructions specify the minimum recovery period to follow the most strenuous items. The consideration possessing the greatest import for test administration in the organizational sense is for the teacher, if free to stipulate order, to begin when possible with mass or large group items and funnel down to items for which a progressively decreasing number of multiple stations can be provided, ending with any dual or individual station items that are to be included. This approach minimizes delays and overall represents the most expedient arrangement, but obviously it should not be followed if it would result in a serious violation of the aforementioned considerations in test order that would affect test integrity.

This ordering consideration has implied a test organizational pattern whereby all students upon reporting proceed from station one through the numerical order to the last item. In circumstances wherein the items appear to lend themselves to arrangement without any discernible ordering effect, as with certain motor ability and motor fitness tests, and mass testing is desired, a second pattern may be utilized. For this, students upon reporting are divided into approximately equal-sized groups with one group assigned initially to each testing station. Rotation proceeds numerically upward and, for all but the group starting at station one, from the last number back to the first and so on until all items have been completed. In considering the two patterns, assuming applicability of the second, preference should be given to the identical pattern for all testees, inasmuch as the second pattern assumes negligible ordering effect and in reality renders comparative interpretation of test scores somewhat improper unless there is evidence from an analytical study that indeed no effect exists.

Testing Stations. Once the order of tests is settled, attention centers on the setup of equipment, upon which the efficiency of test administration depends. The arrangement of equipment and testing stations to result in a relatively smooth flow of traffic through a feasible and plausible sequential order presents an enticing challenge to the test administrator. The arrangement is largely a function of the space needs of the various test items in relation to the space available. The teacher should analyze carefully the actual dimensions required for each test item, and include sufficient space around each station to assure that testees do not feel restricted. This also involves space provision for traffic routing to and from each station. The teacher should give careful thought to the best way of organizing the available space to accommodate the different test items in terms of their particular space needs within the prescribed or desired sequential order of testing. As is readily discernible, this responsibility necessitates putting down on paper a complete layout and details for the testing. In the diagrams for test layout, all dimensions for various test items should be carefully followed.

To be in proper perspective, the time required for a given number of testees to complete each item should be made approximately the same by providing identical multiple stations for items that prove to be more time-consuming. For example, Fig. 6–1 represents a flow chart for the items of the AAHPER fitness test to be given during one class period in the illustrative problem. The sit-ups prove to be the most time-consuming item, so four stations are provided. According to the chart, two stations for pull-ups should handle a group of junior high school boys in the same time as the four stations for sit-ups. The same is true of the two standing broad jump stations, and the provision of one station for the shuttle-run, where two boys can perform simultaneously, is also geared to handle a like number of boys in a comparable amount of time.

To illustrate the principle of proceeding from a mass testing station to multiple stations, assume that no order is specified for the four items included in Fig. 6–1. It is readily apparent that the major limiting factor in the most expeditious and efficient administration of these items is the placement of the sit-ups second rather than first, inasmuch as this item lends itself to mass administration. Accordingly, applying the principle of arranging items in reverse order of the time required for each station the preferential arrangement becomes: sit-ups, standing broad jump, pull-ups, and shuttle run. The testing would begin with the sit-up test being given in two sections, each scoring for the other. The standing broad jump was placed second for two reasons: the provision of an additional one or two stations should pose no problem in order to expedite the testing; and it provides a break between two comparatively strenuous exer-

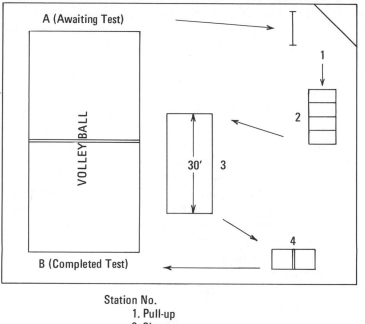

Station No.
1. Pull-up
2. Sit-up
3. Shuttle-run
4. Standing broad jump

Fig. 6–1. Flow chart for first of two periods of the AAHPER fitness test.

cises. The last two items would both accommodate two testees at a time, with the shuttle run being the slowest test item in the organizational scheme.

When the same time is required at a single station for each test, rotation is facilitated without the provision for additional stations. Occasionally, multiple stations might be desirable for one or more test items but cannot be provided, perhaps for reasons of equipment shortage, lack of testing assistance, or the like. Then it becomes necessary to have individuals move on from one station to another as soon as they finish a test, taking their individual record with them. When comparable time is needed at each station, the testees can rotate as a group from one station to another with a group score sheet, or move on individually if desired.

Should the facilities, that is, available space, necessitate a change in the testing area or dimensions for a given test item, any alterations should be kept the same for all comparable administration of the same test. Along this line it should be remembered that, where space does not permit provision of actual area as specified in the test instructions, or where there is any other test modification, the test results cannot be compared to published norms. Basic to planning the arrangement of equipment for a test is the admonition not to schedule more tests than can be conveniently and effectively administered for a given class or testing period. Nothing disrupts purposeful administration of tests more than including too few or too many items in the testing period.

The end result of deliberations as to best utilization of space should be a chart showing the relative arrangement of testing stations and the flow of traffic from one station to the next. Reference has already been made to the flow chart, Fig. 6–1, for the first period of administering the motor fitness test in the illustrative problem. Inasmuch as the teacher desires to administer this test in a sequential order, there will be some students inactive prior to their turn at station No. 1, and students beginning the test first would finish ahead of the others. The volleyball game provides an activity station for students awaiting, or having completed the tests. Presumably, the teacher has trained student leaders with each of the testing groups or squads and assigns himself to station No. 3 with a split-hand stop watch to test two students at a time on the shuttle-run.

When the flow chart is established, a trial run is desirable to check its operation and the adequacy of time provisions, while at the same time furnishing an opportunity to test the readiness of the equipment and facilities for the test. Once the chart becomes accepted, a diagram should be prepared for display; and provisions should be made to mark clearly each testing station with appropriate titles, numbers, or letters in addition to indicating the traffic route from one station to the next.

Directions. Closely associated with the flow chart and its intended purposes is the matter of appropriate directions for the overall administration of the test, including the traffic flow and the previously mentioned instructions for assistants and also the matter of proper instructions concerning the actual test performance. The emphasis of all directions involving the testees should reflect the desire to secure the wholehearted cooperation and interest of the testees. In essence these directions constitute the standardized content that affords the basis for pre-testing orientation. As such, the test instructions should explain the purpose of the test in order to make it appealing and meaningful to the students, so that the development of student interest in the test will be fostered. Student interest in the test becomes imperative if the test is to possess value, since value depends upon the trustee doing his best; that is, effort exerted becomes a function of interest. The desired spirit of the test can be enhanced through carefully and purposefully designed directions leading to favorable student attitudes toward the test and testing. By so doing, the crux of much teacher objection to testing is obviated, namely adverse student attitudes.

It may be argued that a discussion of the preparation of test directions should be included under the earlier attention to directions as part of test selection and also test construction. Actually, directions to a large extent stipulate the administrative procedure, and the teacher merely conforms, if the test is to be applied as is. Notwithstanding, the teacher needs to understand what constitutes good test directions. Consequently, the specific attention accorded to administration herein seemingly affords the most logical point for delineation of the fundamental concerns in test directions.

Some guiding principles that should govern the preparation of suitable instructions for a test have been succinctly and vividly depicted by McCall, as:

1. Test instructions should be as brief as is consistent with an adequate understanding of what is to be done.
2. Test instructions should employ a demonstration and preliminary test.
3. Test instructions should be adapted to and uniform for all who are to be tested.
4. The order of test instructions should be the order of doing.
5. Test instructions should be broken into section units.
6. Test instructions should equalize interest.
7. Test instructions to pupils should be accompanied by instruction to examiners.[2]

These principles are equally applicable to instructions for physical performance or written tests. Implicit in the instructions should be the recognition that in the best interest of time, effort, and clarity necessary instructions and demonstrations should be given to the entire group at the beginning of the testing period. To epitomize some of the salient points embodied in these principles, it should be stressed that the instructions be as brief as possible without sacrificing the adequacy deemed necessary and be always consistent with the subsequent use of the results.

"A picture is worth a thousand words" effectively sums up the importance of affording a demonstration and preliminary test practice when appropriate. For physical performance tests, demonstration and practice vivifies the interpretation of test technique and virtually eliminates the possibility of misconstruing a description of the action. The provision of different instructions as needed to be appropriate for different levels of age and ability of students is desirable, so that all testees will fully comprehend the test and also feel that the test is geared to their level. Understanding the test is also furthered by sequential arrangement of in-

2 William A. McCall, *Measurement* (New York: The Macmillan Co., 1939), pp. 80–89.

structions as the items are to be done and by arranging the instructions to pertain to meaningful action units or sequence, that is, a seemingly natural division or part. The point is that the testee must fully realize how to proceed in executing the various parts of a test or action and in what order. Adherence to the aforementioned principles will assure the provision of instructions that will nurture and enhance the value of the test and its results.

The utilization of audio-visual materials in conjunction with test directions enhances effectiveness and saves valuable time in test administration. In addition to use of visual media—slides, loop films, diagrams, etc.—to supplement or substitute for demonstration, the practicality and advisability of giving verbal instruction by means of tape recording warrants special mention. Not only does this technique afford standardization of instructions for the test as a whole, but also for the different test items. For example, the administration of the Harvard Step Test is greatly facilitated by a tape recording of all directions and preparatory practice, including the pulse counting routine, followed by the stepping cadence for the required period and complete instructions and timed intervals for pulse counting and recording. Such a procedure frees the teacher and testing assistants to supervise the testing more directly and eliminates the need for continual repetition of a tedious task with subsequent groups, one wherein considerable chance for error exists.

Timing of Events. Throughout this book, stress is placed upon the importance of providing specified conditions for testing, so as to facilitate any desired comparison of results. The desirability of maintaining the proper order of events in this light has already been indicated. It is also important to maintain the intended or recommended timing of items to insure that all tests reflect the influence of comparable conditions. The timing of items should be so arranged that the interval lapse between the items remains reasonably the same and never is less than the minimum time recommended in the directions or deemed necessary for satisfactory recovery from strenuous events. In many instances this matter of timing becomes an important variable and, hence, should not be overlooked. Some published tests invite the teacher to administer the items however it may be desired as to timing, that is, all at one session or spread over two or more sessions. Preferably the teacher should establish a definite timing pattern between events and adhere to it to facilitate assured comparability of scores derived from present and subsequent administrations. The element of safety is also involved in the timing of events. That is, the timing of items should be so arranged as not to present a risk to safe participation, such as when inadequate provision is made for recovery from a physically demanding event.

Safety Aspects. Consideration of safety in administering tests extends well beyond that inherent in the timing of events. In testing, as in teaching, the teacher must be alert to safety hazards and practices inimical to the well-being of students. Safety necessitates careful consideration, particularly when there are a number of stations involved. Then the concern is not only for the test participants at a given station but also for those in transit from one station to another. Test administrators must be alert to insure that the equipment, assistants, and testees at all times represent the desired characteristics regarding safety. Defective equipment may not only present safety hazards but also may adversely influence test results; thus further illustrating the interrelatedness of the many considerations implicit in test administration.

Other safety concerns center around the testee's preparedness for the test itself. Medical clearance should preferably be a prerequisite for student participation in a physical performance testing program, and for strenuous tests and endurance items it becomes imperative. The regular school medical examination, sometimes augmented by special check-ups, constitutes the usual basis for medical approval of participation. Another concern in this category is warm-up. For some test items a warm-up period is advocated in addition to the pre-test practice in the test itself to prevent injury or engender maximum performance. The general controversy surrounding the value of warm-up as a prerequisite for physical performance applies to the testing context. And similar to the general interpretation, the teacher may wish to justify warm-up activity primarily in terms of the psychological benefits that may accrue for the testing situation. A final concern regarding preparedness for testing is provision that testees have adequate background and experience for tests of muscular strength and endurance to minimize possible debilitating effects. A frequently observed example has been the administration of sit-up tests to students whose activity background has included no attention to the abdominal muscle group or experience with the sit-up test. The resulting discomfort and potential harm can be readily perceived.

A final category of safety aspects focuses on avoidance of physical tasks for which evidence suggests possible detrimental effects attributable to the inherent nature of the task. Experience has shown that some physical education teachers fail to analyze testing and exercise practices critically in light of a fundamental comprehension of kinesiology and exercise physiology. Consequently, test items entailing practices that are known or suspected to be potentially injurious in nature are included in testing programs. Two exercises, whose use is highly questionable and should be contraindicated or at least restricted as test items, serve to illustrate this concern, namely, straight leg raise and hold while supine, and forcible deep squats as in squat jumps. The former has in the past seen considerable use as Test No. 3 of the Kraus–Weber Tests. Yet astute kinesiological analysis indicates that straight leg raising should be avoided until the abdominal muscle group possesses sufficient strength to stabilize the pelvis and so prevent the forced exaggeration of the lumbar curve with its undesirable potential consequences. Dr. Kraus devised this item as a screening measure and specifically admonished users to avoid indiscriminate use of it or repetition of the practice as an exercise for those deficient in abdominal strength. Notwithstanding this cautionary note, some teachers, apparently oblivious to the implications of kinesiological analysis, have persisted in having students who lack the requisite abdominal strength practice this task. Similar circumstances surround the use of a forcible deep squat test item or exercise (against time or for maximum repetitions). Concerted study has been directed to the effect upon knee-joint stability of full squats with heavy resistance or forcible jumping, leading to authoritative recommendations that such exercise be modified to avoid full or near-full knee flexion.[3] Accordingly, the continued use of the squat jump and the squat thrust (at least with deep squating) as test items warrants serious questioning in light of available evidence and until specific study resolves the likelihood of injurious effects.

Knowledge Tests. A discussion of the many considerations in administering a test would be incomplete without recognition of some of the salient factors involved in and peculiar to administering knowledge tests. Perhaps the most noteworthy difference between a test of physical performance and a knowledge test is that the latter is largely a mental activity and, as such, necessitates attention to factors in administering the test that will insure the existence of optimum conditions for concentration. Comfort and quiet should characterize the testing situation. Inherent in comfort are such factors as adequate ventilation and illumination, appropriate seating and seating arrangement, and freedom from needless distractions.

Administering knowledge tests in gymnasiums or activity rooms presents many problems. Inasmuch as in many schools there are no classroom facilities available for physical education classes, this necessitates conducting written tests in the gymnasium. The problem for a comfortable writing surface can be resolved by providing students with a 12- by 18-inch piece of ⅛-inch-thick tempered hardboard, that will fit comfortably on their laps. Students can be grouped centrally in the bleachers, or on the floor if necessary, with a reasonable distance between them. Students should be given all necessary test materials and test directions before beginning the test. This practice eliminates the distrac-

[3] Karl K. Klein, *The Knees: Growth, Development and Activity Influences* (Greeley: All American Productions and Publications, 1967), p. 64.

tions that result when the instructor gives further explanation regarding the test or answers specific questions during the test. Should the instructor feel such interruptions are necessary, he should group his comments together to eliminate repeated disturbance and also make a note to revise or recommend revision of the test or test directions in an endeavor to eliminate recurrence of such a situation. A test that requires a number of comments to clarify questions or directions obviously reflects poor construction.

In beginning the test, it is suggested that the papers be distributed and placed face down after all the students have been seated. If the papers are left face down until the teacher requests they be turned over, there is less tendency for students to read ahead and perhaps miss part of the explanation by the teacher, resulting in misinterpretation or lack of understanding by the student.

A disturbing practice prevails when students are permitted to leave their seats as soon as they finish the written test. The best interests of all are generally served by requesting everyone to remain seated until all are finished. When the range of time between those completing the test first and last becomes rather great, the teacher might ask all students who have finished at a certain time to leave quietly. This procedure might be repeated after another time lapse, if necessary. In instances where early dismissal from a test is permitted, provisions should be made to insure that such students leave the test room immediately. Occasionally early test finishers are allowed to shoot baskets or the like while their classmates finish a test. The distraction presented by such a practice is evident.

When a test sheet or booklet is used in conjunction with an answer sheet, the test forms should be numbered consecutively, and each student should place the test form number on his answer sheet. This will afford a check to insure that all forms are returned; and, if they are not, it will show whose form is missing.

The use of answer sheets for written tests in physical education should be encouraged. Although answer sheets make for an extra piece of paper to hand out and collect when the test is given, the advantages outweigh this inconvenience. With answer sheets considerable saving is made on the amount of paper, since the test forms may be used repeatedly. For instance, assume that five classes of 40 seventh-grade boys were to be given a soccer knowledge test consisting of four pages. Without an answer sheet, 200 copies of the four-page form would be required. With an answer sheet, the teacher would need 40 test forms and 200 answer sheets—360 sheets of paper as compared to 800 sheets. In the event this test is used with the seventh grade next year, three sheets of paper are saved on each student. It should be realized that the paper referred to above also required secretarial services and duplicating equipment and materials to produce the test copies for use, incurring additional expense.

Answer sheets save student time once the student becomes familiar with the sheet and its use. A further advantage of answer sheets lies in the fact that they can be scored more quickly, accurately, and conveniently than the conventional question-answer form. With a little thought the teacher can design an answer sheet that might be used with a variety of selection and supply test items and, consequently, eliminate the need for making a special answer sheet for each test. Figure 6–2 serves as an example of such an answer sheet. In using this sheet the test form or booklet is numbered accordingly by appropriate grouping of different test item types. Conceivably the teacher might wish to design two answer sheets—one to accommodate most selection type test items and the second for supply and the remaining selection type items.

One admonition deserves mention regarding the use of answer sheets, particularly in grades 3 to 6, where evidence exists that test reliability tends to decrease due to errors in recording the intended response on a separate sheet rather than as part of the test item itself. The importance of taking extreme care to put the desired response in the proper place for each item should be stressed to the testees.

Regardless of whether an answer sheet or the conventional test form is employed, the teacher should construct a scoring key when appropriate. The conventional test form can be rendered suitable for a scoring key by arranging blanks or spaces for answers on the left-hand side of the page. A scoring key can be constructed in the following manner.

1. Place a sample answer sheet or conventional test form over a piece of heavy paper (such as a manila filing folder) with a piece of carbon paper between the two.
2. Encircle the numbers of selected questions that will serve to position the key on the answer sheet or test form.
3. Encircle the correct response for alternative-response or multiple-choice items (or other selection items for which this format is applicable), and draw a line to indicate size of blank on which fill-in answers will be noted.
4. Remove the heavy paper key and on it punch out the circled responses and cut out the blank lines.
5. Alongside the blanks, cut out to accommodate fill-in (supply) answers; the correct answer can be noted.
6. In the case of conventional test form, this process must be repeated on the same or different scoring keys for each page of the test form.

To use the scoring key, it is first positioned on the answer sheet or test form by means of the selected question cutouts. Then a red mark

Score_____   Test No._____

Examples: Name_____

                1 2 3 4 5   Course_____

True–False   ( ) (X) ( ) ( ) ( ) Section_____

Multiple–choice ( ) ( ) ( ) (X) ( ) Date_____

Matching   b

Fill–in (other)   Shuttlecock

    1 2 3 4 5   1 2 3 4 5

1. ( ) ( ) ( ) ( ) ( ) 51. ( ) ( ) ( ) ( ) ( ) 101. _____
2. ( ) ( ) ( ) ( ) ( ) 52. ( ) ( ) ( ) ( ) ( ) 102. _____
3. ( ) ( ) ( ) ( ) ( ) 53. ( ) ( ) ( ) ( ) ( ) 103. _____
4. ( ) ( ) ( ) ( ) ( ) 54. ( ) ( ) ( ) ( ) ( ) 104. _____
5. ( ) ( ) ( ) ( ) ( ) 55. ( ) ( ) ( ) ( ) ( ) 105. _____
6. ( ) ( ) ( ) ( ) ( ) 56. ( ) ( ) ( ) ( ) ( ) 106. _____
7. ( ) ( ) ( ) ( ) ( ) 57. ( ) ( ) ( ) ( ) ( ) 107. _____
8. ( ) ( ) ( ) ( ) ( ) 58. ( ) ( ) ( ) ( ) ( ) 108. _____
9. ( ) ( ) ( ) ( ) ( ) 59. ( ) ( ) ( ) ( ) ( ) 109. _____
10. ( ) ( ) ( ) ( ) ( ) 60. ( ) ( ) ( ) ( ) ( ) 110. _____
11. ( ) ( ) ( ) ( ) ( ) 61. ( ) ( ) ( ) ( ) ( ) 111. _____
12. ( ) ( ) ( ) ( ) ( ) 62. ( ) ( ) ( ) ( ) ( ) 112. _____
13. ( ) ( ) ( ) ( ) ( ) 63. ( ) ( ) ( ) ( ) ( ) 113. _____
14. ( ) ( ) ( ) ( ) ( ) 64. ( ) ( ) ( ) ( ) ( ) 114. _____
15. ( ) ( ) ( ) ( ) ( ) 65. ( ) ( ) ( ) ( ) ( ) 115. _____
16. ( ) ( ) ( ) ( ) ( ) 66. ( ) ( ) ( ) ( ) ( ) 116. _____
17. ( ) ( ) ( ) ( ) ( ) 67. ( ) ( ) ( ) ( ) ( ) 117. _____
18. ( ) ( ) ( ) ( ) ( ) 68. ( ) ( ) ( ) ( ) ( ) 118. _____
19. ( ) ( ) ( ) ( ) ( ) 69. ( ) ( ) ( ) ( ) ( ) 119. _____
20. ( ) ( ) ( ) ( ) ( ) 70. ( ) ( ) ( ) ( ) ( ) 120. _____
21. ( ) ( ) ( ) ( ) ( ) 71. ( ) ( ) ( ) ( ) ( ) 121. _____
22. ( ) ( ) ( ) ( ) ( ) 72. ( ) ( ) ( ) ( ) ( ) 122. _____
23. ( ) ( ) ( ) ( ) ( ) 73. ( ) ( ) ( ) ( ) ( ) 123. _____
24. ( ) ( ) ( ) ( ) ( ) 74. ( ) ( ) ( ) ( ) ( ) 124. _____
25. ( ) ( ) ( ) ( ) ( ) 75. ( ) ( ) ( ) ( ) ( ) 125. _____
26. ( ) ( ) ( ) ( ) ( ) 76. _____   126. _____
27. ( ) ( ) ( ) ( ) ( ) 77. _____   127. _____
28. ( ) ( ) ( ) ( ) ( ) 78. _____   128. _____
29. ( ) ( ) ( ) ( ) ( ) 79. _____   129. _____
30. ( ) ( ) ( ) ( ) ( ) 80. _____   130. _____
31. ( ) ( ) ( ) ( ) ( ) 81. _____   131. _____
32. ( ) ( ) ( ) ( ) ( ) 82. _____   132. _____
33. ( ) ( ) ( ) ( ) ( ) 83. _____   133. _____
34. ( ) ( ) ( ) ( ) ( ) 84. _____   134. _____
35. ( ) ( ) ( ) ( ) ( ) 85. _____   135. _____
36. ( ) ( ) ( ) ( ) ( ) 86. _____   136. _____
37. ( ) ( ) ( ) ( ) ( ) 87. _____   137. _____
38. ( ) ( ) ( ) ( ) ( ) 88. _____   138. _____
39. ( ) ( ) ( ) ( ) ( ) 89. _____   139. _____
40. ( ) ( ) ( ) ( ) ( ) 90 _____   140. _____
41. ( ) ( ) ( ) ( ) ( ) 91. _____   141. _____
42. ( ) ( ) ( ) ( ) ( ) 92. _____   142. _____
43. ( ) ( ) ( ) ( ) ( ) 93. _____   143. _____
44. ( ) ( ) ( ) ( ) ( ) 94. _____   144. _____
45. ( ) ( ) ( ) ( ) ( ) 95. _____   145. _____
46. ( ) ( ) ( ) ( ) ( ) 96. _____   146. _____
47. ( ) ( ) ( ) ( ) ( ) 97. _____   147. _____
48. ( ) ( ) ( ) ( ) ( ) 98. _____   148. _____
49. ( ) ( ) ( ) ( ) ( ) 99. _____   149. _____
50. ( ) ( ) ( ) ( ) ( ) 100. _____   150. _____

Fig. 6–2. Master answer sheet for written tests.

(or other suitable color) is placed in every space not containing a mark or, in the case of fill-ins, not containing the answer noted on the answer sheet. The teacher should then examine the answer sheet or test form as the score is totaled to note any discrepancies, such as the checking of more than one alternative in an alternative-response question. An enterprising teacher might well discover another way to construct a scoring key that better meets the needs of a particular situation.

Rating Scales and Self-Report Instruments. Realization of the potential scientific authenticity and overall value of rating scales and self-report instruments is contingent upon their being administered in a manner and setting conducive to eliciting uninhibited response from testees. Hence, the need for brief attention to the particular concerns characterizing administration of them becomes evident.

Self-report instruments—be they attitude scales, personality inventories, or sociometric tests—are essentially written tests and, as such, the administrative considerations described for knowledge tests are applicable. The matter of testing rapport, while an important aspect in all testing, takes on special significance because of the peculiar nature of the qualities involved and the vital need for candid, honest response, despite the supposed "right- or wrong-ness" of it in the social context. The test administrator should become familiar with the discussion of effecting rapport and related concerns in ratings and self-reports as presented in Chapter 5 in the context of construction of these instruments. Succinctly stated, basic to and beyond the conditions stipulated in the directions for each instrument, the teacher should insure that the testing atmosphere reflects the requisite seriousness of purpose in the testing in order to derive important information for use in individual guidance, determining teaching and program effectiveness, and related purposes. The students should understand that the administration of self-report scales and inventories is clearly divorced from the usual knowledge test that is graded. In the actual administration of the instrument the students should be sufficiently well spaced so that they can feel certain that their response will not be seen by any other person. Further, they will need to be assured or, more properly, convinced that their response will remain confidential. Also, in sociometric tests students need assurance that no one will be informed of his own or anyone else's rating.

Conditions surrounding the administration of rating scales are basically identical, whether behavior or physical performance is being rated. Relevant concerns are discussed particularly in Chapter 4 and supplemented by Chapter 5, pertaining to the construction of scales for rating performance and behavior, respectively. These include adequate planning for rating, factors affecting rating, orientation and use of several raters, the importance of rater warm-up, and common errors in rating. In administering the application of a rating scale the teacher should pay particular heed to insure:

1. Appropriate orientation and pre-rating indoctrination to the rating setting and students (that is, "warm-up") for raters.
2. Adequate time to render a rating at the time of observation.
3. Adherence to the specified rating procedure.
4. Plausible equalization of ability when rating requires competitive and/or cooperative performance.
5. Practical scheme to facilitate identification of students by raters, as needed.
6. Uninhibited observation by raters.

Relative to selecting raters the teacher should recognize that, given a satisfactory scale and setting for rating, the key factor in the application of a rating scale is that each rater must be *both willing and able* to give an "unbiased" judgment.

Check List for Administering Tests.   Both the many different factors to be considered in administering a test and the importance of each of them necessitate a procedural guide.   The use of such a guide, as exemplified by the following check list, permits the teacher to proceed with test administration with reasonable dispatch, feeling assured that all necessary considerations will be covered and in preferential order.

1. Prepare a definitive organizational plan for the test with a flow chart, required signs and station directions, and test record forms.
2. Provide, as necessary, adequate pre-test orientation for testers and testing assistants at a time prior to the actual test session.
3. Prior to arrival of testees check to verify proper arrangement and satisfactory condition of facilities and equipment according to plan.
4. Organize the testees as planned when they report.
5. Provide demonstration and explanation in accordance with test directions along with practice trials and warm-up activity, when permitted.
6. Administer the test in compliance with its directions, giving keen attention to test rapport and consistent motivation, the safety element, and control of testing conditions to avoid measurement errors.
7. Be alert to anticipate and resolve problems that might arise during the testing and note suggestions for improving the test administration.
8. Insure that test scores are recorded promptly, neatly, and accurately and submitted upon completion of the testing.

Scoring the Tests

After the test is administered, the next step in the testing program logically follows, that of scoring the test—seeing how well it was done. A discussion of scoring actually encompasses two aspects: how it is arrived at—determining the score for a particular item, including ways and devices to facilitate this scoring; and how it is recorded—providing for a record of the score.

While the matter of adequate measuring and recording devices should be provided for when organizational details are resolved and the procedural considerations are included with the administrative aspects, specific comment was withheld for this discussion of scoring. It should be understood that, as for any phase of the test, the scoring procedure and devices should be stiipulated in the directions for administering the test. The targets, lines, and other scoring aids must be accurate and identical with that prescribed for the test and used in prior and future tests. Needless to say, the comparability, and consequently a lion's share of the value, of a test lies in the assurance that the scoring devices and procedure are the same.

As an illustration, assume that a softball throw for accuracy is one of the items on a motor fitness test and that the teacher draws the concentric circle target on the wall every time before the test is given. By exercising reasonable care with a string and a piece of chalk, the teacher should be able to approximate very closely the same target as prescribed by directions. However, without deliberate effort, the present target might vary appreciably from the prescribed dimensions and consequently affect the scoring as compared to other targets. The most reliable target is provided by painting the circles on a gymnasium wall or a movable object such as plywood, hardboard panel, canvas, or lightweight mat, In many instances the later types prove most practical through preserving the beauty of the facilities and affording flexibility in using the target in different locations. However, for many targets, such as a field for softball throw for distance, attention to care in lining the scoring areas is the only solution. Lightweight canvas or plastic can be used for floor targets in badminton and volleyball and similar activities where scoring zones are desired to cover a limited area. Painting starting lines and measuring lines at 1-inch intervals on mat covers is common practice for use with the standing long jump.

The concentric circle target affords a good example to show different ways to facilitate scoring. The various score value areas might be painted different colors, and the score value can be placed in each space. Taking the cue from the use of a metal tell-tale in squash rackets, tin or another suitable may be used on alternate target circles to afford a reliable means of discerning between close shots by complementing visual perception with an audible cue.

Lines and other necessary markings must often be placed on courts or playing areas. Lime dispensed by a field line marker meets the needs for turf or ground areas. On floors and other indoor surfaces, masking tape or quick-dry washable paints warrant use to line and mark scoring areas. It is usually good practice to experiment with a sample area by applying a small amount of masking tape or washable paint to the surface in question, and then removing it shortly to ascertain whether the finish is harmed in any way.

On the field two different marking schemes are used. For distance events where limited control is a factor, such as football or softball throw for distance, parallel lines are used. Often the testing field is lined off with sufficient width to permit two testing stations. Concentric markings, usually arcs, are utilized for distance events in which control or accuracy is not a factor, such as the discus or shot-put. The spacing between markings, whether parallel or concentric, depends upon the distance and range of performance. In the shot-put the distance and range of performance are comparatively small, so the lines might be at 1-foot intervals, covering the range from just under to just over the expected poorest and best performances. A 5-foot interval would be suitable for the other distance events mentioned above, either for concentric or parallel markings.

To facilitate measurement to the nearest specified unit between field markings (and indoor lines as applicable) a specially marked measuring rod proves advantageous. To illustrate, for measurement to the nearest foot with 5-foot field markings a 5-foot rod would be marked at foot and half-foot intervals. When the number of testees is relatively small, considerable time can be saved by marking the field at large intervals, such as 5 or 10 yards, and using a tape to measure the intervening distance; or at 5-foot intervals in instances where 1-foot lines would ordinarily be preferred and using a 5-foot scoring rod. The teacher should be cautious in the use of such supplementary measuring aids to insure that they are aligned in the desired direction to give the actual distance. In instances when tape measurement is utilized it is expeditious to mark the trials for a number of testees with indicators (for example, tongue depressors) and thus read a number of distances at one placement of the tape.

The scoring of items involving elapsed time poses a challenge to efficient administration without sacrificing test integrity, particularly in reference to the minimal accuracy that can be tolerated. While individual timing for speed events is preferable, sheer numbers of students may render it impractical. If so, two or more individuals can be tested with a standard stop watch in one of two ways: *set distance* with the timer calling out time by seconds; or *set time* utilizing zone markings. In the first instance each runner or swimmer has a judge (or partner) at the finish line who records the time to the nearest second as announced when the testee reaches the finish line. The use of a large digital timing clock suitably located in a swimming pool affords an example of a feasible alternative to announcing times. When zone markings are used, each testee has a judge who determines and records what zone he was in at the elapsed time as announced by the timer. The results in this instance can be expressed as so many feet or yards covered in the allotted time or adjusted to indicate time for a set distance. For example, to administer the 50-yard dash in this manner the teacher would have the proper zone noted at the expiration of 6 seconds. The score for each zone would be the distance covered or expressed as converted time for 50 yards based on distance traversed in 6 seconds. The track or swimming pool must be appropriately marked to indicate the different zones, either on the side or, for running, on the track itself. Zone spacing of one yard for sprint events and two yards for distance is generally deemed most feasible. In practice the set time method appears more suited for sprint events, wherein announcing time lacks necessary accuracy and the number of zone markings is restricted to a relatively small area. The set distance is more amenable to events of considerable distance where time to the nearest second is satisfactory and the zone markings would encompass a much greater area of the course. For both methods the judges should be admonished to remain alert to determine the score accurately and to avoid anticipating the actual point or time of finish.

The set time and set distances methods of scoring illustrate the principle of modifying the administrative procedure for a test item to render it feasible for teacher use in certain situations. That these adaptations tend to compromise the accuracy of scoring somewhat and, therefore, its reliability should be evident. Accordingly, the teacher should administer such modifications in method so as to minimize loss of accuracy; evidence indicates that satisfactory reliability can be attained with the above modifications. However, it behooves the teacher to ascertain the effect of similar adjustments in administrative procedure for other test items before initiating their implementation.

Another method of timing more than one individual at a time can be used when split-hand stop watches are available, and with little if any sacrifice in accuracy. A trained timer can time accurately the performance of two participants with such a watch providing the students are not equal in ability. Slight discrepancies in timing accuracy may occur in very close finishes, since the two buttons must be pressed in a prescribed order. However, this may be obviated by careful pairing of students so that their ability differs somewhat. With just two such watches and a trained assistant, the teacher can time four students simultaneously and accurately and often more quickly and with less confusion than the two other previously mentioned mass methods.

The great reliance placed by most physical education teachers on timing as a method of scoring affords justification for discussing the salient aspects implicit in proper utilization of stop watches. These can be divided into three categories: selection, care, and use. Serious consideration should be given to the selection of quality watches with preference shown for 1/10 second, 30-second sweep, split-hand type. Although use of a split-hand adds slightly to the initial cost, the teacher virtually gains another watch, plus the feature of timing sequential parts of a total performance with one watch when desired. The 1/10 second feature provides the maximum accuracy that the teacher might need, while also permitting more precise determination to the nearest 1/5, ½, or 1 second units, as may be preferred.

The care accorded to the watch is a determining factor in its accuracy and longevity. Recommended practice is to have stop watches examined annually by a reliable craftsman, and serviced and calibrated as necessary. The teacher should check the watches against one another at specified intervals throughout the testing program in order to remove any malfunctioning ones and establish any correction factor or read-out value to be applied to a particular watch to render its reading accurate and identical with the other watches. An effective method of checking two watches is to start and stop them simultaneously by placing the stems against one another and pressing the watches together. Simple devices can be devised easily for simultaneous checking of more than two watches. Watch readings should be compared for a time interval approximating the mean time for the events involved. Hence, if the watches are to be used for 50-yard dash and 600-yard run-walk, the synchronization should be checked for mean times of both items for the group concerned. An error of .1 second at 50 yards would be unchanged over 600 yards if caused by a mechanical impediment in the start–stop mechanism. But the same error would be increased appreciably for the 600-yard event if the actual watch movements were unsynchronized. Given the desired calibration and synchronization of watches, it is imperative that caution be exercised in handling and using the watches in accordance with the manufacturer's recommendations and other practices designed to maintain their accuracy. Prevention of sudden jolts during storage or use is essential. The popular practice of suspending a watch from a cord encircling the neck permits needless jarring and should be supplanted by a finger loop attached to the watch, necessitating continual holding by the timer.

Proper use of stop watches encompasses their users as well as their care. The teacher should utilize only experienced timers in a testing situation, and provide prerequisite experience for training timers during class activity and test practice sessions. Unfortunately, whenever timing is employed—test, trials, or sports competition—the accuracy of the results is often assumed with little or no heed paid to standardization of procedure. The disturbing misconception that "anyone can serve as a timer because accuracy is a sole function of the watch" appears to be all too prevalent. On the contrary, there is much more involved in reliable timing than meets the eye. The teacher must understand and impart to the timers that accuracy is a function of both the watch and its proper use; both must meet certain specifications for accuracy to ensue. Neither a proficient timer with an inaccurate watch nor an unqualified, inept timer with an accurate watch can produce accurate results.

Timing error attributable to improper use may entail circumstances affecting the response of the timer or the actual operation of the watch. To avoid this first source of error it becomes essential that the timer: (1) has an unobstructed view at the start and finish; (2) starts the watch upon sight stimulus (for example, gun fire or hand signal) rather than sound, except when within immediate proximity of the starter; (3) is aligned in the vertical plane projected through the finish line; and (4) responds instantly yet without anticipation upon a legitimate finish. Occasionally undue concern may be expressed over the apparent slow response of some timers at the start and finish. In reality this is of no consequence, since the slow reactor will obtain the same elapsed time as the faster reacting timer, as long as both timers react consistently.

In operating the watch this matter of consistency represents the prime concern, and standardized procedure is advocated to minimize, if not eliminate, the variable factors that are likely to be encountered. Factors such as extraneous arm action, and taking up the slack in the watch stem, are of no particular concern if performed identically at the start and finish. But inasmuch as little likelihood exists of guaranteeing this consistency and nothing is gained by their use, they should be eliminated. Analysis of timing practices will reveal timers who involve little or no arm action upon starting the watch but use vigorous arm action when stopping it, thus introducing a timing error. To insure consistent watch operation it is recommended that the timer: hold the watch so that the end of the index finger contacts the end of the stem; and depress the watch stem firmly and quickly without any arm movement.

The final aspect regarding the use of a stop watch involves accurate reading of it. Ideally the same person should read all watches to minimize reader error. For instance, the teacher or a testing assistant might read the watches of timers assigned to the 50-yard dash. Where this is not feasible, each timer should read his own watch with line of vision perpendicular to the watch face and apply any applicable correction factor or read-out to determine the recorded time without influence from any interested observer—testee or anyone else. The amount of space needed to accommodate this brief description of timing is indicative of the importance that should be attached to providing for proper selection, care, and use of stop watches to insure that the time recorded as the test score is indeed accurate.

The teacher should be always alert to discover new ways of facilitating scoring. The use of sets of numbered tongue depressors serves as an illustration. With each student being assigned a number, these number markers can be used to identify trials in ball throws for distance, to indicate the highest number of foul shots made in three trials, and the like.

When scoring a test item entails counting—be it the number of task repetitions, markers passed, or the like—the teacher should be alert to capitalize on ways to simplify the process and reduce the probability of error occuring. The sidestep test on the New York State Physical Fitness Test exemplifies the application of this principle. For this test two side lines are equally spaced from a center line, and the task consists of sidestepping from the center line to touch the floor just over one side line, then cross the center line to touch the floor beyond the opposite side line, and so on until time expires. The number of line-crossings constitutes the score. It is evident that the job of the counter can be simplified considerably by counting the number of times the testee crosses the center line. Then the score is derived by multiplying this count by two and adding one if he had crossed a side line after last crossing the center. A similar adjustment to simplify counting can be made to any item in which paired movements or cycles of performance are elicited, such as on the treadmill exercise item on the New York test or dribbling a ball around a pattern of obstacles.

As part of the concern of determining of scores, the teacher should be cognizant of common errors that occur in measuring physical performance with a view to minimize if not avoid them. While these errors were described under specific considerations for constructing physical performance measures in Chapter 4, they warrant brief mention as challenges to effective implementation of test scoring procedure. They can be categorized as errors relating to: observation, landmarks, distance, instrument accuracy, instrument design, and rating. Errors of observation probably occur most often and encompass two facets—observation of performance, and reading of instruments. Timers and finish judges should be positioned in the vertical plane of finish. Raters should be placed so as to cover the most important angles of perspective in the performance. In reading instruments such at watches and other dial instruments, and see-through rulers and grid devices, precaution should be taken to avoid errors attributable to parallax and uniocular rather than biocular vision. The caution concerning landmarks is to insure that they are placed when the testee assumes the testing position. For example, skin markings over certain anatomical points may become displaced and invalid if the individual changes his postural attitude or body positioning. To measure distance for jumps, throws, and the like, in addition to the concern for observational errors it is important that the tape is properly aligned in respect to both the desired line of direction and the point of origin (for example, outside of restraining line for standing long jump rather than the inside).

Instrument accuracy entails not only verification as to satisfactory operation and calibration of the instruments, whether they are, for example, timing devices or force gauges, but also checking that they are used properly. Avoidance of errors related to instrument design necessitates that the instrument be appropriate in such aspects as size and range of measurement for the group to which it is to be applied; for example, size of the manuometer for measuring hand grip strength of elementary school children. In the matter of rating errors the concern of the teacher is somewhat different in the present context of scoring. Provision for preventing the prevalent rating errors described in Chapter 4, namely, generosity, halo, central tendency, and logical errors, needs to be accomplished in the orientation of raters. The teacher's concern with rating at this point in the scoring process is to discern any appreciable discrepancy among raters. As discussed in the use of judges' rating as a validity criterion for physical performance tests in Chapter 4, if the ratings of a judge fail to result in a minimum correlation coefficient of .80 with the scores of each of the other judges, that judge's ratings would not be used.

Providing for a record of the score achieved on a test deserves careful and critical consideration, since the results should be kept in a meaningful, systematic manner; the end product of which should be functional records. The teacher has primarily three types of score records to choose from, namely: individual student score card, group or squad record, and station record or record of total class. The decision as to which type or combination will best serve the purpose for a given test depends largely upon the circumstances surrounding the test, such as the type of test, number of testing personnel, and the hike.

Certain considerations apply to all types of score records. Deliberate planning is necessary to provide for all the data to be noted in a particular arrangement. Space should permit recording all trials allowed in the test, the total raw score, and the converted scale score, when appropriate. The arrangement of the score card or sheet should reflect the logical sequence to minimize recording errors, and the general format of the record should be designed to engender accuracy and neatness.

The use of individual student score cards personalizes the testing program, making the individual feel the benefit and meaningfulness of the tests for him. Test meaningfulness is fostered especially when score cards include a cumulative record, as appropriate, of test performance. It is furthered by provision of achievement levels for the test so that each student can compare his score with normed scores and convert the raw score to some form of standard scores. When possible, all achievement scales for a test battery should be included on the score card. Then the student can obtain a profile of his performance by drawing a line through his score on each test. The inclusion of a composite battery score on the card renders it complete.

For many and varied reasons, it may be deemed neither practical nor desirable to include all the aforementioned data on the individual score card. Often a separate report form may appear more desirable for the student to note his achievement scores and draw his profile. A table for converting raw scores to the appropriate form of standard scores should be posted when not included on the individual score card or when the other types of score cards are employed.

Individual score cards may become mutilated after continued use or lost, which poses a problem. Recording the scores from the individual card that the student handles during each test onto a larger, all-inclusive master card for individual students helps to minimize this problem but necessitates clerical time. Despite this concern, the value of individual cards should be obvious. The student knows his score as the test is going on and can immediately evaluate his performance in terms of himself and others. In addition the use of individual score cards affords flexibility in test administration by allowing individuals to move from one station to another when permissible.

The format of individual score cards will vary with the type of test items and the information that the teacher wishes to include. Sometimes it is practical to devise a score card on which the pattern of response on test trials can be charted rather than simply noting the individual and/or total scores for the trials. Such a procedure provides valuable information for appraisal and guidance in learning physical skills. Figure 6–3 shows a pictorial record of trials for a softball target throw consisting of two series of ten trials. On it the recorder notes the approximate point of target impact for each trial by number and totals the points earned for each series. This illustration is intended to be

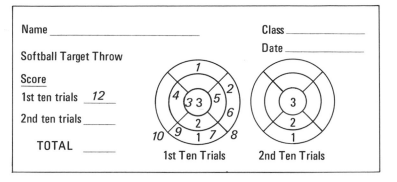

Fig. 6–3.   Pictorial score record.

suggestive of possible variations in the format of score cards. Other test items can be included on the card, and the pictorial target may be printed on the reverse side if desired.

A score card variation to avoid the legibility problems that may occur when students write scores on individual record cards warrants mention. It consists of arranging the test items across the card so that the scores falling within the range that is expected can be printed in columns beneath the respective items (Fig. 16–1). The score is then recorded by simply encircling the correct figure under each test item. A blank can be placed at either end of each column to record scores outside the printed range. This variation readily lends itself to printing the normative scale alongside the raw scores when desired. When a wide range of scores is encountered so that printing all scores is prohibitive, a compromise scheme may be suitable—such as printing a column of blanks from _____.0 in tenths to _____.9. Then the recorder writes the second time in the blank representing the proper tenth.

Group or squad score cards are often used when a group of students is being tested together. Thereby, the scores are recorded by the tester or squad leader on the group card for each member at each station. The third type of score record—station or class score sheets—is nothing more than a complete listing of the names of all class members that is kept at each station. As such it can be used with either type of station rotation —group or individual. When students are tested individually, the scores may also be recorded on individual score cards. This double scheme provides an expedient means of obtaining both class and individual records; the former being necessary for computational purposes when data processing is not available. The station score sheet lends itself readily to use for multiple test items as well as for single item tests with a large number of subjects, while at the same time it limits handling of test scores to testing personnel. Both group and station score sheets provide for convenient administration but have the disadvantage of necessitating the transposing of scores to individual records.

In choosing the most suitable type of score record, consideration should be given to the age level and behavioral characteristics of the students involved, both of which have implications for the decision. Related to the type of score record is the matter of who does the actual recording of the scores. To the extent feasible it is recommended that the teacher or responsible testing assistants note all scores, whether on individual, group or class records, as observed directly or reported by partners. Permitting students to record their own scores introduces the enticement of cheating to attain better scores, and increases the likelihood of recording errors and also mistakes attributable to poor legibility. Acknowledgeably, some teachers will wish to have students record scores either to facilitate test administration or as part of an honor-respecting class atmosphere.

For the illustrative problem station score sheets and/or individual score cards would appear best for recording motor fitness test scores, especially in view of the longitudinal nature of the testing across grade levels. Station score sheets would warrant use for the skill tests in soccer, tumbling, and tennis, which are related to instructional units and a matter of class record in that context.

Suggestions to Facilitate Test Administration and Scoring. In the foregoing discussions dealing with administering and scoring tests many considerations have been incorporated to simplify, expedite, and otherwise improve the testing process. The varying nature and specificity of such suggestions restricted the number that could be covered without unduly distracting from the intended overall continuity of thought. Notwithstanding, because of the importance of some considerations that were omitted, attention to a concise listing of further suggestions appears warranted. Along with the earlier ideas, the items listed below are intended to be illustrative rather than all-inclusive. Hopefully they will elicit other practical ideas from the teacher; other in the sense that those listed have themselves been derived from the application of teachers' ingenuity to their testing experience. As a word of caution, in considering possible innovations in administering tests the teacher should make certain that the idea involved does not provide a cue to or aid in attaining the desired performance; in other words, the idea should not serve as a performance facilitator. For an example, the provision of a rope four feet above the volleyball net as a guide to judge the minimum permissible height for a set-up test affords a cue to performance; one of particular benefit to lesser skilled individuals. Thus the implications of such innovations for facilitating performance as well as administration becomes important.

Additional suggestions to facilitate the administration and scoring of tests include:

1. Number individual score cards for each class to expedite alphabetical arrangement.
2. Inform the school custodian of the testing schedule so that the facilities will be in satisfactory condition, for example, to avoid having the gymnasium floor waxed just before conducting sidestep and shuttle run tests.
3. When available, use audio-hailers outdoors and sound systems in large indoor settings for organizational purposes.
4. Recognize the effect of ability grouping on performance and the resultant score. The very competitive and highly motivational effect that occurs when students are close in ability tends to elicit their best performance as well as making scoring easier in some events, such as softball throw or similar distance-covered items.
5. Standardize test procedure, as desirable, within the latitude of test directions. Two illustrations can be shown by reference to the 50-yard dash. The practice of requiring all students to use the stand-up start affords a baseline for comparison devoid of the influence of various starting techniques, if so desired. Running all subjects in groups (rather than some in groups and some alone, as convenient) eliminates an important variable, namely, motivational effect of a competitor.
6. Put a large X about 3 to 5 yards beyond the finish line and have students run until they reach it. This eliminates the tendency of some individuals, particularly the younger ages, to slow down as they approach the finish line.
7. Place balance beams or heavy ropes, to cite two examples, on the floor to contain rolling balls for throwing or volleying items.
8. In multiple station target or distance throws, have the tester give commands for students to throw and retrieve balls in order to systematize the routine, thus promoting safety and minimizing delays caused by inordinately slow testees.
9. Utilize percussion instrument or metronome to facilitate counting of balance items (time held) when the starting time of different testees may vary.
10. Use a device that applies the principle of a movable right-angle arm that slides along a graduated guide rail for quick and accurate measurement of standing height or standing long jump on surfaces where permanent markings are impractical.
11. House a sliding board scaled in suitable units within a supporting framework for simple and accurate determination of extent

flexibility and vertical jump and reach trials, for example, by permitting zero adjustment of the board at the starting position so that trial results can be read directly from the board.

Presenting the Results

After the tests are scored, the step of presenting the results begins. Actually the beginning was made by the provision of cumulative results, and achievement scales on or supplementary to the individual score cards or other records. Presenting the results encompasses several different levels—the individual, each class group, and the program as a whole.

Directing attention first to individual results, the teacher should give consideration to effective and early presentation of the results. Fullest benefits accrue from a test only when the score is made known to the student in proper perspective and as soon as possible. The crux of the matter regarding presenting individual results lies in the availability of a cumulative record form, when appropriate, along with the table for conversion of raw scores into normative scale scores. When results are presented in this manner, the individual can readily compare his performance with his previous scores and with his peers in a particular group or grade level. The availability of state or national norms provides the basis for further comparisons for the individual student as well as an appraisal for the class or grade level performance. For the illustrative problem the teacher should present the results of the soccer, tumbling, and tennis skill tests in terms of class, and perhaps grade level, performance. The scores on the motor fitness test could be presented in light of state and national norms as well as class and grade level performance. If the teacher in the problem extends the testing into the eighth grade next year, the cumulative results can be compared at that time.

As thought turns to the presentation of results in terms of the physical education program the need for effective portrayal of tabulations and graphs becomes apparent. However, this certainly does not preclude the utilization of pictorial portrayal of results to enhance meaningfulness on an individual or class basis as deemed appropriate. The basic intent of visual presentation is to facilitate understanding of the "total picture" by expressing the results in a two-dimensional format to show either the comparative frequency or the cumulative frequency of the various scores falling within the performance range. The different possible formats of visual presentation begin with the basic tallied frequency distribution (Table 2–1) and its simple graphic transposition, the *line graph* (frequency polygon, Fig. 2–6). Drawing vertical lines with connecting horizontal lines centered on and through the plotted points alters the line graph to form a staircase effect, known as a *histogram*. Separating and spacing contiguous columns in the histogram gives a *bar graph*. And another useful type, *symbolic graph*, consists of using symbols (for example, crude figure of a person) to represent a specified number of cases, such as 10, and fractional symbols to approximate intervening numbers— half of a figure for 5 cases. Adaptations of the above types of graphs may be incorporated, such as a sectioned bar graph wherein two colors or solid and unfilled portions of a bar are used to indicate the number of boys and girls, for example, comprising each column or bar. The graphic illustration of percentiles (cumulative frequency percentages) lends itself best to line graph (Fig. 2–9) or histogram format.

The choice of which format to utilize is largely a function of the circumstances characterizing a particular situation and the thought and ingenuity that the teacher wishes to apply. In preparing an appropriate presentation of results the teacher should endeavor to express them simply, clearly, and concisely in a manner compatible with the understanding of the group involved and with the purpose served in presenting the results. This implies portraying the basic facts in condensed form so that the outstanding points for emphasis will be evident. The same care that typified the foregoing steps in the testing program should be exercised in presenting the results to assure that fullest value is derived.

Certain additional considerations apply to tests of associated learning and are noteworthy. The discussion of a knowledge test, no less than the actual writing of the test, should be an educational experience. The teacher should center the discussion about the subject matter content of the test and not upon the appropriateness or quality of the questions involved. The practice of returning written tests to the class for discussion purposes should be avoided. Not only does such a practice tend to distract from class activity, but it also provides the opportunity for students to become familiar with specific test items. This latter concern actually constitutes a loss or compromising of test items, which represents a serious matter in the development of good tests and as such should be recognized in presenting the test results.

Interpreting the Results

The interpretation of results is closely connected with their presentation. Actually, the presentation should be made in light of the intended attention given to interpreting the results. That is to say, the efficacy of interpretation becomes a function of the way in which, and how effectively, the results are presented. One of the important stipulations concerning testing holds that the test results should find significant use in the program and be properly interpreted to testees in order to derive full potential from the test as a teaching device. This final step in the testing program serves to show what the results indicate in terms of teaching and learning. The relation of the test and its results to practice and performance of physical activities or general physical attributes, as appropriate, should be made manifest to each student. As the final step in the testing program, it is both anticipated and desired that the test results will be interpreted in a manner that will contribute toward resolving the problem as defined.

As in presenting the results, the approach to interpreting the test results should contain several prongs: one should be aimed at a meaningful depiction of the significance of the test findings for each individual, another prong should be directed toward a clear understanding of the meaning of test results on a class group or grade level basis, and a third should be focused on the implications and ramifications of the results for the physical education program in overall perspective. In interpreting the results the teacher should strive for a desirable relationship of emphasis between comparison with oneself and with others, fostering the concept of the individual as his own best norm. Not only is purposeful, direct emphasis in interpreting the results important, but also the timing of the endeavor to explain the score is an essential matter. The general rule should be that results are explained as soon after the test is given as possible. This behooves the teacher to make certain that time commitments at a given time will permit rapid scoring and availability of results. If such is not the case, the test administration should preferably be withheld until the results can be made available and interpreted without undue delay. Some teachers mistakenly assume that interpretation purposes have been served when results are posted or otherwise made available. In such cases, not only is the full worth of a test not attained, but the possibility of misuse or misinterpretation exists. Only when the meaning of results have been explained to and comprehended by the students and other individuals concerned has the responsibility for interpretation been fulfilled.

Reference to the illustrative problem should serve to elucidate this concern. The scores on the various tests of the motor fitness test will indicate the achievement level of each individual and the class as a whole in terms of available local norms and national norms. What does this mean for each individual, each class, and the physical education program? Perhaps, the scores on the standing long jump disclose that individually and collectively the students attained a low achievement level. What is this attributable to—limited ability, little emphasis in elementary education, poor teaching situation, or some other factors? How to meet this need becomes the challenge for the program. When this test is repeated, students can compare the two performances in terms of both the actual score and also the achievement levels for the class, seventh grade, and nationally. Repeating the test also provides evidence relative to the effectiveness of the program in the development of qualities measured by the standing long jump.

Mention should be made of considering and interpreting the results of a test or tests in view of the findings revealed by similar or related tests. For example, a poor score on the standing long jump might be attributable to poor skill or lack of development in leg power. If this score was also associated with a poor score in a running event and a vertical jump but good scores in softball throw and pull-ups, further evidence is available to enhance the meaning of the test results. This attention to other test scores in interpreting a given test result predicates the necessity for a functional record system wherein the test performance of each individual can be analyzed and interpreted in light of performance in other related tests. It is this concern for the interrelatedness of performance of an individual on various tests and the cognizance of this interrelatedness in interpreting test performance that leads quite naturally to the theme and content of the next chapter, which deals with overall appraisal of the individual. Accordingly, the interdependency, unity concept of the traits and abilities of individuals should permeate the interpretation of test results.

This interpretation step completes the description of the process and factors in organizing and administering a testing program, such as posed by the illustrative problem, and should equip the teacher to meet similar challenges effectively. And to summarize succinctly and emphatically the important considerations in the actual administration of tests, the teacher's concern is twofold: (1) to effect desirable testing rapport by instilling an understanding on the student's part of what is being tested and its meaningfulness together with providing a well-organized test setting that is conducive to eliciting his maximum performance; and (2) to administer each test carefully and efficiently in accordance with a specified procedure so as to derive full value from the test in a minimum of time without risk to safety. As a final comment, the admonition regarding the importance of providing the specified conditions for a test to permit desired comparisons cannot be overemphasized. Meticulous conformance to directions in test administration is imperative if comparison of scores for the same individual or between students, classes, teachers, schools, and school districts are to be meaningful rather than distortive and misleading.

APPLICATION OF ELECTRONIC DATA PROCESSING

As in all facets of education, and indeed of society in general, electronic data processing (EDP) has virtually opened new horizons in physical education measurement.[4] Tasks which were heretofore impractical, if not impossible, are not only realizable through utilization of EDP, but are accomplished expeditiously and at very reasonable cost. Through EDP the teacher need not be at all concerned with the arduous chore inherent in hand scoring and compiling of test results. It then becomes possible to utilize measurement to the extent that the teacher deems desirable rather than being restricted by the time available for processing test results.

To depict the use of EDP in physical education measurement in proper context, it should be stressed that data processing can render invaluable assistance in the overall organization and conduct of physical education programs, beginning with budget planning and scheduling of classes, through the instructional process to the grading, report card, and program evaluation aspects. To illustrate, through an inquiry regarding uses made of EDP by administrators of school physical education programs in New York State,[5] it was found that, in addition to measurement tasks, data processing was employed for a number of other purposes, among them to provide information on entering students; to identify special needs groups, for example, physically handicapped; to handle budget and accounting practices; to plan facility usage and schedule classes; to assign lockers and combination locks; and to furnish desired statistical information on intramural and interscholastic sports programs.

In addition to these uses, two instructional applications of computer programming seemingly possess great potential value for physical education—computer assisted instruction (CAI), and computer retrieval system (CRS). CAI enables students to complete an instructional unit on an individual basis at a pace compatible with their ability, along with provision for instructional guidance in light of learning errors. One noteworthy application of CRS is in computer based resource units (CBRU) consisting of instructional objectives with corresponding learning experiences, resource materials, and evaluation information. To utilize CBRU, teachers select certain instructional objectives for their classes and are furnished with a computer print-out containing the respective learning experiences, resource materials, and evaluative measures for these objectives. It is also possible to prepare independent study print-outs for individual students with CBRU.

[4] For an introductory resource to EDP the reader is referred to: Howard W. Stoker, *Automated Data Processing in Testing* (Guidance Monograph Series III: Testing; Boston: Houghton Mifflin Co., 1968). For application to physical education see: Henry J. Montoye (ed.), *Principles and Operational Practices, An Introduction to Measurement in Physical Education*, Vol. 1 (Indianapolis: Phi Epsilon Kappa Fraternity, 1970), Chap. 6.

[5] Research Committee (C. R. Meyers, Chairman), New York State Council of Administrators of HPER, 1969, unpublished survey.

Turning to the application of EDP to physical education measurement, working directly from test scores recorded on special cards or answer sheets electronic data processing can provide the teacher with individual and group results for one test or a battery of tests and also individual profile records, grades, and report cards, as desired. Also, from this basic input EDP can produce the necessary data for test item analysis and related aspects of test construction as well as other statistical analyses. To gain the desired total perspective the teacher should be familiar with the essentials and general procedure in the application of EDP to physical education measurement.

In order to utilize data processing most efficiently it becomes necessary to develop a carefully devised routine, which begins with recording the answers on written tests or scores for physical performance tests on special mark-sense answer sheets or cards with electrographic pencil. The end-product of EDP is a print-out of results as programmed, including the performance of individual students in raw scores and their corresponding normative scores. Several school districts in New York—Bethlehem, Dryden, Pittsford, and Rochester—pioneered the implementation of EDP to handle motor fitness test results and afford a basis for describing the procedure involved. The first step is the development of a mark-sense card, such as the $3\frac{1}{4}$ by $7\frac{3}{8}$ inch card for Bethlehem Central School District shown in Fig. 6–4. The format and content of the card may vary, depending upon the test items included and other information that is desired. A card is prepared for each student in the school district, and every year a new card is reproduced from a master card in the data processing center. After the cards are printed, they are sorted alphanumerically by school, grade, sex, and teacher for all students, as well as by instructional period for grades 7–12. The cards are then distributed through each school to the physical education teachers. As part of the test orientation, each teacher explains to the students the need for careful handling of the cards and the proper use of the special electrographic pencils in filling the mark-sense bubbles fully with a dark mark to record test scores. In the elementary schools some teachers do not permit children to handle these cards and make other arrangements for recording the scores on the cards. When students record scores, it is advisable to have the cards scanned to insure that they all are properly marked without extraneous marks, which would complicate the processing. After the test has been completed and the scores recorded, the mark-sense cards are returned to the data processing center. The results are produced on a print-out for each school or teacher, alphanumerically arranged by student, grade, and sex for each test item and showing raw scores, achievement levels or scale scores, percentiles if needed, and total motor fitness scores. The disposition of the information provided on the print-out

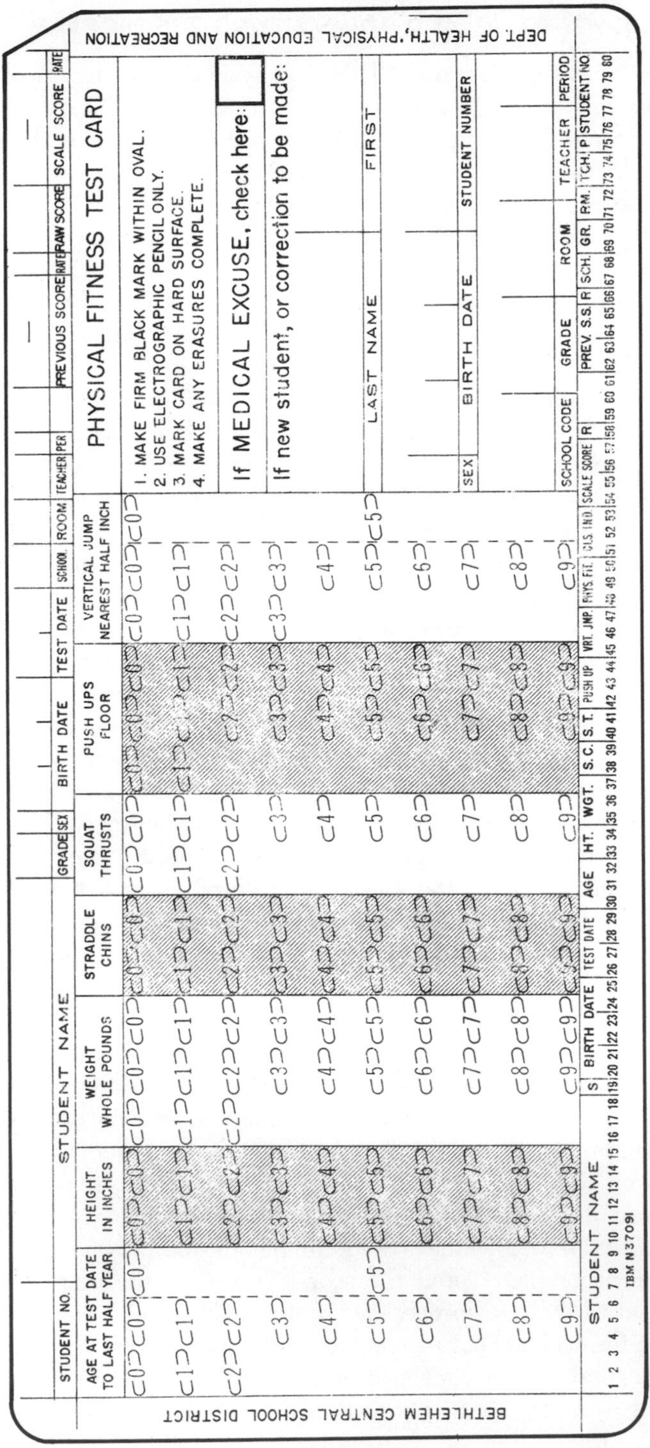

Fig. 6-4. Data processing card for physical fitness test—Bethlehem Central School District.

varies; it may be transferred to permanent record cards or made part of a cumulative data processing record system.

Another illustration of the effective application of EDP utilizing a similar procedure involves the Muscatine-Scott County School System, Bettendorf, Iowa.[6] Its Department of Research and Development has organized and provided data processing for 12 school districts for analysis of AAHPER Fitness Tests administered in the fall and spring, including a key scheme to identify students whose scores qualify them for a Presidential Fitness Award.   As a final example, in 1971–72 the Jefferson County Schools implemented a system with the acronym, AFTARS (AAHPER Fitness Test Analysis Reporting System), comprised of a set of computer programs which generates statistical and management reports.[7] With AFTARS the school system has realized a saving of $13,000 in reduced clerical tasks per test cycle for some 25,000 students. Computer print-outs include a personal profile for each student (display of pretest results can be incorporated), class composite records, quarterly school by grade reports with district-wide totals, and best performance reports.

A written test would be scored and reported in a manner similar to the above, using either the same type of card with columns running lengthwise or a standard mark-sense answer sheet. The teacher can work in conjunction with the data processing center to develop appropriate cards for other tests to be handled as described. Also, with the necessary computer programs the teacher can have the scores of any tests subjected to certain statistical analyses and reported in print-out format as described in Chapter 2.

As mentioned, the application of EDP in physical education measurement extends beyond the concerns in administering a testing program that involve test scoring and analysis of results. EDP has literally provided the important break-through in the construction of teacher-made tests by eliminating the tedious and time-consuming computational tasks involved. This includes the computation of correlation coefficients for establishing validity, reliability, and objectivity for tests of all types of learning, and multiple correlations and regression equations encompassed in constructing physical performance test batteries. Another application of EDP in test construction concerns the definitive process of item analysis for written tests, and as applicable in part for attitude scales and inventories, is discussed in the section on item analysis in Chapter 5.

In planning the organization and administration of a testing program the teacher should utilize any consultatory services available to assist in

[6] Paul J. Staskey, "Computer Scoring of AAHPER Youth Fitness Tests," *Journal of Health-Physical Education-Recreation,* XLI, No. 7 (September, 1970), 63.

[7] Descriptive material can be obtained from: Jefferson County Schools, 809 Quail St., Lakewood, Colorado 80215.

determining ways in which EDP may be employed to accomplish the avowed purposes better. Furthermore, it may well be possible to achieve other purposes that previously were either not deemed feasible or not within the realm of possibility without EDP.

SELECTED REFERENCES

1. BARROW, H. M. "The ABC's of Testing." *Journal of Health-Physical Education-Recreation,* XXX, No. 5 (May–June, 1962), 35–37.
2. BOVARD, J. F.; COZENS, F. W.; and HAGMAN, E. P. *Tests and Measurements in Physical Education,* 3d ed. Philadelphia: W. B. Saunders Co., 1949.
3. MONTOYE, HENRY J. (ed.). *Principles and Operational Practices (An Introduction to Measurement in Physical Education,* Vol. 1). Indianapolis: Phi Epsilon Kappa Fraternity, 1970.

Part II

AREAS OF MEASUREMENT

The intent in this Part is to present the specific tools of physical education measurement in light of the total perspective in which they should be used. To do so, the interrelatedness of the various areas of measurement is depicted first as the basis for discussion concerning the different tests in each area. The tests deemed to be most desirable in the various areas will then be described definitively, and other available tests will be listed along with sources so that the teacher will be cognizant of all the available tests in each area. Additionally, discussion of any characteristics peculiar to the different measurement areas and their implications for test selection, construction and administration will be included.

7

Overall Appraisal
of the Individual

THE INTERRELATION OF MEASUREMENT AREAS IN
OVERALL APPRAISAL

In the desired approach measurement is utilized to afford a realistic
total picture of the individual, even though virtually all of the tests involve specific qualities or skills. Seemingly the tendency in the past has
been to envision the individual as an aggregate of findings or scores in
various areas of measurement. As illustrated in Chapter 1, when dealing
with specific emphases in testing, it is not difficult to lose sight of the
unity concept of the individual. This should not and will not happen
if stress is placed upon the whole relationship of the individual in evaluating his development in terms of the objectives of physical education.
Presumably the teacher of physical education desires to foster the overall
development of each individual through activities that involve the four
developmental areas covered by the objectives (see Chapter 1). Consequently, testing and appraisal should be directed toward this total perspective. This approach is exemplified by the total fitness concept of
individuals in which heed is paid to fitness in four aspects—physical, emotional, mental, and social. Also, recent research findings have revealed
the interrelationships between the physical, emotional, and social aspects
of the development of individuals and the interweaving of their deviations.

Properly conceived, then, overall appraisal does not entail segregating

251

different aspects of the individual for study, inasmuch as each aspect is not a separate entity in itself to be added to other such entities that would then comprise the individual. Rather, attention is directed in overall appraisal to the whole relationship, of which the various measurement areas are a part and in which each area is considered to be one aspect of the individual, intertwined and blended with the other aspects. One of the strong points of physical education is that if any teacher in the school has the opportunity to see children "all in one piece," it is the teacher of physical education. Coupled with this is the fact that in physical education situations, an individual's development physically and organically, in skills and personality, can be readily observed and studied. In this light testing should contribute to a realistic picture of the individual by disclosing the comparative relationship of the various qualities embodied in this "one piece."

AN ILLUSTRATIVE PROBLEM

An illustrative situation should serve to facilitate better comprehension of the concern in this chapter—the "whole relationship." Such a situation might be a junior high school, including grades seven through nine for both boys and girls. (It might be assumed that the illustrative program in Chapter 6 has now expanded to encompass all classes in the junior high school.) The teacher desires to use tests that will contribute to a comprehensive picture of each student as an individual. Before appropriate tests can be selected, the teacher must recognize the various areas of measurement that can contribute to overall appraisal and realize specifically the relative value of this information. Figure 7–1 serves to illustrate the many and diverse tools that may be used to disclose information pertinent to overall appraisal. Once the characteristics and potential use of each measurement area are determined, the teacher is in a position to consider the many different tests under each particular area, as will be presented in subsequent chapters.

AREAS OF MEASUREMENT

The areas of measurement embodied in overall appraisal in physical education constitute primarily the many avenues through which physical education activity affects an individual's development. These may be enumerated as:

Strength
Motor fitness
Cardiovascular function
Anthropometry

Organic Growth and Development	Understanding and Attitudes	Skills and Abilities
Physical and medical examinations and health appraisals	Observation, informal and systematic	Observation
Orthopedic, posture examination	Observation guides	Tests of activity skills
Body-type and movement appraisals	Medical and physical examinations and health appraisals	Check lists
Records of growth-age-height-weight records (Wetzel Grid Graph, Pryor Chart)	Cumulative records—profile interview	Rating scales
Records of physical activity	Summarization of findings	Teacher-constructed tests
Cardiovascular tests	Case conferences, informal conferences	Student-constructed tests
Strength tests and appraisals	Students' statements of goals	Situation tests
Relaxation tests	Self-appraisal	Standardized tests
Coordination tests	Anecdotal records	Marks and grading
Mobility tests	Teacher-constructed tests	Self-survey and self-appraisals
Observation	Student-constructed tests and forms	
Psychotherapeutic reports	Group-constructed tests and appraisal forms	
Self-appraisal	Situation tests	
Time schedules	Standardized tests	
Diet regimes	Sociometric and role-playing techniques	
	Projective tests	
	The unfinished story	
	The wishing well	
	Check lists	
	Rating scales	
	Student-interest lists	
	Interest inventories	
	Student questionnaires	
	Time schedules	
	Diary autobiography	
	Case studies	
	Marking and grading	

Fig. 7–1. Tools to use in finding student needs. (From Rosalind Cassidy) *Curriculum Development in Physical Education*, p. 282. © 1954 by Harper & Row and reprinted by permission.

Body mechanics
General qualities of motor performance
Sports skill
Knowledge and understanding
Attitudes and behavior

These different areas are identified on the basis of representing factors that are peculiar to a given quality but, because of the interrelatedness of the qualities, in addition to the particular quality that characterizes an area it may in some instances include one or more other areas. Strength and cardiovascular function exemplify areas that bear singular identity, whereas motor fitness connotes some consideration of strength and cardiovascular function as well as those factors that are peculiar to the area of motor fitness, as will be described.

These areas of measurement are generally conceived as being within the province of the physical education teacher. In addition and basic to these areas are the health or medical examination and related physical and mental health appraisal techniques. While the physical education teacher will not be responsible for the health examination and other measurement as may be included in the guidance records, these instruments provide pertinent information for overall appraisal as well as for its relation to other measurement areas.

Information from Health and Guidance Records

Considerable information can be derived from health and guidance records for use in overall appraisal of the individual and in divulging limitations and other factors affecting the conduct of activity or measurement in the various areas. The implications and recommendations derived from the health examination, other health appraisal techniques, health habits survey, and pertinent guidance records provide both direction and comprehension to an individual's overall appraisal. These implications and recommendations should be made evident to the physical education teacher by the doctor, guidance counselor, or other trained person, as appropriate, rather than resulting from deduction by the teacher without benefit of technical assistance and with the likelihood of errors of omission and interpretation.

The most fundamental evaluation instrument in considering the individual as a whole is an adequate health examination, because not only does any functional impairment of the body reduce its capacity for physical activity, but also it is realized that all factors influencing one's life likewise affect the organic system. The value of the health examination is twofold: It discloses the need for limiting or modifying physical activity, and it reveals the basic reason for comparatively poor or unusual performance in a particular skill or quality. Supplementary health appraisal measures, such as vision and hearing tests and teacher observation records, provide valuable information for the health records.

The importance accorded the health examination suggests that the experience be a deliberative examination thorough enough to meet its purpose. The all-too-common cursory examination that has characterized many school situations has engendered a false sense of security in students when existing defects have not been discovered and also has appeared to intimate that medical examinations possess relatively little importance. Much improvement can be made in health examinations through the use of appropriate record forms. The importance of recording the results of the medical examinations on a specific form is twofold: It defines certain minimum standards, and it provides some assurance of the adequacy of the examinations. Inasmuch as the health examination is fundamental to the physical education program, the teacher should make known the need for a satisfactory health examination and use the results.

Like the health examination and resulting records, the guidance records should be available to the teacher of physical education as a source of information to render the overall appraisal of an individual more complete and ultimately to chart more effectively the course of physical education experience for an individual. Since appraisal in physical education entails the total personality, all available school records should be drawn upon for implications and recommendations affecting a given individual.

Strength

The first of the areas of measurement generally conceded to be the responsibility of the physical education teacher is that of strength—the capacity for muscular force and the maximum tension that can be instantly developed and applied to an imposed resistance. That strength is related to or a factor involved in the other areas of measurement is obvious. Strength is inextricably a part of total fitness in its many aspects, ranging from efficient body mechanics and postures to skill in physical education activity. Its existence may be characterized by two levels— minimal and optimal. Minimal strength consists of the amount that is essential so that a skill or function may be performed adequately. Optimal strength refers to the amount necessary for the highly desired level of performance or functioning.

Strength provides the answer to how well the body part in question functions as measured by muscular force. It is generally ascertained either for a specific muscular action (hip flexion) or for a particular muscular activity (push-ups), and is categorized as either *static* (isometric contraction) or *dynamic* (isotonic contraction) strength. Strength may be measured by recording devices ranging from an ordinary spring scale to an electronic myodynemeter for static testing, as in the case of hip flexion or back-lift. Also strength may be expressed as the number of executions of a muscular action in functional or dynamic testing, such as push-ups, or as time for a sustained static effort, such as holding a half push-up position. Laboratory instrumentation can be devised to ascertain the amount of force exerted during dynamic testing, but it is impractical for teacher use.

From this description it becomes apparent that strength in the general connotation has two components—muscular strength and muscular endurance. *Muscular strength* refers to force exerted in a single maximum effort, either static or dynamic. *Muscular endurance* refers to the amount of work that can be done through sustained effort in a given task, either static or dynamic. Dynamic testing of muscular endurance can be accomplished in two ways: by maximum repetitions, and repetitions within a prescribed time. Although muscular strength and endurance are clearly related, they are different, so that for the same muscle action individuals scoring best in tasks of muscular strength will not necessarily attain a comparable ranking in tests of muscular endurance. This is attributable to the fact that stronger muscles can sustain a smaller proportion of maximum strength than do comparatively weaker muscles.

An analysis of prevalent motor fitness tests will reveal that a considerable number of the items measure one or both components of strength, thus affirming that strength is valued highly as an indicant of motor and physical fitness. The continued emphasis on strength as a reflector of total fitness is attributable to the fact that strength is a relatively objective measure, is influenced by emotional problems, and is affected by illnesses producing a systemic reaction, such as tonsillitis and the common cold.

Hence, strength represents a quality of the individual that lends itself quite readily to measurement and constitutes an important factor in overall appraisal.

Motor Fitness

Motor fitness refers to that neuromuscular condition that permits strenuous work; the basic components of motor fitness being such factors as strength—primarily as muscular endurance, speed, agility, endurance, power, and flexibility. It entails the basic elements of vigorous physical activity. The term "motor fitness" came into being during World War II to describe that condition that (1) involved more than muscular strength and muscular as well as systemic endurance (the three aspects that represent the basic connotation of physical fitness) but (2) did not encompass more than basic body coordination and fundamental skills (characteristic of motor abilities and performance tests, such as hand-eye or foot-eye coordination, and balance). The reader will note that generally tests designated as physical fitness tests are actually tests of motor fitness by this definition. Physical fitness is generally used to refer to the functional capacity of the individual for a specific task or mode of living. Motor fitness might be conceived as physical fitness in action involving basically fundamental skills.

Thus motor fitness adds to the components of physical fitness, namely, muscular strength and endurance, and cardiovascular function, the factors of speed, agility, power, and flexibility. For clarification purposes these "additives" are defined as: *speed*—rapidity of movement to accomplish a specific task, such as the 50-yard dash; *agility*—ability to change, both rapidly and accurately, the position or direction of the body through large ranges of movement; *power* (muscular or explosive) —exertion of maximum muscular force in the shortest possible time interval to accomplish a specific task, composed of both speed and strength; and *flexibility*—extent of the range of movement of articulating body segments about a joint which is specific to that joint and generalizable only as a profile of the specific joints measured.

So conceived, motor fitness encompasses efficient performance under demanding conditions in lifting, carrying, climbing, running, dodging, jumping, and swimming. Herein, to eliminate misunderstanding, all tests comprised of motor fitness components will be classified as motor fitness tests, regardless of their titles. As an area of measurement, motor fitness represents an important consideration of overall appraisal, namely, the functioning of the individual that is fundamental to all physical activity.

Cardiovascular Function

The area of measurement concerned with cardiovascular function consists for the most part of attempts at measuring certain variables to indicate the functional organic status or physiological fitness of the body as reflected by the strength and endurance of the heart and efficiency of the circulatory system in adjusting to work situations. The variables generally used include pulse rate and blood pressure, recorded under various conditions. The importance of these internal factors lies in the fact that they are capable of modifying muscular action and, therefore, are basic and should logically be accorded first consideration in any inclusive estimate of physical ability. The level of cardiovascular function is indicated through endurance activity that not only elicits strength and endurance of the particular muscles involved in the activity but also depends greatly on the effective functioning of the circulatory system. Furthermore, cardiovascular function is intricately related to the efficiency and capacity of the respiratory system to effect the exchange of oxygen and carbon dioxide essential to support vigorous activity. To recognize this some authorities refer to this area by other descriptive titles, such as cardiovascular–respiratory, cardiorespiratory, or circulatory–respiratory endurance. Herein the traditional terminology is retained with full realization that the vital relationship of the respiratory system is implicit within cardiovascular function.

Since activity of sufficient vigor to determine the degree of stress on the cardiovascular mechanism is generally involved in tests of this type, the school physician usually has a direct or indirect role to play in its utilization. The prime concern of the physical education teacher in tests of cardiovascular function is to make a quantitative assessment of the individual variations in ability of the cardiovascular system to meet conditions of stress. Needless to say, information relative to cardiovascular function serves as a valuable adjunct to the health examination in contributing to overall appraisal of the individual.

Anthropometry

Anthropometry simply stated consists of making external measurements of the human body. These measurements may be either objective (using special instruments such as calipers) or subjective (using a list of characteristics or a description of categories to guide judgment). The results can be used to appraise body build, nutritional status, and posture. Body build includes the size and proportions of the individual; whereas nutritional status refers to the relationship in development between skeletal, adipose, and muscular tissue. The use of anthropometry in appraisal of posture—referring to the symmetry of the body and its parts—will be accorded specific mention as part of the body mechanics area of measurement.

For centuries measurements of body size and proportions have been studied because of the relationship between these measurements and body function and beauty. Because of the present value of anthropometry as well as the significance of previous findings, it is an important aspect of physical education measurement and is considered to be the most important aspect by some authorities. The teacher of physical education will recognize that the great value affixed to anthropometrical measurement lies largely in research and the ensuing implications for teaching, rather than the general utility of this measurement directly in teaching. Relative to body build, certain relationships have appeared between body type and various performance abilities. A knowledge of this will enable the teacher to direct student interest to appropriate activities in addition to the general use of indicating developmental needs. Anthropometrical studies have resulted in methods for analyzing individual growth and development that constitute vast improvement over the use of tables for comparison.

The physical education teacher is in a vital position to observe growth and development and nutritional status of students. On the basis of this observation, the teacher can render individual help or referral, provide developmental activity, or take any action that seems appropriate. In this manner anthropometry can contribute significant information pertinent to overall appraisal of the individual.

Body Mechanics

Body mechanics as used herein encompasses posture, connoting a static position, and posture in action, which entails efficient alignment and mechanical functioning of the body in activity. Body mechanics has been aptly defined as: ". . . the mechanical correlation of the various systems of the body with reference to the skeletal, muscular, and visceral systems and their neurological associations."[1] The values attached to good body mechanics may be summarized as functional efficiency, esthetic, and preventive—which is related to functional efficiency but singled out to emphasize obviating certain chronic orthopedic difficulties often encountered in later life. Since definitive evidence is lacking to indicate the specific relationship between posture and physiologic functions, no special mention is made of the health value, other than that implied in functional efficiency. Authorities concede the apparent existence of health value but point out the present dearth of objective evidence.

Measurement in the area of body mechanics has been largely subjective, although certain objective techniques have been devised. Recently progress has been made in the refinement of subjective appraisal with a suitable pictorial rating form for teacher use and transparent rating grids to record observation of landmarks. Expert opinion affords the basic criterion in appraising body mechanics, and in essence this opinion reflects consensus as to what comprises good body mechanics. Heretofore the lack of precise testing instruments and methods for measuring posture that are generally satisfactory and practical for teacher use has been a deterrent not only in measuring status and progress in body mechanics but also in giving warranted emphasis to body mechanics in the physical education program. It should be realized that poor body mechanics may indicate weakness in other areas, e.g., strength of certain muscle groups, or may in itself cause problems in other areas, such as motor abilities or skill performance. As such, body mechanics constitutes an integral part of overall appraisal.

[1] *White House Conference on Child Health and Protection,* Report of the Subcommittee on Orthopedics and Body Mechanics, "Body Mechanics—Education and Practice" (New York: Appleton-Century-Crofts, Inc., 1932), p. 5.

General Qualities of Motor Performance

In physical education there are certain general measures of motor abilities, capacity, and learning power that possess immense value in revealing the "total picture" of an individual for appraisal. The author arbitrarily refers to these aspects of appraisal as general qualities of motor performance or skill.

At this point it should be noted that "general" is used in this context to connote *representativeness* rather than *inclusiveness*. Research has clearly disclosed the specificity rather than generality of motor abilities and, consequently, the fallibility of the concept of general motor ability in the all-inclusive sense.[2] Properly perceived, tests of general qualities afford due recognition to the specificity of motor abilities and are merely representative of the specific abilities that are sampled by them. Thus, according to this connotation, "general" refers to the compilation of those specific abilities that are included and has relevance only to them. Some individuals will possess more of the specific abilities that comprise a general test than other individuals and thus rank better in general (representative) motor abilities. Also, it is important to recognize the differentiation between this area of measurement and motor fitness. Whereas tests of general motor qualities may include some items occasionally found in motor fitness tests, the purposes served are not the same. For example, the standing long jump will be used to disclose explosive power relative to body weight on motor fitness tests and jumping ability on tests of general qualities. Additionally, tests of general motor qualities introduce the elements of hand–eye and foot–eye coordination, and balance that are defined as beyond the purview of motor fitness. To define these elements, *hand–eye* and *foot–eye* coordination refer to the ability to perform a task involving interrelated visual perception and hand or foot action in a sequentially smooth manner resulting in efficient and accurate movement; and *balance* is the ability to hold the body in a given position for a length of time (static), or to maintain equilibrium while performing a task, for example, beam walking (dynamic).

Broadly conceived, these general motor qualities reflect the total personality—physical, mental, emotional, and social aspects—in the performance of a variety of total body activities and do not purport to indicate skill in any particular sports activity. Specifically, these general qualities may be enumerated as general motor abilities, capacity, and educability. *General motor abilities* entails one's present performance level—the efficiency with which a person executes motor skills. *General motor capacity* means an individual's innate potentialities for performance in motor

---

[2] F. M. Henry, "Specificity vs. Generality in Learning Motor Skill," *Proceedings of the College Physical Education Association,* 1958, pp. 126–128.

skills, the limit to which an individual may be developed. The capability of an individual to learn new skills is termed *general motor educability*.

Tests designed to measure educability must obviously present motor problems that are new to the students. Tests of motor capacity generally include an educability type of test item in addition to agility and other prognostic-type items. In view of the difficulties implicit in endeavoring to separate innate from acquired skill in the specific abilities involved in motor performance, the teacher must select the test or battery of tests that appears most valid as representative of the particular type of general motor qualities that is to be measured.

Tests involving any of the three general motor qualities possess great usefulness in physical education for classification or equating individuals and groups, as well as for specific purposes such as diagnosing and prescribing activity to meet individual needs. Ability grouping by such general qualities has proven very practical in physical education, since individuals or groups may be equated for a range of activities without changing the grouping and on the basis of one test. In addition to this practical aspect, educators agree that provision to equate the abilities of individuals and groups is a necessity if full potential benefits are to be derived from physical activity programs—referring specifically to development in all areas, but particularly social and emotional. Teachers note that with ability groupings students can be inspired and taught in light of their ability, which is difficult if not impossible in classes comprised of individuals with widely varying abilities. Similarly, students have been noted to favor classes based upon general motor abilities groupings.

In interpreting the results of measurement of general motor qualities, as in other areas of measurement, the teacher is admonished to exercise sound judgment and view these findings in total perspective as influenced by all other test results and other sources of pertinent information. These tests of general qualities do not measure such traits as interest, perseverance, and initiative. Neither is previous experience in specific activities considered. Consequently, no substitute exists for teacher judgment based on such sources as observation and previous knowledge of the student in interpreting and applying the results of tests of general motor qualities.

Sports Skill

Sports skill refers to ability to perform in a particular sport or dance. It is specific for each activity, such as soccer, tumbling, or tennis. Sports skill utilizes organic power for performance along with a proper combination of such qualities as eye–muscle coordination, agility, rhythm, timing, speed, and poise for application in a particular sports activity.

Sports skill constitutes a fundamental aspect of physical education; and without sufficient skill for satisfying participation in physical activities, the avowed objectives of physical education cannot be attained. As part of this, basic competency in skills serves as an incentive for continuing to use these skills as part of living and thus contributes to a richer and happier life through the benefits derived from wholesome activity.

Viewed in this light, appraising sports skill is an important phase of measurement in physical education and comprises an integral part of overall appraisal of the student as an individual and as part of a group and of the physical education program. Knowledge of the level of ability in a particular sports activity as disclosed by a skill test serves a number of uses: (1) for diagnostic purposes in analyzing ability to show need or deficiencies in skill, (2) for equating ability of students to facilitate learning and vitalize competition, (3) to ascertain improvement in skill as a basis for grading and evaluating teacher effectiveness, and (4) to motivate students to avail themselves of the opportunity to learn and practice the skills.

Knowledge and Understanding

In skill learning does the individual learn anything besides the skills per se? The answer is evident to anyone who has developed proficiency in a particular sports skill or talked to beginners and experts in a given activity. The experienced and skillful participant displays a wealth of knowledge that is not possessed by the beginner. This realm of associated learning (cognitive domain) encompasses information related to physical education and the particular activity involved, such as the need for and the many values derived from wholesome activity and the value of systematic progression in training, to cite two examples. Associated learning also involves information directly concerned with a specific activity. The knowledge and understanding pertaining to the activity directly include (1) historical development of the sport, (2) purposes of sport and its general value to participants, (3) terminology and rules governing the activity, (4) playing etiquette, (5) techniques embodied in performance, and (6) offensive and defensive strategy. For clarification purposes the reader is reminded of the differentiation made in Chapter 5, in which knowledge was described as implying awareness of facts, beliefs, or other information; whereas understanding was depicted as entailing knowledge and, in addition, cognizance of the applicability and significance of it.

The importance of assessing an individual's knowledge and understanding as an aspect of one's overall appraisal seems apparent. Fuller comprehension of an individual's performance in other areas of measurement will result from an appraisal of associated learning, and certainly the reverse will hold true. In addition, tests of knowledge and understanding may serve as a pretest to determine present knowledge and understanding and deficiencies for instructional purposes, to ascertain the level of knowledge and understanding after instruction as a basis for grading and evaluating teaching efficacy, and to motivate learning by indicating the definite relationship of associated learning to performance in the activity. Generally speaking, tests of associated learning are in written form and should be so regarded herein, unless otherwise stated. However, it should be mentioned that oral response to specific questions and observation of performance in the activity are indicative, with some limitation, of the knowledge possessed by an individual. The undue time requirements necessitated in these latter methods make their use as the principal means of appraisal impractical. Nevertheless, they possess value as a means to supplement findings on written tests to the extent that seems warranted. In reality observation of performance provides the true test of associated learnings that are directly involved in performance; namely, is this learning functional?

Attitudes and Behavior

The expression "last but not least" certainly pertains to consideration of concomitant learning (affective domain)—attitudes and behavior—in overall appraisal of the individual. The nature of the factors involved in this area makes it the most difficult of all areas to measure. Yet concomitant learning pervades and has a decided influence on performance in all other areas. This area might properly be termed the "looking glass," since it reveals the character of the effect of physical education experiences on the individual. It is this effect, manifested in attitudes and behavior, that will influence one's social and emotional development and as such exert a lasting impression. Thus these concomitant learnings are not delimited to physical education activities per se but include the broad areas of development constituting the objectives of physical education. The teacher's concern, then, entails two facets: the development of wholesome attitudes, appreciations, and habits toward physical education and the development of desirable attitudes and behavior through participation in physical education activities.

The importance of attitudes is further enhanced in view of the vital role attitudes play in determining the amount of learning that takes place. What a student wants to do affects both the quantity and quality of learning. The value derived from measuring concomitant learning far transcends the difficulty encountered. Certainly the teacher will find it easier to measure what a student can do, as is the case in many other areas of measurement, than to ascertain what an individual wants to do, likes to do, and will do. In the event the school guidance office neither administers nor has access to records of psychological or personality testing, the physical education teacher should enlist the support and cooperation of the guidance personnel in undertaking any such form of testing. From guidance specialists the teacher can undoubtedly derive valuable assistance in testing attitudes and behavior peculiar to physical education situations. Measures of concomitant learning have a number of uses, such as helping to identify factors least liked and those most liked by students, aiding in providing insight into individual and group behavior patterns, providing information that will enable the teacher to create an atmosphere conducive to the development of wholesome social attitudes and behavior, and at the same time suppress any undesirable attitudes or behavioral manifestations. Without such appraisal the teacher can not know how effective the learning experiences have been in bringing about the desired development in an individual or the class as a whole.

The tools that the teacher may use to obtain information pertinent to this area of measurement include various types of questionnaires or inventories, social distance tests, behavior frequency check lists, and rating scales. Through the use of broad measuring devices such as educational and psychological tests, the teacher is in a better position to appraise development and needs in social and emotional development and plan for individual differences as appropriate. Actually this information is best obtained through the guidance office, where the teacher can receive the desired information along with technical interpretation of the findings. A final means of assessing attitudes and behavior is to provide for a record of observation of behavior exemplified during instruction, performance, and (in many cases) competition. This might take the form of anecdotal records. Alert teacher observation will provide pertinent information that will give some indication of the validity of concomitant learning revealed by other measurement devices. Such observations, together with the findings derived from other measures of concomitant learning will enable the teacher to evaluate an individual's attitudes and behavior in light of and in relation to the other areas of measurement, thus resulting in a completed picture of the individual—overall appraisal.

SUMMATION AND RESOLVING THE ILLUSTRATIVE PROBLEM

In this chapter the authors have endeavored to present an overview of the various areas of measurement that contribute to a comprehensive overall appraisal of the individual and how they dovetail, intertwine, and are interdependent in effecting the whole relationship. As a word of caution, when using the sum of the parts approach in overall appraisal, the teacher should be alert to the fact that part examination may lead to abstraction, based on a sort of reconstruction, that fails to restore the entity that originally existed. It then behooves the teacher to look beyond the whole as the sum of its parts and to consider the whole relationship. This whole relationship or entity is destroyed by analysis, revealed by synthesis.

On the basis of what each area of measurement contributes to the overall appraisal and the interrelationship between areas, the teacher must decide what areas to include in the testing program. Despite how meager a beginning is made in the testing program, the overall appraisal of the individual should be kept in mind, and the areas selected should reflect this "whole-relationship" approach. At this point it should be recognized that consideration of the areas of measurement for use should be based on a knowledge of the tests available and the feasibility of constructing tests in each area. This will be accomplished in the ensuing chapters—suffice it at this point to realize this need.

In analyzing the contributions of various measurement areas to total appraisal of the individual, the teacher may decide not to utilize measurement from a given area or areas. Perhaps an adequate test, appropriate to the teacher's program, does not exist. Or the teacher may feel that the necessary time for testing in a particular area cannot be justified in light of its significance and importance for the program objectives. Perhaps, because of the interrelatedness of the areas, a test categorized in another area may include an item or items that provide a satisfactory indication of the quality in question for overall appraisal within the purposes of the program. To illustrate this latter point, conceivably the teacher may consider the AAHPER Youth Fitness Test items to represent the areas of strength, motor fitness, and general motor abilities adequately for the illustrative problem, at least as the beginning. (Acknowledgeably an item included to assess motor fitness may also reveal important specific abilities for the desired complex of general motor abilities; for example, standing long jump and shuttle run are basic components of motor fitness but also have relevance as specific abilities to discern general motor abilities that encompass jumping, and speed and agility.) The approach in selecting appropriate areas should be to choose different areas and include testing from within the various areas to the extent warranted by the teaching situation, with a view toward eventual inclusion of totally adequate measurement from each area.

How might the provision for overall appraisal be resolved for the illustrative problem? The teacher may decide to include representative measurement from each area, however meager, and utilize tests encompassing more than one area when appropriate. As already mentioned, strength, motor fitness, and general motor qualities would be represented

on the AAHPER Youth Fitness Test, although it is most properly categorized as a motor fitness test. The remaining areas would have to be
studied to find the most appropriate tests. Continuing the hypothetical
resolution of the problem, a modification of the Harvard Step Test might
fit into the program nicely as a measure of cardiovascular function. The
teacher may decide to continue from the elementary grades use of the
height and weight charting on the Wetzel Grid from the area of anthropometry. An appropriate posture rating scheme, such as that included in the New York State Physical Fitness Test (see Chapter 10),
would be an integral part of the body mechanics program. For sports
skills, the teacher may choose to add gradually, as they are available or
constructed, achievement tests in the various activities to supplement
those already included at the seventh-grade level—soccer, tumbling, and
tennis. As soon as possible, the teacher may devise suitable concise skill
pretests to be given at the beginning of each instructional unit. In the
area of knowledge and understanding, the teacher may plan to devise a
general written test for each grade—seventh, eighth, and ninth—encompassing the activities to be taught during the year. These tests would
be administered at the beginning of school in the fall. In addition to
this general pretest, a written test might be given upon completion of
the instructional unit in each activity during the year. The teacher
might use the findings of psychological testing as noted on the guidance
records to appraise individual need and development. Plans may also
include the construction of a physical education attitude inventory to be
given to the seventh-grade students annually.

With the decision as to the different types of measurement to be used
in the program for boys and girls, grades seven to nine, comes the necessity for some means of summation of the results to facilitate overall appraisal. Seemingly this suggests a carefully devised cumulative record
for each student in physical education, as illustrated in Chapter 16. The
informational data contained on the cumulative record should be arranged in a manner that shows the interrelationships between the different areas of measurement and a picture of all-round developmental
progress, clearly disclosing not only the amount but also the quality of
development. To the extent possible, the cumulative record should use a
graphic presentation or profile of results to facilitate developmental assessment and prognostication. Full realization of the potential value of a
carefully planned overall appraisal of the individual will never be reached
without an appropriately designed and readily understandable cumulative record. The desired synthesis of the whole relationship will be
engendered to the degree that the "subject" is made photogenic, which
constitutes the challenge in providing for a suitable record of overall
appraisal.

Having presented the areas of measurement in proper perspective as they are embodied in overall appraisal, attention can now be directed to a further understanding of the characteristics of measurement in each area along with a delineation of available tests for consideration. As previously inferred, the final decision as to what areas are included in overall appraisal resides in the availability of suitable tests and the practicality of constructing appropriate measures.

SELECTED REFERENCES

1. CASSIDY, ROSALIND. *Counseling in the Physical Education Program.* New York: Appleton-Century-Crofts, Inc., 1959.
2. COWELL, CHARLES C. "Evaluation versus Measurement in Physical Education." *Journal of Health and Physical Education,* XII, No. 9 (November, 1941), 499.
3. COWELL, C. C., and SCHWEHN, H. M. *Modern Principles and Methods in Secondary School Physical Education,* 2d ed. Boston: Allyn and Bacon, Inc., 1964.
4. MONTOYE, HENRY J. (ed.). *Principles and Operational Practices (An Introduction to Measurement in Physical Education,* Vol. 1). Indianapolis: Phi Epsilon Kappa Fraternity, 1970.

8

Testing Strength and Motor Fitness

HISTORICAL BACKGROUND

Almost from the beginning of physical education in the United States, physical education teachers have been looking for tests of strength as basic indicants in appraising the physical status of children and youth in their programs. The actual origin of the development of strength testing is lost in antiquity. Since time immemorial, man has assessed strength dynamically through feats of strength and lifting. Findings in an Egyptian tomb include two artistic works dated about 2500 B.C. and picturing strength developing exercises. The first recorded effort to measure strength statically is attributed to French anthropologists who invented strength dynamometers in the late seventeenth century. The first reports of studies on the physical strength of man that ensued were dated in 1702. By 1821 when Coulomb published studies, certain characteristics and inaccuracies common to strength testing were realized. The fast that the biggest man was not necessarily the strongest man on dynamometer tests stimulated interest in such tests and the search for an explanation of this apparent paradox.

The pioneering tests of strength in the United States primarily utilized dynamometric methods. Beginning in 1880, Dr. Dudley A. Sargent began a systematic study of Harvard students as a basis for determining physical standards for American college men. This effort resulted in what Sargent

[1] D. A. Sargent, "Intercollegiate Strength Tests," *American Physical Education Review*, II (December, 1897), 216.

called the Intercollegiate Strength Test,[1] consisting of lung capacity and strength of back, legs, grip, and arms. Back and leg strength was measured on a dynamometer. Grip of right and left hands was measured by a manuometer. A wet spirometer served to measure lung capacity. Arm strength was determined by the number of parallel-bar dips and of pull-ups, which followed the dips; the dips and pull-ups representing functional or dynamic test items. Upon publication of this test, a number of colleges and universities began using it. Thus, Sargent gave origin to the thought of combining strength tests into a formal battery to measure physical ability. Actually the basic test items used on Sargent's test were described rather thoroughly in book form as early as 1892, along with explanation of a number of anthropometric measurements for use in the YMCA.[2] The transition in physical education measurement from basic anthropometry, as instigated by Hitchcock in 1861, to utilization of strength testing apparatus followed the realization that the important factor was the strength of a muscular action and not the size of a muscle, that is, function as opposed to appearance. Furthermore, the early attention to muscular strength reflected the prevalent physical education program emphasis, namely, gymnastics.

During the time that Sargent was developing his test, three other contributions were being made to strength testing—invention of the ergograph, a test devised by Galton, and the development of the Universal Dynamometer. In 1884 Mosso first developed the ergograph, the principle of which saw application in a number of modified devices in the years to follow. Succinctly described, the device was designed to ascertain the character of repeated muscular contractions resulting when the index or middle finger was flexed and relaxed for the purpose of providing an indicant of an individual's muscular power and general condition.[3] In 1890 Francis Galton devised a test to measure physical efficiency as desired for civic and business personnel. He realized that strength measurements comprise but a part of physical efficiency and was the first person to utilize coordination and accuracy items in endeavoring to determine physical ability. Galton's test included breathing capacity, strength tests with reference to height and weight, quickness of response to visual or audible cue, vision, hearing, and color sense.[4]

The Universal Dynamometer was the end result of Kellogg's work with various dynamometers in his search to find a suitable instrument for measuring the strength of various muscle groups primarily for thera-

[2] Luther Gulick, *Manual for Physical Measurements* (New York: YMCA, 1892).
[3] R. Burton-Opitz, "Tests of Physical Efficiency," *American Physical Education Review*, XXVII (April, 1922), 153.
[4] G. L. Meylan, "Marks for Physical Efficiency," *American Physical Education Review*, X (June, 1905), 106.

peutic purposes.[5] Kellogg believed that an accurate rating of an individual's strength must be based on tests of all the important muscle groups and that a single group indicated very little. With his dynamometer Kellogg tested the strength of a variety of muscle groups, including nine different muscle groups of the arm and shoulder, eight different muscle groups of the hip and leg, four groups of the trunk, and four muscle groups of the neck. The practicality of use by schools and colleges is limited by the relative immobility and cost of the apparatus. The principle essential to the operation of this dynamometer involves the application of pressure by a piston to raise a column of mercury and, thereby, indicate the amount of pressure by the height of the column.

The same therapeutic emphasis that motivated Kellogg's work characterized the next significant step in the development of strength tests— Martin's resistance test.[6] In 1915, while involved in the aftermath of a poliomyelitis epidemic, Martin realized the need for a type of strength test to compare normal and affected muscle groups. He introduced the principle of resistance to pull and measured the breaking or elongation force, rather than strength exertion through an active effort. An ordinary flat-faced spring balance served as the measuring device, since it could be adjusted quite readily to meet varying conditions of proper alignment and pull. Martin's test involved eleven muscle groups on each of the upper extremities and ten groups on each of the lower extremities. However, the undue length of this original test prompted the adoption of a short form involving the strength of four pairs of muscle groups—pectoral, forearm flexors, thigh adductors, and thigh abductors. The short form correlated well (.94) with total strength as measured by the original battery. This high relationship led to the recognition of the general principle that the strength of a few muscles serves as a good indicator of the strength of the body as a whole. Hence, Martin made a lasting contribution to strength testing.

With the exception of Martin's work, the first quarter of this century saw the interest in strength testing decline from that manifested at the turn of the century. However the flame was rekindled when Rogers published his dissertation based on Sargent's Intercollegiate Strength Test.[7] Rogers standardized the testing procedure, constructed norms,

5 J. H. Kellogg, "The Value of Strength Tests in the Prescription of Exercise," *Modern Medicine Library*, II, 1896.

6 E. G. Martin, "Tests of Muscular Efficiency," *Physiology Review*, I (July, 1921), 454. This constitutes the only source of directions available.

7 Frederick Rand Rogers, *Physical Capacity Tests in the Administration of Physical Education* (New York: Bureau of Publications, Teachers College, Columbia University, 1925), Contributions to Education No. 173.

ran statistical validation studies, and developed the Physical Fitness
Index and the Strength Index. His work disclosed the relationship between muscular strength, physical condition, and athletic performance
and provided the boom to the development of physical education measurement. In recent years the only appreciable change in strength testing from the Rogers Test has been the increased use of functional or
dynamic testing (e.g., pulls-ups) and less stress on static testing (e.g.,
dynamometer tests).

The development of motor fitness testing resulted from the emphasis
during World Wars I and II on tests of the physical fitness of individuals
to disclose functional capacity for work. The basic and limited concept
of physical fitness—muscular strength, muscular endurance, and cardiovascular endurance—was expanded during World War II to include fundamental coordination and skills reflective of speed, agility, power, and
flexibility and was termed "motor fitness."

AN ILLUSTRATIVE PROBLEM

The focus of this chapter is provided by looking at the problem posed
in Chapter 7, specifically in terms of appropriate tests of strength and
motor fitness. What test of strength and what test of motor fitness, if
any, would be suitable for a junior high school physical education program, grades seven to nine, for boys and girls in light of overall appraisal? The answer lies in a critical analysis of the various tests that
are available.

In the ensuing presentation of available tests it will be noted that
a number of test items are part of different tests of strength or motor
fitness. The basic description of these items is contained in Appendix B
to avoid needless repetition and general reference. In delineating the
items for the various tests no further description of these common items
will be given, unless a particular difference or modification exists or
specific clarification seems indicated.

STRENGTH TESTS

Based on the description of the various measurement areas in Chapter
7, as introductory to the presentation of strength tests, suffice it to
reiterate two points. "Strength" is used in the context connoting two
components—muscular strength and muscular endurance. And strength
tests may be classified as either static or dynamic, wherein the distinguishing characteristic is movement.

Rogers Strength Test [8]

The Rogers Strength Test includes seven items—lung capacity, strength of right and left grip, back lift, leg lift, push-ups, and pull-ups; the latter two are combined to indicate arm strength. The gross score on these test items is referred to as the *Strength Index* (SI) and is derived by adding the scores for each item. Prior to administering the test, the age, height, and weight of the individual is recorded—age in years and months, height to the nearest half-inch in stocking feet, and weight to the nearest half pound in gym attire and stocking feet.

Lung Capacity. A wet spirometer (Fig. 8–1) is used to measure the number of cubic inches of lung capacity, that is, the amount of air that can be expired following fullest inhalation. In administering the spirometer test:

1. The spirometer should be placed at a height to permit testee to stand fully erect while inhaling.

2. Two deep breaths should be taken to obtain full inhalation before the test.

3. For the test, the inhalation should be full and steady.

4. Exhalation should be slow, steady, as complete as possible, and done with care that air does not escape through the subject's nose or around the mouthpiece.

5. The subject should bend forward in an effort to expel the maximum amount of air.

6. The tester should observe the indicator closely to note the highest reading.

7. The tester should note any discrepancies in technique of test performance, such as taking a second breath, and have the subject take the test again after clarifying the causative factors necessitating a retest.

Grip Strength. Grip strength is measured by a manuometer or hand dynamometer (Fig. 8–2) and expressed as pounds of pressure. In administering tests of first the right and then the left grips:

---

[8] Frederick Rand Rogers, *Physical Capacity Tests in the Administration of Physical Education* (New York: Bureau of Publications, Teachers College, Columbia University, 1926); and *Physical Capacity Tests* (New York: A. S. Barnes & Co., Inc., 1931). Norms are also available in SR (selected references) 3, 4, and 7.

Fig. 8–1. Wet spirometer. (Courtesy of Nissen Medart Corp.)

1. After chalking his hand, the subject places the manuometer with the convex edge between the first and second joints of the fingers with the dial facing inward.

2. During the test, the hands should not be allowed to touch anything.

3. A sweeping movement down or up with the elbow slightly flexed is generally used in squeezing the manuometer.

4. The manuometer is read to the nearest pound, and the dial is then set to zero.

Back Lift. A dynamometer mounted on a wooden bench with an adjustable chain and handle constitute the apparatus for measuring back lift (Fig. 8–3). The dynamometer scale reads from 0 to 2,500 pounds

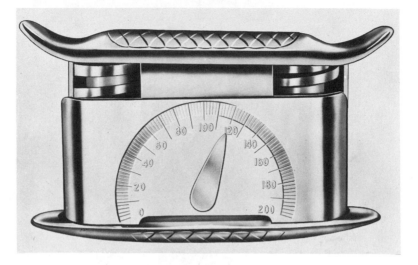

Fig. 8–2. Manuometer. (Courtesy of Nissen Medart Corp.)

in 10-pound intervals or units. A maximum indicator hand is connected to the dial hand and remains at the high point of a subject's pull. The handle may be taped to facilitate grasping by subjects. In administering the back lift test:

1. The testee stands on the apparatus with feet about 6 inches apart and parallel, positioned so that the internal malleoli of the ankles are opposite the dynamometer attachment to the base. Footprints painted on the base will facilitate proper positioning of subjects.

2. Gymnasium shoes should be worn. Under no conditions should high heels be worn during the lift.

3. After drying the hands with chalk, the testee assumes an erect standing position with fingers extending down the thighs so that the tester may adjust the bar to touch the finger tips.

4. The testee flexes at the hip so as to bend forward slightly with knees straight and grasps the bar near both ends with a combined grasp—one palm facing forward and the other palm facing backward. Caution is taken to insure that trunk is inclined only slightly forward, so as not to place an undue strain upon the low back.

5. Upon instructions the testee lifts steadily and forcibly directly upward, while the tester grasps his hands firmly to prevent slipping.

Fig. 8–3. Back dynamometer. (Courtesy of Nissen Medart Corp.)

6. The back should be almost erect at the end of the lift, and the feet should remain flat on the base. In either case of infraction, a retest should be given after proper chain adjustment is made. Lateral sway and backward lean should not be permitted. The tester should also be alert to detect any sudden jolt caused by a kink in the chain and resulting in an invalid reading.

Leg Lift. The same apparatus used for the back lift is necessary for the leg lift in addition to a webbed belt. The latter comprises a modification of the test technique to facilitate test administration and favorably influences test results.[9] The leg lift is the most difficult of the strength tests to administer. In administering it:

[9] Edgar W. Everts and Gordon J. Hathaway, "The Use of the Belt To Measure Leg Strength Improves the Administration of Physical Tests," *Research Quarterly* IX, No. 3 (October, 1938), 62.

1. The subject assumes the same basic position on the testing apparatus as for the back lift.

2. The chain is lengthened from one to two links as used for the back lift to permit a slight knee bend (115 to 125 degrees extension) with back erect while subject grasps the center of the bar, palms facing inward, by the pubic bone.

3. The belt is attached by a loop to the right end of the bar as viewed by the subject and then carried around behind the subject as low as is comfortable over the buttocks and hips. The free end of the belt is secured by looping it over, down, and around the other end of the bar and then tucking it between the body and the standing part of the belt on top of the bar. By so doing, the belt will hold securely during the lift but can be easily detached upon completion.

4. For the lift, the bar rests against the subject's thighs with hands either remaining in the middle of the bar or placed at opposite ends.

5. Upon instructions the subject lifts steadily and forcibly, directly upward.

6. Upon completion of the lift the knees should be nearly, yet not fully, extended to assure that maximum effort was recorded. Too much or not enough knee extension is regulated by adjusting the chain for retesting. Twisting the chain is often done to make length adjustments less than that provided by changing from one link to the next.

Pull-ups.[10] The suggested apparatus for this test consists of a horizontal bar from which rings are suspended. Audible counting is prescribed. In scoring, improper performance of a trial receives half-credit on the first four occurrences, after which no credit is allowed. For the girls the rings should be adjusted to the level of the apex of the sternum.

Push-ups. A 5-minute rest should be allowed between pull-up and push-ups tests, unless less than three pull-ups were recorded. The same concerns of audible counting and half-credit for faulty performance apply to push-ups as well. The test for boys consists of performing *dips*, whereas the girls' test is as previously described in Appendix B.

Arm Strength. Arm strength is computed by substituting the proper quantities in the following formula.

$$(\text{Push-ups} + \text{pull-ups}) \left(\frac{W}{10} + H - 60 \right)$$

[10] The reader is reminded that basic descriptions of common test items are contained in Appendix B.

where W = weight in pounds

H = height in inches (Disregard $H - 60$ if height is less than 60 inches)

Arm strength is the only item in the Rogers test that entails dynamic strength, that is, performance in pull-ups and push-ups as opposed to static strength testing using a dynamometer.

Scoring. Adding the scores made on lung capacity, right and left grips, back strength, and leg strength to the above computed arm strength gives the Strength Index. The SI serves as an indicant of general athletic ability and not of physical fitness. The strength index norms are based upon sex, weight, and age; for the leg lift, they are available either with or without the belt.[11]

Physical Fitness Index. On the basis of the achieved SI and the normal SI taken from the norm charts, the Physical Fitness Index (PFI) is computed, using the following formula.

$$PFI = \frac{\text{Achieved SI}}{\text{Normal}} \times 100$$

The PFI serves as a measure of basic fitness reflected in the status of general health and based primarily on muscular strength and muscular endurance. In interpreting the PFI, the median is 100, the first quartile equals a score of 85, and the third quartile is a PFI score of 115. Individuals scoring 85 or under are generally retested to verify the score. If the score is confirmed, a study with necessary referral is made to disclose the causative factors of low fitness and to derive an appropriately planned developmental program. Extremely high PFI scores should also be viewed analytically to detect possible instances of overstimulated, highly nervous, or overtrained individuals.

Regarding validity of the test, Rogers found that SI correlated about .85 with an athletic index composed of track and field and skill events. A study of PFI validity revealed about .65 correlation with medical judgment. Rogers initially obtained reliability and objectivity coefficients for the seven PFI test items ranging from .86 in the case of leg strength to .97 for lung capacity. Practice effects have been negligible. Corrected self-correlations for the battery was about .94, while those for the various test items ranged from .96 to .99. Rogers found the objectivity of SI to be .94.

Proposed PFI Test Modifications. The PFI battery has been the object of continual study and a number of suggested changes, perhaps the most

---

[11] Norms for boys and girls 8 to 18 and men and women 19 to 38 are available from Nissen Medart Corp., Cedar Rapids, Iowa.

significant to date being the utilization of the belt in the leg lift in 1938. Kennedy demonstrated that a cable tensiometer could be substituted for the back and leg dynamometer, which would result in comparable findings and no appreciable loss of validity.[12] An 800-pound capacity tensiometer was used for the back lifts and in conjunction with a lever system for the leg lifts to record performance up to 2,400 pounds. Clarke and Carter undertook a simplification of this battery from boys (N = 356) at different school levels to provide a means of estimating the true SI.[13] From this and related studies Clarke compiled a summary of equations (covering four school levels from upper elementary through college—boys and girls) which resulted in multiple correlations ranging from .977 to .998 between the SI and various test items comprising the simplified battery.[14] These equations enable the teacher to estimate the SI for each student, and hence the PFI, based on the leg lift and one or two additional tests.

McCloy Strength Test [15]

Whereas the Rogers Strength Test constituted a modification of the Intercollegiate Strength Test, the McCloy Strength Test represents a revision of the Rogers Test. The McCloy Test was designed to overcome three shortcomings of the Rogers Strength Test: (1) Breathing capacity does not represent a measurement of strength. (2) The arm strength scoring was found to penalize unjustly the small individual possessing little ability in pull-ups and dips and at the same time unjustly benefit the individual with above-average ability in these actions. (3) The method of positioning girls for pull-ups resulted in keeping the short girls so erect as to permit them to perform a disproportionate number of repetitions.

To correct these alleged shortcomings, the McCloy Test eliminated breathing capacity and revised the arm strength formula and the pull-ups for girls. Arm strength was determined by the following formula:

Boys:

Pull-up- or dip-strength score (in pounds) = 1.77 weight
+ 3.42 (number of) pull-ups or dips − 46

12 Frank T. Kennedy, "Substitution of the Tensiometer for the Dynamometer in Back and Leg Lift Testing," *Research Quarterly*, XXX, No. 2 (May, 1959), 179.

13 H. H. Clarke and G. H. Carter, "Oregon Simplification of the Strength and Physical Fitness Indices for Upper Elementary, Junior High, and Senior High School Boys," *Research Quarterly*, XXIX, No. 4 (March, 1959), 3.

14 H. Harrison Clarke, *Application of Measurement to Health and Physical Education* (4th ed.; Englewood Cliffs, N.J.: Prentice-Hall, Inc., 1967), p. 167.

15 Charles McCloy and Norma Young, *Tests and Measurements in Health and Physical Education* (3d ed.; New York: Appleton-Century-Crofts, Inc., 1954), pp. 129–53.

Pull-up-dip-strength score (in pounds) = 3.42 (number of) (pull-ups + dips) + 3.54 weight − 92

Girls:

Pull-up-strength score (in pounds) = .67 weight + 1.2 (number of) pull-ups + 52

Push-up-strength score (in pounds) = .78 weight + 1.1 (number of) push-ups + 74

The girls' pull-up was modified by using the horizontal bar instead of the rings and adjusting the height of the bar to within a half-inch of the lower level of the sternum.

The *General-Strength Score* consists of the sum of the strengths in pounds of the right grip, left grip, back lift, pull-ups, and push-ups. McCloy noted that this unweighted strength score represents with a high degree of accuracy the total strength of the skeletal musculature with the exception of trunk and hip flexors. A *General-Strength Quotient* is derived by dividing the unweighted strength score by the norm for strength according to sex, age, and weight and then multiplying this value by 100.[16] Thereby, a score of 100 indicates average strength for a given sex, age, and weight. In predicting strength, the validity of the general-strength quotient is reported as .94, the reliability as .94, and the objectivity as high.

McCloy devised an *Athletic-Strength Score* for boys by weighting the test items in his strength test to indicate the total strength usable in athletic performance. Either of the following formulas are used.

Long form:

Right grip + left grip + .1 back lift + .1 leg lift + 2 pull-up-strength score + push-up-strength score − 3 weight

Short form: As above without back and leg lift.

An *Athletic-Strength-Quotient* is obtained by dividing the athletic-strength score by the norm for strength according to age and weight given in the reference and then multiplying this value by 100. Using both test forms, McCloy obtained validity correlations of .91 for athletic-strength quotient with a criterion measure of six track and field events.

Through factor analysis McCloy has identified two elements in strength tests, namely, "pure" strength and strength dependent upon body size. To compute "pure" strength for boys, he advocated the formula:

.5 (left + right grip) + .1 back lift + .1 leg left + McCloy pull-up-strength score + McCloy dip-strength score

16 For norms based on leg lift without belt see *ibid.*, pp. 136–41.

This measure is deemed more suitable than either of the formulas for athletic-strength scores when strength is used as an indicant of general motor achievement. However, no norms are presently available.

Kraus-Weber Tests of Minimum Muscular Fitness [17]

Perhaps the most controversial test in physical education and yet the most provocative and influential test in terms of the significance of its findings for physical education and the American mode of living has been the Kraus-Weber Tests of Minimum Muscular Fitness. These tests were developed over a period of 18 years through the interest and experience of Dr. Hans Kraus in the relation between low back disorders and poor level of muscular fitness. The six tests selected for school children purportedly represent the most valid tests of a large battery administered in clinical experience. These tests are intended to indicate a level of strength and flexibility for certain key muscle groups below which the functioning of the body as a healthy organism seems to be impaired. While the authors do provide a means of scoring partial movements, as described herein the tests are graded on a pass or fail basis. As devised, it is intended that no warm-up be permitted prior to administering the tests.

Text 2: Abdominal Muscle Strength Minus Psoas (Fig. 8–4B.)
From a supine-lying position, neck firm, with feet held down by examiner, the testee rolls up into a sitting position.

Test 2: Abdominal Muscle Strength Minus Psoas (Fig. 8–B.)
From a supine-lying position, neck firm, knees flexed, heels close to buttocks, and feet held down by examiner, the testee rolls up into a sitting position.

Test 3: Psoas and Lower Abdominal Muscle Strength (Fig. 8–4C.)
From a supine-lying position with neck firm, the testee flexes both hips to raise the heels 10 inches and holds for 10 seconds while the examiner counts.

Test 4: Upper Back Muscle Strength (Fig. 8–4D.)
From a prone-lying position, neck firm, with pillow under hips and lower abdomen, and examiner holding the feet down, the testee raises chest, head, and shoulders and holds this raised position for 10 seconds while the examiner counts.

Test 5: Lower Back Muscle Strength (Fig. 8–4E.)
From a prone-lying position, arms on table with head resting on them, examiner holding chest down, the testee raises his legs off the table with knees straight for 10 seconds while the examiner counts.

[17] Hans Kraus and Ruth P. Hirschland, "Minimum Muscular Fitness in School Children," *Research Quarterly*, XXV, No. 2 (May, 1954), 178.

Test 6: Back and Hamstring Muscle Length (Fig. 8–4F.)

From an erect standing position without shoes, the testee bends slowly downward to touch the floor with the finger tips, holding contact for 3 seconds. The examiner should hold the knees of testee to prevent or detect any bend. Bouncing is not permitted.

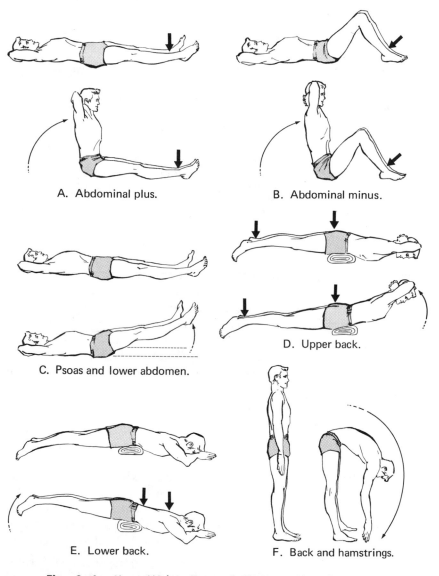

A. Abdominal plus.

B. Abdominal minus.

C. Psoas and lower abdomen.

D. Upper back.

E. Lower back.

F. Back and hamstrings.

Fig. 8–4. Kraus-Weber Tests of Minimum Muscular Fitness.

Kraus and Hirschland administered these tests to 4,458 American school children, urban and rural, and compared the results with those of 3,156 European children. This comparison disclosed failures of 57.9 and 8.7 per cent by American and European children, respectively. Subsequently a number of studies have been made in this country to determine the status of American children in different communities and after different types of physical education experiences. The findings derived from use of these tests on American school children have revealed several interesting relationships.

1. There is a direct, positive relationship between the caliber of the physical education program and performance on these tests.
2. Vigorous body-building activity occurring between repeated tests was noted to increase test performance.
3. The flexibility test produces the greatest number of failures. Girls have only about half the number of failures in flexibility as boys. In both sexes, the failures increase with age.
4. American children score well in minimum back strength.
5. For both sexes, a strength increase is manifested as age increases.

The validity of the Kraus-Weber Tests as measures of muscular fitness is often questioned. Attention should be directed to the fact that these tests were intended to indicate a minimal level of muscular fitness only. Criticism of their validity as measures of anything beyond their purpose is unjust, and, accordingly, their use for other purposes is improper. Also, many thoughtless physical educators have utilized the test items as exercises in themselves as the best means of developing muscular strength, and in so doing in the case of Test 3 (as suggested by test directions also) may be subjecting their students to an undesirable and possibly detrimental practice. These tests are economical both in terms of equipment and time; 2 minutes of testing time being required for each testee.

Cable-Tension Tests

Like the spring balance test of Martin, the cable-tension tests were originally developed by Clarke for use in testing the strength of individual muscle groups in orthopedic disabilities. The tensiometer, an instrument used to measure the tension of aircraft control cable, was adapted for use in muscle testing to record the pounds force exerted upon a cable as the result of a given muscular action. Thirty-eight different tests were devised involving muscular action of the fingers, thumb, wrist, forearm, elbow, shoulder, neck, trunk, hip, knee and ankle.[18] In developing these

---

[18] The current techniques and necessary equipment for administering the different cable-tension strength tests are described in: H. H. Clarke and D. H. Clarke, *Developmental and Adapted Physical Education* (Englewood Cliffs, N. J.: Prentice-Hall, Inc., 1963), pp. 73–96.

tests Clarke directed attention to determining which body position and joint angle resulted in the strongest muscular action for each test, as well as the influence on the test results of the position of the pulling strap and the effect of gravity.

The basic equipment consists of the tensiometer and a pulling strap, appropriate for the action involved, to which may be attached a 12- to 18-inch length of $\frac{1}{16}$-inch flexible cable leading to a 3-foot link chain. A Pacific cable tensiometer is shown in Fig. 8–5, secured to an aluminum

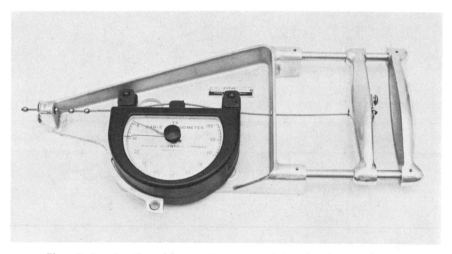

Fig. 8–5. Pacific cable tensiometer and hand grip attachment.

hand grip attachment. Figure 8–6 presents the test of knee extension to illustrate the testing procedure and equipment. The subject assumes a backward-leaning position on a table and extends his leg to an angle of 115 degrees at the knee with the pulling strap midway between knee and ankle joints at a right angle to the leg and hooked to the lower end of the table. In executing the test, caution must be heeded that the subject does not lift his buttocks, flex his elbows, or make other movements in an effort to enhance his test performance.

These tests have seen application in a number of studies. Clarke studied the effectiveness of the Wakim-Porter strain gauge, spring scale, Newman myometer, and the cable tensiometer.[19] The cable tensiometer possessed the greatest precision for strength testing as indicated by objectivity coefficients (.90 or above on 33 of the 38 tests and .82–89 for the others) and appeared to be the most stable and generally useful of

[19] H. Harrison Clarke, "Comparison of Instruments for Recording Muscle Strength," *Research Quarterly*, XXV, No. 4 (December, 1954), 398.

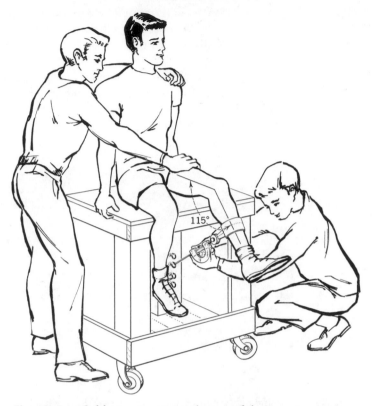

Fig. 8–6. Cable-tension strength test of knee extension.

the four instruments studied. Harrison developed Hull-scale norms for twelve of the tests for boys 7, 9, 12, and 15 years of age.[20] Clarke and Schopf constructed a battery of cable-tension strength tests for upper elementary schools boys ($N = 826$), grades 4–6. The battery consists of shoulder extension, trunk extension, knee extension, and ankle plantar flexion tests, which resulted in a multiple correlation of .98 with a composite criterion of 18 cable-tension tests. This study demonstrated the feasibility of using a battery of three or four cable-tension tests as a valid indicator of the overall body strength for upper elementary school boys.

Based on this finding, a project was undertaken at the University of Oregon under the direction of Dr. H. Harrison Clarke to develop valid short batteries for both boys and girls, grade four through college. This

[20] James Harrison, "The Construction of Cable-Tension Strength Test Norms for Boys Seven, Nine, Twelve and Fifteen Years of Age," Microcarded Master's Thesis, University of Oregon, 1958.

project culminated in a test manual describing the development of the tests and norms and containing complete directions and norms.[21] For validation (N = 576) the mean of the 25 most feasible of the 38 cable-tension tests constituted the criterion. The minimum number and specific strength tests needed to reflect adequately the total musculature were selected by multiple correlation. The tests selected for boys were shoulder extension, knee extension, and ankle plantar flexion which yielded multiple correlations of .963, .965, .955, and . 928 for upper elementary, junior high, senior high, and college levels, respectively. The tests and R's for girls were: (a) upper elementary school (.936)—shoulder extension, hip extension, and trunk flexion; (b) junior high school (.941)—shoulder extension, hip extension, and trunk extension; and (c) senior high school (.955) and college (.947)—shoulder flexion, hip flexion, and ankle plantar flexion. Two different battery scores are available, namely: Strength Composite (SC)—a gross score for the three tests, comparable to Rogers' Strength Index; and Strength Quotient (SQ)—Achieved Strength Composite/Normal Strength Composite × 100, comparable to Rogers' Physical Fitness Index.

Torpey conducted a leg extension test on 450 boys and girls, grade one to six, to determine the success with which such a test could be given as an educational experience for various reasons in a normal physical education class.[22] It was found that a class of about 28 children could be tested in 60 minutes by an experienced tester.

In using these cable-tension tests the matter of positioning and stabilization warrants careful attention in order to insure maximum reliability and objectivity. The tests as devised necessitate two testers—one to handle the tensiometer and pulling assembly and another to hold the subject in the proper position. Utilization of supporting straps might conceivably eliminate the need for one of the testers and at the same time remove the human variable from the stabilization function.

Three recognized limitations of the cable-tension technique are: (1) at least two tensiometers or a lever system with one tensiometer is necessary to cover the complete range of muscular force, (2) no aircraft tensiometer presently is sensitive enough to record force less that 5 pounds, and (3) some scale non-linearity is likely to occur within the range of tension covered, particularly before the middle. Notwithstanding, cable-tension testing presently constitutes a practical means of instrumentation for school application. Additionally, the previously de-

---

[21] H. H. Clarke and R. A. Munroe, *Test Manual: Oregon Cable-Tension Strength Test Batteries for Boys and Girls from Fourth Grade Through College* (Eugene, Oregon: University of Oregon, 1970).

[22] James E. Torpey, "Strength Tests for Young Children—A Pilot Study," *Research Quarterly*, XXXI, No. 2 (May, 1960), 238.

scribed mechanical adaptation of the cable tensiometer by Kennedy to function as a back and leg dynamometer, and the illustrated hand grip attachment afford versatility at considerable saving in cost.

Other Measures of Strength

MacCurdy Physical Capacity Test.[23] As determined by MacCurdy's test, physical capacity deals with the type of performance and achievement involved in vigorous team games and sports. The test is designed to measure the strength of large muscle groups and is intended for use in classifying high school boys into homogeneous grouping for physical education. The test items are identical to those of the Rogers Strength Test with the exceptions that the vertical jump is substituted for lung capacity; leg lift is without the belt; and arm strength in pushing and pulling is measured by a manuometer with a push–pull attachment, rather than by performance of chins and dips. The *Physical Capacity Index,* based on the formula of power = force × velocity, is computed by multiplying the total force in pounds of the dynamometer test items by the velocity, as measured by the vertical jump in inches, and dividing by 100.

The test was validated for senior high school boys, largely 16 to 17 years of age, using a dichotomy of athletes and non-athletes as the criterion. Biserial correlations of .93 for 200 cases, ages 15.5 to 20; .88 for 108 16-year-olds; and .86 for 109 17-year-olds were obtained. Reliability was computed to be . 93, and objectivity was also high. No norms were reported. However, the study presented growth curves for boys from 10 to 20 years of age in muscular velocity, muscular power, athletic performance, and muscular force.

Wendler Strength Index.[24] Wendler used the "Universal Dynamometer" to test 47 muscle groups of 474 men. Using the sum of these tests as the criterion, a multiple correlation of .933 was obtained with a short battery of thigh flexors, leg extensors, arm flexors, and pectoralis major. The best prediction of total strength, .956, was obtained on a battery including the foregoing tests except thigh flexors and with the addition of anterior trunk extensors, foot extensors, and thigh extensors. A multiple correlation of .938 was reported for six tests for women. Norms were not reported.

[23] H. L. MacCurdy, *Test for Measuring the Physical Capacity of Secondary School Boys* (New York: Bureau of Publication, Teachers College, Columbia University, 1933).

[24] Arthur J. Wendler, "An Analytical Study of Strength Tests Using the Universal Dynamometer," *Supplement to the Research Quarterly,* VI, No. 3 (October, 1935), 81.

Larson Strength Test (High School Boys and College Men).[25]   Larson proposed a test of dynamic strength for classifying high school boys and college men into homogeneous grouping for general motor performance. The test items consist of chins, dips, and vertical jump. Using a 15-item composite motor ability criterion, a validity correlation of .82 was obtained for college men and for high school boys. Scoring tables are given to convert raw scores into weighted standard scores for each test, along with a classifying device.

Stansbury Strength Index (High School Boys).[26]   As a predictor of the strength of high school boys, Stansbury proposed a strength index, derived by the following formula.

1.4 (8-pound shot-put in feet) + standing broad jump in inches
+ weight in pounds

Norm charts are available, and a *Physical Efficiency Index* is computed by dividing the strength index by the norm score and multiplying by 100. A correlation of .843 was reported between Stansbury's SI and Rogers' SI.

Carpenter Weighted Strength Test (Elementary School Children).[27] Carpenter proposed weighted strength tests and physical efficiency indices for grades one to three. Back and leg lift strength is eliminated because of the difficulty encountered in measurement on young children. The following formulas are used.

Boys' strength = .1 standing broad jump in inches + 2.3 (4-pound shot-put in feet) + weight
Girls' strength = .5 standing broad jump + 3 shot-put + weight

Tables for finding norms are included in the reference.

Anderson Weighted Strength Test (High School Girls).[28]   Anderson conducted an experimental study with 300 high school girls to note the validity of strength tests in predicting athletic performance. The test items consisted of McCloy's Strength Test, thigh flexor strength as determined by the Martin technique, and push and pull strength with the hand dynamometer and attachment. The items used as the criterion measure were the 40-yard dash, standing broad jump, running high

[25] Leonard A. Larson, "A Factor and Validity Analysis of Strength Variables and Tests with a Test Combination of Chinning, Dipping, and Vertical Jump," *Research Quarterly*, XI, No. 4 (December, 1940), 82.

[26] Edgar Stansbury, "A Simplified Method of Classifying Junior and Senior High School Boys into Homogeneous Groups for Physical Education Activities," *Research Quarterly*, XII, No. 4 (December, 1941), 765.

[27] Aileen Carpenter, "Strength Testing in the First Three Grades," *Research Quarterly*, XIII, No. 3 (October, 1942), 328. Scoring tables are also available in SR 4.

[28] Theresa Anderson, "Weighted Strength Tests for the Prediction of Athletic Ability in High School Girls," *Research Quarterly*, VII, No. 1 (March, 1936), 136.

jump, and basketball throw for distance. A validity coefficient of .55 was obtained for the test and .53 for a short form consisting of weighted results of thigh flexion, push, and leg lift. Reliability and objectivity of .90 was reported, and T-score norms are available.

In another study Anderson conducted with high school girls, tests of push, pull, vertical jump, forward bends, squats, and thigh flexors were added to the McCloy Strength Test.[29] Noteworthy of the findings was the correlation of .65 between McCloy Strength Quotient with vertical jump and the criterion—subjective athletic ability ratings of 300 girls. Norms were not reported.

Scott Push and Pull Tests.[30]   Scott devised two static strength tests of the arm and shoulder girdle for women using the manuometer with push-pull attachment. These tests are the vertical pull and the push and pull. The vertical pull test consists of one-handed simulated chinning action from a standing position against a wall. Reliability reported on successive trials was .90 for 55 college women and for 54 primary-grade elementary school children was .88. Using a spring scale instead of the manuometer, the reliability coefficient was .95 on successive trials for 140 college women. A validity coefficient of .59 was reported with Rogers Short Index. The second test, push and pull, consists of holding the manuometer close to the chest with arms horizontal and pulling against the handles and then pushing against the handles, using the heel of the hand if desired. Successive trial reliability was .91 with 62 college women. Validity was .49 with Rogers Short Index. T-scales for college women freshmen and sophomores are presented in the reference.

Progressive Resistance Exercise.   Since the early 1950s a type of test initiated by orthopedic surgeons for use as the basis for a muscular rehabilitation and development program has seen use in schools and colleges with normal as well as debilitated students. This exercise testing program is referred to as progressive resistance exercise.[31] The tests that are basic to this program consist of determining the 10-Repetition Maximum of a muscle group, viz., the maximum weight that can be moved through the desired range of motion 10 times. Through the use of a specially designed table and pulley arms and weights, this method permits the testing of almost any group of muscles that function together. Exercises involving little equipment and important muscular action have been used in schools and colleges. For example, the knee extension exercise

[29] Theresa Anderson, "Studies in Strength Testing for High School Girls," *Research Quarterly*, VIII, No. 3 (October, 1937), 69.

[30] M. Gladys Scott and Esther French, *Measurement and Evaluation in Physical Education* (Dubuque: W. C. Brown Co., 1959), pp. 288–92.

[31] Thomas L. DeLorme and Arthur L. Watkins, *Progressive Resistance Exercise* (New York: Appleton-Century-Crofts, Inc., 1951).

necessitates only an iron boot for adjustable weights and a padded table. While no norms exist for interpreting results, the reference cited provides a definitive description of procedure and equipment, which in turn are suggestive of applicability for the physical education teacher. This testing may obviously require more student time than certain tests of static strength (dynamometer and cable tension) but nevertheless may constitute a practical means of dynamic testing of selected muscle groups to give readily interpretable results on an inter- as well as intra-individual basis.

Research in Strength Testing. Research in strength testing continues to follow the two-pronged approach that has characterized it since the beginning. This approach concerns analysis of the intrinsic problems of muscular actions to indicate the desired positioning of the subject for valid results on the one hand and the development of measuring instruments and appropriate equipment and devices for facilitating assumption and maintenance of the desired position for testing on the other hand. In addition to determining the most effective position for a particular action, the first concern entails an analysis of the type of stabilization necessary for the action and the need for and effect of artificial counterpoise. The means of support should permit free movement in the desired action yet provide stability and effective positioning for counterbalancing muscular action. To illustrate what is meant by counterpoise, for arm depression in a sitting position, a strap across the upper legs would permit resistance to slight hip flexion on the same side as the arm action to counterbalance the arm action.

To devise appropriate support for a testing position is part of the second concern in strength testing research. This support is best provided by means of comfortable strapping in conjunction with a suitable table, a bench, and semireclining supports and pads. In addition to positioning equipment, the development of improved measuring devices is also implicit in the second concern. Researchers have directed attention to adapting or devising instruments that afford measurement of the complete range of muscular force, are accurate and adaptable, and provide a written record or tape of performance.

A development in the field of muscle testing that has manifested significant progress in both of the aforementioned concerns is the electronic myodynagraph designed by Beasley along with a carefully devised system of positioning.[32] It has been used to gather data on normal and

---

[32] This equipment and method of muscle testing was developed under the auspices of the U. S. Public Health Service and the National Foundation for Infantile Paralysis and is described in: Willis C. Beasley, "Instrumentation and Equipment for Quantitative Clinical Muscle Testing," *Archives of Physical Medicine and Rehabilitation,* XXXVII, No. 10 (October, 1956), 604.

impaired muscle groups of subjects ranging in development from elementary school children to outstanding university athletes.[33] The Beasley myodynagraph is a standardized instrument that offers a means for measuring muscular strength from 0.1 to 1,600 pounds with an accuracy of 1 per cent at any level. The actual measurement of force is made by a light cable tensiometer unit housed in a small insulating plastic cylinder, which responds linearly with stable calibration to axial tension loads. Fixation is obtained by various coupling lines, such as nylon cord, webbed strapping, chain, and steel cable, depending upon the maximum force anticipated. The tensiometer is used to measure direct force at right angles to the point of attachment to the body segment. By inserting a small block and tackle between the tensiometer unit and the fixed point, in addition to isometric tension it is possible to measure elongation force, which consists of the increased external force needed to overcome this initial tension and elongate the contracted muscles. A photoelectric ink recorder provides a record of the maximum amount, character, and duration of muscular effort. A specially devised rack of angle iron is utilized to provide varied fixation points and to facilitate positioning of a subject, so that any one of a large number of muscular actions can be tested. Considerable thought is also reflected in the appropriate strappings and padding of equipment that contribute both to accuracy and comfort in positioning the subject.

While the cost and elaborateness of the Beasley equipment render it impractical for teacher use, the principles and techniques for proper positioning in selected muscular actions and the associated supportive equipment that were developed may warrant consideration in test construction. It is anticipated that continued technological advances will result in electronic instrumentation that is technically, physically (as to size), and economically within the realm of feasibility for teacher use. Special laboratory adaptations of electronic instruments have already approached this end. For example, either a linear variable differential transformer (LVDT) or strain gage together with a suitable light-weight portable readout instrument can now be obtained at a moderate price, making easily readable and accurate instrumentation a reality. The prime concern in adapting a feasible electronic device for recording muscular force lies in the desire to overcome the limitations of the aircraft cable tensiometer as adapted by Clarke for this purpose, especially the tendency to exhibit some non-linearity within the range of tensional force covered. And while considerable progress has been made in strength testing in historical perspective, the need for further investigation con-

---

[33] The author participated in an unpublished research project at Yale University utilizing this equipment under the direction of Dr. Beasley, 1951 to 1954.

tinues, particularly in terms of positioning techniques and instrumentation that are readily applicable to the school population.

Specific Considerations

As the basis for knowledgeable selection, construction, and administration of strength tests, it is imperative that the teacher be cognizant of certain concerns that are peculiar to strength testing, as well as considerations fundamental to physical performance tests in general as described in earlier chapters. The specific considerations for strength testing follow.

1. *Instrument calibration.* The concern for the accuracy of instruments used for strength testing entails two aspects: certification by the manufacturer or a qualified technical inspector; and periodic on-site checks by the teacher. The frequency of calibration checks will be determined by the care and use, or lack of it, accorded to the instrument. After authoritative certification of instrument calibration, the teacher should apply an on-site calibration check before any change is likely to occur. Periodic re-checks can then be used to affirm a continued state of calibration and detect discrepancy. A practical on-site scheme consists of suspending special weights to record readings from the dynamometer or cable tensiometer over the range of force to be measured. The readings on each check should obviously remain the same for the respective weights. The special weights may be either a set of certified weights (rather impractical, costwise) or a set of improvised weights which have been certified and marked as to their precise weight. To illustrate, one 5-pound, two 10-pound, one 25-pound, and one 50-pound weights afford a means of checking the calibration of a dynamometer or cable tensiometer at 5-pound intervals from 5 to 100 pounds. Murray has described several procedures for checking the accuracy of testing instruments.[34]

2. *Determining testing angles.* The proper joint angles for static strength testing can be determined by a goniometer, template, or Leighton flexometer (see Chapter 10). In essence the template is a nonadjustable goniometer and consists of a life-size pattern for the prescribed angle cut from hardboard for placement in or on the joint involved as positioning is fixed. The flexometer, while more time-consuming to use, affords the most accurate determination. Close attention to accurate positioning is important not only for comparison between subjects but, perhaps more importantly, for re-tests on the same subject. Relatively slight variations in

[34] Kenneth Murray, "Calibration and Uses of Fitness Tests in Westmount High School, Quebec," *Supplement to the Research Quarterly,* XXVIII, No. 2 (March, 1935), 12.

angular positioning may alter the force exerted, depending upon the particular muscular action and angular range. For example, using a back-leg dynamometer Linford and Rarick found that variations of knee angle within angles of 135 to 165 degrees did not produce significant differences in recorded leg strength, whereas angles between 115 and 134 degrees resulted in significantly lower leg-strength scores.[35] And a study of cable-tension testing disclosed a curvilinear relationship between knee extension strength and 13 joint angles ranging from 60 to 180 degrees extension, in contrast to a linear relationship between shoulder-flexion strength and joint angles.[36]

3. *Grip strength.* Of the various static strength measures, grip strength appears to be most practical for teacher use. Also, since the inclusion of this item in the Rogers Test, studies have disclosed a direct relationship between an individual's grip strength and varying states of general body condition. Evidence has confirmed the suspicion that the grip span affects the reading obtained on manuometers or hand dynamometers. It is essential that the same grip device, and the same span setting if adjustable, be used for retesting. In studies of college men and women, instruments with adjustable grip settings gave the best results at a medium-small setting (5.25 cm) regardless of the grip size,[37] and pending corroborative study it would appear prudent not to exceed this setting for school use. When testing with a manuometer (see Fig. 8–2), it should be placed with the dial facing the palm of the hand as stipulated in the directions for the Rogers Test and not with the dial outward as prescribed by Fleishman.[38] The basis for this preference has been well confirmed.[39]

MOTOR FITNESS TESTS

Recent national concern over youth fitness, instigated to a large extent by the findings of the Kraus-Weber Test, has been manifested in the

[35] A. G. Linford and G. L. Rarick, "The Effect of Knee Angle on the Measurement of Leg Strength of College Males," *Research Quarterly*, XXXIX, No. 3 (October, 1968), 582.

[36] H. K. Campney and R. W. Wehr, "An Interpretation of the Strength Differences Associated with Varying Angles of Pull," *Research Quarterly*, XXXVI, No. 4 (December, 1965), 403.

[37] D. J. Cotten and Allen Johnson, "Use of the T-5 Cable Tensiometer Grip Attachment for Measuring Strength of College Men," *Research Quarterly*, XLI, No. 3 (October, 1970), 454.

[38] Edwin A. Fleishman, *The Structure and Measurement of Physical Fitness* (Englewood Cliffs, N.J.: Prentice-Hall, Inc., 1964), p. 166.

[39] D. B. Van Dalen, and C. A. Peterson, "A Comparative Study of the Administration of the Manuometer," *Physical Educator*, VII, No. 2 (May, 1950), 52; and C. L. Wear, "Further Study of the Administration of the Manuometer," *Physical Educator*, IX, No. 3 (October, 1952), 82.

development of several tests that are categorized as motor fitness tests. Motor fitness, to reiterate in brief the description given in Chapter 7, is conceived to be a limited but fundamental aspect of motor abilities that emphasizes capacity for efficient performance in vigorous work or athletic effort. California and New York are two states that responded relatively promptly in devising such tests. While the order of test presentation remains arbitrary, it seems appropriate to begin with the national test.

AAHPER Youth Fitness Test [40]

The AAHPER Youth Fitness Test was originally devised in 1957 by a committee of the Research Council of the AAHPER as a means of surveying the fitness of American youth as revealed by what a nationwide sampling of boys and girls in the various grades could do relative to selected aspects of fitness. During the 1957–58 school year, 8,500 children in grades five to twelve in 28 states were tested with the fitness test items and norms were derived. In 1960, percentile norms were prepared for college men based on approximately 2,200 students in eight institutions located throughout the United States. Similarly, norms were derived for college women from over 4,800 freshmen and sophomores in 57 institutions throughout the country. In 1965, new percentile norms were developed both on age and on the Neilsen-Cozens (California) Classification Index based on administration to a nationally representative survey of 9,200 boys and girls, ages 10 to 17 years. The same test items were used for the norm revision, except for inclusion of the flexed-arm hang instead of the modified pull-ups for girls.

The items for the revised test are:[41] (1) pull-ups (boys), or flexed-arm hang (girls); (2) sit-ups to a maximum of 100 for boys or 50 for girls; (3) 40-yard shuttle run on a 10-yard course retrieving two blocks, better of two trials; (4) standing broad jump; (5) 50-yard dash with commands, "Are you ready? Go;" (6) softball throw for distance; and (7) 600-yard run-walk to cover the distance as fast as possible, time recorded in minutes and seconds. It is suggested that the first four items be administered in one period and the remaining items in a second period, with a reasonable warm-up prior to the testing. The original test manual also included three aquatic tests without norms. The current manual contains the 1960 norms for college men and women, thus including the modified pull-ups rather than the flexed-arm hang for women. No statistical evidence of scientific authenticity is presented in the manual. However, consensus

[40] AAHPER Youth Fitness Test Manual (Rev. ed.; Washington, D. C.: American Association for Health, Physical Education, and Recreation, 1965). Norms are also available in SR 3, 4, and 7.

[41] The reader is reminded that basic descriptions of common test items are presented in Appendix B.

of available studies indicates that the reliability for all items is quite satisfactory. Some controversy does exist regarding the preferable number of trials for the different multi-trial items, but contradictory findings among critics afford no justification for change.[42]

The AAHPER Test has seen extensive use, despite some rather important limitations which should be recognized as illustrative of factors to avoid. One shortcoming involves the use of pull-ups and the flexed-arm hang which do not provide an adequate record of performance, because of the inability of some testees to score at all and the limited range of scores. Examination of the percentile norms for pull-ups for boys discloses that a score of 0 is assigned a percentile rank of 25, 25, 25, 20, 10, 5, 5, and 0 for ages 10, 11 and on through 17. A similar picture is obtained for the flexed-arm hang for girls with the high percentile rank being 15. Another shortcoming is found in the sit-up test wherein the method of scoring stipulates an arbitrary maximum which imposes a ceiling, thus failing to accommodate the total range of possible performance. The sit-up norms for each age, 10 to 17 years, assign a percentile rank of 85, 85, 80, 75 ,70, 65, 70, and 70 for the maximum of 100 sit-ups for boys; and 70, 70, 70, 75, 85, 85, 85, and 85 for the maximum score of 50 for girls. A third limitation concerns the 600-yard run-walk for which the directions stipulate three alternative test sites—track, football field (7 corners for 600-yards), and 50 by 50 yard square open area (11 corners); but no indication is given as to the type of running course on which the reported norms are based. The likelihood of disparity in performance time among the three different courses has been confirmed by a study on college men ($N = 100$).[43] It was found that the time scores for the track were significantly better than those for the other courses, and the times for the football field perimeter were significantly better than for the square course. (Strong intercorrelations were obtained— $\gamma = .82$ to $.87$—for the different running courses, indicating that the course had relatively little effect upon performance standing within the group. Also, test–retest reliability was good for the above courses; r's of .95, .92, and .92 in respective order.) Because of these limitations, the norms for the test items involved possess little, if any, value. For the arm-strength and sit-up events the shortcoming extends beyond the norms to the restricted value of the record of performance for individuals

[42] Studies that exemplify this disparity include: (1) Stephen E. Klesius, "Reliability of the AAHPER Youth Fitness Test Items and Relative Efficiency of the Performance Measures," *Research Quarterly*, XXXIX, No. 3 (October, 1968), 809; and (2) Cary Marmis, *et al.*, "Reliability of Multi-Trial Items of the AAHPER Youth Fitness Test," *Research Quarterly*, XL, No. 1 (March, 1969), 240.

[43] D. J. Cotten and Amarjit Singh, "An Evaluation of the Administration of the 600-yard Run-Walk on Three Testing Areas," *Research Quarterly*, XL, No. 1 (March, 1969), 226.

as well as groups. The final limitation to be mentioned, and one commonly expressed by teachers, is the "uncombinability" of item scores to get a composite or battery score with norms when desired, which constitutes a serious disadvantage of percentile norms.

AAHPER Special Fitness Test for the Mentally Retarded.[44]   In 1968 selected items from the AAHPER Youth Fitness Test were modified to render it appropriate for assessing the physical fitness of mentally retarded children. The modifications were:, (a) flexed-arm hang is the arm and shoulder girdle strength item for boys and girls; (b) sit-up is limited to one minute; (c) run-walk distance is 300 yards. Test development statistics are not given. Percentile norms are presented for each item by sex for ages 8 through 18 years, based on 4,200 educable mentally retarded boys and girls in the public schools of continental United States. The manual also contains a description of and standards for an incentive award system.

New York State Physical Fitness Test [45]

In 1958 a test was published for New York State designed to provide schools with a convenient instrument for periodic evaluation of status and progress in physical fitness of boys and girls in grades four through twelve. This test resulted from cooperative efforts of the State Education Department, testing and research experts (as revealed by an impressive list of consultants), and physical education staff members and school district administrators. The seven basic components, which are measured by this test to obtain a total physical fitness score, and the test items used to measure each component follow. Test–retest reliabilities are reported for each item as determined for grades 5, 8, and 11 in six school systems (N = 841) in 1963.

Posture
Posture Rating Chart.   Each pupil is rated on the basis of comparisons with figure drawings illustrating posture for 13 different body segments (see Chapter 10 for description). Reliability: boys–.96, .98, .97; girls–.93, .99, .98.

Accuracy
Target Throw.   The subject makes 20 overhand throws (two series of 10 throws separated by at least one other performer or equivalent time) with a 12-inch regulation softball. The target is a 2-foot circle (outside diameter), with the center 4 feet from the floor. The target distance is 30 feet from the throwing line for all girls and boys, grades four to six, and 35 feet for boys, grades seven through twelve. The total number of target hits (line

---

[44] *Special Fitness Test Manual for the Mentally Retarded* (Washington, D. C.: American Association for Health, Physical Education, and Recreation, 1968).

[45] *The New York State Physical Fitness Test: For Boys and Girls Grades 4–12* (1966 Rev.; Albany: State Education Department, 1966).

included) from behind the throwing line is the raw score. Reliability: boys
—.77, .79, .84; girls—.74, .79, .78.

Strength

For grades four through six, boys and girls, this is measured by the *Modified (or Bench) Push-up Test* with feet placed against a wall. The *Pull-up Test* with reverse grasp is used for boys and girls, grades seven through twelve. The chest must be pulled to the bar in the girls' modified test. Reliability: boys—.91, .93, .91; girls—.86, .86, .78.

Agility

Sidestep. The subject starts standing astride a center line and sidesteps alternately left then right across the center line and between two side lines 8 feet apart. The left foot must touch the floor beyond the left-hand line, and the right foot must touch the floor to the right of the right-hand line. The head and body must not be turned, and the feet cannot cross. The raw score is the number of line-crossings (center line included) made in 10 seconds. Reliability: boys—.75, .66, .77; girls—.72, .69, .77.

Speed

50-Yard Dash. The time to the nearest half-second is the raw score. Reliability: boys—.75, .84, .87; girls—.78, .89, .84.

Balance

Squat Stand. The subject squats with hands placed inside of the feet and slightly more than shoulder width apart, fingers pointing forward, and elbows against the inner knee surface. The subject then leans forward into a balanced position with the feet off the floor. The number of full seconds that the feet are off the floor constitutes the raw score. If balance is lost within 5 seconds, a second trial is allowed; the better of the two trials is counted. Reliability: boys—.88, .95, .95; girls—.72, .92, .98.

Endurance

Treadmill. The subject begins from a modified front-leaning-rest position, in which the hip and knee on one side are fully flexed so that the knee is between the arms and the thigh against the chest. The test movement consists of exchanging the position of the feet with both feet leaving the mat during the change. The number of leg changes performed in the specified time comprises the score. The time interval is 1 minute for boys, grades seven through twelve, and 30 seconds for boys, grades four through six, and all girls. Reliability: boys—.73, .92, .82; girls—.88, .87, .84.

Total score reliabilities without posture for grades 5, 8, and 11 were .89, .88, .89 for boys, and .87, .90, .89 for girls. Total score reliabilities with the posture component were .91, .90, .91 for boys, and .89, .91, .91 for girls. Statistical validity for the battery is not reported. Based on the scores for 1,645 ninth-grade boys and girls in 1956, the correlations between each component score (test item) and the total physical fitness score ranged from .35 to .67. The intercorrelations among the component scores ranged from −.02 to .49, with 36 of the 42 intercorrelations being .30 or below.

It is stipulated that the test order should be as listed when more than one item is administered during a class period. The reference cited is intended to serve as a manual for teachers and contains test directions, record forms, and norm tables derived from administering the test in 1962 to 10,855 pupils in 30 school districts geographically representative of the state, with the exception of the New York City school system. C-scale norms, expressed as achievement levels, are reported for boys and girls at each grade level with percentile rank equivalents for each component and for total scores with and without posture. The basic statistics (mean and standard deviation) computed for grades 5, 8, and 11 in the 1963 reliability study are reported in Table C-1 in the Appendix for each item and total scores, boys and girls.

New York State Physical Fitness Screening Test [46]

This test was developed in response to the recommendation of the President's Council on Physical Fitness that the basic school program include a screening test for the identification of physically underdeveloped pupils. Accordingly, the specific purpose of the New York screening test was to provide schools with a measuring instrument for boys and girls in grades four through twelve that requires little if any equipment, can be administered in one class period, and will provide a reasonable estimate of the pupils' physical fitness status. As designed it also provides specific information regarding four components of physical fitness that is useful in individual appraisal as well as evaluating performance of classes, grades, or other school groupings. The four components of physical fitness that were selected from those identified in research for the New York State Physical Fitness Test and their respective test items follow, with test–retest reliability computed for grades 5, 8, and 11 in seven public schools (N = 1,043) in 1963.

1. Agility: *Sidestep.* As described for the New York State Physical Fitness Test. Reliability: boys—.84, .75, .85; girls—.83, .77, .88.[47]
2. Strength: *Sit-up.* One complete sit-up is counted each time the testee returns to the starting position, if elbow touched knee. Alternate knee touch is encouraged, but infractions are not penal-

[46] *The New York State Physical Fitness Screening Test:* For Boys and Girls Grades 4–12 (1968 Rev.; Albany: State Education Department, 1968).

[47] These coefficients represent approximately .10 increase over those computed for this item on NYSPF Test in the same year with a slightly smaller N.

ized. Time limit: 1 minute for all girls and for boys in grades
4–6; 2 minutes for boys in grades 7–12. Reliability: boys—.92, .92,
.93; girls—.92, .85, .90.

3. Speed: *Dash.* The running course consists of two turning markers
(e.g., Indian clubs) placed on lines 45 feet apart with unobstructed
space at either end. Upon command, "Ready—Go," the testee
starts from behind the starting line and on the right of the marker
and runs to and around (counterclockwise) the second marker
and back to the first marker, rounding it counterclockwise to complete one lap. On the final lap the subject runs across the line and
on the right of the marker for the finish. The distance varies for
grades as follows: 1½ laps (45 yards) for all pupils in grades 4–6
> 2 laps (60 yards) for girls in grades 7–12
> 3 laps (90 yards) for boys in grades 7–9
> 4 laps (120 yards) for boys in grades 10–12

The raw score is the time recorded to the nearest half-second.
Multiple station testing with individual timers or the teacher calling the elapsed time to scorers as *"seven – five – eight – five"* is
suggested. If a marker is knocked down, the course is run again
after a rest period. Reliability: boys—.88, .78, .95; girls—.91, .95,
.87.

4. Endurance: *Squat-thrust.* In the squat position the arms may be
between, outside of, or in front of the bent knees. Time limit:
30 seconds for all girls and boys in grades 4–6; 1 minute for boys
in grades 7–12. Reliability: boys—.86, .83, .96; girls—.88, .91, .82.

Total score reliabilities for the four items were .90, .92, .94 for boys,
and .91, .92, .90 for girls. Statistical validity for the battery is not reported. The correlations between each item and total physical fitness
scores ranged from .65 to .76, based on 363 eighth-grade pupils in 1963,
and the intercorrelations among the items ranged from .21 to .50.

The manual contains details regarding development of the screening
test and complete directions and administrative suggestions, record
forms, and C-scale norms. All four items can be administered to a class
of 30 to 40 pupils within 30 minutes. The prescribed testing order is as
listed above. It is suggested that items one, two, and four be given on
a group basis with partners to one-half of the group at a time. The
norms are expressed as achievement levels (C-scores) for boys and girls
at each grade with percentile rank equivalents for each item and total
scores. The norms were derived from 11,145 pupils in 30 school districts
geographically representative of the state, exclusive of New York City.
The basic statistics for grades 5, 8, and 11 as computed in the 1963 reliability study are reported in Table C-2 in the Appendix for boys and
girls for each item and total scores.

This test has seen extensive use largely because of its administrative feasibility and the essentiality of the four components of physical fitness measured, in addition to the further advantage of a battery norm when a composite picture is desired.

The CAHPER Fitness-Performance Test [48]

This test was developed as the basis for establishing national norms of physical performance for Canadian children and youth. Although the particular combination of items in the test is unique, familiar items were utilized to permit comparison with other published tests. The test items for boys and girls are: (1) 1-minute speed sit-up, bent-knee; (2) standing broad jump, better of two valid trials with three practice trials allowed; (3) 40-yard shuttle run on a 10-yard course retrieving two objects, better of two trials from prone-lying starting position with hands at side of the chest and forehead on the starting line; (4) flexed-arm hang, reverse grasp with eyes kept at bar level and bar 6 feet from the floor; (5) 50-yard run; and (6) 300-yard run, three circuits on a 50-yard straightaway course with turning marker. The first three items are given on one day and the rest on a second day, with no alteration of testing order as listed for the second day. Prior test orientation and item practice are prescribed.

The manual contains test directions, instructions for the teacher, percentile norms, and the mean and standard deviation for each item and age, boys and girls; the last of which (basic statistics) are reported in the Appendix in Table C-3 for boys and Table C-4 for girls. The normative group included 8,998 boys and girls in 135 schools throughout Canada, selected to constitute a proportionally representative sample. Information concerning scientific authenticity is not presented, nor are item intercorrelations. Without this information, a shortcoming would appear to be posed by the inclusion of the 300-yard run for the stated purpose of indicating stamina or endurance. Available evidence affords the basis for questioning the validity of this item. Also, the limitation of the flexed-arm hang, as noted earlier for the AAPHER Test, was manifested by its failure to provide a score for some of the lower percentile ranks.

California Physical Performance Test [49]

This test for boys and girls, ages 10 through 18, reflects a deliberative study and revision of a six-item test adopted for use by California school

[48] The CAHPER Fitness-Performance Test Manual: For Boys and Girls 7 to 17 Years of Age (Ottawa: Canadian Association for Health, Physical Education and Recreation, 1966).

[49] The Physical Performance Test for California (Revised; Sacramento, California State Department of Education, 1971).

districts in 1966. The revised test was adopted in 1970 by the California State Board of Education, and its selection was based upon the following criteria: (a) involvement of some of the natural skills of human beings (running, jumping, and climbing); (b) inclusion of some measure of cardiorespiratory endurance; (c) involvement of a minimum amount of equipment; (d) administration geared to teachers with a minimum of experience; and (e) administration which requires a minimum amount of time.

The test events selected were: (1) standing long jump, 3 successive fair trials (not including fouls); (2) knee bent sit-up for time—60 seconds, heels not more than 12 inches from the buttocks, ankles held down, and elbows contacting the floor upon return; (3) side step, as for the New York test; (4) chair push-up—maximum of 50, done with feet on floor against the wall and hands grasping near corners of seat with partner firmly supporting the chair (non-folding type); (5) pull-ups; and (6) jog-walk, scored as the number of the 110-yard segment in which testee is at the expiration of six minutes. The order for item administration is not prescribed, but it is recommended that test events involving the same parts of the body not be given on the same day.

No test development statistics are reported. Percentile norms for boys and for girls are presented for each age (N = 1,060–1,277) 10 through 18 years, together with mean and standard deviation on each item. These are reported in summary form as basic statistics and quartiles in the Appendix herein, Table C–5 for boys and Table C–6 for girls. The test booklet covers the test purposes definitively as well as test administration and use of results. Development and warm-up activities, and common faults are given for the different test items. EDP forms are available.

The rationale for changes made in this revision for the California test warrants mention for resource purposes for the teacher in test construction. The softball throw for distance was eliminated because of administrative problems cited by teachers and supervisors. The time allocation for all ages on the knee bent sit-up was set at 60 seconds, since little difference was noted in performance for 30, 60, and 90 seconds on the previous test. The side step was added at the request of teachers and supervisors to include agility, balance, and coordination. The jog-walk for six minutes was selected as a more appropriate measure of cardiorespiratory endurance than the 600-yard distance, which some pupils could sprint. Of particular interest and in contrast to the AAHPER Test, the knee bent sit-up for time has replaced the straight leg sit-up because experimentation and analysis indicated the former to be the better measure of abdominal strength and endurance.

Indiana Motor Fitness Tests

Motor fitness tests for college men,[50] high school boys and girls,[51] and elementary school children[52] were developed at Indiana University. The test items involved in one or more of the various levels of tests, with supplementary description as necessary, follow.

1. *Chins.* With either forward or reverse grasp.
2. *Straddle Chins.* Students are paired up according to height. Testee lies on his back and partner stands astride erect and facing him. Testee clasps hands by a fingerhold with his partner and executes a pull-up, keeping his body straight and until the chest meets firm resistance from the partner's thighs. The partner should maintain straight supporting arms throughout.
3. *Push-ups.* For girls, the push-ups are performed from the knees, which are flexed 90 degrees.
4. *Vertical Jump.* Subject toes a line 1 foot in front of and facing the jumping board to mark the standing reach for the reaching hand.
5. *Standing Broad Jump.*
6. *Squat Thrust (20 seconds).*

College Men. In constructing a test for college men, Bookwalter proposed four Motor Fitness Indices involving the first five of the foregoing test items.

Index   I. (Chins and push-ups) × vertical jump ÷ 100.
Index II. (Chins and push-ups) × standing broad jump ÷ 100.
Index III. (Straddle chins and push-ups) × vertical jump ÷ 100.
Index IV. (Straddle chins and push-ups) × standing broad jump ÷ 100.

The use of a twelve-item criterion that was composed of at least two measures each of strength, velocity, motor ability, and endurance resulted in validity correlations of .86, .82, .84, and .81 for Indices I to IV, respectively. Although Index I or III is preferable, the acceptable valid-

[50] Karl W. Bookwalter and Carolyn W. Bookwalter, "A Measure of Motor Fitness for College," *Bulletin of the School of Education*, Indiana University, XIX, No. 2 (March, 1943); Karl W. Bookwalter, "Further Studies of Indiana University Motor Fitness Index," *Bulletin of the School of Education*, Indiana University, XIX, No. 5 (September, 1943).

[51] State of Indiana, *Physical Fitness Manual for High School Boys*, Bulletin No. 136, Department of Public Instruction, Indiana, 1944; State of Indiana, *Physical Fitness Manual for High School Girls*, Bulletin No. 137, rev. ed., Department of Public Instruction, Indiana, 1944.

[52] C. C. Franklin and N. G. Lehsten, "Indiana Physical Fitness Tests for the Elementary Level (Grades 4–8)," *The Physical Educator*, V, No. 3 (May, 1948), 38. Norms are available for all tests in SR 7 and in SR 1 for school tests.

ity of all indices permits use of the index most appropriate to a given teaching situation. The reference contains six-sigma scale norms established for 705 university men in a physical fitness program for the five tests, achievement scales based on McCloy's Classification Index I for each of the indices, and a rating scale for interpreting a derived index.

High School Boys and Girls. The motor fitness test for high school boys and girls is composed of test items 2, 6, 3, and 4. A validity of .77 was found using a criterion of 12 motor fitness items. The test score is computed by multiplying the sum of the raw scores on straddle chins, squat thrusts, and push-ups by the vertical jump score and then dividing the result by 10 and rounding off to the nearest whole number—the motor fitness score. Norms are available based on the McCloy Classification Index for boys and height-weight class divisions for girls. A specially designed score card is also found in the references cited.

Elementary School Children. The four-item test for high school boys and girls was adapted by Franklin and Lehsten for boys and girls, grades four to eight. The reference contains norms for each of the six groups determined from McCloy's Classification Index I. While the validity is not reported, this test is deemed important in view of the scarcity of such tests at the elementary level.

Other Motor Fitness Tests

The JCR Test.[53] This is a 3-item test comprised of the vertical jump to the nearest inch, chinning, and a 100-yard shuttle run performed on a 10-yard course with a backboard (at a 40-degree angle with the floor) at either end to facilitate reversal of direction. The standing reach for the vertical jump is measured with the reaching hand and its side toward the board. The items are to be administered in the order listed. The test purports to measure ability in fundamental motor skills that reflect the basic elements of power, strength, speed, agility, and endurance. Extensive validation was reported with four different criterion measures, resulting in coefficients ranging from .59 to .90. The .90 correlation was obtained with a 19-variable criterion comprised of items from accepted physical fitness tests. Total score reliabilities on different studies ranged from .91 to .97. Item test–retest reliabilities for two groups (N = 135 each) were reported as a .89 for jump; .92, .95 for chins; and .80, .81 for run.

The comparative test simplicity and satisfactory scientific authenticity suggest the potential value of this test to the teacher in appraising motor fitness for subjects with whom chins pose no appreciable scoring prob-

[53] B. E. Phillips, "The JCR Test," *Research Quarterly*, XVIII, No. 1 (March, 1947), 12.

lem. The reference includes six-sigma scale scoring tables based on male officer candidates, 18 to 45 years of age (N = 3,783) as well as equipment diagrams and specifications.

COOPER MODIFIED JCR TEST.[54] To simplify administration of the JCR in British schools Cooper modified the suggested order and items as follows: (1) shuttle run without turning board but with foot-touch over the line, (2) chins done on bar or beam, and (3) vertical jump, standing reaching-hand height taken while facing the board. Scientific authenticity is not reported regarding the modifications, which were made to facilitate administration. Norms and the fitness rating scale are given based on 900 English Midland schoolboys, ages 11 through 16 years.

Oregon Motor Fitness Tests.[55] Three different tests of motor fitness for Oregon schools were developed to cover grades four through twelve, boys and girls, in large part through the efforts of graduate students at the University of Oregon and Oregon State University. The items comprising the test for *upper elementary school boys* are: (1) standing broad jump, with trials on which testee falls back being repeated; (2) floor push-ups; and (3) knee-touch sit-ups, scorer kneels and holds feet down, firmly against his knees. For *junior and senior high school boys* the test consists of: (1) pull-ups; (2) jump and reach (vertical jump), chalk held to mark and reaching height taken with side to the wall; and (3) 160-yard potato race. The test item for *girls at all school levels* are: (1) hanging in arm-flexed position; (2) standing broad jump; and (3) crossed-arm curl-ups—a variation of the bent knee sit-up in which the testee raises the trunk to an erect sitting position a maximum number of times with arms folded against the chest and feet held down firmly by a partner, and without pausing or bouncing.

Multiple correlations of the tests ranged from .90 to .94 with a criterion comprised of a number of items representing the motor fitness elements identified as: arm and shoulder girdle strength and endurance, abdominal strength and endurance, muscular power, running speed and endurance, agility, and trunk flexibility. Other test development statistics are not given. T-scale scoring charts are reported (N = 8,900).

North Carolina Fitness Test.[56] This test was constructed to provide a measure of the elements of motor fitness that would be appropriate and easily administered in the North Carolina schools, grades four through

[56] *North Carolina Fitness Test* (Raleigh: State Department of Public Instruction, 1961). Norms are also available in SR 1.

[54] N. C. Cooper, "The JCR Fitness Test," *The Leaflet*, LXIV (May, 1963), 30; and described with norms in SR 3.

[55] *Motor Fitness Tests for Oregon Schools* (Salem, Oregon: State Department of Education, 1962). Rating norms are also available in SR 4 and 7.

twelve. The test items for boys and girls are: (1) bent-knee sit-ups for 30 seconds—done with alternate twisting to touch knee with opposite elbow, no resting, elbows touching the floor to minimize bouncing, and feet held flat on the floor; (2) side stepping for 30 seconds—starting with one foot touching a side line, testee begins side stepping with the other foot to touch on or over a second line 8 feet away and moves back and forth between the lines while facing forward and without crossing the feet to score as many line-touches as possible; (3) standing broad jump, fouls counting as trials; (4) pull-ups for 30 seconds (boys age 12 through 17); or modified pull-ups for 30 seconds (all girls, and boys age 9 through 11)—for equipment, two chairs of equal height (at least 30 inches) are positioned to enable two students to sit in them and securely support a bar 4 feet long and 1 inch in diameter; and (5) squat thrusts for 30 seconds. All items should be given in one period. It is suggested that the class be divided into five squads with each squad assigned to one of the test items and then rotating in the sequence listed until all items have been completed. The reference includes tabular presentation of means and standard deviations and percentile norms for boys and girls, ages 9 through 17 (N = 9,336). Details and descriptive statistics pertaining to test development are not reported.

Fleishman Basic Fitness Tests.[57] Fleishman conducted an extensive correlational study of physical fitness items beginning with 100 in the pre-testing stage, 60 in a pilot study and finally 14 tests administered to more than 20,000 boys and girls in 45 American cities to cover nine basic factors that were identified. The basic fitness factors and their respective items (with reliabilities) selected from this study were: (1) *extent flexibility*—extent flexibility test (.90); (2) *dynamic flexibility*—dynamic flexibility test (.92); (3) *explosive strength*—(a) 100-yard shuttle run on 20-yard course with foot-touch over the line on turns (.85), and (b) softball throw for distance without moving the feet (.93); (4) *static strength*—hand grip as for Rogers Test except that dial faces outward, best of three trials taken with at least a full minute of rest intervening (.91); (5) *dynamic strength*—pull-ups with underhand grip, i.e., palms facing (.93); (6) *trunk strength*—leg lifts (.89); (7) *gross body coordination*—cable jump (.70); (8) *gross body equilibrium*—balance stand (.82); and (9) *stamina*—600-yard run-walk as AAHPER Test to nearest second (.80).

The intercorrelations among the items ranged form .02 to .52 with 34 of the 36 coeffiicents below .33. When necessary, the battery length can

[57] Edwin A. Fleishman, *Examiner's Manual for the Basic Fitness Tests* (Englewood Cliffs, N. J.: Prentice-Hall, Inc., 1964); and E. A. Fleishman, *The Structure and Measurement of Physical Fitness* (Englewood Cliffs, N. J.: Prentice-Hall, Inc., 1964).

be reduced by eliminating the softball throw and still cover the basic nine factors. The test order is not prescribed other than that the extent flexibility factor should precede the dynamic flexibility test, and 600-yard run-walk should be the last or only item in a session. Percentile norms are reported for boys and girls, ages 12 through 18 years, although the age spread is more restricted for some items. A percentile equivalent table is provided for converting to stanine scale to permit combining tests into a battery index. The second reference contains norms for the other four of the 14 tests in the normative sampling, namely, standing broad jump, 50-yard dash, dodge run, and hold half sit-up. As a note of interest, the inappropriateness of pull-ups as a test for girls was indicated by the fact that zero pull-ups were assigned percentile ranks from 50 to 70 for ages 13 through 18.

Washington Elementary School Physical Fitness Test.[58] A 5-item physical fitness battery has been designed for use by the self-contained classroom teacher with elementary school boys and girls 6 to 12 years of age in the state of Washington. The tests include (1) standing broad jump—one practice and one trial; (2) bench push-ups—performed on a chair 14 to 17 inches high with feet against the wall; (3) curl-ups—bent knee sit-up while tester holds one hand on top of insteps and the other on top of knees; (4) squat jump—starting from crouch with fingers on mat and jumping up until feet are about 4 inches from mat and repeat; and (5) 30-yard dash—time to the nearest half-second. A maximum of 50 executions is allowed for each of the strength and endurance items— 2 ,3, and 4. Separate McCall T-scale norms are available for boys and girls (N = 2,100). T-scores for the tests are totaled to give the physical fitness battery score. Both individual test and total battery scores are interpreted in terms of rating of superior (top 15 per cent), average (next 35 per cent), poor (next 35 per cent), and very poor (bottom 15 per cent). Test development statistics were not reported.

Glover Physical Fitness Test Items for Primary Grade Children.[59] On the basis of content (face) and jury validation, Glover selected the following motor fitness items for use with boys and girls in grades one through three: (1) standing broad jump; (2) shuttle race—5 laps on a course around two wastebaskets placed on the inner side of lines 40 feet apart; (3) seal crawl—in a front leaning rest position with fingers pointing backward and resting on top of the instep, the testee pulls the body

[58] Glenn Kirchner, *Elementary School Physical Fitness Test* (Cheney, Wash.: Washington Association for Health, Physical Education and Recreation, 1959). Norms are also available in SR 7.

[59] Elizabeth G. Glover, "Physical Fitness Test Items for Boys and Girls in the First, Second, and Third Grades,: Microcard Master's Thesis, The Woman's College, University of North Carolina, 1962; and reported with norms in SR 1.

from starting to finish lines 20 feet apart with the score being the time to the nearest tenth of a second for the first hand to touch the finish line; and (4) sit-ups (bent knee) for 30 seconds, feet held flat by partner. Respective item reliabilities were reported as .83, .86, .82, and .84. Percentile norms are available for children (boys and girls together) ages 6 through 9 years.

Purdue Motor Fitness Tests. Motor fitness test batteries have been developed at Purdue University for senior high school girls and pre-adolescent boys. For the former Arnett studied four short batteries and recommended one consisting of modified pull-up, 600-yard run, and standing broad jump (validity, .755; reliability, .848).[60] Ismail and Cowell devised four batteries for boys 10 to 12 years of age.[61] The regression equation for battery I is: 3.319 standing broad jump + 1.596 softball throw for distance + 15.371 chins + 188.640. The other batteries include two of the three items. Validity ranged from .876 to .904 with 12-item composite criterion; estimated reliability for battery I was .817.

PCPF Screening Test.[62] As a means of identifying physically under-developed boys and girls, 10 years of age and older, the President's Council on Physical Fitness proposed the following test items and minimal standards: (1) pull-ups for boys—minimum number of 1, 2, and 3 for age brackets of 10–13, 14–15, and 16–17 years, respectively; or modified pull-ups for girls—8 for all ages; (2) sit-ups—14 for boys, 10 for girls; and (3) squat thrusts for 10 seconds—4 for boys, 3 for girls. Test development data were not given.

Marine Corps League Physical Fitness Test.[63] The Marine Corps League has designed a program for ages 3 through 12 to encourage development in basic exercises and to award scores indicative of general physical fitness. The program consists of the following five competitive exercises: pull-ups (modified for girls); bent-knee sit-ups, with feet held down; standing broad jump; push-ups (modified for girls); and shuttle-run—300 yards around markers 60 yards apart for grades 7–12, and 40 yards on a 10-yard course retrieving two blocks for grades 3–6. Raw scores are assigned point values to a maximum of 100 for each item on two bases, for individual records and for meet scoring. Participating

[60] Chappelle Arnett, "The Purdue Motor Fitness Test Batteries for Senior High School Girls," *Research Quarterly*, XXXIII, No. 3 (October, 1962), 323.

[61] A. H. Ismail and C. C. Cowell, "Purdue Motor Fitness Test Batteries and a Development Profile for Pre-Adolescent Boys," *Research Quarterly*, XXXIII, No. 4 (December, 1962), 553.

[62] *Youth Physical Fitness: Suggested Elements of a School-Centered Program* (Washington, D. C.: U. S. Government Printing Office, 1961).

[63] *National Marine Corps League Physical Fitness Program*, School Edition (Marine Corps League, 939 N. Kenmore Street, Arlington, Virginia 22201).

schools administer the tests in the spring, and students attaining 250 or more points are eligible to receive a "Certificate of Athletic Accomplishment." Regional interscholastic invitational meets are conducted annually in four divisions for junior and senior high school boys and girls. The manual contains directions and scoring scheme for three alternate exercises recommended for individual purposes and intramural competition; these are softball throw for distance, 50-yard dash, and 600-yard run-walk.

A.A.U. Physical Fitness and Proficiency Test.[64] The Amateur Athletic Union of the U.S. has published standards designed to motivate boys and girls to increase athletic sports participation for the development of physical fitness. Certificates of achievement are available for youngsters who meet the standards in five required and one optional events. The required events are sprints, walk and run, sit-ups, pull-ups, and standing broad jump. The optional items are push-ups, softball throw for distance, continuous hike for distance, and running high jump. The distances vary for age in running and walking items, and modified pull-ups and push-ups are prescribed for girls and for boys under 10 years of age. Separate standards apply to boys and girls, presented in two-year age categories from 6 to 15 and in final grouping for 16 to 18 year-olds.

The University of Illinois Motor Fitness Tests.[65] Cureton identified by factor analysis six components of motor fitness—balance, flexibility, agility, strength, power, and endurance. Two tests batteries were developed: one of 14 items, and another with 18 items and requiring no apparatus. The 14-item Motor Fitness Screen Test includes foot and toe balance, squat stand, trunk extension flexibility, trunk flexion, sitting, extension press-ups, man lift and let down, leg lifts and sit-ups, medicine ball put, Illinois Agility Run, skin the cat, bar or fence vault, chinning, standing broad jump, and mile run. Validity was .87 with a 30-item criterion; reliability, .91. For situations requiring more administrative simplicity a 7-item Short Screen Test was proposed, scored as pass or fail, to screen those poor in ability without demanding a strenuous effort for the majority of individuals. The items include dive and roll, medicine ball put, bar vault, chinning, leg lifts and sit-ups, breath holding, and man lift.

Associated with the Illinois Tests but not included in the basic reference are the Motor Fitness Tests for High School Girls,[66] consisting of two forms—a single period test of 6 items and a double period test of 12 items. The following pairs comprise the items included: foot and

[64] Amateur Athletic Union, 231 West 58th Street, New York City.

[65] Thomas K. Cureton, *Physical Fitness Appraisal and Guidance* (St. Louis: The C. V. Mosby Co., 1947), Chap. 13.

[66] Mary E. O'Connor and Thomas K. Cureton, "Motor Fitness Tests for High School Girls," *Research Quarterly,* XVI, No. 4 (December, 1945), 302.

toe balance and dizziness recovery; trunk extension and trunk flexion; kneeling jump and Illinois Agility Run; sit-ups and kneeling push-ups; basketball throw and standing broad jump; and squat thrust (30 seconds) and Brouha Step Test. Test item correlations with the composite item score ranged from .39 to .62. Norms are available, based on a limited sample.

Cleveland Motor Efficiency Test (High School Boys and Girls).[67] An 8-item test of motor fitness has been developed in the Cleveland senior high schools. The items include agility run, trunk flexion, standing broad jump, squat balance (boys) or foot balance (girls), pull-ups, and a step test. No validity is reported. Norms are given, based on the scores of 9,000 boys and 9,000 girls.

U.S. Office of Education Tests. The U.S. Office of Education was instrumental in the development of several motor fitness tests through appointing a special committee on wartime physical education for high school and also for college. The reports of these committees included suggested fitness test items.[68]

The test for high school boys involves selecting 10 items according to a specified procedure from the following: push-ups, pull-ups, dips, rope climb (15 feet), bar vault, sit-ups, hanging half lever, leg lift, forward bend, back twist, potato race, jump and reach, standing broad jump, running high jump, 100-yard dash, 440-yard run, and 880-yard run. The test for high-school girls includes standing broad jump, basketball throw for distance, potato race, sit-ups, squat thrust (10 seconds), push-ups, or pull-ups. Validity is not reported. Scoring scales are available, and for the girls performance levels are available along with information relative to the amount of improvement to be expected.

The test for college men entails selection of 10 items from three categories: *arm and shoulder girdle*—pull-ups, push-ups, rope climb (20 feet), dips, and bar vault; *abdomen*—sit-ups, squat thrust (20 seconds), leg lift, and leg raising from a hanging position; and *back and legs*—jump and reach, squat thrust, standing broad jump, 100-yard dash, 880-yard run, and running high jump. The test for college women includes 5 items: *endurance*—run-ratio (50 yards to 200 yards), continuous squat thrusts, or any of the cardiovascular tests; *arm and shoulder girdle*

[67] H. V. Fitchpatrick and George Kozacs, *Motor Efficiency Tests,* Bulletin No. 37, Bureau of Education Research (Cleveland: Cleveland Public Schools, 1944).

[68] Committee Report, "Physical Proficiency Levels for High School Girls," *Education for Victory,* III, March 3, 1945 and May 3, 1945; U. S. Office of Education, *Physical Fitness Through Physical Education for the Victory Corps,* Pamphlet No. 2 (Washington, D. C.: U. S. Government Printing Office, 1942); U. S. Office of Education, *Handbook on Physical Fitness for Colleges and Universities* (Washington, D. C.: U. S. Government Printing Office, 1943).

strength—chinning, floor dips, hanging in an arm flexed position, and dynamometer tests of shoulder retraction; *abdominal strength*—sit-ups, and sit-ups in V position; *foot strength*—20-yard hop and hopping in place; and *body control*—the Humiston Test, run-jump-throw test, and a test of posture. No validity is reported for either the men's or women's test.

NSWA Physical Performance Test (High School Girls).[69] A Research Committee of the National Section on Women's Athletics [70] devised a motor fitness test that includes (1) standing broad jump; (2) basketball throw; (3) potato race—as AAHPER Test shuttle run; (4) push-ups; (5) pull-ups, bar 42 inches above floor, reverse grasp, pull to chest-to-bar position; (6) sit-ups, feet 24 to 30 inches apart, fingers touching behind neck; (7) squat thrust (10 seconds), to indicate agility; and (8) squat thrust (30 seconds), as a partial measure of endurance. When limiting factors prevent giving the 8-item test, a short form may be used consisting of standing broad jump, basketball throw, potato race *or* 10-second squat thrust, sit-ups, and push-ups *or* pull-ups. A sigma-scale scoring table is available, along with a table of expected improvement, based on the actual improvement of 4,500 girls in 25 different high schools.

Iowa Physical Fitness Battery (College Women). Scott and French describe a number of test batteries, consisting of various combinations of 6 test items.[71] Six of these batteries along with the correlations with the criterion—work output on the ergometer—are listed below.

Chair stepping, sit-ups	.634
Vertical pull, chair stepping, sit-ups	.666
Vertical pull, obstacle race, sit-ups	.650
Vertical pull, sit-ups, bounce, chair stepping	.669
Vertical pull, obstacle race, sit-ups, bounce	.651
Vertical pull, obstacle race, sit-ups, bounce, chair stepping	.686

T-scales for these tests appear in the reference, affording the basis for making a student profile chart showing comparative scores on the separate tests as well as a single composite score.

California Physical Fitness Pentathlon (Junior High School to Junior College Boys).[72] In this fitness pentathlon the test items are divided

[69] Eleanor Metheny (Chairman), "Physical Performance Levels for High School Girls," *Journal of Health and Physical Education*, XVI, No. 6 (June, 1945), 308. Scoring table is available in SR 4 and 7.

[70] Now designated as the Division for Girls' and Women's Sports (DGWS), AAHPER.

[71] M. Gladys Scott and Esther French, *Measurement and Evaluation in Physical Education* (Dubuque: W. C. Brown Co., 1959), chap. 8.

[72] "The California Physical Fitness Pentathlon," *Bulletin of the California State Department of Education*, XI, No. 8 (November, 1942).

into the following groups: I—standing broad jump, standing hop, step and jump; II—pull-ups, rope climb, push-ups; III—combination 75- and 150-yard run, 150- and 220- and 300-yard run; IV—bar snap for distance, bar or fence vault; and V—frog stand, sit-ups, Burpee Test. One event is selected from each group and scaled scores are totaled. Available norms are based on the California classification plan. Scientific authenticity is not reported.

Elder Motor Fitness Test (High School Boys).[73] For this test Elder utilized the composite score on 14 motor fitness items as the criterion for selection of test items. The test includes push-ups, standing broad jump, trunk flexion, Cozens' dodge run, and squat thrusts (20 seconds). The test differentiated well between eight groups categorized according to their "physical fitness" and ranging from outstanding athletes to students with poor attendance due to illness. Six-sigma scale norms are available, based on the California classification plan.

Illinois High School Physical Condition Test (High School Boys).[74] A five-item test consisting of pull-ups, squat jumps, sit-ups, push-ups, and 1-mile run was developed in Illinois for high school boys. Standards of performance are available for ages 13 through 18.

Physical Fitness Achievement Standards for Youth (High School Boys).[75] Through the AAHPER-Armed Forces Committee, the Armed Forces proposed certain physical fitness achievement standards to assist in promoting physical fitness among high school youth. Standards were established in two areas, physical performance and aquatics. The Physical Performance Standard consists of five tests, one selected from each of the following (achievement levels appear in parentheses):

Group 1   Hop, step, and jump—three trials (24 feet); three continuous broad jumps, three trials (22½ feet); jump and reach (vertical jump, 19 inches); or standing broad jump (87 inches)

Group 2   Rope climb, one trial (15 feet in 20 seconds); pull-ups (6); dips (6); or sit-ups (45)

Group 3   150-yard shuttle run, 25-yard course (27 seconds); or hurdle dodge run (38 seconds)

Group 4   Softball throw, three trials with 15-foot run (175 feet); basketball throw, three trials with 15-foot run (81 feet); or medicine ball put, three trials from 7-foot circle with 6-pound ball (37 feet)

Group 5   300-yard run (42 seconds); or 250-yard shuttle run, 25-yard course (49 seconds)

[73] Haskell P. Elder, "Appraising the Physical (Motor) Fitness of Junior High School Boys," Microcard Doctoral Dissertation, Springfield College, 1958.

[74] *Illinois High School Physical Condition Test and Standards of Performance,* Bulletin No. 6, Office of Public Instruction, State of Illinois, September, 1944.

[75] AAHPER-Armed Forces Committee, "Physical Fitness Achievement Standards for Youth," *Journal of AAHPER,* XXII, No. 5 (May, 1951), 13.

The Aquatic Standard is comprised of five test items—relaxed self-support, swimming strokes, 200-yard distance swim, submerge and underwater swim, and jumping and self-support.

The established achievement levels represent the mean performance of an approximately representative national sample of young men of college entrance age. No adjustment is made for age, height, or weight.

All-around Muscular Endurance Test (High School Boys and Young Men).[76] Cureton and associates proposed a three-item test selected from 28 tests of endurance for males between 15 and 25 years of age. The items are pull-ups, sitting tucks, and mile run. The *sitting tuck* is performed from a sitting position, hands on hips, and legs extended with feet about 6 to 8 inches from the floor. The test action consists of flexing hips and knees fully so as to draw knees to the chest and then return to starting position. The score is the number of flexions performed with the feet being kept off the floor. Norms are available.

Yale Physical Fitness Test (College Freshmen).[77] A test was devised at Yale University to appraise the motor fitness of freshmen students. The six-item test was selected on a twofold basis—capable of being administered accurately with little equipment, and significant in indicating the overall strength of different body parts. The test items and the minimum standards for the physical education program are pull-ups (8), push-ups (25), sit-ups (50); fence vault (4 feet 6 inches), standing broad jump (86 inches), and vertical jump (18 inches). Statistical analysis of scientific authenticity and norms are not available. The Harvard Step (Brouha) Test was initially included in the battery as an endurance measure but was discontinued because of the testing time involved with large numbers.

Tests of United States Armed Forces

Since the beginning of World War II, the Armed Forces have developed and put to extensive use motor fitness tests designed primarily to be given to large numbers in a short period of time and with little necessary equipment. Although the military connotation of fitness and the age group (except for college) may render the appropriateness of some of these tests questionable for teacher use, they do at least possess value for resource purposes.

Navy Standard Physical Fitness Test.[78] The Navy Test was the first

[76] T. K. Cureton, *et al.*, "Endurance of Young Men," *Society for Research in Child Development*, X, Serial No. 40, No. 1, 1945.

[77] T. Erwin Blesh and Alfred E. Scholz, "Ten-Year Survey of Physical Fitness Tests at Yale University," *Research Quarterly*, XXVIII, No. 4 (December, 1957), 321.

[78] United States Navy, *Physical Fitness Manual for the U. S. Navy*, Bureau of Naval Personnel, Training Division, Physical Section, 1943, chap. 4. T-scores are also available in SR 4.

physical fitness test of the Armed Forces to be devised and used extensively. It consists of the following items: (1) squat thrust for 1 minute;
(2) sit-ups, feet held down with soles against the knees of an assistant;
(3) push-ups, starting from the down position; (4) squat jumps; and
(5) pull-ups. Test directions stipulate a pretest warmup, instruction,
demonstration and practice trials of test items, and also a 5-minute rest
between items. T-scores constructed from the raw scores of conditioned
naval personnel are available. Test development statistics for the test
are not reported.

Army Air Force (AAF) Physical Fitness Test.[79]   The Army Air Force
devised a test involving these items: (1) chinning; (2) sit-ups—maximum number done in 2 minutes, feet held down with soles against knees
of an assistant; and (3) 300-yard shuttle run—a stake 18 inches high is
placed in the center of 4- to 6-foot lanes on both starting and finish
lines, subject must run around stakes, and time is to the nearest second.
Indoors, the shuttle run is 250 yards on a 25-yard course with 45-degree
angle turning boards. Scores on the three items were combined by a
standard scoring scale and norms were prepared. The test correlated .86
with the sum of 15 selected items used as the criterion. In 1956, as the
test for the Air Force (USAF), it was modified by eliminating the time
limit for sit-ups.[80]

Army Tests.   The *Army Physical Efficiency Test*[81] was devised as a
10-item test and, in the interest of adminstrative economy, was revised
to include seven and then five items—pull-ups, squat jumps, push-ups,
sit-ups, and a 300-yard shuttle run on a 60-yard course. An alternate
battery for indoors includes either a 250-yard shuttle run or 60-second
squat thrust for the 300-yard shuttle run. The *Army Specialized Training Division Test*,[82] for which two days are needed, includes push-ups,
squat jumps, sit-ups, pull-ups, 100-yard pick-a-back carry, Burpee test
(squat thrust for 10 seconds), and a 300-yard run.

Subsequently, three other Army tests were published. The *Army
Minimum Physical Fitness Test*[83] consists of one item selected from each
of the following six pairings: squat bender *or* squat stretch; push-ups *or*
8-count push-ups; sit-ups *or* body twist; leg over *or* leg spreader; squat

[79] Leonard A. Larson, "Some Findings Resulting from the Army Air Force Physical
Training Program," *Research Quarterly*, XVII, No. 2 (May, 1946), 144.

[80] Air Force Manual, 160–26, *Physical Conditioning* (Washington, D. C.: U. S.
Government Printing Office, 1956).

[81] U. S. Army, *Basic Field Manual*, FM21–20, Physical Training (Washington,
D. C.: U. S. Government Printing Office, 1946).

[82] Services of Supply, ASTP, *Programs of Physical Training* (Washington, D C.:
War Department, 1943).

[83] Department of the Army Technical Manual 21–200, Change No. 4, *Physical
Conditioning* (Washington, D. C.: U. S. Government Printing Office, May 26, 1965).

thrust *or* mountain climber; and stationary run *or* half-mile run. The *Physical Combat Proficiency Test* [84] entails five items—40-yard low crawl, horizontal ladder hanging travel, dodge run and jump, grenade throw, and one-mile run. The items for the *Airborne Trainee Physical Fitness Test* [85] and minimum standards are: (1) chins—6; (2) knee bender for 2 minutes—80, standing with hands on hips, feet slightly apart, thumbs on the back, and elbows retracted the subject bends the knees fully, leaning forward from the hips, puts arms between the legs until extended fingers touch the floor, and then returns to the starting position; (3) push-ups—22; (4) bent-knee sit-up without support—20; and (5) 1-mile run—8½ minutes.

The *WAC Physical Fitness Rating* [86] utilized by the Women's Army Corps included knee dips or full dips, sit-ups, wing lifts, and squat thrusts. Directions for administering and scoring are found in the reference.

Marine Corps Physical Fitness Test.[87]—This test, designed to ascertain a minimal level of physical fitness for corpsmen, consists of the following items and standards for under age 30 and age 30 and over: pull-ups (5,2); push-ups (28,18); sit-ups for 2 minutes (20,15); squat thrusts for 1 minute (26,21); and 300-yard shuttle run (53 and 57 seconds). The reference contains a scoring chart for the Reserve Physical Fitness Test points, except for the recent substitution of squat thrusts for leg lifts, available from the author.

Specific Considerations

Basic to knowledgeable selection, construction, and administration of motor fitness tests, it becomes essential for the teacher to understand important characteristics that are peculiar to tests of this type or necessitate more specific explanation to supplement the concerns previously discussed for constructing and administering physical performance tests. The specific considerations for tests of motor fitness are arbitrarily classified for discussion purposes into two groups; one dealing with prevalent oversights in existing tests and the second with other considerations.

Common Shortcomings in Available Tests. Some testing oversights have been briefly mentioned in the foregoing description of available

[84] *Ibid.*

[85] Department of the Army Technical Manual 21–200, Change No. 3, *Physical Conditioning* (Washington, D. C.: U. S. Government Printing Office, July 11, 1963).

[86] WAC Department, *WAC Physical Fitness Rating*, Training Circular No. 40 (Washington, D. C.: U. S. Government Printing Office, 1944).

[87] J. T. Fisher, "Marine Corps Physical Fitness Programs," *Journal of Physical Education*, LXV (March–April, 1968), 120; and personal correspondence with the author at West Chester State College in Pennsylvania.

tests. Neither the format nor purpose of these descriptions afforded adequate coverage of salient test limitations. But particular attention to common shortcomings is most important in view of the (a) apparent tendency of many teachers to accept published tests without critical analysis and (b) failure of test users to recognize fundamental errors or limitations in tests. Only through identification and avoidance of these shortcomings can tests be improved and render their potential contribution in terms of meaningful results. Common shortcomings in available tests include the following:

1. *Inadequate record of performance.* The failure to provide an adequate record of performance is especially vital in instances where test items are combined to form a composite or battery score; otherwise the limitation is confined to difficulty in rendering meaningful interpretation of score performance on a particular item. Prevalent shortcomings of this type primarily entail an incomplete determination of minimum and/or maximum performance scores and may be attributable to (a) the inappropriate nature of the test task itself or (b) the imposition of an arbitrary repetition maximum or insufficient time restriction. Both of these shortcomings were illustrated in the description of the AAHPER Test. First, the pull-ups and flexed-arm hang were too difficult for many individuals so that no score record, other than zero, was possible with the attendant difficulty in normative scoring. Second, the arbitrary maximum for sit-ups leaves a similar lack of differentiation among a sizeable upper group who attain the maximum. The latter problem can be obviated by establishing a time limit of sufficient duration to give a reasonable spread among the best performers. Acknowledgeably, too short of a time allocation will also be unduly restrictive. The rationale offered for including pull-ups and flexed-arm hang as measures of arm and shoulder girdle strength and endurance rather than alternative items (e.g., push-ups, modified pull-ups) is better reliability; for example, the California and Fleishman Tests offer this explanation. However, any gain in reliability is more than offset by the loss of a complete score spectrum that is essential for meaningful interpretation. Matters of this sort should be resolved by continual search for better items and interim use of the best all-round item in terms of reliability and score record. The test items cited are merely illustrative of the shortcoming and not all-inclusive.

2. *Item inappropriateness.* This shortcoming concerns the overall appropriateness of a given test item as a measure of the particular quality involved. Several examples serve to show the scope of this concern. First, items are designed in a manner resulting in a contamination of two or more component qualities that should be disassociated in order to render meaningful interpretation possible.

To illustrate, the sidestep as a test of agility can be easily contaminated by extending the time limit to the point that muscular endurance comes into play. The New York Tests use what appears to be a reasonable time limit of 10 seconds on this item, while the North Carolina Test prescribes 30 seconds and acknowledgeably expands the purpose to measure agility, endurance, and speed. Another aspect of component validity is exemplified by the continued utilization of items after available evidence indicates poor validity. The inclusion of the 300-yard run-walk as a measure of endurance in the CAHPER illustrates this concern.

A further example of item inappropriateness deals with continued use of the straight leg sit-up as a measure of abdominal strength and endurance. Kinesiological analysis and research evidence reveals that the hip flexor muscles not only contribute appreciably to the sit-up with straight leg but might have a detrimental effect in instances when the abdominal muscles are incapable of pelvic fixation to prevent the iliopsoas from pulling the lumbar spine into forced hyperextension. (This concern was expressed in relation to a Kraus-Weber test item in Chapter 6 under safety aspects implicit in test administration.) The straight leg sit-up is still used in the AAHPER Test and some others, notwithstanding the findings of the California test study which led to substitution of the knee bent sit-up for time because of evidence substantiating that it is a better measure of abdominal strength and endurance. To pose another challenge to appropriateness from a different aspect, the feasibility of alternate elbow to knee touch as used in the straight leg sit-up on the AAHPER special test for mentally retarded would appear questionable in terms of the concentration task it presents to such subjects, one that is irrelevant to the basic test purpose.

3. *Uncombinability of scores.* Although most existing tests reflect identification and consideration of important components of motor fitness, many afford no means of combining scores into a composite test or battery score. Thereby these tests limit interpretation to the profile of performance in each test item; not to belittle in any sense the tremendous importance of this in individual overall appraisal. However, many teachers find a single index of total test performance an additionally valuable statistic for interpretation purposes. Teachers can derive their own standard score or scale derived from it to determine a composite test score, but have no published test norms for comparison. Some teachers who are uninformed in measurement erroneously develop their own total scores by adding percentiles, which suggests the desirability of test manuals depicting the fact that total score norms are not available and that the teacher cannot derive them simply by summation of the percentile ranks for the various items.

Other Considerations. Among important considerations for the teacher to bear in mind are the following:

1. *Reliability.* Several concerns relating to reliability warrant mention.

    a. The great effect of motivation upon physical performance and the necessity to standardize motivational procedure to minimize variation was discussed under specific considerations for physical performance tests. The varying need for motivation among age groups was clearly shown in a reliability study of the AAHPER 600-yard run-walk test.[88] Reliability coefficients of .65 (girls) and .76 (boys) in grade 11 were obtained on essentially the same students involved in an earlier reliability determination of .92 at the junior high school level, disclosing the need for more teacher motivation at the senior high school level on a stressful event.

    b. Regarding test length and reliability for the shuttle run, Fleishman's study pointed to the use of one trial on the shuttle run at 100-yard distance rather than giving two or more trials over a shorter distance.[89]

    c. Pertaining to the reliability of dynamic strength and endurance items, there is some evidence that the score on a single trial for push-ups, sit-ups, and pull-ups is as reliable as the mean or better of two trials on separate days ($N = 152$, elementary and secondary school boys).[90] Thus not only does the nature of these items render more than one trial rather impractical, but the lack of increased reliability using two trials indicates that more than one trial does not appear warranted. The teacher should not confuse this consideration with, nor extend it to include, the use of multiple trials on less taxing physical performance items (e.g., vertical jump, softball throw), as discussed elsewhere.

    d. Particular heed should be paid to insure satisfactory completion of required test action, such as reaching the proper top position in push-ups, pull-ups, and sit-ups. Laxity in proper scoring will affect test reliability appreciably.

2. *Norms and body weight.* Analysis of correlational studies concerning items of muscular strength, endurance, and power discloses a definite and important relationship of scores with body weight. This suggests the desirability of developing norms based on body weight, as well as age and sex, for tests of these factors to facilitate meaningful interpretation of results.

3. *Abdominal strength and endurance.* Although some controversy

---

[88] N. R. Askew, "Reliability of the 600-Yard Run-Walk Test at the Secondary School Level," *Research Quarterly*, XXXVII, No. 4 (December, 1966), 451.

[89] Fleishman, *The Structure and Measurement of Physical Fitness*, p. 120.

[90] L. W. McCraw and B. N. McClenney, "Reliability of Fitness Strength Tests," *Research Quarterly*, XXXVI, No. 3 (October, 1965), 289.

exists regarding the validity of the sit-ups as a measure of abdominal strength and endurance, empirical evidence points to continued study of this item for teacher use. The author's experience in testing students from elementary school through university at varying ability levels suggests a strong relationship between abdominal strength and endurance and overall muscular strength and endurance, based upon both static and dynamic tests. Unpublished studies under his direction in New York schools and test development data for the New York State screening test (NYSPFST) have shown that the sit-up correlates better than any other single item (r's $> .84$) with the composite score for either State test—long form (NYSPFT) or screening test. The sit-up does not represent an item on the former but is included in the four-item screening test. While further corroboration is desirable, all evidence suggests teacher use and experimentation as appropriate with the sit-ups as a basic indicator or predictor of overall motor fitness as well as, more specifically, muscular strength and endurance. While a basic screening item for overall motor fitness will not remove the need for more definitive testing of its components for the profile aspect, it can prove extremely valuable as a readily administrable gauge of motor fitness.

4. *Muscular or explosive power.* The two events that are primarily and most directly concerned with the ability of the body to develop power relative to its weight are the standing broad jump and vertical jump. The former has been used more often in tests as a measure of power although, compared to the vertical jump, skill learning and growth and development changes appear to affect it more and the judgment of legal jumps and point of landing render it somewhat more difficult to administer. The case for teacher consideration of the vertical jump was substantiated by Van Huss and Heusner who, after critical analysis of different tests used to measure power, concluded, "The best single measure of the individual's overall body power is the vertical jump." [91]

5. *Inimical practices.* The teacher should apply his or her analytical understanding of kinesiology and exercise physiology to avoid test items that cannot be administered in a manner devoid of possible detriment to the well-being of testees. The very nature of some test tasks poses potential risks which must be controlled to justify their use. The problem in this context associated with straight leg sit-ups is mentioned above (item 2) along with reference to the discussion of safety aspects in Chapter 6. To obviate repetition at this point referral should be made to this earlier discussion to note the admonition regarding test items entailing leg lifts or forcible deep squats, such as squat thrust and squat jump.

[91] Henry J. Montoye (ed.), *An Introduction to Measurement in Physical Education,* Vol. 4, *Physical Fitness* (Indianapolis: Phi Epsilon Fraternity, 1970), p. 18.

RESOLVING THE ILLUSTRATIVE PROBLEM

After analyzing the available tests of strength and motor fitness, a decision must be reached by the teacher as to what test or tests, if any, would be suitable for boys and girls in junior high school. Granted, many circumstances other than desirability will shape the decision, but attention is focused upon resolving the problem on the assumption that modest requests for testing needs can be met. To illustrate, a cable tensiometer with grip attachment and possible back-and-leg adaptation might be a justified expenditure; whereas the more costly and decidedly less versatile manuometer and back-and-leg dynamometer would be more difficult to justify.

Analysis of strength tests might suggest to the teacher consideration of the McCloy Strength Test as the most comprehensive yet practical test of strength. However, as mentioned in resolving the problem for overall appraisal, the motor fitness test that is selected might contain proper strength items to suffice, at least for the outset of the testing program.

Upon careful, critical review of available motor fitness tests it becomes evident that the likelihood is not very great of finding a test that will be totally satisfactory both in terms of desirable test characteristics and suitability of content for particular teacher needs. Thus the teacher may use a test that best meets the needs, regardless of limitations or choose to make warranted modification of one or more items in a test. In this context several motor fitness tests might warrant consideration for this problem, namely, New York, Indiana, and AAHPER Tests. The New York Tests afford the teacher the choice of a longer test encompassing some components of general motor abilities (and with or without posture) or a basic four-item motor fitness test. The advantage of the Indiana Tests lies in the availability of related test batteries covering grade four through college. The teacher might choose the AAHPER Test, with or without modification to overcome recognized limitations, for its coverage of motor fitness components, including a cardiovascular endurance item, and elementary school to college norms. It should be realized that other tests selected in the remaining areas of measurement will influence the choice, and certainly the choice of a motor fitness test will influence the selection in other areas.

SELECTED REFERENCES

1. BARROW, HAROLD M., and McGEE, ROSEMARY. *A Practical Approach to Measurement in Physical Education,* 2d ed. Philadelphia: Lea and Febiger, 1971.
2. BROWN, HOWARD S. "A Comparative Study of Motor Fitness Tests." *Research Quarterly,* XXV, No. 1 (March, 1954), 8.

3. CAMPBELL, W. R., and TUCKER, N. M. *An Introduction to Tests and Measurement in Physical Education.* London: G. Bell & Sons Ltd, 1967.
4. CLARKE, H. HARRISON. *Application to Measurement to Health and Physical Education,* 4th ed. Englewood Cliffs, N. J.: Prentice-Hall, Inc., 1967.
5. CLARKE, H. HARRISON *Muscular Strength and Endurance in Man.* Englewood Cliffs, N. J.: Prentice-Hall, Inc., 1966.
6. HUNSICKER, P A., and DONNELLY, R. I. "Instruments to Measure Strength." *Research Quarterly,* XXVI, No. 4 (December, 1955), 408.
7. MATHEWS, DONALD K. *Measurement in Physical Education,* 4th ed. Philadelphia: W. B. Saunders Co., 1973.
8. MONTOYE, HENRY J. (ed.). *Physical Fitness (An Introduction to Measurement in Physical Education,* Vol. 4). Indianapolis: Phi Epsilon Fraternity, 1970.

9

Cardiovascular Tests

THE CARDIOVASCULAR FUNCTION [1]

Tests of cardiovascular function represent attempts to determine the physiological fitness of the body as indicated by the reaction of the heart and circulatory system in adjusting to stress conditions. Since the conditions of stress that the individual meets most often are those imposed by exercise and gravity, cardiovascular tests are based largely upon the response of the individual to these variations in the external environment.

Briefly described, the cardiovascular function entails the ability of the heart and the circulatory system to supply fuel to the muscles and take away waste products. This demand is directly proportional to the intensity of muscle activity. During vigorous exercise, the demand is greatly increased over resting, so that the heart's activity must be accelerated and the circulation speeded. The efficiency and intensity of muscular activity depends upon the adequacy of the cardiovascular function. Muscles can operate efficiently only to the extent that fuel and waste materials are handled expeditiously by the heart and circulatory system. In comparison with a poorly conditioned individual, the heart and the circulatory system of a trained or conditioned body typically manifest less change in the variables upon assuming a different position or under work conditions and also return to normal sooner after activity. The interrelatedness of the respiratory system and cardiovascular function should be realized; for unless the respiratory system is capable of handling the gaseous needs and wastes efficiently and adequately, the cardiovascular function will be impeded, and vice versa.

---

[1] The reader is reminded that the basic description of cardiovascular function and its relation to other measurement areas is discussed in Chapter 7.

The variable elements most frequently utilized as indicants of cardiovascular function are pulse rate, systolic and diastolic blood pressures, and venous pressures—taken under various conditions such as before and after exercise or in different body positions. These elements are determinable by non-laboratory tests that require a minimum of technical training and are relatively simple to administer. Although impractical for teacher use, cardiovascular function may be measured in the laboratory by tests of oxygen consumption, minute volume of circulation, carbon dioxide determination, and blood composition. Of the physiological variables that reflect the internal bodily efficiency in response to exercise, the pulse rate appears the easiest to measure, the most reliable, and the most sensitive. It represents a linear function of oxygen consumption and is highly correlated with physical fitness, summing to a very useful indicant of reaction to cardiovascular stress. Since the pulse rate does not represent a complete test of cardiovascular function, one or more other variables may be used as a supplement to afford a more complete picture.

In actuality measurement of cardiovascular function is a complex matter, as revealed by the many factors known to influence heart rate and blood pressure, such as age, sex, diurnal changes, changes in position, exercise, season and climate, altitude, air and water movements, loss of sleep, digestion, respiration, metabolism, and emotional and nervous conditions. Nevertheless, comparing measurements of certain variables taken at different times under similar conditions furnishes the trained examiner with some indication of the efficiency of a subject's heart and circulatory system—appraisal of the cardiovascular function.

HISTORICAL BACKGROUND

The invention of the ergograph by Mosso in 1884 gave rise to the development of cardiovascular tests. Mosso disclosed that the ability of a muscle to perform depended upon the efficiency of the circulatory system and that interference with the nutritive functions of the body decreased the power to do work. These findings instigated recognition of the relationship between physical condition and muscular activity. Hence, the development of cardiovascular measurement was the direct outcome of the findings of the physiologists' interest in the strength of muscles.

Bowen appears to have been the first physical educator to publish results of a study of cardiovascular function.[2] Specifically, he studied the relationship of pulse rate to exercise and physical fitness and recognized that the pulse rate is influenced by the speed and amount of effort

[2] W. P. Bowen, "Changes in Heart Rate, Blood Pressure and Duration of Systole Resulting from Bicycling," *American Physical Education Review*, VIII (1903), 8.

as well as age, physiological condition, posture, and mental state of the subject. Bowen recommended better standardization of the method and conditions governing the observation of pulse rates. In 1905, Crampton (see page 349) proposed a rating scheme to approximate the general condition of a person by observing changes in the cardiac rate and arterial pressure on assuming an erect position. McCurdy's work resulted in a simple test of condition in 1910.[3] Four years later Meylan, Foster, and Barach each proposed physical efficiency tests. Basically, Meylan's[4] and Foster's (see page 345) tests involved the elements of general condition, rhythm and character of pulse rate, blood pressure, and a test of the heart's response to exercise. Barach (see page 348) devised a test to yield an index of efficiency based on blood pressure and pulse rate.

In 1916, Barringer (see page 348) proposed a test to show the relationship between blood pressure and physical deficiency. Shortly after, Schneider (see page 325) devised a test involving cardiovascular adjustment to general physical fitness in an endeavor to overcome shortcomings of the Crampton and Foster Tests. Schneider's test recognized more factors than any previous test and found considerable use in ascertaining fatigue and conditions for flying during World War I.

As a result of these early tests and the work of many researchers, the importance of this phase of testing in establishing the relationship between physiological systems and the reaction of the body as a whole became recognized. From this beginning, test developments have represented efforts to divulge the efficiency of the cardiovascular function, with particular reference to methodology conducive to administration in groups without costly and delicate equipment.

Two noteworthy findings have contributed appreciably to the direction of recent test development efforts. Using the Balke Treadmill Test,[5] Billings and associates reported that the time required to reach a heart rate of 150 beats per minute serves as a valid indicator of capacity for more strenuous work.[6] A subsequent study substantiated that submaximal tests of cardiovascular fitness provide information which compares favorably with maximal test results.[7] This evidence that exhaustive exer-

---

[3] J. H. McCurdy, "Adolescent Changes in Heart Rate and Blood Pressure," *American Physical Education Review*, XV (June, 1910), 421.

[4] G. L. Meylan, "Twenty Years Progress in Tests of Efficiency," *American Physical Education Review*, XVIII (October, 1913), 442.

[5] A test to detremine the duration of exercise with increasing intensity that is required to produce a heart rate of 180 beats per minute as described in: B. Balke, *et al.*, "Work Capacity After Blood Donation," *Journal of Applied Physiology*, VII, No. 3 (November, 1954), 231.

[6] C. E. Billings, *et al.*, "Measurement of Human Capacity for Aerobic Muscular Work," *Journal of Applied Physiology*, XV, No. 6 (November, 1960), 1001.

[7] J. T. Truett, H. Benson, and B. Balke, "On the Practicality of Submaximal Exercise Testing," *Journal of Chronic Diseases*, XIX, No. 6 (June, 1966), 711.

cise is not required to appraise cardiovascular condition affords justification for avoiding, or at least minimizing, the motivational, other psychological, and safety limitations associated with tests demanding all-out effort. The other important finding in terms of its implications for test development was the evidence presented by Balke that various run-walk tests, scored as distance covered in a given time, represented valid indicators of maximum oxygen intake attainable.[8] The influence of both of these findings is reflected in some of the recent tests of cardiovascular function.

AN ILLUSTRATIVE PROBLEM

To provide focus for the presentation of available tests in this chapter, the question is posed: what cardiovascular test, if any, appears suitable for junior high school physical education for boys and for girls in light of the testing program as a whole, i.e., overall appraisal? In attempting to resolve this question, it is assumed that the teacher will have no technological assistance from the school health services. However, the tests presented include some in which the teacher may need such help from the school nurse or doctor. These are included for situations where trained assistance is available and such a test appears appropriate.

DESCRIPTIONS OF BASIC PROCEDURES

To facilitate presentation of the different tests, a description will first be given of the methodology employed with certain measurement and exercise techniques that are common to a number of cardiovascular tests. No further mention of the item involved will be made in discussion of the various tests in which it is used, unless a difference exists or specific clarification seems desirable.

Pulse Rate. In taking the pulse rate, it is suggested that the index and middle fingers or middle three fingers of one hand be placed in the slight groove formed on the wrist above the base of the thumb and slightly toward the inside. Actually, the groove lies between the radius and the first prominent tendon on the inside of the wrist. Moderate pressure should suffice to locate the pulse. Caution should be heeded that the thumb is not used to find the pulse, inasmuch as the slight pulse discernible in the tip of the thumb may interfere with or be mistaken for the subject's pulse. The fingers may approach the subject's wrist from

[8] Bruno Balke, *A Simple Field Test for the Assessment of Physical Fitness*, CARI Report 63–6 (Oklahoma City: Civil Aeronautical Research Institute, Federal Aviation Agency, 1963).

either direction—from the inside as when the subject takes his own pulse or from the outside with the examiner using the wrist nearer to him.

The pulse of the testee should be located prior to the test, so that it can be readily relocated when needed. The pulse is counted for 15 seconds and multiplied by 4 to obtain the rate per minute. The 15-second count is used to minimize errors in counting and also because of the rapid dropoff or fluctuation following exercise and the desirability of estimating pulse rate at the peak and at specific interval points.

An alternative method of pulse counting is mentioned at this point and will be referred to specifically as the carotid pulse when reported in a given test. The carotid pulse can be located by holding the fingers vertically and placing them alongside the neck just in front of the ster-nocleido-mastoid muscle.

Blood Pressure. Measuring blood pressure involves the use of a sphygmomanometer for which specific instruction and practice is desirable. In making blood pressure observations, it must also be realized that a number of factors affect blood pressure, such as age, sex, posture, eating, exercise, and temperature. Detailed instructions for taking blood pressure have been prepared by the American Institute of Medicine.[9]

To observe the blood pressure, the arm and body of the subject should be as relaxed as possible and his mind at rest. The cuff is wrapped snugly around the left arm, level with the heart. The examiner firmly places the stethoscope bell on the brachial artery just above the elbow and slightly toward the inside. Next, the cuff is inflated by the bulb until no pulse beat is audible, and then slowly released. When the first pulse sound becomes audible, the examiner notes the reading on the mercury column or gauge in millimeters Hg; this is the *systolic pressure.* The cuff pressure is released continually until a dull, forceless beat is heard; this is the *diastolic pressure.* When both pressures are recorded, they appear as a fraction, with systolic pressure over diastolic pressure. Time permitting, good procedure dictates taking a practice reading in order to relieve apprehension and remove any friction in the machine. Preferably, observations should be made at the same time of day and at least 2 hours after a meal.

Stepping Exercise. To perform the stepping exercise, the subject starts from a standing position on both feet and places his lead foot on a bench or stool of specified height; then he steps up and puts the other foot alongside the lead foot to assume an erect position. Immediately the testee steps down to the starting position beginning with the lead

[9] *Instructions for Taking Blood Pressure* (New York: The American Institute of Medicine, 1939), p. 37. These are also presented in George H. Deaver, *Fundamentals of the Physical Examination* (Philadelphia: W. B. Saunders Co., 1939), p. 216.

foot, thereby completing one step. The exercise is repeated a specified number of times for a specified amount of time according to the cadence counted by the tester or kept by a suitable contrivance such as a metronome. The choice as to which foot serves as the lead foot lies with the subject; right-footed individuals lead with the right foot and left-footed subjects with the left.

SELECTED TESTS

Schneider Test [10]

The Schneider Test, the first comprehensive cardiovascular test, resulted from a study involving 2,000 pilots during World War I and was revised slightly in 1923. The test involves six observations: reclining pulse, standing pulse, pulse increase on standing, pulse increase from exercise, pulse return to normalcy after exercise, and change in systolic pressure from reclining to standing. The test procedure follows:

1. *Reclining.* After the subject has reclined for 5 minutes, (a) the normal reclining pulse rate is determined by counting continuously in 20-second intervals until two consecutive counts are identical, then this figure is multiplied by 3 and recorded; and (b) the systolic pressure is taken by auscultation two or three times to assure a reliable reading and recorded.

2. *Standing.* After rising and standing for 2 minutes, the normal standing pulse rate is determined by counting continuously in 15-second intervals until two consecutive counts yield the same result, multiplied by 4 and recorded. The systolic pressure is taken as before and recorded.

3. *Increases upon standing.* The differences between reclining and standing pulse rates and systolic pressures are computed and recorded.

4. *Exercising.* The subject steps up and down on a chair 18½ inches high five times in 15 seconds as timed by a stop watch. In performing the exercise, the subject stands with one foot on the chair on the count "one" and keeps this foot on the chair until five steps are completed with the other foot. Then both feet are together on the floor after 15 seconds.

5. *After exercise.* The after-exercise standing pulse rate is determined immediately at the completion of the 15-second exercise period on the 15-second basis and recorded.

[10] A succinct report of the test is given in Peter V. Karpovich, *Physiology of Muscular Activity* (4th ed.; Philadelphia: W. B. Saunders Co., 1953), pp. 264–67, as presented by E. C. Schneider and D. Truesdell, "Daily Variations in Cardio-Vascular Conditions and a Physical Efficiency Rating," *American Journal of Physiology,* LXVII (1923), 193. Scoring table is also available in SR (selected reference) 4 and 8.

6. *Return to normal.* The pulse is counted continuously in 15-second intervals from cessation of exercise until the rate returns to normal, at which point the elapsed time in seconds from the end of the exercise to the beginning of the first normal 15-second pulse count is recorded. If the pulse fails to return to normal within 2 minutes, counting is discontinued and the number of beats above normal is recorded.

7. *Score interpretation.* The scores derived for each of the six observations are interpreted in light of a scoring table. The final index score was originally devised from an empirical weighting of the separate test items.

The reliability reported for this test ranges from .54 to .89, with high correlations representing studies in which the test was administered with extreme care. Objectivity is routinely about .80. While research reveals that this test is related to endurance and may shed light upon improper cardiovascular function as a supplement to the medical examination, it cannot be used to determine fitness for strenuous physical work. The Schneider test possesses value for situations where need exists for a mild test of circulatory efficiency, and it can be given two or three times. In an endeavor to improve the method of scoring, Hindman developed a nomograph for this test.[11] Cureton proposed a slight modification of the scoring system upon considered application of the test.[12]

Tuttle Pulse-Ratio Test [13]

Taking the original idea from English researchers at Guy's Hospital in London, Tuttle devised a test to serve as an index of physical efficiency based on the ability of the heart to compensate for exercise. Justification for a pulse-ratio test was found in the fact that one's physical condition has a definite effect upon the rate of heart beat and the time involved in return to normalcy after exercise. Tuttle defined *pulse ratio* as the ratio of the resting pulse rate to the rate after exercise, found by dividing the total pulse beats for 2 minutes after a given amount of exercise by the normal resting pulse for 1 minute. The test procedure follows:

1. The sitting pulse rate is determined by counting for 30 seconds after the rate becomes constant, doubling the number, and recording the result as "normal pulse."

[11] Darwin A. Hindman, "Nomographs for Interpolating Scores on the Schneider Test," *Research Quarterly*, IV, No. 4 (December, 1930), 26; also presented in SR 8.

[12] T. K. Cureton, *et al.*, *Endurance of Young Men* (Washington, D. C.: Society for Research in Child Development, 1945), Monograph X, No. 1, Serial No. 40, p. 210; also reported in SR 6.

[13] W. W. Tuttle, "The Use of the Pulse-Ratio Test for Rating Physical Efficiency," *Research Quarterly*, II, No. 2 (May, 1931), 5.

2. The subject then performs the stepping exercise for 1 minute on a stool 13 inches high. Twenty such steps are taken by boys, fifteen by girls. The number taken is recorded as S_1.

3. Beginning immediately upon completion of the exercise, the subject's sitting pulse is counted for 2 minutes.

4. The total pulse for 2 minutes is divided by the normal pulse for 1 minute to give the "first pulse ratio" (r_1).

5. The subject remains seated until the pulse has returned to normal, at which time additional exercise is begun. The testee performs 35 to 40 steps in 1 minute; the actual number is recorded as S_2.

6. Immediately upon completion of the second exercise bout, the subject's sitting pulse is counted for 2 minutes.

7. The repeated total 2-minute pulse is divided by the normal pulse for 1 minute to give the "second pulse ratio" (r_2).

8. The number of steps required to obtain a 2.5 pulse ratio (S_0) is then computed by means of the formula:

$$S_0 = S_1 \frac{(S_2 - S_1)(2.5 - r_1)}{r_2 - r_1}$$

Determination of S_0 can be made easier by constructing a chart with the steps plotted on one axis and pulse ratios on the other. Then the point representing r_1 for S_1 is marked, as is the point showing r_2 for S_2. These two points are connected by a straight line and S_0 is read directly from the chart where the line and 2.5 pulse ratio intersect.

The established norms are: boys 10 to 12 years of age—33 steps, boys 13 to 18 years of age—30 steps, adult men—29 steps, and adult women—25 steps. An efficiency rating is proposed to put results on a percentage basis, using 50 steps per minute as the amount of exercise necessary to produce a 2.5 ratio in a highly efficient individual. The formula is:

$$EF = \frac{(\text{number of steps for 2.5 ratio})}{50} \times 100$$

Later, a simplified version of the test was suggested by Tuttle and Dickinson in which only one exercise about employing 30 steps was used.[14] A correlation of .93 was obtained between this simplification and the ratio derived from two stepping exercises.

In terms of scientific authenticity, little evidence exists to warrant the use of this test to measure general physical condition. Tuttle found

[14] W. W. Tuttle aud R. E. Dickinson, "A Simplification of the Pulse-Ratio Technique for Rating Physical Efficiency and Present Condition," *Research Quarterly,* IX, No. 2 (May, 1938), 73.

that the efficiency rating of athletes increased appreciably during the season and then commonly decreased after the season. He also reported this test to be a reliable indicant of proficiency in gymnastics. Investigation has disclosed a high correlation between the efficiency rating of this test and endurance in sprint running. Poor correlation has been noted with a measure of general muscular endurance. Another study concluded that the reliability failed to warrant test usage with college women. Test-retest reliability coefficient reportedly average about .80.

Results of the pulse-ratio test corroborate the findings by medical doctors concerning the status of the cardiovascular system. Accordingly, this test is regarded as one of the most useful of the cardiovascular tests for detecting pathological hearts and possesses value as a supplement to the medical examination. In using this test to check the condition of the heart, the procedure follows: After the subject's pulse has returned to normal and the number of steps needed to obtain a 2.5 ratio has been computed, the subject performs the computed number of steps in 1 minute. Then the pulse is counted and a third pulse ratio is computed, as before. If this new ratio is more than .07 above or below 2.5 and substantiated by subsequent testing, the individual should be referred to a physician, since a defective heart appears probable.[15] The simplified form appears more practical for the purpose of medical diagnosis.

Harvard Step Test (College Men) [16]

Challenged by the need for a simple circulatory test of physical fitness during World War II, Brouha and his associates in the Harvard Fatigue Laboratories developed a test for college men purporting to measure the general capacity of the body to adapt itself to and recover from hard work. Concisely described, the test consists of observing pulse reaction to 5 or less minutes of stepping exercise on a 20-inch bench. The test procedure follows:

1. The subject performs the stepping exercise on a 20-inch bench at the rate of 30 steps per minute for 5 minutes, or as long as he can up to the 5-minute maximum. The cadence of 120 counts per minute may be kept by announcing, "up, 2, 3, 4, etc." The lead foot may be changed during the test, but no more than three times.
2. Immediately upon completion of the exercise, the testee sits down preparatory for three pulse counts. The pulse is counted for 30 seconds and recorded, beginning at 1 minute, 2 minutes, and 3 minutes after cessation of exercise. The carotid pulse is suggested for this test.

[15] Henry Sievers, "A Simple Method of Detecting Abnormal Hearts by the Use of the Pulse-Ratio Test," *Research Quarterly*, VI, No. 2 (May, 1935), 36.

[16] Lucien Brouha, "The Step Test: A Simple Method of Measuring Physical Fitness for Muscular Work in Young Men," *Research Quarterly*, XIV, No. 1 (March, 1943), 31. Scoring table is available in SR 1 and 3.

3. The scoring is done by the formula: [17]

$$\text{Index} = \frac{\text{Duration of exercise in seconds} \times 100}{2 \times \text{sum of pulse counts in recovery}}$$

Fractions are discarded in using the formula above. This calculation is simplified for all testees completing 5 minutes of exercise by use of a table provided in the reference. This table gives the index for the various sum-of-pulse counts. A less precise scoring basis may be used for subjects failing to finish the full exercise bout and for whom pulse counts were not obtained.

Duration of Exercise	Index Score
Less than 2 minutes	25
2 to 3 minutes	38
3 to 3½ minutes	48
3½ to 4 minutes	52
4 to 4½ minutes	55
4½ to 5 minutes	59

4. The index is interpreted according to the following standards.

Below 55	Poor physical condition
55 to 64	Low average
65 to 79	High average
80 to 89	Good
Above 90	Excellent

A Rapid Form of this test has been developed in which only a single pulse count is taken (1 minute after exercise) and the exercise remains the same.[18] The score for the Rapid Form is derived by the formula:

$$\text{Index} = \frac{\text{Duration of exercise in seconds} \times 100}{5.5 \times \text{pulse count}}$$

The reference contains a table to facilitate scoring. After derivation, the score is interpreted in terms of general physical fitness as below 50—poor, 50 to 80—average, and above 80—good.

As evidence of validity for the original test, Brouha utilized the criterion of a work index based upon endurance treadmill running, maximum heart rate per minute, and blood lactate level. Study of Harvard undergraduates disclosed that athletes scored higher and had

---

[17] Although not included in the reference, for cadence of 30 steps per minute the formula can be alternatively expressed as:

$$\text{Index} = \frac{\text{Number of steps} \times 100}{\text{Sum of recovery pulse counts}}$$

[18] R. E. Johnson and S. Robinson, "Selection of Men for Physical Work in Hot Weather," Appendix I, CMR, OSRD, Report 16, Harvard Fatigue Laboratory. Scoring table is also available in SR 5 and 7.

less variable scores than non-athletes, and that their scores increased with continued training and decreased upon discontinuing training. For the most part, correlational studies by other researchers involving physical strength and endurance items, and maximum work capacity have disclosed little relationship with the Harvard Step Test (HST). Reported reliabilities generally exceed .82 and go as high as .94.[19] The range of test reliability and its relation to testing conditions is illustrated by a report of coefficients of .84 (N = 31) with college men and the same tester counting all pulses, and .65 (N = 119) with grade 8 boys counting their partners' pulses without prior experience.[20]

The test has seen wide application both in physical fitness testing programs and in research studies. Together with its modifications for other age levels and girls and women HST comprises the most widely used test of heart rate response to standard submaximal exercise. Studies to refine scoring and other slight modifications (see NARSS modification) hold promise for improving validity and reliability as a measure of cardiovascular function. Two possible drawbacks of the test exercise itself, as advanced by some critics, are the extreme height of the bench and the fact that acute local muscular fatigue may be produced. With reference to the former, a considerable number of studies representing a diversity of populations of children and adults divulge virtually no correlation of the step test results with stature, weight, leg length, bi-iliac diameter, and surface area.

The Rapid Form is easier to administer, results in only a small loss of accuracy (as reflected by high correlation between single and summed post-stepping pulse counts), and may be used as a quick procedure for selection or classification purposes. Based on tests given to several hundred healthy convalescing young men, Karpovich and his associates considered the scores of the Rapid Form preferable to those of the original test and accepted a score of 75 as the minimum for "good" condition.[21] Citing other supportive studies, Montoye concluded that the last two pulse counts are not at all necessary and preference should be given to use of the single 60–90 second count.[22]

Early Modifications of the Harvard Step Test. Modified versions of HST were soon developed to make it applicable to different groups and have entailed primarily a change in bench height and exercise duration.

---

[19] Henry J. Montoye (ed.), *An Introduction to Measurement in Physical Education*, Vol. 4, *Physical Fitness* (Indianapolis: Phi Epsilon Kappa Fraternity, 1970), p. 59.

[20] Carlton R. Meyers, "A Study of the Reliability of the Harvard Step Test," *Research Quarterly*, XL, No. 2 (May, 1969), 243.

[21] Karpovich, *op. cit.*, p. 270.

[22] Montoye, *op. cit.*, p. 62.

COLLEGE WOMEN.[23] To render the test appropriate for college women, the bench height was set at 18 inches and the duration of exercise at 4 minutes. The sequence of pulse counts and scoring formula remain the same as for college men. A specially devised chart to facilitate determination of the physical fitness index was constructed. The six-category classification for interpreting men's scores is also applicable for women.

WOMEN.[24] Sloan proposed modification of HST by using a 17-inch bench for women with the same cadence, exercise duration, and scoring formula for men. This was based on data indicating that the same arbitrary performance standards are applicable with the same validity as for the men's test.

HIGH SCHOOL BOYS.[25] The step test was modified for high school boys, 12 to 18 years of age, by shortening the exercise duration to 4 minutes and reducing the bench height to 18 inches for boys with body surface areas less than 1.85 square meters. The surface area can be readily determined from height and weight by using body surface charts such as the nomograph in Fig. 9–1. Otherwise, the test procedure and scoring remains the same as for college men. A score calculation table is available in the reference. A score of 45 may be assigned to subjects who do not finish, to obviate counting the pulse for drop-outs. And a score of 55 is advocated for those who finish but lag or otherwise do less work than the test demands. In interpreting scores in terms of physical condition, the following may be applied: 50 or less—very poor, 51 to 60—poor, 61 to 70—fair, 71 to 80—good, 81 to 90—excellent, and 91 or more—superior.

HIGH SCHOOL GIRLS.[26] To adapt the step test for high school girls, the bench height was reduced to 16 inches and the exercise duration shortened to 4 minutes. The sequence of pulse counts and scoring formula was not changed. An alternative scoring plan may be used for girls not completing the full exercise bout as follows: 2 minutes—score of 25, 2½ minutes—30, 3 minutes—35, and 3½ minutes—40. A score of 45 is assigned to girls who, although finishing the test, lagged behind, crouched, or otherwise showed evidence of doing less work than de-

[23] Harriet L. Clarke, "A Functional Physical Fitness Test for College Women," *Journal of Health and Physical Education,* XIV, No. 7 (September, 1943), 358. Scoring table is available in SR 3.

[24] A. W. Sloan, "A Modified Harvard Step Test for Women," *Journal of Applied Physiology,* XIV, No. 6 (November, 1959), 985.

[25] J. Roswell Gallagher and Lucien Brouha, "A Simple Method of Testing the Physical Fitness of Boys," *Research Quarterly,* XIV, No. 1 (March, 1943), 23. Scoring table is available in SR 1 and 3.

[26] Lucien Brouha and J. Roswell Gallagher, "A Functional Fitness Test for High School Girls," *Journal of Health and Physical Education,* XIV, No. 10 (December, 1943), 517. Scoring table is available in SR 1 and 3.

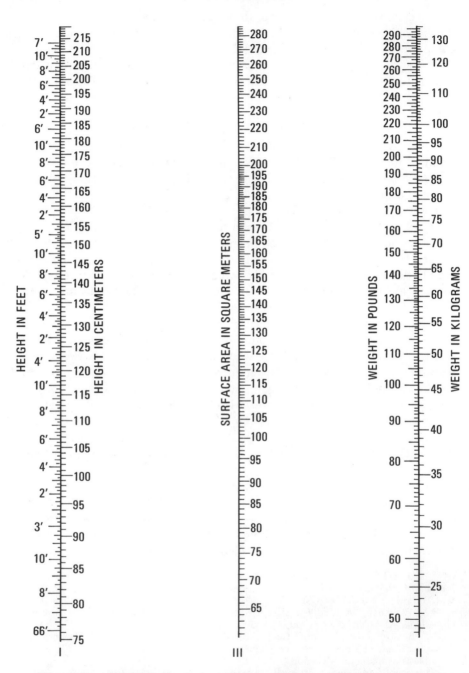

Fig. 9–1. Dubois Body Surface Chart. (Cited in Gallagher and Brouha, *op. cit.*, p. 29, as prepared by Boothby and Sandiford of the Mayo Clinic.)

manded by the test. A score calculation table but no classification scale is available for high school girls.

ELEMENTARY SCHOOL BOYS AND GIRLS.[27] The step test was modified for boys and girls below 12 years of age by reducing the height of the bench to 14 inches and setting the exercise duration at 3 minutes for 8 to 12 years and at 2 minutes for 7 years and less. The remaining test procedure and scoring was unchanged. To facilitate score interpretation, the average performances found for three age groups are presented.

7 and under	40 (N = 225)
7 to 10	57 (N = 725)
10 to 12	61 (N = 650)

Scores above the group mean are considered good or excellent and scores below as poor or very poor.

KARPOVICH REVISION (Convalescent Men).[28] In a study of 88 men convalescing from rheumatic fever, Karpovich and his associates reduced the stepping rate from 30 to 24 per minute on a 20-inch bench, since it was an easier rate for the subject to maintain and for the tester to count without a pendulum or metronome. The original scoring table was modified slightly.

Later Modifications of the Harvard Step Test. Continued analysis and application has led to further modifications of the HST. The basic characteristics of these test variations are compared in Table 9–1 along with those previously presented.

MODIFIED HST APPARATUS.[29]—Patterson and his associates modified the HST apparatus for use with men by the provision of a horizontal bar slightly above shoulder height in the vertical plane of the back of the step for a handhold by the subject. Several horizontal bars were used to accommodate subjects of different heights, as shown in the action sequence in Fig. 9–2. This apparatus appeared to overcome to a great extent two important limitations in bench stepping: the skill needed for unassisted stepping; and the restricted total muscle mass involved in the exercise because of insufficient use of arm, shoulder, and thoracic musculature and the resultant local muscle fatigue in the legs.

[27] L. Brouha and M. V. Ball, *Canadian Red Cross Society's School Meal Study* (Toronto: University of Toronto Press, 1952), p. 55. Scoring table is also available in SR 3.

[28] P. V. Karpovich, *et al.*, "Physical Reconditioning after Rheumatic Fever," *Journal of the American Medical Association*, CXXX, No. 17 (1946), 1198.

[29] John L. Patterson, *et al.*, "Evaluation and Prediction of Physical Fitness Utilizing Modified Apparatus of the Harvard Step Test," *American Journal of Cardiology*, XIV, No. 6 (December, 1964), 811.

Table 9–1. Summary Chart of Specifications for HST and Modifications

Test	Score Form[+]	Bench Height[++]	Duration in Minutes	Steps per Minute
College men—HST	LF; RF	20	5	30
NARSS modified HST (men)	RF with correction	20	5	30
Karpovich revision (convalescent men)	LF	20	5	24
High school boys (age 12-18)				
Body surface $\geqslant$ 1.85 sq. m.	LF	20	4	30
Body surface $<$ 1.85 sq. m.	LF	18	4	30
Women (Sloan)	LF	17	5	30
College women (Clarke)	LF	18	4	30
High school girsl (age 12-18)	LF	16	4	30
Elementary school boys and girls				
Age 8-12	LF	14	3	30
Age under 8 years	LF	14	2	30
Cardiovascular Efficiency Test				
(secondary school girls and college women)	RF	18	3	24
Kent State University Test (college women)	60-90 second pulse count	18	1	30
Tecumseh Study Test (age 10-69, males and females)	60-second heart rate	8	3	24

[+]LF = Long Form Index—3 pulse counts.
　RF = Rapid Form Index—1 pulse count.
[++]in inches.

NARSS Modified HST.[30]—Carver and Winsmann have proposed a New and Rapid Stepping Score (NARSS) formula to overcome scoring inadequacies of the HST. One of these is that the scores of subjects who do not complete the prescribed work are largely a function of the duration of stepping and can be increased simply by lengthening the stepping period, while the scores of subjects completing the stepping are solely dependent upon the response of the heart to the work. As another shortcoming of the conventional HST scoring, motivational differences influence scores so that the physical capacity of individuals who do not extend themselves is underestimated. With NARSS, although motivational differences and local muscle fatigue may cause variations in the duration of stepping, these discrepancies in duration appear to exert little effect upon the estimated fitness, while they may result in large invalid differences using the conventional formulas. NARSS consists of the addition of a correction factor to the Rapid Form of HST, which tends to produce the same estimated

[30] R. P. Carver and F. R. Winsmann, "Study of Measurement and Experimental Design Problems Associated with the Step Test," *Journal of Sports Medicine and Physical Fitness*, X, No. 2 (June, 1970), 104.

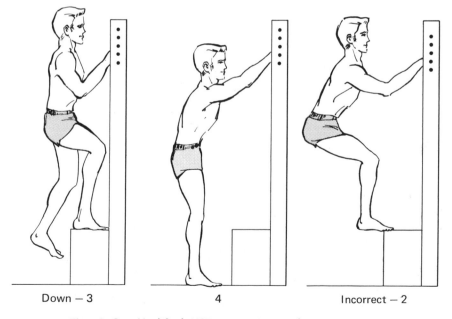

Fig. 9–2. Modified HST apparatus and action pattern.

5-minute score regardless of stepping duration, as disclosed by an experiment with men (N = 12) involving stepping durations of 1, 3, and 5 minutes. The formula is:

$$\text{NARSS} = \frac{\text{Duration (in seconds)} \times 100}{5.5 \times \text{pulse count}} + .22 \, (300 - \text{Duration})$$

To effect standardization of testing technique for the HST it is recommended that: (a) horizontal bar apparatus (Patterson, *et al.*) is grasped with both hands and adjusted so forearms are horizontal when standing on the bench, (b) a recording device is used for counting cadence, (c) no crouching or bouncing is permitted, (d) subjects lagging more than one step behind are stopped and assumed to be at the exhaustion point; and (e) the pre-test resting pulse should be counted to screen out subjects with rates over 100 per minute, since high initial rates invalidate the score. The investigators are optimistic regarding the general applicability of NARSS formula with the standardized testing technique, recognizing the need for substantiation by field experience.

CARDIOVASCULAR EFFICIENCY TEST (High School Girls and College Women).[31]—Skubic and Hodgkins modified the HST for girls and women by using an 18-inch bench, 24 steps per minute cadence, and 3-minute duration with one pulse count, namely, 60–90 seconds post-exercise. The HST Rapid Form index formula was adapted slightly to read:

$$\text{Cardiovascular Efficiency Score} = \frac{\text{Number of seconds completed} \times 100}{\text{Recovery pulse} \times 5.6}$$

The test clearly differentiated among highly trained, moderately active, and sedentary testees, and reliability was determined as .82 (N = 27). Norms were developed for junior high school girls (N = 686) and senior high school girls (N = 1,332) from 55 schools, and college women (N = 2,360) from 66 colleges throughout the country.[32] The means and standard deviations of CE scores for these respective groups were: 50.73, 10.03; 48.61, 9.67; and 48.90, 10.40. The rating charts include CE scores for all testees and pulse counts for those completing the stepping.

[31] Vera Skubic and Jean Hodgkins, "Cardiovascular Efficiency Test for Girls and Women," *Research Quarterly*, XXXIV, No. 2 (May, 1963), 191.

[32] Jean Hodgkins and Vera Skubic, "Cardiovascular Efficiency Test Scores for College Women in the U. S.," *Research Quarterly*, XXXIV, No. 4 (December, 1963), 454; and Vera Skubic and Jean Hodgkins, "Cardiovascular Efficiency Test Scores for Junior and Senior High School Girls in the U. S.," *Research Quarterly*, XXXV, No. 2 (May, 1964), 184. Norms are available in SR 4.

KENT STATE UNIVERSITY TEST (College Women).[33]—For the KSU Test the 60–90 second post-exercise carotid pulse is counted by each subject after stepping onto an 18-inch bench, 30 steps per minute for one minute. A correlation of .71 (N = 41) with the criterion of Skubic-Hodgkins CE Test was reported for validation. Reliability for test-retest on consecutive days was .73 (N = 31). As evidence of the accuracy of self-palpated counting of the carotid pulse, a correlation of .91 (N = 31) was obtained with stethoscopic determinations. This test distinguished the fit from the non-fit, and discriminated between degrees of improvement in cardiovascular efficiency in average college women but not in women athletes who possess a high level of cardio-vascular fitness.

TECUMSEH STUDY TEST (Males and Females, Age 10–69).[34]—As part of an extensive community health study, Montoye and associates modi-fied the HST to involve an 8-inch bench at 24 steps per minute for 3 minutes to investigate the heart rate response of males and females, aged 10 to 69 years (N = 5,264). Test development statistics are not presented. The metabolic cost of this test was found to be about 5 times the basal metabolic rate and deemed probably not sufficiently strenuous for most young subjects. The reference includes percentile rank norms, means and standard deviations for the 1-minute post-exercise heart rate as determined for 2-year groupings for ages 10–11 through 18–19 (N = 1,435) and 10-year groups from 20–29 through 60–69 years (N = 2,542).

MANAHAN-GUTIN ONE-MINUTE STEP TEST (Ninth Grade Girls).[35]— In a study (N = 40 ninth-grade girls) to ascertain the predictive va-lidity of selected step tests using the 600-yard run-walk as the criterion, Manahan and Gutin concluded that the two-count one-minute step test is reasonably valid (r = .824) and reliable (r = .952). Unsatisfactory validity was found using the Skubic-Hodgkins test. Two minute four-count and two-count step tests and a one-minute four-count step test comprised the other tests studied.

The one-minute two-count step test is performed on an 18-inch bench with a student counter holding the testee's hands. The testee begins the test with the right foot on the bench, straightens the right leg, and without placing the left foot on the bench, returns to starting

[33] V. P. Harvey and G. D. Scott, "The Validity and Reliability of a One-Minute Step Test for Women," *Journal of Sports Medicine and Physical Fitness*, X, No. 3 (September, 1970), 185.

[34] Henry J. Montoye, *et al.*, "Heart Rate Response to a Modified Harvard Step Test: Males and Females, Age 10–69," *Research Quarterly*, XL, No. 1 (March, 1969), 153.

[35] Joan E. Manahan and Bernard Gutin, "The One-Minute Step Test as a Measure of 600-Yard Run Performance." *Research Quarterly*, XLII, No. 2 (May, 1971), 173.

position with left foot on the floor. The score is the number of returns completed in one minute. The subject is permitted to change lead foot if necessary. Nonsignificant correlations of .135 and .276 were found with height and weight, respectively. Test statistics are not reported. The test authors deem it a practical indoor alternative for the 600-yard run, since it lends itself well to group testing in a gymnasium. Certainly more definitive study of this test as a measure of cardiovascular function appears warranted.

The Ohio State University Step Test (Men, Age 18–60)[36]

The OSU Step Test was developed as a submaximal test of cardiovascular fitness for use with men, 18 to 60 years of age, to overcome the adverse criticism of available tests as to extreme strenuousness and also, for HST, leg muscle fatigue and discomfort. Bench exercise with a hand bar was chosen as the work task for several reasons; administrative ease and economy; constant workload for the subject; and skill is not an important factor. The test was designed to avoid heart rates exceeding 150 beats per minute during exercise in order to permit application to a wide age range regardless of fitness classification. It was based on evidence that the time required to reach this rate is a valid indicator of cardiovascular capacity for exhaustive work.[37] The test equipment consists of the split-level bench apparatus shown in Fig. 9–3 and either a prerecorded tape of the test or a stop watch and metronome. The test consists of 18 innings of 50 seconds in duration, with each inning divided into a 30-second work period followed by a 20-second rest period. The procedure follows:

1. To begin the test the subject adjusts the bar height to the level closest to his standing height and then stands immediately in front of the 15-inch bench. The subject listens to the instructions and a complete inning to become acquainted with the procedure. Then he grasps the bar with both hands and, upon commands "ready" and "up," begins the stepping exercise for the work period of the first inning according to cadence commands of "up, up, down, down." The testee must step completely onto the platform in assuming a full standing position on each cycle.
2. At the 30-second mark the commands "stop" and "find your pulse" are given. Beginning at second "5" of the rest period upon command —"count" the testee takes his radial or carotid pulse for 10 seconds until the commands "stop" and "prepare to exercise" are given at second "15" of the rest period. The subject records the

[36] R. L. Kurucz, E. L. Fox, and D. K. Mathews, "Construction of a Submaximal Cardiovascular Step Test," *Research Quarterly*, XL, No. 1 (March, 1969), 115.
[37] Billings, *op. cit.*

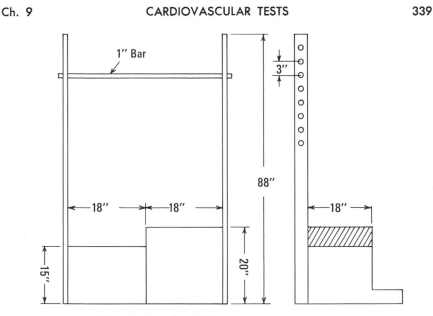

Fig. 9–3. The OSU step test apparatus.

pulse count and awaits the commands to start the next work period.

3. The test is terminated upon completion of 18 innings or when the pulse count reaches 25 beats, that is, 150 per minute. The score is the number of the inning in which the pulse reaches the 150 per minute rate. Testees who complete 18 innings without reaching the pulse count maximum are arbitrarily assigned a score of 19.

4. The workload for the different work periods is scheduled in three continuous phases of six innings each as follows: I—24 steps per minute cadence on a 15-inch bench; II—30 steps per minute cadence on a 15-inch bench, and III—30 steps per minute cadence on a 20-inch bench. After the pulse count for inning six, the subject is informed of the cadence increase beginning with inning seven. Just prior to the start of inning thirteen the subject is directed to move to the 20-inch bench.

The test development data on 75 volunteers from 19 to 56 (mean = 34) years of age were reported as mean innings and standard deviations for age classifications as follows: 19–29 years (N = 28)—12.4, 4.7; 30–40 years (N = 30)—13.0, 4.0; and 41–56 (N = 17)—11.8, 3.4. A validity of .94 was obtained with the criterion—Balke Treadmill Test—on a random selection of 30 (ages 19 to 56) of the 75 subjects. A test and retest on successive days for 24 (ages 19 to 56) randomly selected subjects yielded a reliability of .94. The test development study afforded corroborative evidence of the effect of the modified HST apparatus. A lessened energy requirement was manifested with the bar ($N = 7$), apparently attributable to the greater anatomical stability it provides, and its recommended use permits testing a wider range of subjects.

Summarily, it was found that the OSU Test proceeds gradually and does not overstrain the individual so that even subjects in poor condition can be evaluated, while still building up to a more strenuous exercise so that the highly fit can be measured; and with simple scoring.[38] Considered study of the application of this test to the school-age population appears warranted, notwithstanding the concern of providing sufficient benches suitable for group administration to render it practical for teacher use.

Callan Modified OSU Step Test (Boys, Grades Four through Six).[39] Callan devised an adaptation of the OSU Step Test for use with boys in grades four through six. The modifications embodied were (a) depth of bench was reduced to 13½ inches; (b) height of the second bench was lowered to 18 inches; (c) hand bar is adjusted at testee's eye level; (d) pulse count is taken by the tester with a stethoscope; and (e) the criterion for cessation of exercise is a pulse rate of 29 for 10 seconds (174 bpm). Other than these modifications, the test is conducted and scored as described for the OSU Test. Test development data for the three grades ($N = 153$) yielded a mean of 13.5 innings, standard deviation of 4.0, and test-retest objectivity of .963. The performance of fourth-grade boys was significantly better than that of fifth- and sixth-grade boys. Weight proved to be a more important factor in performance than age, and height had no significant effect. For validity ($N = 6$), a coefficient of .897 was obtained using the criterion of a modified treadmill test,[40] and a correlation of .955 was found between energy expenditure and work done in vertical lifting.

Cotten Modified Ohio State University Test.[41] Cotten developed a modification of the OSU Step Test to render it satisfactory for mass testing in a class situation. The modifications consisted of: use of 17-inch bleacher step for all phases; elimination of the handbar; and a cadence of 36 steps/minute for Phase III. A 15-minute rest period precedes the test, during which time instructions and pulse counting

[38] Donald K. Mathews, *Measurement in Physical Education* (4th ed.; Philadelphia: W. B. Saunders Co., 1973), p. 256.

[39] Donald E. Callan, "A Submaximal Cardiovascular Fitness Test for Fourth, Fifth and Sixth Grade Boys." Unpublished Doctoral Dissertation, Ohio State University, 1968.

[40] Mathews, *op. cit.*, pp. 26–27.

[41] Doyice J. Cotten, "A Modified Step Test for Group Cardiovascular Testing," *Research Quarterly*, XLII, No. 1 (March, 1971), 91.

practice occur. Subjects are paired, and the partner of the testee sits on the second bleacher step so that the testee can rest in front of him for the pulse counting after each inning. With 34 male physical education majors this modified test yielded a validity coefficient of .84 with the Balke Treadmill Test and a reliability coefficient of .95. The lower validity, compared to .94 for OSU Test, was attributed to the elimination of the handbar and the change in work load increase in the third phase. Students were able to complete the test relatively easily and within one class period. Reliability of .75 was reported with high school boys (N = 40) using different partners on the retest and with obvious counting errors noted by the examiner.

F-EMU Step Test (College Women).[42] At Eastern Michigan University, Witten developed a modification of the OSU Step Test to render it appropriate for college women. The changes entailed: 14- and 17-inch bench heights; no hand bar; and 5 innings in each phase for a total of 15 innings. Testees rested for 15 minutes, seated in a chair. With 20 female freshmen the F-EMU Test resulted in a validity coefficient of .85 with the Balke Treadmill Test for a heart rate of 168 bpm. Ninety-five per cent of the subjects reached 168 bpm within 15 innings, so that the fourth phase of the experimental study was eliminated, involving 5 innings of 30 steps per minute on a 20-inch bench. Correlation of pulse count by testees with simultaneous EKG recording was .95. A mean of 9.8 innings ($s = 3.1$) to reach the criterion pulse count of 28 (168 bpm) and test-retest reliability of .90 were obtained with another group of 51 female freshmen.

The 12-Minute Test

Running Endurance as a Measure of Cardiovascular Fitness. Introductory to a description of the 12-Minute Test, brief mention of the evolvement of a run-walk test as a measure of cardiovascular fitness seems appropriate. While not a test of cardiovascular function in the strict and usual sense, it is highly correlated with a recognized criterion of cardiovascular fitness and most appropriately classified in this measurement area. But the distinction between endurance and cardiovascular function should be realized. The latter refers to the capability of the circulatory–respiratory system to adapt to increased metabolic demands, such as exercise. Endurance or work capacity, in addition to the capability implicit in cardiovascular function, depends upon other factors such as individual skill in performance, motivational level, and the inclination to extend oneself fully in exhaustive effort. The vari-

[42] Chet Witten, "Construction of a Submaximal Cardiovascular Step Test for College Females," *Research Quarterly*, XLIV, No. 1 (March, 1973), 46.

ability contingent upon these factors is obvious, so that individuals with comparable cardiovascular function cannot be expected to give similar performance in running or comparable "general" endurance unless, coincidentally, the resultant effect of the other variables is the same. This distinction is readily discernible by the kind of measurement utilized. For endurance tests the variable measured is fastest possible time to accomplish the distance or task. Whereas in tests of cardiovascular function the parameter is one (or more) of the variables directly a part of the function itself, for example, heart rate.

Distance runs (or running endurance) have for some time been used as a measure of cardiovascular endurance (or aerobic work capacity). In the quest to eliminate the skill variable the concept of the endurance ratio was introduced, entailing the proportion between the performance times for a short dash and a long run, which indicates how well speed is carried over the longer distance. Through factor analysis McCloy found an endurance ratio, namely, 300-yard run divided by 6-second run, to have a high factor rating (.88) with circulatory–respiratory endurance.[43] Use of the AAHPER Fitness Test has enabled interested teachers to determine an endurance ratio, such as:

$$ER = \frac{\text{50-yard dash in seconds} \times 12}{\text{600-yard run-walk in seconds}} \times 100.$$

Despite their potential value in physical education measurement, the limited attention to validation of the different ratios affords no reasonable basis for evaluation.

Attention seemingly focused on the long run alone as a practical measure of cardiovascular fitness about the end of World War II, when 90 per cent of 10,282 school boys completed the 600-yard run-walk without experiencing difficulty. Correlations up to .66 with maximal oxygen intake have been reported for this event, as have reliabilities as high as .92 to .95 involving different running courses. These findings then led to evolvement of the 12-minute test by the question posed as to whether extending the distance would improve scientific authenticity to a desirable level and present any particular problems concerning the motivational and related aspects implicit in exhausting performance. The breakthrough in this context was a test developed by Balke which predicted maximal oxygen intake satisfactorily in terms of the maximum distance covered by a subject in a 15-minute run.[44]

The 12-Minute Run-Walk (High School Boys and Girls, and Men). As a result of extensive study involving U. S. Air Force personnel and

[43] C. H. McCloy, "A Factor Analysis of Tests of Endurance," *Research Quarterly,* XXVII, No. 2 (May, 1956), 213.

[44] Balke, *A Simple Field Test for the Assessment of Physical Fitness.*

civilians, Cooper modified the time duration and scoring of the Balke test and proposed the 12-minute test as a readily administrable and valid measure of cardiorespiratory fitness.[45] His findings disclosed a validity coefficient of .90 with treadmill measurements of oxygen consumption and aerobic capacity, whereas 600-yard and 1-mile runs correlate comparatively poorly. Table 9–2 presents the interpretative scoring chart developed on 12-minute distances covered by men.[46] To simplify the administration to large numbers, Cooper prepared a rating chart based on the time required to run 1.5 miles, as illustrated in Table 9–3.[47] However, good correlative data between the 1.5 mile run and the 12-minute test are not yet available.[48]

Table 9–2. Twelve-Minute Performance (Miles)

Physical Fitness Category	Age (in years)			
	17-29	30-39	40-49	50-59
Excellent	1.75+	1.70+	1.65+	1.60+
Good	1.50-1.74	1.45-1.69	1.40-1.64	1.35-1.59
Fair	1.25-1.49	1.20-1.44	1.15-1.39	1.10-1.34
Poor	1.0-1.24	1.0-1.19	0.95-1.14	0.90-1.09
Very poor	<1.0	<1.0	<0.95	<0.90

Table 9–3. 1.5 Mile Test for Men

Fitness Category	Age (in years)			
	Under 30	30-39	40-49	50+
Excellent	10:15 or less	11:00 or less	11:38 or less	12:00 or less
Good	10:16-12:00	11:01-13:00	11:39-14:00	12:01-14:30
Fair	12:01-14:30	13:01-15:30	14:01-16:30	14:31-17:00
Poor	14:31-16:30	15:31-17:30	16:31-18:30	17:01-19:00
Very poor	>16:30	>17:30	>18:30	>19:00

Doolittle and Bigbee administered this test to grade 9 boys as follows: [49]

[45] Kenneth H. Cooper, "A Means of Assessing Maximal Oxygen Intake," *Journal of the American Medical Association*, CCIII, No. 3 (15 January, 1968), 201.

[46] Kenneth H. Cooper, "The Role of Exercise in Our Contemporary Society," *Journal of Health-Physical Education-Recreation*, XL, No. 5 (May, 1969), 22.

[47] Kenneth H. Cooper, *The New Aerobics* (New York: Bantam Books, Inc., 1970), p. 31.

[48] Kenneth H. Cooper, personal correspondence. September 27, 1971.

[49] T. L. Doolittle and Rollin Bigbee, "The Twelve-Minute Run-Walk: A Test of Cardiorespiratory Fitness of Adolescent Boys," *Research Quarterly*, XXXIX, No. 3 (October, 1968), 491.

1. The subjects ran on a measured quarter-mile grass track, divided into eighths with the start numbered 0. They were instructed to: (a) run for the entire 12 minutes but, if walking became necessary, not to walk more than one-eighth of a lap at one time; (b) increase the pace during the final minute, if able, and put forth their best effort; and (c) stop running when a gunshot signalled the end of the run.
2. Testees were notified of the remaining time at 9, 11, and 11½ minutes. A partner recorded the highest lap and lap-segment completed when the gun sounded by encircling the proper number for each appearing in a columnar arrangement on the score card.

A reliability of .94 was computed when the subjects (N = 153) were retested five days later without knowledge of the results on the first test. It was noted that most testees were able to run for the entire 12 minutes. A validity coefficient of .90 was obtained on nine randomly selected subjects from the study sample, using the criterion of maximal oxygen intake test on a bicycle ergometer. These nine subjects subsequently completed a 600-yard run-walk test on the same grass track, giving a validity of .62 with the same criterion. The administration of the 12-minute run to ninth-grade boys was found to be equally as feasible as the 600-yard run-walk in addition to its improved validity and reliability. In a subsequent study, identical reliability coefficients of .89 were obtained for grade 9 and 10 high school girls (N = 100) and grade 9 junior high school girls (N = 45), and r = .92 for combined group reliability.[50]

In the application of this test the teacher may wish to divide the running course into zones smaller than the 55-yard units described above. Although this will admittedly entail more time for course layout, it would appear justifiable in terms of the finer discriminatory power in scoring with an anticipated improved reliability. Further, the feasibility of using time rather than distance as the test criterion warrants consideration, inasmuch as teacher practicality and score discrimination would be enhanced. However, validation evidence as to appropriate distances for various age groups is needed.

Other Measures of Cardiovascular Function

McCurdy-Larson Organic Efficiency Test (College Men).[51] McCurdy and Larson devised a test purporting to measure the functional effi-

---

[50] T. Doolittle, J. Dominic, and J. Doolittle, "Reliability of the Twelve-Minute Run-Walk When Employed with Adolescent Girls," *Abstracts Of Research Papers,* Boston Convention of AAHPER, 1969, p. 7.

[51] J. H. McCurdy and L. A. Larson, "The Measurement of Organic Efficiency for the Prediction of Physical Condition in Convalescent Patients," *Research Quarterly,* VI, No. 4 (December, 1935), 78.

ciency of the circulatory–respiratory systems and involving 5 items selected on the basis of apparent significance in measuring organic efficiency with emphasis on endurance. The 5 items were selected after a statistical study of 26 items commonly used for experimentation in the area of functional tests and included (1) sitting diastolic blood pressure, (2) breath holding 20 seconds after exercise, (3) difference between normal standing pulse rate and that 2 minutes after exercise, (4) standing pulse pressure, and (5) vital capacity. The exercise consists of performing a given number of steps in 90 seconds on a special two-step stairs. The number of steps is determined from a table according to the age and weight of the subject. By combining the weighted scores of the 5 test items, the *organic efficiency index* is obtained. Originally classification standards were provided, but subsequently the authors prepared scales for three age groups—18 to 34, 35 to 49, and 50 to 80. After further research, a short test was developed possessing a validity coefficient comparable to the complete battery and involving sitting diastolic pressure, breath-holding after exercise, and standing-pulse pressure.

To determine validity two groups were used: varsity swimmers in "good" condition and infirmary patients after respiratory infections. The resultant biserial *r* of .833 may be misleading, since the normal group was omitted. The reported reliabilities range from .67 to .80, and carefully controlled conditions must prevail. This test represents one of the more satisfactory cardiovascular tests. Its use by teachers may be limited by the elaborate methodology necessitated and the time limitations; one subject can be tested in 15 minutes.

Foster Test (High School Boys).[52] This test, another early cardiovascular test, is based on the fact that exercise increases the heart rate almost in direct proportion to exercise intensity. Foster standardized the exercise, determined the reaction of high school boys in good physical condition, and constructed norms of condition. The test consists of (1) recording normal standing pulse; (2) running in place for 30 seconds at the rate of three steps per second; (3) counting the pulse for 5 seconds and converting it to the minute rate, both immediately after running and again after subject has stood at ease for 45 seconds; and (4) computing efficiency rating from the scoring table.

Michigan Pulse Rate Test for Physical Fitness (High School Boys and Girls).[53] This test was devised as a possible index of physical condition

---

[52] W. L. Foster, "A Test of Physical Efficiency," *American Physical Education Review*, XIX (December, 1914), 632. Scoring table is available in SR 2 and 7.

[53] "Physical Education in the State of Michigan," *American Physical Education Review*, XXV (April, 1920), 138.

and is easily administered to a class-size group with students counting their own pulses. The test is comprised of (1) counting normal standing pulse; (2) performing a 15-second bout of spot running at a rate of three steps per second; (3) counting standing pulse rate beginning ½, 1, 2, and 3 minutes after cessation of exercise; and (4) rating according to scale based on recovery time. In instances of irregular pulse after running, students are dropped one grade on the scale and advised to consult a physician. The scoring scale follows:

Time To Recover Normal	Grade	Degree of Fitness	Physical Habits or Types
½ minute	A	Fine	Athletic
1 minute	B	Good	Active
2 minutes	C	Fair	Sedentary
3 minutes	D	Poor	Moderately active
Pulse slower after run	E	Very Poor	Invalid

Taylor Pack Test (Men 17 to 46 Years).[54] During World War II, Taylor developed a maximal pack test to examine quickly large groups of men for fitness and endurance in heavy physical exertion. The test procedure follows:

1. To start, the subject stands with his left foot placed on an 18-inch bench, and with the left hand grasps a crossbar positioned directly over the back edge of the bench and 6 feet above the floor. (A crossbar 6 inches lower may be provided for shorter testees.)

2. The subject steps up to an erect position on the bench, touches the right foot to the bench, and immediately descends with the right foot, maintaining the same position of left foot and hand. This cycle is repeated at the rate of 40 per minute as long as possible, while every half-minute upon signal by the examiner and without breaking the rhythm, the testee changes so that the other foot and hand maintain the support position. During the exercise, the subject carries a back-pack containing a 10-pound weight and to which 10 pounds are added at 2-minute intervals.

3. The total time exercised at the required rate constitutes the final score, and the heart rate is counted from 10 to 30 seconds after exercise termination to ascertain if the testee has put forth maximum effort. A scoring scale with a correction factor for height appears in the reference along with average scores and heart rates for different age groups, 17 to 46 years.

Validation depends chiefly on "face validity," that is, the length of time spent in work before becoming exhausted. Scattergram analysis

[54] Craig Taylor, "A Maximal Pack Test of Exercise Tolerances," *Research Quarterly*, XV, No. 4 (December, 1944), 291. Scoring table is available in SR 8.

showed that good general skill scores were achieved only by those with high pack-test scores, but a high pack-test score was not always associated with a good athletic score. Taylor advocates the pack test in preference to the athletic-type test of fitness, since athletic skill is minimized and the psychological influence of competition is absent. This test distinguishes between individuals in the upper score range in comparison to other step tests that are submaximal for well-conditioned men. Since the heart rate after exercise is not at all related to test scoring, like running endurance tests, the pack test is not a test of cardiovascular function in the direct sense.

Carlson Fatigue Curve Test.[55] Carlson devised a test utilizing the generalized fatigue curve—an established and accepted physiological phenomenon—and based on the premise that a true physical test of function should be sufficiently taxing and searching to indicate as nearly as possible the absolute state of physical condition. Purportedly the test measures time rate of work or power (relative to one's mass) that represents the mechanical function most clearly associated with fuel consumption—hence, cardiovascular efficiency. The test consists of 10 innings of spot running (lift and lower the feet alternately just off the floor as fast as possible) with intervening rest periods of 10 seconds, during which the subject records the number of times the right foot touched the floor during the preceding 10 seconds. The fatigue curve measures *production* (work done in terms of total number of "rights" in 100 seconds) and also indicates the percentage of all-out effort or *application*. Fatigue will cause a drop in production for each inning and, if a drop is not manifested, lack of application (or error) is evidenced. As an index of condition, five pulse rates are taken while sitting on the floor; one just prior to exercise and then at 10 seconds and 2, 4, and 6 minutes after exercise. The pulse rate total gives the index of cost for production of the fatigue curve. A plotted curve of pulse rates provides a picture of recovery. The resultant index of condition is based on the normal pulse rate, pulse increase in response to effort, and time and degree of recovery. Carlson proposed that a complete test consists of a series of tests administered one each day; he used a series of ten tests.

Scientific authenticity is not reported. Ohnmacht found that, while reliability coefficients were reasonably high, the test does not possess sufficient validity as a measure of circulatory–respiratory endurance with a composite criterion of the Schneider Test and Barach Index (nonperformance tests to reflect peripheral vascular factors), and an En-

---

[55] H. C. Carlson, "Fatigue Curve Test," *Research Quarterly,* XVI, No. 3 (October, 1945), 169.

durance Ratio (a performance measure).[56] Additionally, unpublished analysis of repeated testing by Meyers suggested that the amount and pattern of learning the spot running technique, associated with its recognized conditioning effect, contributes to the poor validity. In contrast to stepping exercise, in spot running each subject proceeds at his own tempo which avoids interference with the efficiency of different individuals by imposing the same performance pace upon a group. While the test is easily administered to large groups, the score of right foot touches appears to pose a challenge both in terms of accuracy in counting and the limiting effect that attention to counting may exert upon speed. Evidence affirms that the test possesses utility as a conditioning activity, albeit an apparently poor indicant of cardiovascular function.

Barach Energy Index.[57] Barach proposed an index to measure intravascular tension and the energy expended by the circulatory system:

$$EI = \frac{\text{Pulse rate (systolic pressure + diastolic pressure)}}{100}$$

The systolic pressure serves to indicate the energy factor in the work of the heart itself, the diastolic pressure reflects the energy factor in the peripheral resistance, and the pulse rate gives the number of systolic and diastolic phases occurring in 1 minute. All measurements are made in a sitting position after the pulse rate becomes constant. The scores for a robust individual were reported to range from 110 to 160, with 90 and 200 representing the lower and upper normal limits, respectively. A later study of 200 university men found the index to range from 70 to 220, with a mean of 141.[58]

Barringer Test.[59] Barringer developed a test to estimate the functional capacity of the heart based on the principle that a physically deficient individual will manifest a delayed rise in blood pressure after performing a regularly increasing amount of work measured in footpounds. The work consisted of repeatedly raising a dumbbell in a stride standing position from the floor to overhead for a predetermined

[56] Fred W. Ohnmacht, "The Validity of the Carlson Fatigue Curve Test as a Measure of Circulatory–Respiratory Endurance," Microcard Doctoral Dissertation, University of Buffalo, 1962.

[57] J. H. Barach, "The Energy Index," *Journal of American Medical Association,* LXII, No. 7 (February 14, 1914), 525.

[58] Thomas K. Cureton, *Physical Fitness Appraisal and Guidance* (St. Louis: The C. V. Mosby Co., 1947), p. 285.

[59] T. B. Barringer, Jr., "Studies in the Heart's Functional Capacity as Estimated by the Circulatory Reaction to Graduated Work," *Archives of Internal Medicine,* XVII (May, 1916), 670.

number of times, as calculated from the weight and distance involved. The normal heart rate and systolic blood pressure are measured simultaneously prior to work and again after work every 30 seconds for 3 to 5 minutes. This procedure is repeated daily with an increased amount of work performed until the point is reached at which the "delayed rise" appears. No scoring scales are available since the normal cardiac capacity varies considerably in different people.

McCloy Test of Present Health (Adults).[60]   McCloy devised a rating of "present health" based on a study of diastolic pressures, systolic pressures, and pulse rates. To arrive at a rating the Schneider Test exercise is given, after which the following formulas are applied.

Men:
4.46 standing diastolic pressure − standing pulse rate − 3 pulse rate immediately after exercise.

Women:
3 standing diastolic pressure − 3.4 standing pulse rate − pulse rate immediately after exercise + 160

Validity coefficients of .803 and .901 are reported with a criterion of present health for men and women, respectively. McCloy attributes more importance to this rating as a method than to the findings, since the number of subjects was small.

Crampton Blood Ptosis Test.[61]   The Crampton Blood Ptosis Test was a pioneer cardiovascular test designed to appraise the general condition of an individual on the basis of observed changes in heart rate and systolic blood pressure upon standing from a reclining position. The subject reclines until the pulse rate becomes constant; then the pulse and systolic blood pressure are taken. Thereupon, the subject stands and his pulse and systolic blood pressure are taken again after the pulse rate becomes constant. A norm chart applicable to both men and women is available.

The test considers two basic elements: increase in systolic pressure, connoting efficiency, and increase in heart rate, which connotes deficiency. Available evidence suggests that this test fails to reflect differences in athletic condition but does reveal changes in health deficiency. Inasmuch as individual scores tend to differ appreciably, its utility appears limited to situations wherein retests can be given to establish a norm for each individual.

---

[60] C. H. McCloy, "A Cardiovascular Rating of Present Condition," *Arbeitphysiologie*, March, 1931.

[61] C. Ward Crampton, "A Test of Condition," *Medical News*, LXXXVII (September 16, 1905), 529. Rating table is available in SR 4 and 7.

California Group Functional Test (Elementary and Secondary Boys and Girls).[62] In California an endeavor was made to meet the need for a battery of functional tests for elementary and secondary pupils that can be given at the beginning of the school year to a group of 20 to 30 pupils at one time to categorize them into two groups: (1) needing immediate medical examination and (2) apparently able to participate in the physical education program until the regular medical examination is given. The California Test reflects general organic efficiency by such items as determination of body weight in relation to age and height, breath-holding, pulse rate return following body-bending for 30 seconds, potato race (girls) or half-mile run in 3½ minutes (boys), and recording the findings of physical inspection of pupils for corroborative evidence.

SPECIFIC CONSIDERATIONS

The particular characteristics of cardiovascular function as an area of measurement have implications for the selection, construction and administration of tests in addition to those basic to the general categorization of physical performance tests. These specific considerations include the following:

1. *Criteria for tests of cardiovascular function.* A good test should: (a) subject the cardiovascular system to considerable stress in exercise of a general type involving large groups of muscles and for which no special skill is required; (b) while sufficiently demanding, control work intensity so as to minimize the role of motivation; and (c) entail an exercise task for which work load is determinable, reproducible, and reasonably easy so that the mechanical efficiency is kept relatively constant.[63]

2. *Factors to be controlled.* When physiological measures (for example, pulse rate, blood pressure) are taken, it is particularly important to control test anxiety and related emotional factors as physiological aspects so that the pre-exercise state approximates a normal resting level. This entails adequate test orientation, including prior practice if appropriate, and a testing setting conducive to the testee being at ease. A test should not be given: when ambient temperature exceeds 80 degrees Fahrenheit or in

[62] H. R. Stolz, "Group Functional Tests," Circular Letter M30, November 7, 1923, California State Board of Education, Department of Physical Education. Presented in J. F. Bovard, F. W. Cozens, and E. P. Hagman, *Tests and Measurements in Physical Education* (3d ed.; Philadelphia: W. B. Saunders Co., 1949), pp. 81–83.

[63] Adapted from: C. F. Consolazio, R. E. Johnson, and L. J. Pecora, *Physiological Measurements of Metabolic Functions in Man* (New York: McGraw-Hill Book Co., 1963), p. 341.

warm and extremely humid conditions; immediately after a meal; or until adequate recovery from illness, strenuous pre-test activity, or emotional stress. To the extent reasonable, repeated tests should be given at the same time of day. The use of tape recorded test exercise and measurement instructions affords desirable standardization, but the recording should be checked routinely by a stop watch to detect any inaccuracies due to variable power supply or technical problems.

3. *Pulse counting.* Prior training with practice should be given to subjects who count their own or another's pulse. Although this may be handled minimally at the testing session, earlier and concerted attention to it will enhance reliability and objectivity. If the pulse count is to be used to indicate heart rate during exercise, to minimize error it is critical to begin the count as soon as possible after exercise ceases.[64]

4. *Suggestions for step tests.* These include: (a) use of stall bars where available for support apparatus; (b) insuring satisfactory stability of benches; (c) a 14-inch bench with 2, 3, 4, and 6-inch floor blocks constitutes a practical means of adjusting bench height for different groups; (d) benches to accommodate one testee can be made with several heights in one unit; (e) when a metronome is used, a cadence setting of twice the number of steps per minute is recommended (for example, setting of 60 for 30 steps per minute) to give a beat for both up and down stepping positions; and (f) such mechanical cadence beats should be supplemented by verbal count as often as necessary to indicate the correct up and down pattern.

5. *HST interpretation.* Inasmuch as the Harvard Step Test and modifications of it do not give good estimates of maximal oxygen intake, they possess no particular value for inter-individual comparisons and afford basis only for gross classification of subjects. But because the test scores are sensitive to intra-individual changes, the tests are useful for comparison of a given individual at different times.

6. *Running endurance.* While important at all ages, attaining the desired motivation for running endurance is especially difficult with elementary and senior high school levels and necessitates deliberative attention. For elementary school children with all factors weighed in light of available evidence, it appears prudent to limit the distance to 600 yards.

---

[64] Best minimization of error is achieved by allowing approximately 4 seconds to locate the pulse and then counting for 10 seconds, as reported in: W. D. McArdle, L. Zwiren, and J. R. Magel, "Validity of the Post-exercise Heart Rate as a Means of Estimating Heart Rate During Work of Varying Intensities," *Research Quarterly,* XL, No. 3 (October, 1969), 523.

RESOLVING THE ILLUSTRATIVE PROBLEM

Certain basic concerns relative to cardiovascular tests and their administration should be recognized before a teacher decides which of the aforementioned tests, if any, appears suitable for boys and girls in junior high school. While variation exists between tests, all cardiovascular tests necessitate careful control and administration because of the very nature of the function involved and the available means of measurement. This along with questions relating to validity and reliability of some tests accounts for the somewhat limited use of cardiovascular tests by teachers. However, it is contended herein that the cardiovascular function constitutes the most important yet most neglected aspect relating to the physical and organic development objective of physical education and, accordingly, should receive serious and prime consideration as a measurement area.

Despite possible limitations, one of the available tests may be selected to reflect the cardiovascular endurance of students or possibly used as a screening device when a medical examination has not been given or as a supplement to the medical examination. But unless the cardiovascular test fits into the testing program as a valuable source of information pertinent to overall appraisal, its use lacks justification. Conceivably, it may be that a particular test may serve a twofold purpose—devlopmental and measurement; for example, use of the 12–minute run as a developer of and check on cardiovascular fitness. Also, the teacher may decide to use a test with some limitations with a view to eventual revision so as to render it more appropriate for the intended purpose.

While varying program emphases, objectives, and resources will certainly influence the decision to resolve the illustrative problem in the perspective of overall appraisal, the teacher decides to utilize the high-school modifications of the Harvard Step Test for boys and girls. The teacher justifies this selection on the fact that the test: can be rather easily administered to a class with students counting pulses; satisfactorily meets the criteria for a good cardiovascular test (including the exercise being sufficiently demanding without complications of motivation encountered in all-out effort); and has a scoring table to aid in interpreting the results. The use of this test will have no relation to the medical examination except in terms of referral to the school physician for students performing very poorly. The teacher further decides to apply the modified apparatus and NARSS formula on a limited basis in the near future to determine the appropriateness for this age group.

SELECTED REFERENCES

1. BARROW, HAROLD M., and McGEE, ROSEMARY. *A Practical Approach to Measurement in Physical Education*, 2d ed. Philadelphia: Lea and Febiger, 1971.
2. BOVARD, J. F., COZENS, F. W., and HAGMAN, E. P. *Tests and Measurements in Physical Education*, 3d ed. Philadelphia: W. B. Saunders Co., 1949.
3. CAMPBELL, W. R., and TUCKER, N. M. *An Introduction to Tests and Measurement in Physical Education*. London: G. Bell & Sons Ltd., 1967.
4. CLARKE, H. HARRISON. *Application of Measurement to Health and Physical Education*, 4th ed. Englewood Cliffs, N. J.: Prentice-Hall, Inc., 1967.
5. CONSOLAZIO, C. F., JOHNSON, R. E., and PECORA, L. J. *Physiological Measurements of Metabolic Functions in Man*. New York: McGraw-Hill Book Co., 1963.
6. CURETON, THOMAS K. *Physical Fitness Appraisal and Guidance*. St. Louis: The C. V. Mosby Co., 1947.
7. MATHEWS, DONALD K. *Measurement in Physical Education*, 4th ed. Philadelphia: W. B. Saunders Co., 1973.
8. McCLOY, C. H., and YOUNG, N. D. *Tests and Measurements in Health and Physical Education*, 3d ed. New York: Appleton-Century-Crofts, Inc., 1954.
9. MONTOYE, HENRY J. (ed.). *Physical Fitness (An Introduction to Measurement in Physical Education*, Vol. 4). Indianapolis: Phi Epsilon Kappa Fraternity, 1970.

10

Anthropometry and Body Mechanics

The basic description of anthropometry and body mechanics and their relation to overall appraisal, as given in Chapter 7, furnishes the foundation for presenting the various available measuring instruments in each of these areas, preceded by an overview of the historical development.

ANTHROPOMETRY AND ITS HISTORICAL DEVELOPMENT

Anthropometry constitutes the earliest form of measurement in physical education, as one might surmise. Study of the human physique and its proportions began many centuries ago. The early beginnings can be traced to the remote civilization of India, where a treatise called "Silpi Sastri" analyzed the outline of the body by dividing it into 480 parts. Anthropometry evolved in the quest to determine the ideal body proportions, and artists and sculptors directed their study to it as shown by the artwork of early civilizations. Artists comprised the chief workers in anthropometry until 1835 when a mathematician in Brussels, Baron Quetelet, applied purely mathematical methods to discover the physical constants of the human body and proved that the binomial law (law of chance) applies to human proportions. This finding was confirmed about 50 years later by Sir Francis Galton, who systematically analyzed measurements of certain physical constants of English men and women. In 1854, a German named Carus proposed an anatomical basis to determine body proportions. Shortly after this, Zeissing in Belgium and Cromwell in England studied the growth of school children.

The first application of anthropometry in physical education began with Dr. Edward Hitchcock in 1861, when he undertook a study of anthropometrical measurements of Amherst College men, leading to the publication of anthropometrical tables almost annually for 40 years. The aim of anthropometry was depicted by Hitchcock as ascertaining the ideal or typical man as a guide in fostering the development of normal individuals. He provided his students with a chart showing average results associated with different variables, against which the student might plot his own results. In 1886, Sargent published an anthropometrical chart based on 6 years of examining Harvard students. Sargent included lung capacity and certain strength measurements along with various measures of physical proportion and expressed the results in percentiles. From 1885 to 1900, anthropometrical studies were conducted at different collegiate institutions involving close to 8,000 men and women. In 1890, Seaver published what proved to be the pioneer American book on physical measurements of the body; it was subsequently revised twice.

Anthropometrical measurement for assessment of physical status was expanded quite naturally to include consideration of body types and the relation of physique to one's health, immunity from disease, posture, physical performance, and personality qualities. It soon became recognized that a single ideal physique was both impractical and unrealistic. Actually Hippocrates first realized this fact and classified human beings according to two basic physiques—long and thin, or short and thick. Kretschmer, the father of modern body- or somato-typing, defined three types by adding an in-between and referred to them as asthenic (lean), athletic, and pyknic (heavy).

Early attempts to ascertain the nutritional status of individuals consisted of giving a desired weight for a certain height and later included age and sex differentiations. Age-height-weight tables were utilized in some schools for the purpose of discovering malnourished and obese children. Perceiving the inadequacy of height as a basis for predicting body weight, further investigations have resulted in methods of assaying weight that utilize skeletal dimensions and consider the gross proportion of bone, muscle, and fat.

Presently, anthropometry considers individual differences, appraises each subject relative to his structural differences, and determines his potentialities in light of those structural characteristics.

BODY MECHANICS AND ITS HISTORICAL DEVELOPMENT

To foster continuity from the previous discussion of body mechanics in Chapter 7, the twofold importance of body mechanics in overall appraisal is reiterated, namely, as an indicant of weakness in a particular part of the body or its functioning and as a causative factor of problems in other areas, such as motor abilities. The story of the historical development of body mechanics is one of a continuing search for relatively precise testing instruments and satisfactory methods for postural appraisal that are practical for teacher use. Considerable progress has been made, but more is needed.

The beginning of concerted effort to devise suitable means of postural appraisal can be traced to the 1890's when several special instruments appeared. These included devices for revealing the amount of pelvic tilt, exact chest contour and anteroposterior depths at all points of the trunk, and for recording outlines of the body and abnormalities of spinal curvature. Early attempts at posture appraisal were based on the thesis that the centers of gravity of the head, trunk, and legs must be perfectly aligned over one another if the gravitational forces acting on the body are to be in equilibrium. Today this thesis is still propounded; and the body is described as being in good alignment when such points as the tragus of the ear, acromion of the shoulder, middle of the greater trochanter, styloid process of the fibula, and cuboid bone of the foot approximate a vertical line. Early posture tests utilized a gravital line, such as a plumb line or pole, so that the tester could discern the relationship of landmarks to the vertical and to the spinal curvatures.

Not long after the beginnings in postural measurement, Bancroft [1] proposed a triple test—standing, marching, and exercise—to meet the need for a practical test for teacher use. This test afforded a means by which, ideally, the teacher could judge the posture of 40 or 50 pupils in a period of 15 to 20 minutes. In the late 1920's and early 1930's, more emphasis was directed to the development of appraisal techniques possessing practicality for teacher use. Essentially these techniques entailed teacher comparison of either students themselves or their silhouettes with a posture chart exemplifying various types of posture and giving the appropriate ratings. Soon photographs and improved silhouettes replaced the original silhouettes and afforded greater possibilities for objective postural measurement.

A cursory survey of professional literature shows that the 1930's were productive of a number of studies relating to body mechanics. Continued study has led to various proposed measurements and different ways of photographing subjects or obtaining data for objective measurement as well as refined methods of subjective appraisal. Presently there are several satisfactory means of posture appraisal that must be evaluated in light of practicality for a given situation. Further desirable refine-

[1] Jessie H. Bancroft, *The Posture of School Children* (New York: The Macmillan Co., 1913), pp. 197–203.

ments and suggested developments may well manifest themselves in practical use in many situations and under varying circumstances.

AN ILLUSTRATIVE PROBLEM

What anthropometric test and measure of body mechanics, if any, should the teacher select as appropriate for a particular physical education testing program in junior high school? Like all other tests selected, the ones representing the areas of anthropometry and body mechanics must fill a definite niche and comprise an integral aspect of a comprehensive overall appraisal.

All of the tests presented in this chapter are not suggested for teacher consideration. A number are hastily described so as to inform the teacher fully regarding the different forms of tests that have evolved and to engender a more thorough understanding of other tests and realization of the many varied approaches that have been made. It is intended that this material will prove valuable in not only the application of available tests but also their refinement and in the development of teacher-made tests for a particular situation.

ANTHROPOMETRIC TESTS

Weight and Body Build

The ACH Index (Boys and Girls 7 to 12).[2]   After the inadequacy of the age-height-weight tables of the American Child Health Association was manifested through extensive usage, Franzen analyzed various anthropometric measurements made on over 10,000 children in 75 cities in the United States in order to discover possible ways of considering individual differences in body build and type in determining nutritional status. Franzen concluded that the items that possess the greatest significance in ascertaining the amount and quality of soft tissue relative to skeletal build in children ages 7 to 12 are hip width, chest depth, chest width, height, weight, arm girth, and subcutaneous tissue over the upper arm. With these items, it is possible to find the children lowest in certain important respects, namely, arm girth for skeletal build, subcutaneous tissue for skeletal build, and weight for skeletal build. Since the inclusion of all seven items would make an unwieldy test, a comparatively simple combination of three items—upper arm girth (A), chest depth (C), and hip width (H)—was proposed as a screening de-

[2] Raymond Franzen and George T. Palmer, *The ACH Index of Nutritional Status* (New York: The American Child Health Association, 1934). Scoring table is available in SR (selected reference) 4.

vice to select children whose nutritional status warranted study by a physician. It is called the "ACH Index" and is computed as follows:

1. Girth of the upper arm is measured to the nearest centimeter by a steel Gulick tape. The preferred arm is measured in a flexed position with finger tips on shoulder while held at right angles with the body and again in a relaxed position hanging at the side. The two readings are recorded and totaled.
2. With the subject in a natural standing position, the examiner faces the upper left side of the subject and positions the calipers slightly above the nipple line and just below the angle of the left scapula. Measurements for both natural expiration and inspiration are taken over gymnasium clothing to the nearest tenth of a centimeter. The readings are recorded and summed.
3. The hip width is recorded to the nearest tenth of a centimeter with the calipers placed against the most lateral aspect of the greater trochanters.
4. The chest depth total is subtracted from the arm girth sum. The difference is compared to the minimum difference allowed for a child with the given hip width, as found in the scoring table.
5. Cases are referred to a physician when the computed difference is the same or less than that devised from the table.

The test authors proposed two ways of using the index, resulting in different degrees of discrimination. The method suggested for schools selects the lowest 10 per cent of any broad general sampling, of which about 60 per cent are extreme defect cases and over 80 per cent are either extreme defects or those that border on extreme defects. In this way, some extreme defect cases are omitted, but speed and simplicity of measurement are gained. The teacher can administer this test in 2 to 3 minutes for each child.

Since the judgment of an experienced pediatrician is more valuable than such an objective procedure in appraising nutritional status, the appropriateness and applicability of the ACH Index for teacher use would be limited to unusual instances, such as no or very infrequent medical examinations.

Pryor Width-Weight Tables.[3] Pryor devised a test of nutritional status for ages 1 to 41, after studying various anthropometric measurements and realizing that determination of appropriate body weight must consider the bony framework and body structure as well as height, sex, and age. The test procedure entails the following:

1. Record age to nearest birthday.

[3] Helen B. Pryor, *Width-Weight Tables for Boys and Girls from 1 to 17 Years— For Men and Women from 18 to 41+ Years* (2d rev. ed.; Stanford: Stanford University Press, 1936).

2. Record height to nearest ¼ inch without shoes.
3. Record weight to nearest pound without clothes.
4. Measure and record hip width (bi-iliac diameter) to the nearest tenth of a centimeter with calipers next to the skin at the crest of the ilium.
5. Measure with calipers and record the chest width at nipple level to the nearest tenth of a centimeter.
6. Select the appropriate Width-Weight Table in the reference according to sex, age, and chest width (below age 6, chest width is not used).
7. In the proper table, find the appropriate weight in pounds opposite the subject's height and under his bi-iliac diameter. It is necessary to interpolate when the bi-iliac diameter falls between two given values.
8. The actual weight is compared with appropriate weight as the basis for screening individuals with nutritional deficiences. The desired critical screening points should be established by a medical doctor.

Pryor's tables constituted a real advance over the age-height-weight standards. The entire procedure of determining appropriate weight can be accomplished by the teacher in 2 to 3 minutes per pupil. While this test does not consider the fat content, it represents a concerted attempt to consider body structure in determining body weight and lends itself quite readily to teacher use and interpretation in instances where a close check of nutritional status is desired as part of the testing program.

Wetzel Grid.[4]   Wetzel developed a direct reading control chart to show the quality of growth and development for the individual child based on age, height, and weight measures. Two such charts, or *grids*, are available—one for babies and the regular grid for school children. The grid affords a means of determining the direction and rate of growth from infancy to maturity and is based on the assumption that a child represents his own standard of comparison. Wetzel classified the principal varieties of physiques into nine groups from A4 (obese) to A1, M1, or B1 (medium build) to B4 (extremely thin) and divided the grid into seven principal channels, grouping the three medium-build groups in the center channel, obese to the left, and thin to the right.

The grid appears as three different parts, ignoring two vertical scales on the right that are not applicable to teacher use. The left portion

[4] Norman C. Wetzel, *The Treatment of Growth Failure in Children* (Cleveland: NEA Service, Inc., 1948); and ————, "New Dimensions in the Simultaneous Screening and Assessment of School Children," *Journal of Health-Physical Education-Recreation,* XXXVII, No. 5 (May, 1966), 33. Further information and grids are available from Newspaper Enterprise Association, 1200 W. Third St., Cleveland, Ohio 44113.

provides space for recording age, weight, height, and developmental level for every plotting. The center portion contains the Physique Channels, and the Age Schedule of Development appears on the right. To apply the grid, the procedure follows:

1. The date, age, height, and weight are recorded.
2. The pupil's height and weight are plotted on the Physique Channels, and the appropriate developmental level is noted.
3. The age and developmental level of the pupil is then plotted on the Age Schedule of Development, and this plotting becomes a point on the pupil's schedule of development known as an "auxodrome." The auxodrome is a curve showing the age at which a child arrives at any developmental level in the channel. Five standard auxodromes are drawn on the grid to represent the percentage distribution of children reaching the various levels throughout their period of growth. Comparison of the child's auxodrome with the standards will indicate whether the child is normal, advanced, or retardéd in terms of the general child populace.
4. Repeated plottings at regular intervals provide a basis for evaluation of the individual child's progress and future prognosis.

In interpreting the grid, normal development should proceed in a channel and according to schedule. Pupils in the right three channels (B2 to B4) or to the right of the 67 per cent auxodrome should be watched carefully. Any pupil who manifests obvious and persistent deviation from either channelwise progress or expected auxodrome should be studied.

In validating the grid as a means of detecting nutritional and growth disturbances in children, Wetzel compared the grid ratings for 2,093 school children, kindergarten through twelfth grade, with estimates of physicians. A 94 per cent agreement was reported, excluding those children rated as fair and upon whom the physicians evinced difficulty in agreeing. In addition, the grid detected 94.5 per cent of the cases categorized as poor or borderline by the physicians. The usefulness of this technique for its intended purpose has been confirmed by other researchers. But it should not be used as a screening test for the school medical examination, because of evidence of poor correlation. Also, no justification exists on the basis of available research for use of any of the grid measures in classifying students for physical education activities.

The Wetzel Grid provides a cumulative growth record of the student throughout his school years. A word of caution must be stressed, however, for the teacher, regarding the accuracy of initial measurements to assure placement of a child in the proper channel. Improper assignment to a Physique Channel may perpetuate an incorrect growth pattern.

Meredith Physical Growth Record (Boys and Girls 4 to 18).[5] Meredith constructed charts for interpreting height and weight for boys and girls from ages 4 to 18 years. The charts resulted from computation of average height and weight at various age levels of a large number of children in Iowa City from 1930 to 1945. These averages were plotted separately against age to give average height- and weight-age curves. Normal variations from the computed averages are shown on the charts, giving five normal zones for height (tall, moderately tall, average, moderately short, and short) and a similar five-zone classification for weight. The revised charts shown in Figs. 10–1 and 10–2 were derived from white subjects attending Iowa City schools, 1961–63.

In applying the charts, the teacher plots a student's height to the nearest ¼ inch and weight to the nearest ½ pound in the proper zone. If these two points fail to fall in corresponding zones, such as tall and heavy or short and light, the discrepancy is regarded as either a normal stocky or slender build or a manifestation of poor health. The latter instance should be referred to a physician as well as cases in which successive measurements reveal abrupt changing from one zone to another. In general the curves plotted by repeated testing at intervals should follow the same zone pattern if growth is satisfactory.

Pelidisi Formula.[6] A simplified method of locating nutritional deficiency was devised by Pirquet and his staff in Central Europe during World War I when widespread malnutrition appeared. These researchers disclosed that the cube of the sitting height in centimeters is approximately ten times the normal person's weight in grams. Accordingly, it was proposed that the nutritional status of an individual be expressed as a percentage as follows:

$$\text{Pelidisi} = \frac{\sqrt[3]{10 \times \text{weight in grams}}}{\text{Sitting height in centimeters}}$$
$$= 100 \text{ per cent for a normal individual}$$

In interpreting the results, the pelidisi or nutritional index of a well-nourished child approximates 100 per cent, ranging from 95 to 100 with 95 regarded as lower limit of normal. Thin children range from 88 to

[5] Howard V. Meredith, "Interpreting Growth: Ways To Use Height and Weight Measures of School Children," *Saskatchewan Recreation,* Fall 1947, p. 1. Charts and descriptive information are obtainable from the American Medical Association, 535 N. Dearborn St., Chicago, Illinois, 60610.

[6] William E. Carter, "The Pirquet System of Nutrition and Its Applicability to American Conditions," *Journal of the American Medical Association,* LXXVII, No. 20 (November 12, 1921), 1541.

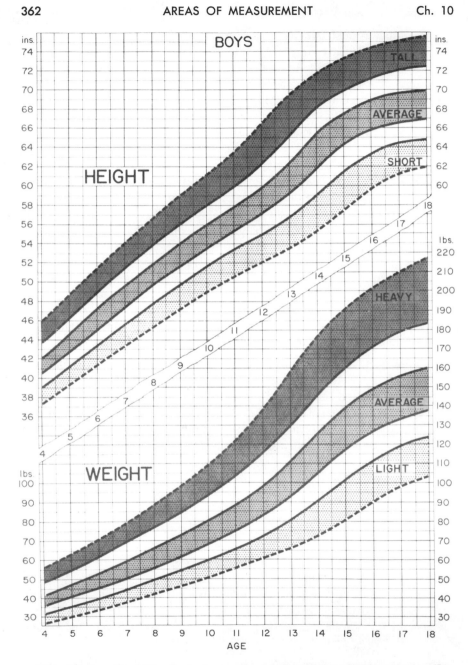

Fig. 10–1. Meredith physical growth record for boys—1963 revision. (Reprinted with the permission of the Joint Committee on Health Problems in Education of the National Education Association and the American Medical Association.)

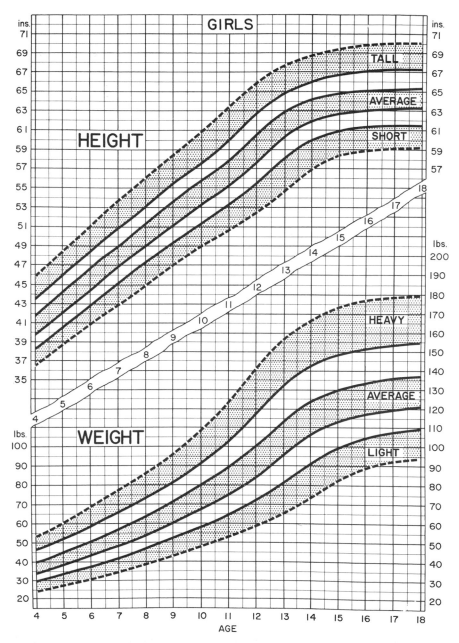

Fig. 10–2. Meredith physical growth record for girls—1963 revision. (Reprinted with the permission of the Joint Committee on Health Problems in Education of the National Education Association and the American Medical Association.)

94 per cent, while an obese child may reach 110 per cent. For adults, a pelidisi below 100 per cent denotes an undernourished state; and 105 per cent suggests reduction in food intake. The reference contains a table for deriving the pelidisi for school children, eliminating any computation. A table for converting pounds to kilograms is also included. This method represents an expedient method of appraising the nutritional status of children for possible teacher use.

Quimby Weight Analysis (Young Men 16 to 22).[7] Quimby devised a weight prediction technique, taking into account differences in skeletal build. The test procedure consists of the following:

1. Measure *height* without shoes to the nearest ½ inch and *weight* without clothes to the nearest pound.
2. Measure *shoulder width* from the rear as the distance between acromion processes with shoulders in a neutral position. This and following measurements, unless otherwise stated, are made with sliding wooden or curved chest calipers to the nearest tenth of an inch.
3. Measure *chest width* at nipple level during normal breathing.
4. Measure *chest depth* with curved chest calipers from the side at nipple level while breathing normally.
5. Measure *hip width* from the front as the distance between the crests of the ilium.
6. The subject's *estimated weight* (EW) is derived by substituting the proper coefficients for his age from Table 10–1 in the basic

Table 10–1. Substitution Values for Quimby Formula

Age	a	b	c	d	e	f
16 1/4	1.82	4.19	5.38	7.99	5.07	225.39
16 3/4	1.03	4.70	5.52	8.82	5.10	189.61
17 1/2	2.14	3.71	5.93	5.49	2.59	199.45
18 1/2	1.91	4.89	8.86	7.80	1.22	229.39
19 1/2	2.18	4.26	7.16	8.20	0.612	217.37
20 1/2	2.16	6.28	8.08	7.50	1.30	257.29
21 1/2	1.08	5.25	8.37	9.09	5.7	229.33
22 1/2	2.23	0.489	13.4	9.43	1.34	214.154

formula and then making the necessary computation. The basic formula is:

[7] R. C. Quimby, "What a Man Should Weigh," *Research Quarterly*, V, No. 1 (March, 1934), 91.

For given age:

$$EW = a(\text{height}) + b(\text{shoulder width}) + c \text{ (chest width)}$$
$$+ d(\text{chest depth}) + e(\text{hip width}) - f$$

The reference contains multiplication tables for each age division. After the various products are calculated, they are totaled and the last figure (f) is subtracted from their total to give the estimated weight in pounds.

Analysis has revealed that out of every 200 individuals who are 10 per cent overweight or underweight, according to height-weight tables, the Quimby formulas show that 100 to 150 weigh what would normally be expected for their skeletal builds. Individuals who vary greatly from the estimated weight, either definitely overweight or underweight, should be observed over a fixed period of time for change in body weight. In administering the test, one teacher can measure 30 to 40 students in an hour with a recorder. Additional time is required to compute the estimated weight. No evidence is available regarding the comparative accuracy of this technique.

Other Measures. CURETON-NORDSTROM SKELETAL INDEX (College Men).[8] The Cureton-Nordstrom Skeletal Index purports to evaluate skeletal size and predict body weight on the basis of measurements of chest breadth, ankle girth, chest depth, hip width, and height. Raw scores are inserted into quick-scoring tables to give five figures that are added, and then a constant is subtracted from the total. Norms are available for college men. With a recorder, approximately 3 minutes are required per student. Reliability and objectivity coefficients are reported as .96, with validity of .94 as a weight predictor.

WELLESLEY WEIGHT PREDICTION TABLE (College Women 16 to 20).[9] A study at Wellesley College of weight prediction methods for college women found height, chest depth, and chest width to be the most effective items analyzed. Utilizing these measures and the weights of 1,580 women representing 19 colleges throughout the United States, the following regression equation was derived.

$$\text{Weight} = 2.6 \text{ (height} + \text{chest depth} + \text{chest width)} - 154.3$$

Height is measured to the nearest ½ inch and chest items to the nearest ½ centimeter at the end of a normal expiration. The weight prediction table merely constitutes a series of solutions for the formula, with the

[8] Thomas K. Cureton, "Weight and Tissue Symmetry Analysis," *Supplement to the Research Quarterly*, XII, No. 2 (May, 1941), 331.

[9] F. C. Ludlum and Elizabeth Powell, "Chest-Height-Weight Tables for College Women," *Research Quarterly*, XI, No. 3 (October, 1940), 55. The prediction table is also available in SR 1.

predicted weight in pounds appearing opposite a given sum of the three measurements. The original study disclosed that the proposed formula is approximately twice as effective (predictive index of .30) in predicting weight as is height alone.

CURETON TISSUE SYMMETRY ANALYSIS.[10] Cureton has proposed a procedure for tissue symmetry analysis to serve as a screening device in selecting the markedly asymmetrical cases for follow-up. A profile chart is presented in percentile scale form to simplify noting a subject's deviation from his own established standard in any important element. Fifteen different linear, circumferential, and skin-fold measurements are taken to determine three indices—skeletal, muscle girth, and adipose —from which weight is predicted. This test is described herein for teacher information only, inasmuch as the elaborate procedure precludes use for teaching purposes. The reference contains complete description and illustrated directions.

McCLOY WEIGHT PREDICTION METHOD.[11] McCoy described a method for predicting normal weight purporting to give just consideration to skeletal build and fat content. Height, chest girth, hip width, and knee width were selected as the most satisfactory measurements for weight prediction. Chest girth and hip width are corrected for deficiencies or excesses of fat as disclosed by measurements of skin and subcutaneous tissue taken with fat calipers on front and back of chest, over the hip, and on the abdomen. Like the Cureton method, this test appears impractical for teacher use but is mentioned to inform the teacher fully as to the extent of available tests.

MAGLISCHO ANTHROPOMETRIC BASES FOR STRENGTH NORMS (Elementary and Secondary School Girls).[12] Maglischo used a strength criterion of the mean of 12 cable-tension tests for upper elementary and 25 tests for junior and senior high school girls to determine those structural measurements that would best reflect strength status from 12 anthropometric measures for 72 girls from each level. The best anthropometric bases for strength norms of girls were concluded to be:

Upper elementary school: Height × cube root of weight + arm girth/ thigh girth ($R = .822$)

10 Thomas K. Cureton, *Physical Fitness Appraisal and Guidance* (St. Louis: The C. V. Mosby Co., 1947), chap. 5.

11 Charles H. McCloy and Norma D. Young, *Tests and Measurements in Health and Physical Education* (3d ed.; New York: Appleton-Century-Crofts, Inc., 1954), pp. 363–72.

12 Cheryl W. Maglischo, "Bases of Norms for Cable-Tension Strength Tests for Upper Elementary, Junior High, and Senior High School Girls," *Research Quarterly*, XXXIX, No. 3 (October, 1968), 595.

Junior high school: Chest girth × standing height + shoulder width ($R = .784$)

Senior high school: Arm girth + shoulder width/hip width ($R = .607$)

Skinfold Measurement

The measurement of skinfold thickness represents the most practical estimate of body fatness for use by the teacher. While usually not practical for general testing purposes, when carefully done it affords an effective means for teacher assessment of body fatness as part of a special purpose program such as weight control or body conditioning. Succinctly, skinfold measurement consists of applying specially designed calipers [13] to determine the thickness of a fold of two layers of skin and subcutaneous fat pinched between the thumb and index finger at selected sites, generally on the right side. Recommended calipers are designed to exert a jaw pressure of 10 grams per square millimeter. Validation of this technique is based upon quite satisfactory correlations with body density disclosed by hydrostatic weighing, determinations of subcutaneous fat by X-ray and incision, and changes in body weight.[14]

Emanating from extensive study, Brozek proposed three minimum sites of skinfolds, namely: (1) *triceps*—at a point midway between the tips of the acromial process and the elbow, lifted vertically (see Fig. 10–3); (2) *subscapular*—at the inferior angle (tip) of the scapula, laterally downward; and (3) *abdominal*—at the side of the umbilicus, taken vertically.[15]

Analysis of available studies reveals that only a slight increase in correlation with the above criterion of total body density results from including additional skinfold sites, which would not appear to justify the time involved. For intra-individual comparison the triceps skinfold alone appears to give satisfactory estimates for teacher use. Montoye indicates that, although the aforementioned three sites plus the *waist* fold (on mid-axillary line just above the chest of the ilium, dorsally upward) are desirable, at least the triceps and subscapular folds should

---

[13] Two calipers are popular: Lange, less expensive and easier to handle (Cambridge Scientific Industries, 527 Poplar St., Cambridge, Maryland), and Harpenden, more accurately read scale (H. E. Morse Co., 455 Douglas Ave., Holland, Michigan).

[14] A concise and illustrated discussion of technique, sites, and validity is presented in: Henry J. Montoye (ed.), *An Introduction to Measurement in Physical Education,* Vol. 2, *Growth, Development, and Body Composition* (Indianapolis: Phi Epsilon Kappa, 1970), pp. 55–65.

[15] Josef Brosek (ed.), *Body Measurements and Human Physique* (Detroit: Wayne State University Press, 1956), p. 22.

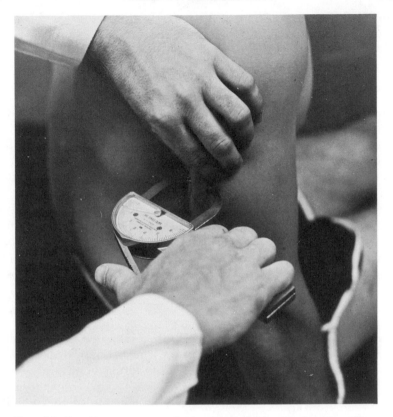

Fig. 10–3. Measurement of triceps skinfold with Lange caliper.

be measured for purposes of comparison with age–sex specific standards to ascertain the relative fatness of individuals.[16]

To obtain maximum scientific authenticity in skinfold measurement it is desirable to:

1. Standardize the procedure for lifting a fold at the different sites and apply the calipers about 1 centimeter from the point at which the fold is taken.
2. Take the reading for each fold between 2 and 5 seconds after the calipers are placed.
3. Ask the subject to move so as to contract the muscle beneath the fold, when doubt exists relative to excluding muscle tissue.

[16] Montoye, *op. cit.*, p. 65. The appendix contains percentile norms, means and standard deviations for the four sites and their sum for each year of age from 5 to 19 and in 5-year groupings from 20 through 69 for males and for females in the Tecumseh Community Health Study.

4. Make measurements early in the morning to eliminate the diurnal variation in the state of hydration.
5. Provide adequate prior practice for the examiner to assure satisfactory reliability.

Body Typology

Somatotyping. The long history of research directed toward the appraisal and classification of body types referred to as "somatotyping" has disclosed considerable evidence that the physique pattern is significant and definitely related to an understanding of the physical, mental, emotional, and social aspects of an individual's development.[17] Particular strides in this direction have occurred in the "modern era" of body-typing, beginning with Kretschmer's identification of three types—pyknic, athletic, and asthenic. A study of professional literature since the late 1920's reveals emphasis on the relatedness of physique types of various propensities such as certain personality characteristics and athletic ability. The general and often-found impressions of the obese individual as jovial and of good humor and the lean individual as high strung or nervous exemplify the association of certain characteristics with particular body types. Present-day anthropological investigations have done much to foster understanding relative to the classification of physiques as well as the predominant behavior and growth patterns associated with specific somatotypes. Certainly, the implications for the teacher of an understanding of various somatotypes and the characteristics of each as related to physical education makes its importance very apparent.

Refinement of somatotyping is attributable to Sheldon and his associates who, after extensive investigation, recognized three primary components of body build that serve as first order criteria for differentiating among individuals.[18] It was realized that individuals can best be classified in terms of the extent to which each primary component appears in their composition rather than specifically as one of three body types. The primary components recognized by Sheldon are (1) *endomorphy,* reflecting a dominance of soft roundness of the body with mass concentration in the center, (2) *mesomorphy,* characterized by a preponderance of muscle, bone, and connective tissues, giving the appearance of a rectangular and rugged body; and (3) *ectomorphy,* reflecting a dominance of linearity and fragility.

---

[17] A comprehensive presentation of somatotyping and its implications for physical education is contained in: Carl E. Willgoose, *Evaluation in Health Education and Physical Education* (New York: McGraw-Hill Book Co., 1961), Chap. 13.

[18] W. H. Sheldon, S. S. Stevens, and W. B. Tucker, *The Varieties of Human Physique* (New York: Harper & Bros., 1940).

In determining the somatotype of an individual, standardized photographic techniques are utilized; and all analyses are made from anthropometric measurements on photographs of front, back, and side views. Each component was originally assigned a rating from 1 to 7 (later, half-points were also used), and the somatotype became a sequential number listing of ratings assigned to the components in the above order. For example, an extreme mesomorph would have a rating of 171, while 117 would characterize an extreme ectomorph. Out of a possible theoretical total of 343, 88 different somatotypes have been described and illustrated in *Atlas of Men,* which also depicts the standardized procedure for somatotyping and, as such, constitutes an important research tool.[19] While considerable study has been devoted to the application of somatotyping to women and children, respective atlases have not been published as yet. Studies of the reliability and objectivity of somatotyping with trained raters have been reported to yield coefficients ranging between .82 and .93. More recently Sheldon modified the original procedure slightly to render somatotyping completely objective.[20]

The requisite training for raters (coupled with the necessity for specialized photographic equipment) limits use even for research purposes in physical education. Recognizing this, Cureton proposed a simplified physique rating that can be applied comparatively easily to rate body types of children subjectively.[21] Cureton's method represents an approximation of the Sheldon procedure and as such may not give precisely the same rating but should prove satisfactory. Three gross aspects—external fat, muscular development and condition, and skeletal development—are rated on a scale of 1 to 7 for each individual. The descriptive scale for the *Cureton Simplified Physique Rating* appears as follows:

A. Scale for Rating Endomorphic Characteristics

1	2	3	4	5	6	7
Extremely low in adipose tissue and relatively small anterior-posterior dimensions of the lower trunk		Average tissue and physical build of lower trunk			Extremely obese with large quantities of adipose tissue and an unproportionately thick abdominal region	

---

[19] William H. Sheldon, *Atlas of Men* (New York: Harper & Bros., 1954).

[20] William Sheldon, "Brief Communication on Somatotyping and Psychiatyping and Other Sheldonian Delinquencies," Maudsley Bequest Lecture, Royal Society of Medicine, London. England, May 13, 1965.

[21] Cureton, *Physical Fitness Appraisal and Guidance,* p. 120.

B. Scale for Rating Muscular Development and Condition

1	2	3	4	5	6	7
Extremely underdeveloped and poorly conditioned muscles squeezed or pushed in the contracted states (biceps, abdominals, thighs, calves)		Average in skeletal muscular development and condition			Extremely developed with large and hard muscles in the contracted state, firm under forceful squeezing	

C. Scale for Rating Skeletal Development

1	2	3	4	5	6	7
Extremely thick and heavy bones, short and ponderous skeleton with relatively great cross-section of ankle, knee, and elbow joints		Average size bones and joints in cross-section and length			Extremely thin, frail bones, tall linear skeleton with relatively small cross-section of ankle, knee, and elbow joints	

Willgoose described another subjective rating procedure as a simplification of somatotyping.[22] First the examiner studies the physical characteristics of the three components and practices observing subjects in gym and swim suits in order to select the primary and secondary components. Then to somatotype a given subject the examiner:

1. Decides on the primary component and rates it on the 1-to-7 scale.
2. Rates the secondary and tertiary components on the 1-to-7 scale to obtain a three-digit somatotype.
3. Calculates the ponderal index (height divided by cube root of weight) and relates it to possible somatotypes.
4. Compares one or two possible somatotypes to illustrations in the *Atlas of Men* and makes the final assessment.

This procedure proved effective in training over 1,200 prospective elementary school teachers. It was found that satisfactory estimation of somatotypes can be obtained for teacher use without the ponderal index or reference atlas and that interested teachers readily learned to derive somatotype ratings through inspection.

Parnell Anthropometric Phenotype.[23] Parnell developed an objective rating of body typology by physical anthropometry based on the following measurements: age; height in inches; weight in pounds; bony

---

[22] Willgoose, *op. cit.*, p. 303.
[23] R. W. Parnell, *Behaviour and Physique* (London: Edward Arnold Ltd., 1958).

breadths (bicondylar distance in centimeters) of humerus and femur; girth in centimeter of flexed biceps and calf; and three skinfolds (Harpenden calipers recommended)—subscapular, suprailiac (waist), and triceps. A 13 half-point standard scale (1–7, mean = 4) was derived from data on Oxford and Birmingham University students (N = 2,063) and arranged on an "Adult Deviation Chart of Physique" for raw scores of the different measures. By encircling the appropriate value for a subject on these standard scales, a profile is outlined which reveals the main characteristics of physical dominance. Parnell uses the nomenclature, Fat, Muscularity, and Linearity, in identifying the components of physique rating to emphasize that the scores are physical measurements and avoid the assumption that the scores describe the same components rated photoscopically by Sheldon. Laubach and Marshall have described, complete with basic statistics, a computer program for calculation of the Parnell phenotype as used in a U.S. Air Force anthropometric survey (N = 2,429 males).[24]

The chief advantage of phenotyping lies in its reliability and objectivity, since it relies on objective physical measurement rather than measurement on photographs and subjective judgment as in somatotyping. Further, phenotyping avoids reliance upon nude photography (to which some subjects object) and the associated cost and delays in photographic processing. For Sheldon somatotyping Parnell recommends combining phenotyping with photography to give objective preliminary estimates which afford better definition, reliability, and objectivity than is possible with photoscopy alone and still largely preserve the essence of Sheldon's dynamic concept of somatotype.

Specific Considerations

In anthropometric measurement the teacher should realize the importance of standardization of technique and should be cognizant of the following specific considerations:

1. *Height and weight accuracy.* While a prime concern in all measurement, accuracy becomes especially important when height and weight are used as the bases for physical growth records; and the particular criticalness of the initial measurement for such records is obvious. Haste should be avoided, and particular heed should be paid to standardized procedure regarding footwear and clothing

---

[24] L. L. Laubach and M. E. Marshall, "A Computer Program for Calculating Parnell's Anthropometric Phenotype," *Journal of Sports Medicine and Physical Fitness,* X, No. 4 (December, 1970), 217.

permitted and the time of day as these affect reproducibility and comparability of results.

2. *Girth and breadth measurements.* The tape or calipers should be aligned in a plane perpendicular to the long axis of the body part involved (e.g., horizontal in chest measurements) and firm but not forcible contact should be applied. The use of flexible metal tapes with tension-equalizing tabs to grasp is recommended. In taking chest girth either maximum (full inhalation) or minimum (full exhalation) measurement, or the mean of the two, should be used rather than a "normal" chest.

3. *Instrument calibration.* All instruments should be periodically checked for accuracy, including technical inspection as appropriate. Weight scales can be checked with certified weights as described for strength testing instruments. The accuracy of height measuring devices can be verified easily but is often overlooked. For skinfold calipers, a small metal block of varying certified thickness can be machined to check the reproducibility of scale readings at selected jaw spacings, and a simple pressure gauge can be devised to check on the pressure exerted by the jaws.

MEASUREMENT IN BODY MECHANICS

Neither the order in which the various measures of body mechanics are presented herein nor the fact that a given measure is described should signify relative importance or general acceptance for teacher use. Some measures are discussed that possess little if any appropriateness per se but provide valuable insight into the development of later techniques and in the construction of teacher-devised methods of appraisal. Inclusion, then, does not necessarily imply that a given test warrants consideration; the criterion of applicability must be carefully observed.

Tests of Anteroposterior Posture

As reflected in the historical development, the prime emphasis in measurement in body mechanics has involved bodily alignment in the anteroposterior plane (as viewed from the side). Most bodily adjustments to gravital force obviously concern the antigravity muscles that function to attain and maintain an erect position. The focus of available anteroposterior posture tests concerns an arbitrary "standard" type of posture rather than the best functioning posture for the indivdual. Progress in measurement of body mechanics has been impeded by the problems involved in establishing desirable standards. The crux of this matter lies in the fact that the basic criterion for evaluating body mechanics is expert opinion, while general consensus does not exist among experts as to the constituency of good posture. Most of the postural standards to date have been based on the assumption that one best posture can be applicable to all, although considerable evidence dictates that such an assumption is not in accord with facts. The individual differences in skeletal architecture and proportions seemingly render it imperative to establish standards in accordance with those differences. Associated with this concern for standards that reflect the best functioning posture for an individual is the need to place deserved emphasis upon the dynamic aspects of posture, body in movement, to supplement the usual static approach that has dominated measurement to date.

Recognition of these important concerns in postural appraisal should temper teacher analysis and consideration of available means of appraisal. To facilitate the presentation of anteroposterior posture tests, they are categorized as subjective and objective and include tests that may also entail appraisal of lateral deviations.

Subjective Anteroposterior Tests. Postural appraisal represents one area of measurement that has relied upon subjective judgment of experts for its development and has been somewhat retarded in the past, in addition to lack of recognition of a "good" posture, by the lack of a satisfactory means of teacher appraisal utilizing subjective judgment. Also associated with this retardation, of course, is the inability to devise a practical objective measurement technique. However, considerable progress has been manifested in the development of standards for subjective valuation of posture, notwithstanding the lack of unanimity as to what comprises good posture.

Silhouette Scales. The first concerted effort to render some standardization to subjective postural appraisal involved utilization of silhouettes or shadow prints of anteroposterior standing posture. This technique consists of making a silhouette of a student and comparing it with a standardized silhouette or set of silhouettes.

BROWNELL SCALE.[25] Brownell developed a scale of 13 silhouettes by statistically analyzing the ranking of a random sampling of 100 silhouettes by judges. The scale is arranged in rank order of numerical units, ranging from 20 to 120, assigned to each silhouette. To apply the scale, the teacher compares a student's silhouette with each example on

---

[25] Clifford L. Brownell, *A Scale for Measuring Antero-Posterior Posture of Ninth Grade Boys* (New York: Bureau of Publications, Teachers College, Columbia University, 1928). Scale also appears in SR 5.

the scale by first beginning at the bottom and working up the scale to find the comparable example. Then the comparison is made again starting at the top and going down the scale to find the comparable example. The posture grade is obtained by averaging the numerical units for the two comparisons.

CROOK SCALE FOR PRESCHOOL CHILD.[26] Crook devised a scale of 13 silhouettes for preschool children by following a procedure similar to Brownell's and based on the ranking of 100 silhouettes by 50 judges. In applying the scale, the silhouette to be graded is moved along the scale from each end until the standard type of posture most similar in quality is found. The average of three separate comparisons constitutes the child's posture grade.

HUBBARD SHADOW-SILHOUETTOGRAPH.[27] Another type of silhouette resulted merely from utilizing additional lighting devices placed in front of the screen. This simple addition changed the silhouette from a black and white outline of body contour to a shadow print. The advantages of the Hubbard method include: (1) shows clearly the difference in shoulder blade height, (2) reveals direction of the spine without special marking, (3) shows muscular development, (4) provides a means of checking foot pronation, (5) makes possible photostatic reproduction and enlargement of negatives when desired, and (6) permits the use of flesh pencil markings on the body to obtain a better check of alignment.

CHRISTENSON TECHNIQUE FOR SILHOUETTE APPRAISAL.[28] To improve silhouette appraisal, Christenson superimposed silhouettes on Brownell scale standards with a projector. The appraisals made by four judges with this technique compared very favorably. Furthermore, the variability of evaluation was appreciably reduced by the superimposition technique in contrast to the usual visual comparison.

KORB COMPAROGRAPH.[29] The Comparograph was developed by Korb to increase the validity of judging silhouettes. An outline of the norm posture appears on the backdrop in front of which the subject stands to have a silhouette made. An A, B, C, or D rating is made by comparing

[26] Billie Louise Crook, "A Scale for Measuring the Antero-Posterior Posture of the Pre-School Child," *Research Quarterly*, VII, No. 4 (December, 1936), 96. Scale also appears in SR 5.

[27] C. H. Hubbard, "Advantages of a New Shadow-Silhouettograph over the Original," *Supplement to the Research Quarterly*, VI, No. 1 (March, 1935), 50.

[28] Cornell H. Christenson, "An Improvement in Technique for Measuring Antero-Posterior Posture," *Research Quarterly*, IV, No. 4 (December, 1933), 88.

[29] Edwin M. Korb, "A Method To Increase the Validity of Measuring Posture," *Research Quarterly*, X, No. 1 (March, 1939), 142.

the silhouette with the surrounding outline of desirable posture. The norm posture represents a composite silhouette outline based on the examination of 2,200 subjects. Korb found that this method of silhouette analysis increased the validity by almost 50 per cent with 76 judges and favorably affected reliability.

New York State Posture Test.[30]   A carefully devised rating chart is included in New York's physical fitness test to judge posture from both anteroposterior and lateral aspects as one of seven basic components. The chart, shown in Fig. 10–4, consists of figure drawings illustrating three types of posture for 13 different body segments. The examples for each segment are arranged horizontally with the desired position (5) shown on the left, mild to moderate deviation (3) in the center, and marked deviation (1) in the remaining figure. The rating assigned to each body segment (5, 3, or 1) is placed to the right of the illustrations in the appropriately numbered space relative to grade level.

A relatively simple procedure is followed to position students for this postural appraisal. A plumb line is hung in front of an appropriate screen with the bob almost touching the floor. A straight line is made on the floor with masking tape extending directly under the bob toward the screen from a point 10 feet away from the bob to a point 3 feet inside the bob.

For the examination, the student first assumes a comfortable and natural standing position between the plumb line and the screen, straddling the short end of the floor line with back to the plumb line. The teacher takes a position on the floor line about 10 feet from the student and rates the lateral posture and feet from the back. Next, the student makes a one-quarter left turn so that the feet lie at right angles to the floor line, while the ankle bone is aligned with the plumb bob. The teacher stays in the same position on the floor line and rates anteroposterior posture.

In scoring each segment, the teacher first observes the student, then reviews the illustrations and descriptions on the rating chart pertaining to a given segment, and finally evaluates the student and records the score. Each segment is scored separately, devoid of influence of the scoring for previous segments. The ratings are summed for all 13 segments to give the total raw score. Norms appearing below are based on a single combined distribution for the 10,855 students tested in 30 different school systems, grades 4–12, in 1962, inasmuch as the differences in the mean grade scores between boys and girls and among the various grades were so small.

[30] *The New York State Physical Fitness Test: For Boys and Girls Grades 4–12* (1966 Rev.; Albany: State Education Department, 1966).

Posture Score	Achievement Level	Percentile Rank
—	10	99
65	9	98
63	8	93
61	7	84
59	6	69
57	5	50
53–55	4	31
49–51	3	16
43–47	2	7
39–41	1	2
13–37	0	1

Test validation is not described. The reliability coefficients ranged from .96 to .98 for boys and .93 to .99 for girls in grades 5, 8, and 11, as reported in the description of the New York State Physical Fitness Test. Meyers has achieved extremely high agreement between raters (objectivity) in brief training sessions with sizable groups of pre-service and in-service teachers. On the basis of professional personnel and teacher experience with it, this rating chart represents a decided contribution to postural appraisal. It reflects progress in rendering some clearly discernible objective basis for subjective judgment. Not only does this rating chart constitute a practical means of rating for the teacher, but also through utilization of diagrams and the scoring system, it fosters teacher comprehension and accuracy in rating. Other subjective appraisal techniques that have entailed consideration of the various body segments have necessitated extensive experience of raters and provided little in the way of illustrative rating guides. As such, these other techniques remain outside the realm of practicality for teacher use.

A discernible but often overlooked shortcoming of this test is the foot arch item. For it a high arch is rated as the desirable standard and flat feet as low, thus presupposing a direct relationship between the height of the arch and the strength and functional efficiency of the foot; for which there appears to be strong contradictory rather than supportive evidence.[31] The teacher may advisedly eliminate this item and rely on the development of local norms for interpretive purposes.

The scoring system has undoubtedly played an important part in engendering the manifested feeling of teacher confidence and satisfaction that has evolved with use of the rating chart. The scheme may be best described as a five-point rating scale in which two intermediate points are eliminated, namely, 2 and 4. By so doing, apparently much

[31] See findings by Cureton and Danford cited in the section on Foot Measurement.

POSTURE RATING CHART

Grade | 4 | 5 | 6 | 7 | 8 | 9 | 10 | 11 | 12

Rater's Initials

Date of Test

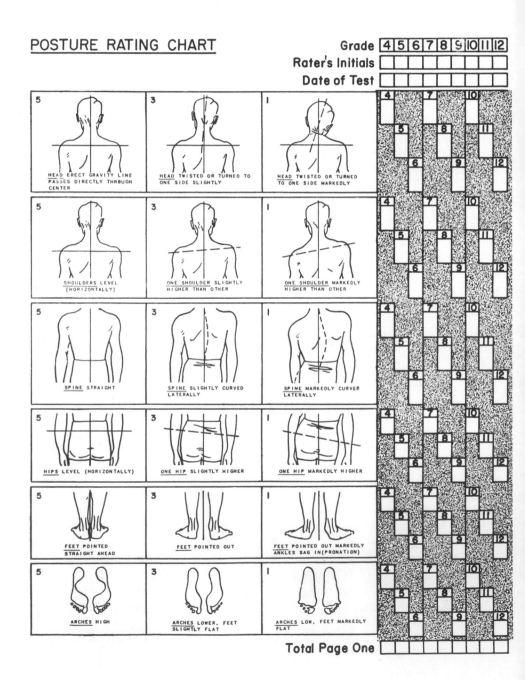

HEAD ERECT GRAVITY LINE PASSES DIRECTLY THROUGH CENTER — 5

HEAD TWISTED OR TURNED TO ONE SIDE SLIGHTLY — 3

HEAD TWISTED OR TURNED TO ONE SIDE MARKEDLY — 1

SHOULDERS LEVEL (HORIZONTALLY) — 5

ONE SHOULDER SLIGHTLY HIGHER THAN OTHER — 3

ONE SHOULDER MARKEDLY HIGHER THAN OTHER — 1

SPINE STRAIGHT — 5

SPINE SLIGHTLY CURVED LATERALLY — 3

SPINE MARKEDLY CURVED LATERALLY — 1

HIPS LEVEL (HORIZONTALLY) — 5

ONE HIP SLIGHTLY HIGHER — 3

ONE HIP MARKEDLY HIGHER — 1

FEET POINTED STRAIGHT AHEAD — 5

FEET POINTED OUT — 3

FEET POINTED OUT MARKEDLY ANKLES SAG IN (PRONATION) — 1

ARCHES HIGH — 5

ARCHES LOWER, FEET SLIGHTLY FLAT — 3

ARCHES LOW, FEET MARKEDLY FLAT — 1

Total Page One

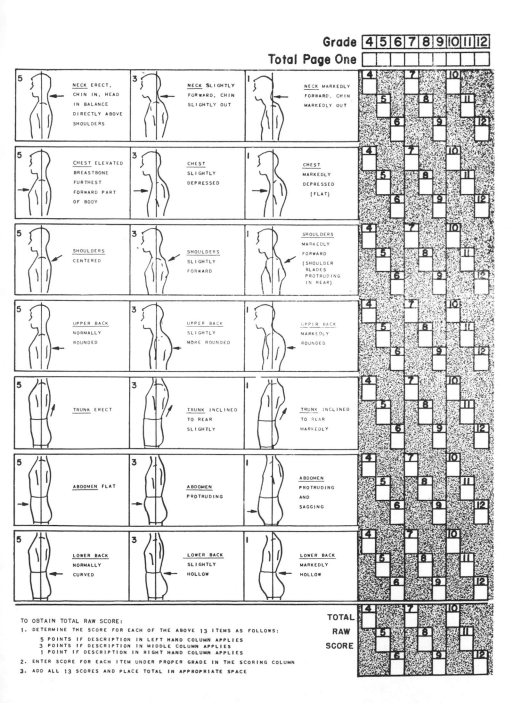

Grade 4 5 6 7 8 9 10 11 12

Total Page One

| 5 | NECK ERECT, CHIN IN, HEAD IN BALANCE DIRECTLY ABOVE SHOULDERS | 3 | NECK SLIGHTLY FORWARD, CHIN SLIGHTLY OUT | 1 | NECK MARKEDLY FORWARD, CHIN MARKEDLY OUT |

| 5 | CHEST ELEVATED BREASTBONE FURTHEST FORWARD PART OF BODY | 3 | CHEST SLIGHTLY DEPRESSED | 1 | CHEST MARKEDLY DEPRESSED (FLAT) |

| 5 | SHOULDERS CENTERED | 3 | SHOULDERS SLIGHTLY FORWARD | 1 | SHOULDERS MARKEDLY FORWARD (SHOULDER BLADES PROTRUDING IN REAR) |

| 5 | UPPER BACK NORMALLY ROUNDED | 3 | UPPER BACK SLIGHTLY MORE ROUNDED | 1 | UPPER BACK MARKEDLY ROUNDED |

| 5 | TRUNK ERECT | 3 | TRUNK INCLINED TO REAR SLIGHTLY | 1 | TRUNK INCLINED TO REAR MARKEDLY |

| 5 | ABDOMEN FLAT | 3 | ABDOMEN PROTRUDING | 1 | ABDOMEN PROTRUDING AND SAGGING |

| 5 | LOWER BACK NORMALLY CURVED | 3 | LOWER BACK SLIGHTLY HOLLOW | 1 | LOWER BACK MARKEDLY HOLLOW |

TO OBTAIN TOTAL RAW SCORE:

1. DETERMINE THE SCORE FOR EACH OF THE ABOVE 13 ITEMS AS FOLLOWS:

   5 POINTS IF DESCRIPTION IN LEFT HAND COLUMN APPLIES
   3 POINTS IF DESCRIPTION IN MIDDLE COLUMN APPLIES
   1 POINT IF DESCRIPTION IN RIGHT HAND COLUMN APPLIES

2. ENTER SCORE FOR EACH ITEM UNDER PROPER GRADE IN THE SCORING COLUMN

3. ADD ALL 13 SCORES AND PLACE TOTAL IN APPROPRIATE SPACE

TOTAL RAW SCORE

indecision is avoided while more valid and reliable ratings are likely. For instance, when either all five points on a five-point scale or a three-point scale designated as 1, 2, and 3 are used, oftentimes the teacher experiences difficulty in reaching a clear-cut decision as to whether a rating should be the lower or higher of two adjacent numbers (e.g., 1 or 2). Elimination of the intervening numbers relegates the choice to the only number appearing on the scale (e.g., 1). Certainly this scheme is not a panacea to all rating problems; neither is it a substitute for thorough understanding of posture and its appraisal by the physical education teacher.

POSTURAL SKAN-A-GRAF.—While not a test but rather a testing aid and recording scheme, the Skan-A-Graf is described in conjunction with the New York State Posture Test inasmuch as it was designed to permit use with this test.[32] The Skan-A-Graf consists of a desk top skanner (i.e., a "plexi-glass" clipboard in a wood base) that serves as a holder for transparent gridlined record charts. The skanner is placed 10 feet from the subject on a level table, and the record chart is clipped to it in a level position. With one eye closed the examiner sights through the grid to view the subject. A colored grease pencil and a straight edge are used to draw three reference lines in each plane. For lateral appraisal lines are drawn through identical points on both sides of the body to indicate ear, shoulder, and hip alignment. For the anteroposterior view the points for the ear antrum, acromion process, greater trochanter, and external malleolus (marked on the subject as necessary) are marked on the grid without changing the line of vision, and the connecting lines are drawn. Retests can be recorded on the same chart using different colored pencils. Three different grid records are available: a two-page New York State rating chart; an individual chart; and a group screening chart.

The Skan-A-Graf affords a practical means of obtaining some form of objective record of an individual's posture when desired. Although no evidence is given regarding scientific authenticity, the lack of precision implicit in the device and its use would appear to render it unsatisfactory in terms of objective measurement. There is evidence from a study involving analysis of photographs to suggest that the use of a grid is more valid and reliable in appraising anteroposterior posture than either a check list or the New York State rating chart.[33] However, grid application to photographs does not present the parallax error problem that

[32] Further information is available from the manufacturer: Reedco, Inc., 5 Easterly Ave., Auburn, New York 13021.

[33] B. Corlee Munson, "An Evaluation of Posture Screening Techniques for Children." Report to the Research Section, AAHPER Convention, Las Vegas, Nevada, 1967.

grid viewing does. Certainly further study with particular reference to viewing subjects through a grid is desirable. As an indication of the potential value of a viewing grid in subjective posture rating, the use of a grid immediately behind the subject has seen considerable endorsement as a means of enhancing accuracy of assessment of lateral deviations.

Yale Subjective Appraisal.[34] A relatively definitive appraisal of posture has seen extensive use at Yale University as an integral part of a body mechanics program in conjunction with an objective technique, described beginning on page 384. This method is depicted in the reference along with illustrations of the various items. The complete posture appraisal consists of considering the relative position or alignment of the neck, shoulders, dorsal spine, lumbar spine, pelvic tilt, overcarriage, chest, abdomen, hips, knees, feet, and lateral deviations of the spine. A taut string is held on the first dorsal and fifth lumbar vertebra to facilitate rating of upper and lower back in anteroposterior curves. For lateral curve examinations, the string is drawn from the seventh cervical to the fifth lumbar vertebras. The postural ratings given on an overall basis fall into four groups: no defects (0), mild indispositions (1), moderate defects (2), and marked to gross disorders (3). The same ratings apply to each item. This technique lacks sufficient illustrative guides to supplement description of the various degrees of deviation regarding the different items. Consequently, considerable teacher experience in observing posture becomes requisite before any semblance of satisfactory reliability and objectivity can be expected.

Iowa Posture Test.[35] The Iowa Posture Test represents an attempt to measure dynamic as well as static posture and is comprised of subjective rating of six functional conditions—foot mechanics, standing, walking, sitting, stooping, and stair ascending and descending. The various factors comprising each condition are rated either 3, 2, or 1 as being a good, fair, or poor manifestation, respectively, of the item in question. The test procedure follows:

1. *Foot mechanics test.* Each subject walks first forward ten steps and back while the tester stands at the side and then toward the tester and back. The teacher or tester makes three separate ratings under foot mechanics: (a) heel-toe walking (first walk), (b) absence of pronation (second walk), and (c) feet parallel (second walk).

[34] W. Phelps, R. J. H. Kiphuth, and C. W. Goff, *The Diagnosis and Treatment of Postural Defects* (2d ed.; Springfield, Ill.: Charles C Thomas, 1956), pp. 118–38.

[35] Published in mimeographed form by the Women's Department of Division of Physical Education, State University of Iowa. A thorough description is available in McCloy and Young, *op. cit.,* pp. 257–61.

2. *Standing-position test.* Viewing from the right side of the subject, the tester makes a rating of correct alignment of body segments and notes on the chart any deviations from the normal.

3. *Walking test.* As the subject walks around a set course, the tester rates two factors from a side view, namely, correct alignment of body segments and weight distribution. The manner of weight carriage is noted on the chart as forward or backward.

4. *Sitting test.* The tester rates two factors in this test—sitting position and rising from sitting position. In checking the former, the tester observes posture in an erect sitting position in a chair and as the subject leans forward about 30 degrees. The second rating is given upon observing the carriage in rising from the chair and walking a few steps.

5. *Stooping to pick up light object.* Each subject is rated on the way in which a small object is picked up and returned to the floor.

6. *Ascending and descending stairs test.* The carriage of the testee is rated during ascent and descent of eight to ten stairs.

Subsequent descriptions have eliminated the stair test. The teacher might choose to add certain other items, such as running and jumping. Suggested test administration calls for dividing the class into groups of 10 or 12 and arranging chairs about 2 feet apart in a row for each group. The tests are performed in this group arrangement, and a group record form is kept on which ratings for each subject are noted and totaled. The original test environment has since been modified from a formal nature to a sociodrama situation. This test has enjoyed considerable success at the State University of Iowa with satisfactorily correct and objective results when scored by experienced physical educators. No statistical evidence is reported on scientific authenticity originally. A later study entailing 250 children resulted in a reliability coefficient of .97.

The value of this test as an aid in motivating better posture has led some authorities to recommend application of it by the inexperienced, poorly trained teacher. This might be questioned in light of the fact that incorrect or poor rating would present a distorted, false picture and cause unwarranted anxiety in underrated cases and ungrounded confidence in overrated instances. That is to suggest that even for motivational purposes alone, the diagnostic instrument should be within the capabilities of the teacher applying it.

Washington State University Test.[36] A screening test was devised at Washington State University to discover students needing a more detailed examination. By means of a check list, the examiner subjectively rates anteroposterior and lateral balance; alignment of the feet and legs

[36] Donald K. Mathews, *Measurement in Physical Education* (4th ed.; Philadelphia: W. B. Saunders Co., 1973), pp. 312–14.

in the standing position; as well as efficiency of the gait as observed from the side, back, and front. A systematized procedure is described for group administration by which approximately 40 subjects may be screened in a 45-minute period. A desirable vantage point for observing gait is obtained by standing at the right angle of a right-angle triangle with 20-foot sides.

Mathews Functional Body Mechanics Appraisal.[37]   Mathews has described a functional body mechanics appraisal resembling the Iowa Test somewhat and encompassing anteroposterior and lateral standing, being seated and rising, walking (front, back, and side views), reaching, ascending and descending stairs, lowering and returning a 5- to 8-pound weight from an overhead shelf, and rope skipping. The score card for recording ratings on a four-point scale in check list format and the administrative flow chart are illustrated in the reference. No test development information is presented.

Objective Anteroposterior Tests. Posture measurement innovations in the 1890's consisted largely of objective techniques dealing with specific aspects of posture. Since then, efforts have failed to devise a practical technique for teacher application, although definite progress has been recorded in this direction. Several different approaches to objective measurement have been made. To engender continuity, the various tests involved in the sequential development of the most promising technique will be presented first. Then, the remaining tests will be discussed in chronological order.

Wellesley Posture Test.[38]   MacEwan and Howe devised a test at Wellesley College that led ultimately through adaptations by other investigators to the most thorough overall objective appraisal presently available. The Wellesley Test consists of making certain measurements on a photograph of anteroposterior standing posture. Recognizing that the actual position of reference points is obscured in the side view by back musculature, scapulae, and breasts, the test authors utilized aluminum pointers, 9 cm. long by 4 mm. wide, to locate the actual reference points. One end of the pointer, exclusive of the 9-cm. length, is bent at right angles to afford a short arm for attachment to the body by a small strip of adhesive tape. Eleven such pointers are used: nine on alternate spinous processes beginning downward from the seventh cervical, one on the prominence of the first segment of the sacrum, and one at the end of the sternum. After locating the body end of each pointer by setting dividers on the visible end, the picture is placed under a special trans-

37 *Ibid.*, pp. 314–17.
38 Charlotte C. MacEwan and Eugene C. Howe, "An Objective Method of Grading Posture," *Research Quarterly*, III, No. 3 (October, 1932), 144.

parent scale to read desired measurements. These are (1) the amount of anteroposterior curvature in the dorsal and lumbar spine, (2) the amout of segmental angulation and body tilt, and (3) the position of the head and neck. The sum of these three measurements gives the posture grade on a scale of 1 to 25, which may be translated into a letter grade from A+ to E−.

Test validity was established with the criterion of the composite rating of six postural specialists; multiple correlation of .812 (N = 834). This method of postural appraisal was discontinued at Wellesley largely because of certain inconsistencies. It should also be noted that taking and processing photographs entail considerable time that must be justified in terms of program objectives. The contribution and significance of the Wellesley method to the development of a satisfactory objective technique cannot be overlooked.

Yale Posture Test.[39] Drawing heavily upon the work at Wellesley and supplemented by the results of investigations at Springfield College (see page 391), Wickens and Kiphuth devised a test utilizing the posture photograph that had been a part of the Yale program since 1919. This test purported to determine objectively anteroposterior spinal curvature and segmental alignment. To facilitate appraisal of segmental alignment, a mark is made with a black flesh pencil on each of the following points: tragus of the ear, front tip of the shoulder, acromion, greater trochanter of the femur, styloid process of fibula, and center of the external malleolus. Aluminum pointers, as designed at Wellesley, are affixed at various points of the body to give requisite reference points for appraisal of anteroposterior spinal curvature and carriage of certain other body parts. A pointer is attached over the following: seventh cervical vertebra, point of greatest convexity in the upper back, point of inflection (where curve changes from convex to concave posteriorly), point of greatest concavity in lower back, the most prominent part of the sacrum, lower end of the sternum, and sometimes on the acromion (when needed to make it visible).

After the aforementioned preparation, the student steps into parallel footprints on the floor with the inner borders 3 inches apart and adjusts his position for the photograph so that the plumb bob falls through the external malleolus. The plumb line itself affords the basic reference in analyzing segmental alignment and body lean in addition to serving as a guide for drawing horizontal lines on the photograph.

To prepare the photographic print for measurement, small perforations are made with a pair of dividers at the body or proximal end of

---

[39] J. Stuart Wickens and Oscar W. Kiphuth, "Body Mechanics Analysis of Yale University Freshmen," *Research Quarterly*, III, No. 4 (December, 1937), 38.

each pointer, through each flesh pencil mark, and on the fleshline at the most protuberant part of the abdomen. Next, the glossy side of the print is placed down on an opaque glass surface illuminated from beneath, such as a mimeoscope, to make the picture transparent. The appropriate lines are then drawn to make the following measurements.

1. *Head and neck* (Angle A [40]). The head and neck position is indicated by the angle between a horizontal line through the seventh cervical vertebra and a line drawn from that vertebra through the tragus of the ear. The size of this angle will vary as the head is thrust forward or backward; and the more the head is thrust forward, the smaller the angle will be.

2. *Kyphosis* (Upper-back roundness, Angle B). The amount of upper-back curvature is found by scaling the angle formed by a line drawn through the point of greatest convexity and the seventh cervical vertebra and a line from the point of greatest convexity through the point of inflection between dorsal and lumbar curves. The greater the roundness of the upper back, the smaller the angle will be.

3. *Lordosis* (Lower-back hollowness, Angle C). The curve in the lower back is shown by an angle formed by a line through the greatest concavity and the point of inflection and a line between the point of greatest concavity and the prominence of the sacrum. This angle of concavity diminishes as the hollowness becomes greater.

4. *Chest* (Angle E). Chest carriage is disclosed by scaling the angle between a horizontal line through the seventh cervical vertebra and a line from the end of the sternum to the seventh cervical vertebra. The higher the chest is carried, the smaller the angle will be.

5. *Abdomen.* To indicate how the abdomen is carried relative to the chest, the angle is scaled as formed by a line through the prominent point of the abdomen and the end of the sternum and a horizontal line through the seventh cervical vertebra.

6. *Shoulders.* The shoulder position is determined by scaling the angle made by a line through the forward tip of the shoulder to the seventh cervical vertebra and a horizontal line through the latter point. Determining the horizontal distance between vertical lines through the above reference points gives a linear rating of forward shoulder position.

7. *Trunk* (Overcarriage, Angle F). The trunk position is ascertained by measuring the angle formed by a horizontal line through the sacral point and a line from that point to the seventh cervical vertebra. As the trunk begins to tilt back over the hips, this angle

[40] The reader is referred to Fig. 10–7 presented under the Modified Yale Posture Test for illustration of the specific angles.

will approach or surpass a right angle. When the angle exceeds 90 degrees, the term "overcarriage" is used to describe the existence of faulty trunk carriage.

8. *Hips.* The position of the hips is shown by the relation of the greater trochanter to the external malleolus and determined by measuring the angle between a line connecting these two points and a horizontal line through the external malleolus.

9. *Knees.* The position of knees relative to being either flexed or hyperextended is determined by scaling the angle formed by a horizontal line through the external malleolus and a line from that point to the styloid process of the fibula. In instances of hyperextension, the angle will be greater than 90 degrees.

Validation of this method began with acceptance of the validity and precision of measurement with aluminum pointers as established in the Wellesley Test. Specific validation was made largely in terms of the relationship of angular and linear measurements obtained to those derived with a wooden conformateur. Correlation coefficients ranged from .619 to .90 for head and neck, kyphosis, and lordosis. Objectivity coefficients involving the same body areas were determined by photographing 30 subjects and then rephotographing them after a different examiner affixed the pointers. The coefficients ranged from .721 to .854 and showed the precision of affixing the pointers and scaling the picture combined with the variability of posture. The grading of duplicate sets of 100 5- by 7-inch pictures by two different examiners resulted in objectivity coefficients ranging from .956 to .966 for the three items. Coefficients of .945 to .979 were obtained in the comparison of results derived from a 5- by 7-inch photograph and when enlarged four times. In essence these investigations have revealed that a high degree of accuracy and consistency can result from the application of the measurement procedures to photographs, and that objectivity for the entire process of preparing and photographing the subject is very satisfactory.

Modified Yale Posture Test.[41] With the advent of a new technique called "PhotoMetric photography," the original Yale Test was modified to capitalize on other possibilities of measurement now afforded. The PhotoMetric technique produces four images of the individual (Fig. 10–5) by a single exposure. This is accomplished by a series of mirrors set at specific positions, as shown in Fig. 10–6, to reflect images onto a bank of mirrors. The camera photographs the bank of mirrors contain-

[41] T. E. Blesh, C. R. Meyers, and O. W. Kiphuth, *PhotoMetric Photography in Posture Evaluation of Yale University Freshmen* (New Haven: Yale University, Department of Physical Education, 1954). Also reported in: T. E. Blesh, C. R. Meyers, and O. W. Kiphuth, "PhotoMetric Posture Pictures," *Journal of Health-Physical Education-Recreation*, XXV, No. 2 (February, 1954), 20; and Phelps, Kiphuth, and Goff, *op. cit.*, pp. 104–18.

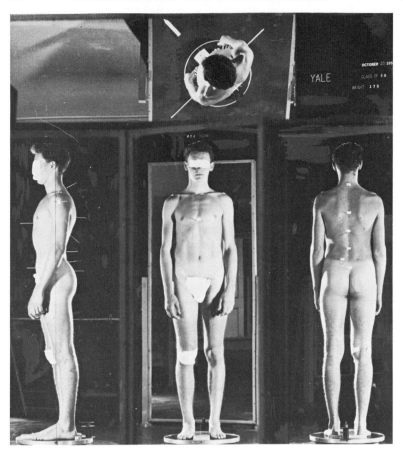

Fig. 10–5. Yale posture photograph.

ing reflections of the subject as viewed from the left side, front, back, and overhead. Both a print and a slide may be prepared from the photographic negative. The PhotoMetric equipment includes projection apparatus by means of which the images can be projected on a screen to half life-size, rendering it possible to make measurements with a tolerance of $\frac{1}{16}$ of an inch in 72 inches. Thereby, this innovation provides two unique photographic features that make additional and improved measurement possible, namely, the half life-size image and the four views of identical proportions on the same negative.

The projected image is approximately five times the size of the image on the photograph used previously. Certain desired measurements that are too small to be made on photographic prints can be taken with reasonable assurance of accuracy. The inclusion of three other views on

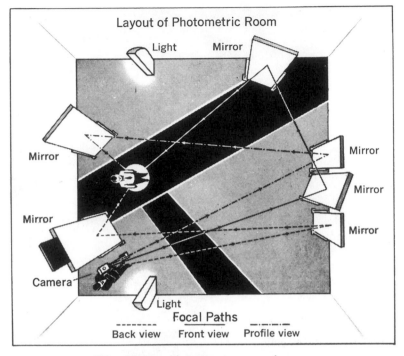

Fig. 10–6. PhotoMetric room layout.

the same negative with the side view permits making certain desired measurements not obtainable on the anteroposterior view. In addition to affording the opportunity for new measurements, the larger working image reduces the multiplication of possible error from ten to two, inasmuch as the image is one-half rather than one-tenth of life size.

Members of the physical education staff with the orthopedic physician at the University analyzed the projected image of a number of subjects to select body landmarks that would be conducive to measurement for posture purposes. As a result of this analysis, the procedure utilized previously for the side view and basically as described under the original Yale Test was continued along with the use of appropriate markings on additional landmarks to facilitate further proposed measurement.

In preparation for the photograph, the following flesh pencil markings are made: *left side*—tragus of ear, tip of acromion, greater trochanter, head of fibula, external malleolus, cuboid bone of the foot (the latter is an addition to the original test markings, while forward tip of shoulder mark was deleted); *posterior*—spinous processes of all vertebrae from seventh cervical downward, root of spine of each scapula, inferior angle of each scapula, and posterior-superior spines of ilia; *anterior*—anterior-superior spines of ilia; and top of shoulders—acromio-clavicular joint. The aluminum pointers described in the original test are applied next along with pointers on the anterior and posterior superior spines of left ilium and on top of the upper arm. The latter pointer serves to provide a readily visible indicant of pointer length. The markings are shown in Fig. 10–5.

After the landmarks are located on the image projected on the screen by measuring the distance of the exact pointer length in from the free end of the pointer, measurement is made of the angles described previously in the original test and pertaining to head and neck position, kyphosis, lordosis, overcarriage (trunk), chest, and hip thrust. A specially designed protractor-ruler is employed to scale the various angles. Certain other measurements were proposed for study to capitalize upon the unique features of the PhotoMetric technique. These include:

1. *Linear measurement of neck position.* The half life-size image makes it practical to measure certain linear distances. Two such measurements may be taken: the horizontal displacement of the tragus of the ear from the seventh cervical vertebra (Fig. 10–7, *aa*) and the linear distance between these two landmarks (Fig. 10–7, *bb*).

2. *Pelvic tilt.* PhotoMetric photography renders considerations of angles to reveal pelvic tilt more feasible. Two angles need study on the side view to determine the more significant indicant of pelvic tilt. The reference points on the left side for both angles are the anterior- and posterior-superior spines of the ilium and the greater trochanter of the femur. The anterior-superior spine of the ilium serves as the vertex for the first angle (Fig. 10–7, Angle *G*), whereas the posterior-superior spine becomes the vertex for the second angle (Fig. 10–7, Angle *D*).

3. *Shoulder displacement.* The relationship of two different angles to the shoulder position warrants study. The first angle (Fig. 10–7, Angle *K*) is proposed to indicate scapular abduction on both sides and is formed by a line through the inferior angle of the scapula to the seventh cervical vertebra and a vertical line through the latter. The second angle (Fig. 10–7, Angle *L*) shows scapular tilt as measured between a line from the inferior angle to the root of the scapula and a vertical line through the root.

The overhead view offers outstanding possibilities of shoulder displacement measurement. Two such measures of forward shoulder position are: using the two acromions and the seventh cervical vertebra as the reference points (Fig. 10–7, Angle *M*); and involving the left acromion, body mid-line, and seventh cervical vertebra (Fig. 10–7, Angle *N*).

4. *Overcarriage.* Another angle (Fig. 10–7, Angle *H*) for consideration as an indicant of overcarriage is formed by a horizontal line through

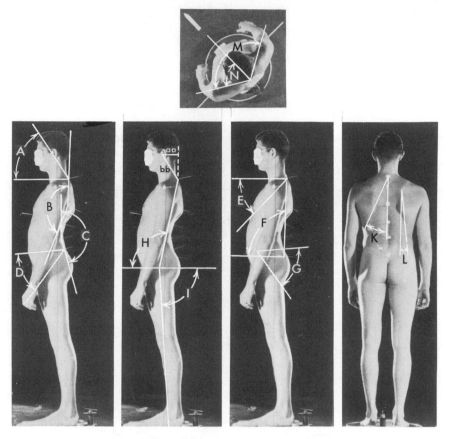

Fig. 10–7. Yale posture measurements.

the greater trochanter and a line from the latter to the seventh cervical vertebra. The use of this angle to disclose overcarriage would facilitate comparing the relationship of the trunk to the legs, since the greater trochanter also acts as the reference point for hip thrust.

The suitability of these proposed measurements has yet to be determined. But notwithstanding, the potential of the PhotoMetric technique in terms of new and important measurement cannot be denied. And although specific restudy of scientific authenticity of the original test items has not been undertaken, a discernible increase seems inevitable in view of increased accuracy with which measurements can be taken.

Certainly the cost of equipment and the time involved render this test impractical for general teacher use. However, when program objectives and conditions warrant use of the most objective postural appraisal available, this technique deserves serious consideration.

Cureton-Gunby Conformateur.[42]   Cureton studied the validity of various posture-testing devices, giving particular attention to the conformateur, spinograph (a spine-tracing instrument), and the silhouettograph. The conformateur consisted of a base supporting a wooden upright with horizontal rods or spindles of identical length arranged vertically projecting through the upright. To use the conformateur, the subject stands with his back to the upright; and the spindles are aligned so that each one just touches the spinous process of a vertebra. Upon completion of spindle arrangement, the spindles are secured in place. Validity of conformateur measurement of spinal curves was established upon comparison with other methods in which 99 per cent accuracy in full size was found for the conformateur and 85 per cent accuracy was attained from 5- by 7-inch photographs or silhouettes. Reliability coefficients on retests a week later proved much better than subjective judgment on the same cases (ranging from .62 to .67 for lordosis and .67 to .80 for kyphosis); objectivity reflected even more improvement over subjective judgment. In light of these findings, Cureton and Gunby devised an improved con-embodying some features of the spinograph and stadiometer. This new conformateur has cadmium-plated rods, a special locking device, adjustable plumb line, and a leveling attachment. Cureton advocates combining the conformateur with the silhouette for best results, inasmuch as deviations of the spine can reportedly be measured with an experimental error as small as 1 per cent, and the entire procedure—picture and measurement—can be completed in 4 minutes.

Massey Posture Test.[43]   Massey developed a criterion composed of the combined ratings of three qualified judges to select the combination of body adjustments that best reflects total body posture. Measurement of 40 selected angles and indices representing segmental alignments were made on 200 silhouettes. The investigation also included relating the findings of Wellesley, Kellogg, and Goldthwait posture tests to the criterion. This study resulted in the selection of four angles as a test of posture. The procedure follows:

1. The Cureton-Gunby conformateur technique is utilized to make a silhouette for which small-angle pointers are used to show invisible points not marked by the conformateur, and pointed pieces of

[42] Thomas K. Cureton, J. S. Wickens, and H. P. Elder, "Reliability and Objectivity of Springfield Postural Measurements," *Supplement to the Research Quarterly*, VI, No. 2 (May, 1935), 81.

[43] Wayne W. Massey, "A Critical Study of Objective Methods for Measuring Anterior-Posterior Posture with a Simplified Technique," *Research Quarterly*, XIV, No. 1 (March, 1943), 3.

adhesive tape serve to mark points easily discernible in the side view.

2. The following points are then perforated on the silhouette: (a) tragus of the ear, (b) mid-point of a horizontal line from suprasternal notch to the spine, (c) mid-point of a horizontal line from fourth lumbar vertebra to the abdominal line, (d) upper tip of the greater trochanter, (e) mid-point of knee joint, and (f) lowest point of external malleolus.

3. Lines are drawn between these points so that the following angles may be scaled: Angle I or abc (head-neck with trunk), Angle II or bcd (trunk with hips), Angle III or cde (hips with thigh), and Angle IV or def (thigh with leg).

4. These angles are recorded as the difference from a straight line (e.g., 170-degree angle is recorded as 10 degrees), and the four figures are summed to obtain the Massey Posture Score.

5. The score may be interpreted according to the following letter-grade scale: 8 to 22 degrees = A, 23 to 36 degrees = B, 37 to 51 degrees = C, 52 to 65 degrees = D, 66 to 78 degrees = E, and 79 to 93 degrees = F.

Massey reported a multiple correlation of .985 for the combination of angles with the criterion and correlations of .560, .71, and .855 with Wellesley, Goldthwait, and Kellogg posture tests, respectively. Correlations in other studies between Massey's posture score and judges' ratings have not approached that reported by Massey.

Howland Alignometer.[44]   As the basis for the development of a means of both measuring and teaching body alignment, Howland determined that the balanced relationship between the tilt of the pelvis and the upper trunk could be shown by two anatomical landmarks—the center of the sternum and the superior border of the symphysis pubis. It was noted that when structural alignment of the trunk approximates the line of gravity, these two landmarks were aligned vertically. Accordingly, she designed a device called an alignometer to ascertain the relationship of these landmarks to the vertical and, hence, indicate structural trunk alignment.

The alignometer consists of a vertical rod to which two adjustable and calibrated pointers are attached. The rod itself is secured to a portable base. The two pointers may be adjusted to meet the varying heights of subjects and also different distances in horizontal projection, the latter being measured on a calibrated scale. To facilitate location of the center of the sternum that the upper pointer must indicate, a special pointer is affixed immediately above and another just beneath the upper pointer.

---

[44] Ivalclare S. Howland, *Body Alignment in Fundamental Motor Skills* (New York: The Exposition Press, Inc., 1953), pp. 78–80.

These special pointers are joined together and to the upper pointer by a calibrated rod. With the subject standing on the base facing the rod, the top special pointer is set at the top or superior border of the subject's sternum; the bottom one is placed at the base of the sternum. Then the calibrated rod shows the distance between the two points; and the sternum pointer is set at the center reading and extended horizontally to touch the subject. The pubic pointer is adjusted horizontally to touch the superior border of the symphysis pubis. When the calibrated readings of both sternum and pubic pointers are identical, a vertical alignment of the landmarks exists.

The objectivity coefficient was found to be .923. The author also reported the existence of a high relationship (.889) between the sterno-pubic line and the distance from the acromion process of scapula to the greater trochanter of the femur, seemingly indicating validity. This device is relatively simple to construct (instructions are contained in the reference) and permits quick measurement.

Cureton Center of Gravity Test.[45] Adapting the original apparatus of Reynolds and Lovett, Cureton and Wickens developed a procedure to show the relation of a subject's center of gravity line to the internal malleoli. The apparatus consists of a balance board with a vertical pin in the exact center and resting on a scale at each end. The subject assumes a natural standing position on the board facing one end, with the internal malleoli at the mid-point by the pin. The scale readings are recorded, and one-half of the predetermined board weight is deducted from the reading at each end. The distance that the gravity line falls in front of the internal malleoli may be determined from a prepared table into which the readings are entered. The reference also contains a percentile rating scale. In the absence of the special table, the location of gravital line may be computed by the following formula.

$$FS\ X = RS\ (BL - X)$$

where X = Distance of center of gravity from front scale
$\quad$ FS = Reading of front scale minus ½ board weight
$\quad$ RS = Reading of rear scale minus ½ board weight
$\quad$ BL = Board length

Having found X, the distance of the gravital line from the internal malleoli (d) is ½ BL − X.

This test requires about 1 minute for each subject and reportedly

[45] Thomas K. Cureton and J. Stuart Wickens, "The Center of Gravity of the Human Body in the Antero-Posterior Plane and Its Relation to Posture, Physical Fitness, and Athletic Ability," *Supplement to the Research Quarterly*, VI, No. 2 (May, 1935), 93.

reflects satisfactory accuracy as indicated by reliability and objectivity coefficients over .90.

Kraus-Weber Posture Test.[46] Kraus and Weber have described an elaborate and rather definitive evaluation of posture that warrants mention for teacher information rather than proposed use. The test includes both structural and functional measurements. Structural measurements encompass chest expansion, scalpulae-spine distance, scapular level, level of anterior-superior spine of ilium, leg length, angle of pelvic tilt, and dorsal kyphosis and lumbar lordosis (based on linear displacement of seventh cervical and lumbar concavity from dorsal convexity). The functional measurements entail maximum degree of active joint range expressed as the total elasticity of three muscle groups—pectorals, hamstrings, and erector spine and hamstrings.

Tests of Lateral Deviation

Tests of lateral deviation refer basically to the spine but broadly conceived should entail the level of head and neck, shoulders, and hip, since these items are discerned in the same view of the body as the lateral spine deviations and are closely related to spinal curves. Regardless of the type of test, subjective or objective, the provision of certain considerations facilitates measurement, namely, such things as plumb line, a grid backdrop, and flesh pencil markings. While the plumb line gives the vertical reference, utilization of a grid backdrop provides horizontal and vertical reference lines. A simple grid, for example, may be constructed by stringing light colored wire at intervals of 4 inches both horizontally and vertically on a 6-foot square frame of 1- by 4-inch lumber. Painting the grid frame black, numbering height readings in white, and placing it against a black background will afford an excellent background to photograph and appraise the level of head, shoulders, and hips. Flesh pencil markings are employed primarily for photographic recording. The rear view of the Yale posture photograph (see Fig. 10–5) illustrates the possibility for analyzing all lateral deviations. A grid could be drawn or superimposed upon the projection screen for the PhotoMetric technique or, for conventional single view photographs, included in the background close to the subject. As previously described the New York State posture test provides a rating of the aforementioned concerns in terms of specific illustrations. Likewise, a grid background would facilitate this means of subjective appraisal and enhance its accuracy.

[46] Hans Kraus and W. Weber, "Evaluation of Posture Based on Structural and Functional Measurements," *Physiotherapy Review*, XXV, No. 6 (November–December, 1945), 267.

While the incidence of lateral spinal deviations does not approximate that for the anteroposterior plane, the significance of such deviations justifies attention to measures of detecting them. Measurement of lateral deviation of the spine is not plagued by lack of agreement as to what is a desirable standard, since no lateral deviation should exist. Thus measurement of lateral curvature is concerned only with the kind and amount of curve.

Taut String Test.[47]   The taut string test of lateral deviations consists of observing the spine in relation to a string stretched from the seventh cervical to the fifth lumbar vertebra. The spinous process of each vertebra between these points is dotted with a flesh pencil. The taut string may be used less objectively without pencil markings as an aid in subjective examinations. The string is not hung vertically from the upper point since many individuals deviate the whole body to one side and a vertical line comparison would lead to a false impression. In analyzing a curve it is first classified according to type as a "C" (single) or "S" curve, wherein the former lies to one side of the line while an "S" curve extends to both sides of the line. The amount of curve is found by measuring the greatest distance between the spine and the string and noting the vertebra at the level where the distance is measured.

This technique may be modified by using inside calipers to measure the curvature and a steel metric rule for determining the amount of deviation.[48] While certain difficulties [49] are acknowledged, this modified version was found to be slightly superior to the scoliometer as described below.

Scoliometer.   In 1906, Fitz described a scoliometer to plot graphically and measure lateral spine curvatures in addition to showing the deviation from the vertical, lateral pelvic tilt, and shoulder level.[50] This scoliometer consisted of a piece of transparent celluloid 16 by 52 cm. ruled longitudinally and crosswise with two small levels attached. Flesh markings were made on the subject.

Clarke and Shay studied this instrument as a measure of lateral curvature only, omitting the levels.[51] An objectivity coefficient of .89 was reported on successive tests without re-marking the back. This correlation was reduced to about .60 with several days between tests.

[47] Phelps, Kiphuth, and Goff, *op. cit.*, p. 134.
[48] H. H. Clarke and C. T. Shay, "Measurement of Lateral Spinal Deviations," *Black and Gold of Phi Epsilon Kappa*, XVII, No. 2 (March, 1940), 38.
[49] Also reported in SR 1.
[50] George W. Fitz, "A Simple Method of Measuring and Graphically Plotting Spinal Curvature and Other Asymmetrics by Means of a New Direct Reading Scoliometer," *American Physical Education Review*, XI, No. 1 (March, 1906), 18.
[51] Clarke and Shay, *loc. cit.* Illustrated and discussed in SR 1.

Foot Measurement

For the most part, tests of foot measurement represent attempts to measure functional foot efficiency. Pronation, rolling onto the inner margin of the foot, is the most generally accepted criterion of foot weakness and strain. The multitude of foot complaints by adults has provided impetus to the search for measures of foot function. Individual variance in structure has complicated test construction and interpretation.

The Iowa Posture Test (see page 381) provides for rating three aspects of foot function—heel-toe walking, absence of pronation, and feet parallel —on a three-point scale as revealed in performing a short walk. Some of the other tests described earlier also include subjective appraisal of the foot, static and/or functional. Other tests in this category have endeavored to utilize objective measurement of the foot itself as an indicant of functional foot efficiency.

Footprint Angle. The early practice of making footprints to evaluate the foot subjectively in terms of the longitudinal arch led quite naturally to a standardized measurement of the arch on the print. Schwartz originated the footprint angle on the assumption that arch angles increase steadily as arches become higher.[52] Cureton later provided substantiation for this assumption by obtaining high correlations between the footprint angle and the height of the imprints made in moist sand.[53] High reliability was reported for this original angle but no objectivity. Clarke refined the technique for determining the arch angle and obtained coefficients of .97 and .95 for reliability and objectivity, respectively.[54]

Figure 10–8 shows the Clarke footprint angle, which is measured as follows:

1. Line *AC* is drawn between the base of the big toe and the heel bone to represent the medial border of the foot.
2. Line *BD* is drawn from the point at which *AC* touches the imprint on the inner side of the big toe through the point on the edge of the print on the inside of the arch.
3. Angle *BDC* is scaled with a protractor to give the footprint angle.

[52] L. Schwartz, R. H. Britton, and J. R. Thompson, *Studies in Physical Development and Posture*, U. S. Public Health Bulletin No. 179 (Washington, D. C.: U. S. Government Printing Office, 1928).

[53] Thomas K Cureton, "The Validity of Footprints as a Measure of Vertical Height of the Arch and Functional Efficiency of the Foot," *Supplement to the Research Quarterly*, VI, No. 2 (May, 1935), 70.

[54] H. Harrison Clarke, "An Objective Method of Measuring the Height of the Longitudinal Arch of the Foot in Foot Examinations," *Research Quarterly*, IV, No. 3 (October, 1933), 99.

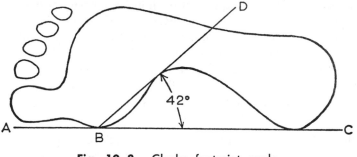

Fig. 10–8. Clarke footprint angle.

Clarke's data derived from college freshmen suggested an average angle of 42 degrees (N-518), while below 30 degrees pointed to the need for corrective measures.

Cureton's investigation revealed that the height of the arch is not a significant factor in functional foot efficiency and delimits the value of the footprint angle to motivational purposes by showing the foot condition. The potential value of periodic footprints for students should be realized, however, since the individual becomes his own standard for interpretation to indicate the need for or effects of corrective or preventive measures.

Pedorule.[55]   Recognizing that individuals with low arches might not necessarily have weak feet, Danford devised the pedorule to indicate the position of the foot in relation to the leg. The pedorule is a rectangle of heavy plate glass 7 inches wide by 9 inches high with the surface marked with parallel lines 0.1 inch apart. It is designed to measure the amount of deflection from a straight line made by the Achilles tendon, since the lower portion of the tendon appears to be deflected outwardly in weak feet. Danford recommends the second of two proposed methods of using the pedorule, in which:

1. The pedorule is positioned at the back of the foot with its center line bisecting the Achilles tendon at the point where the tendon is bowed inward the greatest extent.
2. The number of lines from this point to the tips of the malleoli are counted. Then, the total to the inner malleoli is subtracted from the number for the outer malleoli. The resultant figure represents the tendon deviation from the perpendicular.

---

[55] Harold R. Danford, "A Comparative Study of Three Methods of Measuring Flat and Weak Feet," *Supplement to the Research Quarterly*, VI, No. 1 (March, 1935), 43.

Ideally the foot should be scored 0, showing no tendon deviation. An objectivity coefficient of .94 was reported. Danford found a low correlation (.30) between the pedograph (footprint) and the pedorule, indicating that different factors are measured. This study suggests that the measurement of the Achilles tendon deflection serves as a better method of evaluating feet than measuring the arch. The pedorule shows the distance the tendon deviates from normal and, accordingly, how much the arch has flattened.

Truslow Height-Length Foot Ratio.[56] Based on clinical experience, Truslow noted that the ratio of arch height to foot length serves as a valid determinant of functional foot efficiency. This ratio is computed by dividing the height of the arch by the length of the foot (both in centimeters) and multiplying the dividend by 100. The arch height is measured with a small draftman's triangle while standing and sitting; foot length with a shoe-sizing device while sitting. The test validity lies in clinical validation from many cases. Test development statistics are not reported.

In interpreting the findings, Truslow found a standing ratio of 8 per cent to be a reasonable average for foot efficiency with a range of 7 to 9 per cent considered satisfactory when no harmful factors are present. A low standing ratio compared to a high sitting ratio divulges a temporary muscular weakness.

Flexibility

Tests of flexibility or range of joint motion have been devised to measure the amount of motion in a joint or the degree to which an individual can bend, twist, and fold. While this type of measurement has been discussed since the early 1900's, the real impetus to its development came from the need for effective evaluative means for the orthopedically disabled during World Wars I and II. It is important to recognize that flexibility is specific to each joint or paired joint in question and that these "specific flexibilities" may have little if any relationship to one another; the relationship of flexibility among joints varies within and between individuals. (In essence this is analogous to the concept of general motor abilities.) Thus, there is no general flexibility factor in the usual context of a single index or composite. The only sort of general indicant of flexibility is one derived as a profile of the specific flexibilities for the joints that are included. Unfortunately, a misconception of flexibility as a general factor has been perpetuated by the inclusion of one or two items to measure the component of flexibility on some motor fitness tests.

[56] Walter Truslow, *Body Poise* (Baltimore: The Williams & Wilkins Co., 1943), pp. 142–46.

Goniometer. Although a number of varieties of goniometers have been devised, a common type may be described simply as a 180-degree protractor with a stationary arm projecting from the right side of the protractor and a movable arm hinged at the center. It may be constructed of plastic or metal, and the arms should be 12 or more inches in length. For illustrative purposes, the application of the goniometer can be described for knee flexion, wherein the pivotal center of the instrument coincides with the center of joint motion, and one arm lies along the center line of the lower leg, and the other goniometer arm is similarly aligned on the upper leg. The difference between the readings taken at full extension and full flexion is the range of knee motion. In applying the goniometer, the importance of deliberate, consistent positioning must be realized to assure reliable findings.

Although not practical for general teacher use, an electronic goniometer (*elgon*) has been developed which permits continuous recording in degrees of the angular changes in joints during movement.[57] Briefly described, the elgon is a goniometer on which the protractor is replaced by a potentiometer of the type originally designed for small transistorized audio equipment. Recently Korb[58] devised a simplified electrogoniometer which can be constructed for less than ten dollars for use with a low level d.c. recording device.

Leighton Flexometer.[59] Leighton devised an instrument for measuring range of motion called the "flexometer" and a standardizd testing procedure for 13 different actions initially and for others later to bring the total to 19 different actions, 11 of which apply to both sides; a total of 30 tests. The flexometer (see Figure 10–9) consists of a weighted 360-degree dial and a weighted pointer mounted independently in a case about 4½ inches in diameter. The case is secured to the body segment by a strap. In the operating position, the dial and pointer coincide and point upward. Separate locking devices are provided, and the dial is locked in place when the segment is positioned to begin a test action. The pointer remains free and vertical during the movement and is locked

[57] P. V. Karpovich and G. P. Karpovich, "Electrogoniometer: A New Device for Study of Joints in Action," *Federation Proceedings*, XVIII (1959), 79.

[58] Robert J. Korb, "A Simple Electrogoniometer: A Technical Note." *Research Quarterly*, XLI, No. 2 (May, 1970), 203.

[59] Jack R. Leighton, "An Instrument and Technic for the Measurement of Range of Joint Motion," *Archives of Physical Medicine*, XXXVI, No. 9 (September, 1955), 571. A description and illustrations of the 30 actions and percentile norms on selected tests for males and females at different ages is presented in Chapter 4, "Flexibility," by P. O. Sigerseth in: Henry J. Montoye (ed.), *An Introduction to Measurement in Physical Education*, Vol. 4, *Physical Fitness* (Indianapolis: Phi Epsilon Kappa Fraternity, 1970). Also, description of these tests and the means and standard deviations for a group of 60 16-year old boys is reported in SR 4.

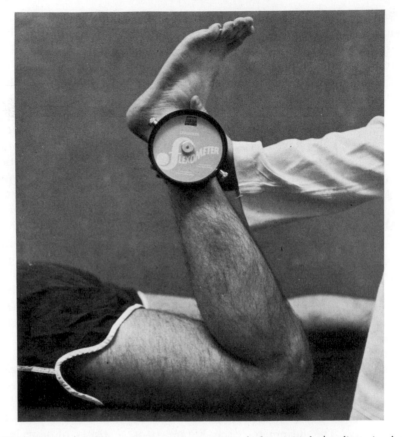

Fig. 10–9. Leighton flexometer positioned for initial reading in knee flexion-extension.

in the point of finished movement. The direct dial reading represents the arc or range of motion. For the original test actions reliability coefficients varied from .889 to .997, and reliabilities for the 30 actions on subsequent studies have fallen within these limits. Average ranges of motion and directions for the different joint actions are given in the reference.

Cureton Flexibility Test.[60] Using a flexi-ruler graduated to tenths of an inch, a meter stick, and a protractor, Cureton devised a test with college men to determine the gross flexibility of back extension, trunk flexion on thighs, shoulder, and ankles. To validate the test, Cureton compared the results of expert swimmers to those of ordinary swimmers.

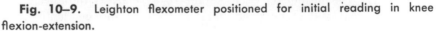

[60] Thomas K. Cureton, "Flexibility as an Aspect of Physical Fitness," *Supplement to the Research Quarterly*, XII, No. 2 (May, 1941), 381.

Reliability coefficients ranged from .70 to .95. Norms and standard scoring tables are available.

McCloy modified the Cureton Test to include consideration for the size of the subject.[61] This was accomplished by expressing, except for the ankle test, the score as a quotient in which the obtained measurement is multiplied by 100, and the product is divided by the length of the body segment involved (trunk and arm).

Scott-French Standing Bend-Reach Test.[62] To show trunk and hip flexibility, Scott and French attached a 20-inch scale, marked in ½-inch units, perpendicular to one edge of a stable bench with the zero end up and the ten-mark at bench level. (An alternative suggestion is to have zero at bench level with readings minus one, two, etc., going up and plus one, two, etc., below the bench.) For the test, the subject stands on the bench with toes to the edge alongside the scale, bends at the hips, and extends fingers in front of the scale. Keeping the knees straight, the subject slowly reaches down as low as possible with the finger tips; the score is the lowest line touched on the stretch. Preferably, two or three practice trials should immediately precede the test. Taking the test score as the last of a series of quick bobs may be done but is not recommended.

A reliability coefficient of .93 is reported as derived with 63 college women. No consideration of extremity length is made, so that an individual with short legs and long arms will score better than a student with a comparable amount of flexibility but average proportioned extremities.

The authors also describe a sitting, bending reach test and tests of upper back extension and shoulder joint range.

Wells-Dillon Sit-and-Reach Test.[63] At Wellesley College a test was developed to measure trunk and hip flexibility and avert the feeling of insecurity and apprehension that may be involved in the standing-bobbing test and that might result in less than maximal effort. In this test the subject sits with the feet flat against a vertical support, knees straight, and bobs downward four times with finger tips reaching forward. The fourth movement is held momentarily, and the reading is noted on the horizontally positioned scale over which the finger tips reach. The vertical support for the test is provided by two stall-bar benches, placed on their sides against the wall and about 12 inches apart. The scale is mounted on the edges of a board running lengthwise and another board running across the center of the scale board at the zero line of the scale.[64] Foot

[61] McCloy and Young, *op. cit.*, pp. 226–27.

[62] M. Gladys Scott and Esther French, *Measurement and Evaluation in Physical Education* (Dubuque: W. C. Brown Co., 1959), pp. 311–13.

[63] Katharine F. Wells and Evelyn K. Dillon, "The Sit and Reach—A Test of Back and Leg Flexibility," *Research Quarterly*, XXIII, No. 1 (March, 1952), 115.

[64] A specially constructed scale-support unit that permits use for sitting or standing bobs is illustrated in SR 4.

prints are drawn on the cross board, one on either side of the stem board running lengthwise. The back of the cross board is placed against the benches to position the equipment securely. The scale reads in ½-inch units from zero, plus going away from and minus going toward the subject's trunk. The lowest line touched by the finger tips of both hands (or the shorter reach if uneven) on the fourth bob represents the test score.

The sit-and-reach test yielded a validity coefficient of .90 with the standing-bobbing test as the criterion. A reliability of .98 was obtained by the split-half method for 100 college women. It was found that scores tended to be consistently higher than scores for the standing-bobbing test, seemingly verifying the supposition that less than maximal effort is obtained in the standing test. As for the standing-bobbing test, the varying extremity lengths are not considered.

Specific Considerations

The peculiar characteristics of body mechanics, like those for other measurement areas, have implications for the teacher relative to selecting, constructing, and administering tests in addition to those that are generally applicable. The specific considerations for measurement in body mechanics include:

1. *Eliciting the posture desired.* The problem of natural or normal versus posed and artificial presents a serious concern in posture appraisal, just as it does in everyday photography. It is imperative, especially in view of the variable nature of posture (both static and functional), that explicit, readily understandable, standardized instructions be given to testees so that they display what is being sought. For example, the requests to stand "normally," "in your best natural position," or "in the best position you can" invite three different responses, each of which reflects different objectives. Intendedly, the first position discloses actuality, the third reflects knowledge and understanding of what good posture is and the ability to attain it, and the second shows the implementation of the third within the context of the normal position for the testee. In the New York State Test the testee assumes a *comfortable and natural* standing position.
2. *Appraisal guides.* While the most practical means of teacher assessment of posture are subjective in nature, utilization of "judgment guides" coupled with strict attention to standardization of procedure enhances the scientific authenticity of these measures and, in essence, tends to "objectify" them. Illustrative posture rating charts and grids placed behind the subject exemplify such aids. When grids are used in taking photographs or slides from which

objective measurements are made, they should be placed as close as possible to the subject to minimize parallax.

3. *Profile of components.* Index or composite (total) scores and norms derived from them defy meaningful interpretation. While such an index may be provided, prime attention should be accorded to the posture profile, i.e., the "appraised value" for each factor or component that is included in the appraisal. Both the specificity of postural components, and the interrelatedness of change in one and its effect upon others, necessitate the profile type of record to render the results useful.

4. *Trunk-hip flexibility.* When the teacher chooses to measure trunk-hip flexibility, it should be limited to intra-individual analysis, i.e., comparison of an individual with his repeated measurements. The variation of arm, leg, and trunk lengths alone among individuals renders inter-individual comparisons and compilation of norms not only impractical but meaningless.

RESOLVING THE ILLUSTRATIVE PROBLEM

As for other areas of measurement, to resolve the illustrative problem for authropometry and body mechanics the teacher must decide which test or tests best provided information vital to an understanding of the individual in the desired perspective of overall appraisal and are compatible with program objectives and needs, still being administratively feasible. These two areas of measurement are concerned with manifestations of growth and development of children and youth that serve as the basis for providing physical educational experiences to foster optimum growth and to contribute to preventing irregularities or detecting, arresting, and correcting any that may develop. That is to say, the teacher should look for tests appropriate for the program that provide an indicant of nutritional status interpreted according to body type and disclose the basic mechanical carriage of the body. The choice of postural appraisal concerning the type of test (subjective or objective, static or dynamic) and a particular test of that type becomes largely a function of the particular situation not only in terms of practicality for the program, but especially in light of teacher competency in body mechanics. As in the case of cardiovascular function, it would seem prudent to elicit the suggestions of the school physician and nurse pertaining to teacher selection of a test. Their cooperation is essential in interpreting the test findings and in endeavoring to integrate fully this aspect of measurement with the school health and guidance records.

Analysis of anthropometric tests for the hypothetical problem might suggest that the teacher consider continuance of the Wetzel Grid as kept for elementary grades, application of the Pelidisi formula, and use of the

Meredith physical growth record charts. To the teacher these appear the most practical and expedient of the available tests. Inasmuch as the Wetzel Grid has comprised part of each student's elementary school record in the assumed situation, it would appear feasible to continue its use; the graphic portrayal of the growth record facilitates interpretation to students.

Study of available body mechanics tests suggests teacher consideration of the New York State Posture Rating Chart, the Iowa Posture Test, and the Howland alignometer. The New York State Test is conducive to expedient, reliable teacher rating of static anteroposterior and lateral posture. The Iowa Posture Test represents a dynamic test. The Howland alignometer serves as both a "teacher" and a tester of anteroposterior trunk alignment. With all factors considered, the cited problem is resolved by use of the New York State Test with the thought of possibly constructing a Howland alignometer as a supplement in the near future to capitalize on its learning-testing potential for students. Use of the New York Test will be undertaken with due recognition of the limitation imposed by the foot-arch item and how to interpret the total test properly in light of this.

SELECTED REFERENCES

1. CLARKE, H. HARRISON. *Application of Measurement to Health and Physical Education*, 4th ed. Englewood Cliffs, N. J.: Prentice-Hall, Inc., 1967.
2. CURETON, THOMAS K. *Physical Fitness Appraisal and Guidance*. St. Louis: The C. V. Mosby Co., 1947.
3. LOWMAN, C. L., and YOUNG, C. H. *Postural Fitness: Significance and Variance*. Philadelphia: Lea & Febiger, 1960.
4. MATHEWS, DONALD K *Measurement in Physical Education*, 4th ed. Philadelphia: W. B. Saunders Co., 1973.
5. McCLOY, C. H., and YOUNG, N D. *Tests and Measurements in Health and Physical Education*, 3d ed. New York: Appleton-Century-Crofts, Inc., 1954.
6. MONTOYE, HENRY J. (ed.). *Growth, Development, and Body Composition (An Introduction to Measurement in Physical Education*, Vol. 2), Indianapolis: Phi Epsilon Kappa Fraternity, 1970.

11

Tests of General Qualities
of Motor Performance

The general qualities of motor performance as explicitly described in Chapter 7 consist of certain measures of motor abilities, capacity and educability that possess great value in affording the "total picture" of an individual for appraisal. This area of testing conceivably begins where tests of motor fitness leave off. In other words, the general differentiation of motor performance from motor fitness tests lies in the addition of coordination and balance components and specific skills. Tests of motor abilities, acquired or potential, serve as invaluable "sighting devices" by which the physical education experiences can be directed more precisely on the target of identified abilities. Such tests find extensive use in grouping students for instruction and competition as well as a diagnostic and prognostic tool to guide instruction in meeting individual needs and appraising the effectiveness with which needs are fulfilled.

As an aid to understanding motor ability tests and their construction, Larson classified research underlying these tests into three categories: (1) studies dealing with those elements basic to skill performance, i.e., the underlying causes or composition of a skill, such as accuracy, speed endurance, control of voluntary movements, agility, balance, body coordination, sensory motor coordination, rhythm, body structure, shiftiness, and strength; (2) studies entailing the fundamental skills in physical education, i.e., the performance characteristics, such as running, jumping, vaulting, throwing, kicking, climbing, and catching; and (3) studies concerned with physical education sport skills, i.e., characteristics of specialized performance, such as skills in gymnastics, basketball, football, and the like.[1]

It should be acknowledged that some measurement critics argue that this area of general qualities, while possessing use for the teacher, should be excluded because of insufficient evidence regarding validity. The point of view espoused herein is that all measurement areas should be defined and described, complete with available tests and due recognition of their limitations. Only then can concerted effort be directed to improvement and refinement of satisfactory instruments within each area. Teachers represent a valuable and viable source for the development of practical and scientifically authentic tests, and thorough coverage of tests in each area affords a challenge, as well as essential resource material, for better test development in areas of need.

HISTORICAL BACKGROUND

The origin of tests pertaining to general qualities of motor performance can be traced to the turn of the nineteenth century and emanated from the desire for measuring speed and endurance as important aspects of physical (motor) ability. Since strength was deemed a minor factor, the prevalent tests at that time were inappropriate. The first physical ability and classification test is attributed to the Normal School of Gymnastics in Milwaukee where a test of student ability in nine events was introduced in 1894. Sargent devised a test of physical efficiency in 1901, comprised of six simple exercises to be performed continuously for 30 minutes. The first comprehensive test entailing the fundamental elements of running, jumping, vaulting, climbing, and the like is credited to Meylan of Columbia in 1904. This test served to turn attention to testing individuals according to the elements involved in play, and by 1916 this emphasis had attained wide acceptance. About 1908, physical ability tests were instituted in the Cleveland Public Schools, while the New York Public School Athletic League began organized competition in three events. In the Cincinnati High Schools, 1910 saw the inception of a button test for all-round efficiency in five events for boys, wherein the boys were divided into two classes with different standards for each. About a year later the St. Louis Public Schools implemented a scoring system for athletic events in which boys and girls were divided into four weight classes with three events in each class. In 1913, the Athletic Badge Tests of the Playground and Recreation Association of America were published for boys and girls to stimulate the achievement of a certain minimum physical standard, striving especially to benefit rural

---

[1] Leonard A. Larson, "A Factor Analysis of Motor Ability Variables and Tests, with Tests for College Men," *Research Quarterly*, XII, No. 3 (October, 1941), 499.

children. From this time a great wave of ability testing engulfed the country. This included Physical Education Efficiency Tests for Grade Schools in Newark, New Jersey, covering seven events with two classifications and standards for attainment according to age, height, and grade; Detroit tests; age aims for Philadelphia Public Schools; and the New York State Physical Ability Test. An important stimulus to testing elementary school boys and girls in this era was the Decathlon Test in California. This era culminated in the demand for a scientifically devised battery of motor tests, readily applicable to large groups. In 1927, to meet this demand, Brace proposed a scale of motor ability tests that has proved valuable in a threefold way: classification of pupils, basis for evaluating achievements, and instigation of a new era of ability testing characterized by attention to scientific authenticity.

A similar development characterized testing for college men wherein intense interest brought about the organization of a national athletic fraternity, Sigma Delta Psi, in 1912 with ability standard minima for membership (see page 424). This provided impetus for college departments to devise tests beginning in 1915 with the University of California Classification Test, which entailed knowledge and skill in agility, defense, and swimming. In 1921, a physical ability test was developed at the University of Oregon to furnish a basis for prescribing the physical educational experience of students. Other tests appeared at different institutions at this time. Such testing ultimately led to a scientifically devised battery of tests that resulted from a study by Cozens and which provides a means to classify college men according to their big-muscle efficiency and to indicate their special weakness.

Attention was not concertedly directed to ability testing for college women until the early 1920's. A "self-testing" program was initiated at the University of Oregon in 1922, with proficiency being determined on the basis of skill alone, and a medical examination being a prerequisite. Other tests at this time utilized the latter as part of the scoring itself. Typical of this was the Barnard Test, a scientifically devised combination of eight tests encompassing motor ability.

It is from this historical background that the development of tests of general qualities of motor performance continues for schools and colleges with due recognition accorded to the specificity of motor skills and the need to define the package or combination of specifics that will satisfactorily represent the general picture that is desired.

AN ILLUSTRATIVE PROBLEM

As for other areas of measurement, the focus of this chapter is provided by the problem posed in Chapter 7 in relation to appropriate tests of general qualities of motor performance. What test of general qualities, if any, seems appropriate for boys' and girls' junior high school physical education in the context of overall appraisal? To afford basis for resolving this question, the teacher must critically review the available tests and determine the importance of what is measured and the efficacy with which the various items are measured.

To permit more concise presentation of tests and avoid needless repetition, descriptions of items common to different tests are presented in Appendix B. In listing the items for the various tests of general qualities, no further description of these basic items will be given, except when a difference or modification exists or special clarification appears necessary.

GENERAL MOTOR ABILITIES TESTS

Tests of general motor abilities are concerned with an individual's efficiency in executing selected motor skills, that is, the present level of performance. The following tests are presented in an arbitrary order giving some semblance to importance either as a test for consideration or as an early test that proved fundamental to the development of subsequent tests.

Cozens General Ability Test (College Men) [2]

Cozens devised a test of general athletic ability for college men through a thorough study utilizing the fundamental elements underlying the skills approach to the measurement of motor ability. In constructing the test the judgment of 52 physical educators was utilized to delineate the seven components deemed most important of those comprising general athletic ability. After more than 40 tests were analyzed and classified under the seven basic elements, one test was selected for each component. The original battery was revised for administrative reasons to the final form, for which the items are listed below. (The basic component and weighting for each item are given in parentheses.)

1. Baseball throw for distance (arm and shoulder-girdle coordination, 1.5). A 12-inch outseam ball is prescribed.
2. Football punt for distance (arm- and foot-eye coordination, 1.0). No warmup.
3. Bar snap for distance (body coordination, agility, and control, .5).
4. Standing broad jump (leg strength and power, and leg flexibility, .9). One practice jump is permitted.
5. Dip (arm and shoulder-girdle strength and endurance, .8).

[2] F. W. Cozens, *Achievement Scales in Physical Education Activities for College Men* (Philadelphia: Lea & Febiger, 1936).

6. Dodging run (speed of legs, and ability to change direction quickly, 1.0). Subjects jog through course as a warmup.
7. Quarter-mile run (speed and endurance, 1.3).

The above order is adhered to as closely as possible in giving the test, with the quarter-mile run always being the last event. To score the test the subject's height-weight classification is first obtained from the appropriate table. This classification and the raw score for an event provide the data to enter the proper achievement table and find the sigma scale score. The weighted sigma score (sigma score times its weighting) for each event is readily derived from a conversion chart. The total of all the weighted sigma scores is interpreted in light of a classification scale. Performance in individual test items may be appraised as follows: superior, 80 and up; above average, 60 to 79; average, 40 to 59; below average, 20 to 39; and inferior, 19 and below. A score falling within the last two categories is regarded as reflecting weakness in that unit of the test battery.

Identical coefficients of .97 for the battery were reported for validity and reliability. The standardized directions and scoring provide for satisfactory objectivity. Both scientific authenticity and practical application suggest teacher consideration of this test on the college level for classification and diagnostic purposes for situations in which the constituent components are appropriate.

Barrow Motor Ability Test (College Men) [3]

As the basis for constructing a valid test of motor ability for college men, Barrow had a jury of experts select eight factors of motor ability and 29 items representing potential measures of these factors. After test-retest administration of the items to 252 college men, two test batteries were selected for the prediction of general motor ability on the basis of multiple correlation with the criterion of total performance on the 29 test items. Correlations of .95 and .92 were obtained from the first and second batteries, respectively.

The first battery includes (assigned weighting for each item is given in parentheses with the reliability):

1. Standing broad jump (2.2, .895).
2. Softball throw (1.6; .928) One-minute throwing warm-up and 15-foot run allowed.
3. Zigzag run (1.6, .795). Subject performs this dodging run by completing three cycles around five obstacles, placed one in each

---

[3] Harold M. Barrow, *Motor Ability Testing for College Men* (Minneapolis: Burgess Publishing Co., 1957); and H. M. Barrow, "Test of Motor Ability for College Men," *Research Quarterly*, XXV, No. 3 (October, 1954), 253.

corner and the center of a 10- by 16-foot rectangle (by going to the right of the center obstacle and circling the two end ones from the left side and repeating the procedure to complete one cycle by returning to the right of the center again). A second trial is permitted when a foul, such as knocking an obstacle over, is committed.

4. Wall pass (1.3, .791).
5. Medicine ball put (1.2, .893).
6. Sixty-yard dash (1.0, .828).

The standing broad jump, zigzag run, and medicine ball put comprise the second battery, intended as a short indoor form.[4] For classification use only, the second battery is preferable, chiefly because of its administrative economy.

The reference contains scoring tables and norms for both the general population of college men and physical education major students.

Humiston Motor Ability Test (College Women) [5]

As a test of present motor ability, Humiston combined a series of items to be performed in sequence against time. It includes the following, arranged in order of execution.

1. Complete a dodging run on a maze course marked by nine chairs and return to a mat at the starting line.
2. Lie down, do a sideward roll on the mat, and rise.
3. Run to and climb over a gymnasium box, 3 feet 6 inches high.
4. Run to a circle on the floor, make a complete turn, and continue running between two barriers.
5. Climb up a perpendicular ladder 14 rungs and descend, touching every rung.
6. Take a basketball from an assistant and run to a rope (stretched between two supports and 7 feet high), toss ball over rope, and catch it.
7. Complete a 60-foot straightaway run to the starting line.

The elapsed time to the nearest tenth of a second for completing these events constitutes the student's score. Percentile norms are based on scores made by 2,195 college women. The course layout requires floor space at least 90 feet in length. Approximately 35 students can be tested

---

[4] T-score norms for this battery for college men and for junior and senior high school boys are reported in SR (selected reference) 1. Scientific authenticity for application to the latter group is not presented.

[5] Dorothy A. Humiston, "A Measurement of Motor Ability in College Women," *Research Quarterly*, VIII, No. 2 (May, 1937), 181.

in a 40-minute period with good organization. The test correlates .81, with the criterion comprised of 15 separate events combined into a composite score. A validity coefficient of .92 with the criterion was obtained when the test items were administered separately rather than as a series. Reliability is reported as .91, with standardized directions and scoring to foster objectivity.

Newton Motor Ability Test (High School Girls) [6]

A test of motor ability was devised at Newton, Massachusetts for high school girls and found useful in aiding teachers to identify markedly superior or inferior students. The test includes three items.

1. Standing broad jump.
2. Hurdles. On a straight 90-foot-long course with 15-inch improvised hurdles, the subject runs upon signal to and over the first hurdle, 15 feet, and over four other hurdles spaced at 9-foot intervals. After the last hurdle, the subject goes around an Indian club 9 feet from the fifth hurdle and runs the course back to the starting line. The subject continues and completes the trial regardless of displaced hurdles. One trial is allowed, and the score is recorded as time to the nearest fifth of a second.
3. Scramble. A tap bell is secured 4 feet above the floor and 10 feet from the wall. The subject begins in a supine position, arms stretched to the side with palms down, and feet against the wall. On signal, the subject rises and runs to tap the bell twice, returns to a supine position, and claps the hands twice on the floor. This procedure is repeated until the fourth double bell-tap. The score is the time taken to the nearest fifth of a second.

To enhance reliability, the authors suggest that each test be given twice (i.e., repeated on a subsequent day) and an average taken as the final score. To compute the motor ability score, the raw score for each item is converted into a point (sigma-scale) score; and these scores are totaled. Achievement scales were derived from tests given to 812 students. This test can be administered to approximately 25 students in a 40-minute period by using three stations.

The test was validated against two criteria: one (.93), comprised of a composite score on 18 objective tests designed to measure power and strength, speed and coordination; and the second (.73) being subjective judgment of experts.

---

[6] Elizabeth Powell and E. C. Howe, "Motor Ability Tests for High School Girls," *Research Quarterly*, X, No. 4 (December, 1939), 81. Scales are also available in SR 4.

Scott Motor Ability Test (High School and College Girls) [7]

After extensive experimentation involving 35 different test items, Scott proposed two test batteries for use in appraising the motor ability of college women and high school girls. *Battery 1* is comprised of the following: basketball throw, 4-second dash, wall pass, and standing broad jump. *Battery 2* consists of basketball throw, standing broad jump, and obstacle run.

Supplementary description is needed to clarify two test items, the wall pass and obstacle race. In the wall pass, the best of two or three trials may be taken, time permitting. For the obstacle race:

The subject lies supine with heels on the starting line and upon signal rises quickly and runs toward a standard. In transit she steps with both feet on each of three 12- by 18-inch rectangles in the line of travel. After running twice around the jump standard, the subject runs to a crossbar 18 inches above the floor and goes beneath it. Then she stands and runs across the first of two shuttle lines to the second and returns to the first—repeating this twice and running across the second line for the finish. The score is recorded as time to the nearest tenth of a second.

The motor ability score can be derived by either of two methods. The first entails transmuting the run scores to T-scores by the appropriate tables (high school girls, college women, physical education major students) and then computing the mean T-score for the test items. The second method involves substitution in the following formulas:

Battery 1:

.7 basketball throw + 2 dash + wall pass + .5 broad jump

Battery 2:

2 basketball throw + 1.4 broad jump − obstacle race

The reference provides a table to simplify multiplication, after which the average is computed. T-score norms are available for interpreting item and battery results.

Validity coefficients of .91 and .87 were obtained for Battery 1 and Battery 2, respectively. The criterion consisted of a composite of judgment rating of experts, T-scores on nine widely varied sports skills, and an achievement score on three fundamental activities. Individual item reliability ranged from .62 to .91. About 30 students can be tested in a 40-minute period with all testing stations operating simultaneously. The second battery appears preferable, since it is easier to administer and

---

[7] M. Gladys Scott and Esther French, *Measurement and Evaluation in Physical Education* (Dubuque: W. C. Brown Co., 1959), pp. 344–63. T-scales are also available in SR 5 for high school girls and in SR 1 for high school girls, college women, and ninth grade boys.

differs relatively little in validity. Experience with this battery for college women has shown it to be very effective in screening those needing special help while also affording a close prediction of achievement rate in physical education skills.

Latchaw Motor Skills Tests (Grades Four through Six)[8]

Latchaw proposed seven tests that were devised from a number of established tests to measure performance in selected motor skills in grades four through six, boys and girls. The tests include:

1. Basketball wall pass. A target area 8 feet wide and 4 feet high at a distance 3 feet from floor is used with an 8-foot-long restraining line 4 feet from the wall. To score, a ball must fall inside, not on, the lines of the target area. After one 10-second practice trial, the better number of successful throws in two 15-second trials is recorded as the score.
2. Volleyball wall volley.
3. Vertical jump. Both starting and jumping heights are recorded by means of a series of 1-inch cloth strips suspended from a horizontal bar at 1-inch intervals, with the longest strip 5 feet from floor and the shortest, 8 feet 11 inches from floor. Each strip is weighted with a penny at its free end to insure even hanging. The score is recorded as the best differential recorded in unlimited trials.
4. Standing broad jump. Score is recorded as the furthest whole inch (e.g., 80 and ⅜ inches becomes 80).
5. Shuttle run. Three round trips are made between two lines, 20 feet apart. Score is the better of two trials, with an intervening rest while a testing partner runs a trial.
6. Soccer wall volley.
7. Softball repeated throws. Upon signal the subject continually throws overhand and retrieves a regulation softball for 15 seconds from within the throwing area. The score is the total of successful throws (balls hitting target line do not count) made in a prescribed time, with the better of two trials being the final score. A 10-second practice period is given. The target area, 5½ feet wide and 10 feet high, is marked on a flat wall 6 inches from the floor. A throwing area, 5½ feet square, is marked on the floor 9 feet from the target. A backstop, 12 feet long and at least 2½ feet high, is placed 15 feet behind the throwing area.

Face validity was accepted for each test; and the tests proved reliable (.77 to .97) for the population measured, which involved a total of 20

[8] Marjorie Latchaw, "Measuring Selected Motor Skills in Fourth, Fifth, and Sixth Grades," *Research Quarterly*, XXV, No. 4 (December, 1954), 439. T-scales are also available in SR 1.

elementary schools representing a cross-section in two states. Analysis disclosed that age, height, and weight factors were not statistically significant in determining performance as measured by these tests. Means and standard deviations were reported for each sex within each grade level.

Johnson Fundamental Skills Test (Elementary School Children) [9]

Recognizing the need for assessment of fundamental skills as a basis for intelligent and constructive programming in physical education, Johnson constructed a test of selected fundamental skills for children in grades 1 to 6. The test items follow.

1. Kicking. The test layout consists of a wall target extending 5 feet from the floor and 10 feet wide, and three floor lines 3 feet long at distances of 10, 20 and 30 feet from the wall. The target is divided into five 2 foot wide vertical areas with assigned point values of 1, 3, 5, 3, 1—left to right. The subject places a soccer ball behind the 10 foot floor line and kicks the ball to the target. Two practice trials and three test trials are made from each line. The score is the sum of the points earned in 9 kicks, with line balls receiving the higher point value.

2. Throw-and-catch. The test setup entails a 3 foot square on the wall, 4 feet above the floor, containing an inner square 10 inches from all sides; and five 2 foot squares on the floor in line with the wall target and spaced 1 foot apart, starting 3 feet from the wall. An 8½ inch playground ball is used for grades 1–3 and a regulation volleyball for grades 4–6. The subject stands with both feet inside the first square and throws the ball underhand at the wall target and tries to catch the rebound, keeping both feet inside the square. Two practice and three test trials are taken in each square. Two points are scored for hitting in or on the inner wall target and for catching a rebound in the air while standing in the floor square. One point is scored for hitting in or on the outer wall target and for catching the rebound in the air on or outside the floor square. The score is the sum of the points for the 15 trials.

3. Jump-and-reach (vertical jump). Score is the best of five trials with standing reach measured with side of the reaching hand toward the board.

4. Zig-zag run. The course consists of four chairs aligned 6 feet apart, and the first chair 6 feet from a 1-foot-long starting line; the last chair 6 feet from a wall. A 6-inch X is placed on the wall 4 feet above the floor. The subject stands behind the middle of the starting line and upon command runs either to the right or left

[9] Robert D. Johnson, "Measurements of Achievement in Fundamental Skills of Elementary School Children," *Research Quarterly*, XXXIII, No. 1 (March, 1962), 94.

of the first chair and zigzags around the others, touches the X, and returns in a similar manner to touch the starting line with a foot. The score is the best of three trials timed to the nearest tenth of a second. Trials are repeated when the start or running pattern is improper or the X is not touched.

5. Batting. A "batter-up" kit (available from Tigrett Industries, Jackson, Tennessee) is positioned so that the plastic ball passes directly over a softball base in its circle of rotation on a nylon cord. The subject faces the base in a batting position and swings the bat at the ball as it passes. Two practice trials and 10 test swings are taken. One point is scored when the bat contacts the ball to propel it at least 270 degrees.

Percentile norms are included by grade and sex based on 2,549 boys and 2,195 girls in seven cities in southern Minnesota. Validity and reliability determinations were made with about 50 boys and 50 girls at each grade level. Validity coefficients using the criterion of classroom teacher rating of each skill on a five-point scale ranged from .03 to .78; seemingly reflecting the lack of discriminatory power attributable to the limited number of rating points and, in some items, score values, plus the limitation implicit in physical performance rating by classroom teachers. Reliabilities ranged from .38 to .97. Statistical analysis indicated that the five tests generally differentiated between levels of ability of the subjects for grades 1 to 5. While the practicality of the batting item in particular may be questioned, the teacher may find this test useful for resources purposes, and in such instances should consult the reliability table in the reference.

Western Motor Ability Test [10]

Yuhasz devised a test with Canadian high school boys and college men as a simple indicant of general athletic ability that has been widely used in schools primarily for classification purposes. The test consists of the better of two trials in: (1) agility run—to nearest one-tenth of a second on course shown in Fig. 11–1, starting from a prone position with hands at sides of the chest and forehead on the floor; (2) standing broad jump—with two or three practice trials permitted; (3) alternate hand wall toss—one minute's practice allowed; and (4) sitting basketball throw. Reliability coefficients for these items were .94, .90, .95, and .89, respectively. A validity coefficient of .90 was obtained with a criterion

[10] As reported in SR 3 complete with norms and also percentile norms for British boys (16 to 19 years), girls (15 to 18 years), and men physical education students. Norms are also available from the test author (M. S. Yuhasz, The University of Western Ontario, London, Ontario) for elementary school boys (N = 812) and girls (N = 801), ages 6 to 13, and for high school girls.

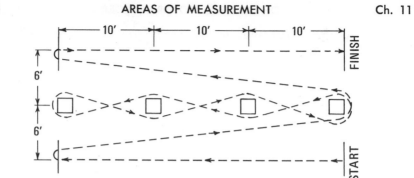

Fig. 11–1. Course for agility run—Western Motor Ability Test.

of basketball playing ability. Item correlations with composite sigma scores ranged from .71 to .82 and item intercorrelations from .46 to .61. Sigma score norms for each item are reported in the reference for Canadian college men and boys (13 to 17 years).

Great Barr Ball Ability Test (English high-school boys) [11]

To fill a void and need in English schools, Gaskin developed a motor ability test for ball games as a basis for ability grouping in physical education wherein considerable emphasis is accorded to basketball, soccer, rugby, and cricket. The test items are listed below, with means and standard deviations for 497 boys 11–12 years of age from two Midland schools. One trial of 30 seconds is given for each item with brief practice permitted.

1. Soccer dribble. The course consists of four obstacles (beam saddles) arranged in a line with 5 feet between each one and from the first obstacle to the starting line. The testee starts from behind this line with the ball at his feet and dribbles it so as to pass as many obstacles as possible on alternate sides without returning to the starting line. The score is the number of obstacles passed. Loose balls must be returned to the point of error with the feet (10.1, 3.2).

2. Padder tennis bat. With both feet behind a restraining line (13 feet from the wall), the testee bounces the ball to strike it against the wall and continues striking the rebounds. The score is the number of legal wall hits, with loose balls being retrieved (9.0, 3.5).

3. Tennis ball catch. The testee throws the ball against the wall so

---

[11] Paul F. Gaskin, "A Motor Ability Test for Ball Games," *British Journal of Physical Education,* II, No. 1 (January, 1971), i. Item and composite T-scores are available from C. R. Meyers.

as to catch it on the fly (without bouncing), while keeping both feet behind a restraining line 13 feet from the wall. The score is the number of legal catches (10.6, 4.7).

4. Basketball dribble. The testee follows the identical course and pattern as for the soccer dribble; scored as the number of obstacles passed. Loose balls are retrieved and put into play at the point of error (13.6, 3.2).

To facilitate group administration, testees began with any of the items but rotated in the sequence listed. A validity of .75 was obtained with the composite T-scores and the criterion of ability ranking in basketball, football, and cricket, and boys scoring well on the test were noted to win the majority of places on the school teams in these sports. A reliability coefficient of .95 was obtained for the total test. Very favorable results were reports after the initial two years of use in terms of improved program effectiveness, and particularly for rugby.

Johnson General Sports Skills Test (College Men) [12]

Johnson developed a battery of tests for college men to assess sports skills involving basketball, soccer, softball, touch football, and volleyball. A sports skill criterion of 25 items was derived by critical analysis of test value and jury judgment. The tests selected correlated .91 as a battery with the criterion and included: (1) basketball dribble—L. W. Johnson test; (2) soccer repeated volleys—Shaufele test; (3) softball distance throw; (4) touch football pass for distance—Borleske test without center pass; and (5) volleyball volleying—Wisconsin test with one trial. Reliabilities for these respective tests were reported as: .86, .84, .83 and .88. To compute the battery score T-scores for each test are multiplied by the weighted regression coefficients and summed. The test multipliers are: (1) 2.8, (2) 0.6; (3) 0.1, (4), 1.0, and (5) 0.4. Norms for the standard group (N = 103) were reported as: 120 or below—inferior; 121–202—poor; 203–286—average; 287–369—good; and 370 or more—excellent. This categorization was based on percentages of 3.5, 24, 45, 24, and 3.5 in the respective groups.

Classification Indices and Achievement Scales

A classification scheme with accompanying achievement scales, similar to that used in Cozens' ability test for college men, has been developed for elementary and junior high school boys and girls and another for secondary school boys. While differing in context from the above measures of general motor abilities these indices and scales afford an indicant

[12] Kenneth P. Johnson, "A Measure of General Sports Skills of College Men," Microcard Doctoral Dissertation, Indiana University, 1956.

of present abilities. The classification index provides a tentative, expedient means of homogeneous grouping by itself in addition to use in conjunction with achievement scales to disclose ability in particular items. As a general admonition, the findings of a study pertaining to the application of the classification index with the AAHPER Fitness Test reflect the limitations involved. "This study indicates that if classification indexes are used, they should be calculated for these specific selected events." [13] In essence, this corroborates the specificity approach to general abilities.

Neilson-Cozens Classification Index and Achievement Scales (Elementary and Junior High Schools)[14] Neilson and Cozens proposed a classification scheme developed in the Oakland, California Public Schools as an adaptation of a 4-point California classification scheme and the classification chart used with the California decathlon chart, both of which emanated from Reilly's plan of rational athletics.[15] This proposed scheme was intended for use with elementary and junior high school boys and girls and is based on the formula:

Classification Index (CI) = 20 age + 5.5 height + 1.1 weight

Table 11–1 presents the chart for readily computing the classification index. The reference that is cited contains a description of 33 different physical education skill tests, scoring tables for each test in terms of each classification index, and detailed instructions for using the achievement scales.

In validating the classification scheme, a correlation of .983, using high school groups, was obtained with the McCloy Classification Index (see below), which was derived scientifically.

Cozens-Trieb-Neilson Classification Index and Achievement Scales (High School Boys).[16] Based on earlier work and a study of 20,000 performance records of boys in a wide variety of individual athletic events, a classification scheme for athletic competition and achievement scales were developed. The formula was derived by taking the average of classification formulas for each of five items—running, jumping, throw-

---

[13] E. A. Gross and J. A. Casciani, "Value of Age, Height and Weight as a Classification Device for Secondary School Students in Seven AAHPER Youth Fitness Tests," *Research Quarterly*, XXXIII, No. 1 (March, 1962), 51.

[14] N. P. Neilson and F. W. Cozens, *Achievement Scales in Physical Education Activities for Boys and Girls in Elementary and Junior High Schools* (New York: A. S. Barnes & Co., 1934).

[15] F. J. Reilly, *New Rational Athletics for Boys and Girls* (Boston: D. C. Heath & Co., 1917).

[16] F. W. Cozens, M. H. Trieb, and N. P. Neilson, "The Classification of Secondary School Boys for Purposes of Competition," *Research Quarterly*, VII, No. 1 (March, 1936), 36.

Table 11–1.   Classification Chart for Boys and Girls *

Exponent	Height in Inches	Age in Years and Months	Weight in Pounds
1	50 to 51	10 to 10-5	60 to 65
2	52 to 53	10-6 to 10-11	66 to 70
3		11 to 11-5	71 to 75
4	54 to 55	11-6 to 11-11	76 to 80
5		12 to 12-6	81 to 85
6	56 to 57	12-6 to 12-11	86 to 90
7		13 to 13-5	91 to 95
8	58 to 59	13-6 to 13-11	96 to 100
9		14 to 14-5	101 to 105
10	60 to 61	14-6 to 14-11	106 to 110
11		15 to 15-6	111 to 115
12	62 to 63	15-6 to 15-11	116 to 120
13		16 to 16-5	121 to 125
14	64 to 65	16-6 to 16-11	126 to 130
15	66 to 67	17 to 17-5	131 to 133
16	68	17-6 to 17-11	134 to 136
17	69 and over	18 and over	137 and over

Sum of Exponents	Class
9 and below	A
10 to 14	B
15 to 19	C
20 to 24	D
25 to 29	E
30 to 34	F
35 to 38	G
39 and above	H

* N. P. Neilson and F. W. Cozens, *Achievement Scales in Physical Education Activities for Boys and Girls in Elementary and Junior High Schools* (New York: A. S. Barnes & Co., 1934), p. 6.

ing, weight and strength, and kicking—and dividing by 10. This was called the Best-fit Index, computed as: 2 age + .475 height + .16 weight. Achievement scales were prepared for 45 different events of which two— 100-yard run and running broad jump—are presented in the reference along with the classification chart and instructions. The California Interscholastic Federation adopted this scheme in 1935.

McCloy Classification Index.[17] McCloy was the first to devise a classification index scientifically, basing it on the relative contributions that age, height, and weight make to performance in a number of achievement tests classified under four fundamental play elements. Although not a test of general motor abilities, this index is presented at this point along with the other indices to afford substantiation for the Neilson-Cozens Index, with which a correlation of .983 was obtained. As a result of his study, McCloy proposed the following:

High School: Classification Index I   = 20 age + 6 height
                                                                         + weight

College Men: Classification Index II = 6 height + weight

Elementary School: Classification Index III = 10 age + weight

Height is omitted for elementary school (Index III), since it proved to be a negligible factor. Age is eliminated in the college index (II), inasmuch as age failed to make any difference after 17. The second reference cited contains proposed divisions for Classification Index I computed for elementary, junior high, and high schools and for Index II for college. The original reference describes the development of the indices and in addition to the above divisions, presents those pertaining to Index III for elementary schools.

Other Tests of General Motor Abilities

As a supplement to other tests listed below and in view of the comparative dearth of tests applicable for secondary school boys, the reader is referred to the Stansbury Strength Index (see page 287) for another test utilized to provide a basis for ability groupings.

McCloy General Motor Achievement Test (Boys and Girls).[18] McCloy describes a test of general motor achievement, which in essence

---

[17] C. H. McCloy, *The Measurement of Athletic Power* (New York: A. S. Barnes & Co., 1932); and C. H. McCloy and N. D. Young, *Tests and Measurements in Health and Physical Education* (3d ed.; New York: Appleton-Century-Crofts, Inc., 1954), chap. 8.

[18] C. McCloy and Young, *op. cit.*, chap. 17.

is present ability. The boys' test is comprised of pull-ups, 50- or 100-yard dash, running or standing broad jump, running high jump, and a weight-distance event—either shotput, basketball throw, or baseball throw. The pull-up strength score is computed by tables according to the formula: 3.42 pull-ups + 1.77 weight (lbs.). The points for the different track and field events are obtained from the prepared tables. The test score is derived using computation tables as: .1022 total track and field points + .3928 pull-up strength score.

The test for girls consists of modified pull-ups with the bar, a dash, a broad jump, and a throw. The actual number of pull-ups and the total track and field points obtained from the boys' scoring tables are entered in the following formula to derive the girls' motor achievement score with the help of computation tables: .42 total points + 9.6 pull-ups. All the necessary tables are contained in the reference.

While evidence of validity is incomplete, in developing this test, the results on individual test elements were correlated with the total score on a large battery of achievement tests. The items selected for the test reflected as high a prediction of general motor ability as any other combination of events.

A general motor achievement quotient can be obtained by dividing the score by the general motor capacity score (see page ■) and multiplying the result by 100. This quotient serves to disclose the relationship of present ability or achievement to innate capacity, with 100 indicating full realization of potential.

Carpenter Motor Ability Test (Primary Grades).[19] Using the same items as in the Carpenter Weighted Strength Test, Carpenter proposed equations for predicting general motor ability for both boys and girls in grades one to three. The *general motor ability score* is derived as follows:

Girls:
   GMAS = Standing broad jump + 1.5 shot + .05 weight

Boys:
   GMAS = Standing broad jump * + 2.5 shot + .5 weight

The shotput is scored as the best of three puts to the nearest foot, performed in the standard manner with a 4-pound shot. Body weight is recorded to the nearest pound.

---

[19] Aileen Carpenter, "The Measurement of General Motor Capacity and General Motor Ability in the First Three Grades," *Research Quarterly*, XIII, No. 4 (December, 1942), 444.
   * This item was erroneously given in the original reference as 2 Broad Jump and subsequently corrected.

A multiple correlation of .84 for girls and .82 for boys is reported with validity criterion of total points on a large battery of events. The reference contains instructions and norm tables for finding the General Motor Capacity Score. Norms specifically for this test are not available.

Cowan-Pratt Motor Coordination Test (Children 3 to 12 Years).[20] Cowan and Pratt studied the hurdle jump, made from both feet over a bamboo pole supported by simple jumping standards, as a test of motor coordination for children of ages 3 to 12. While scientific authenticity is not given, it is shown that skill increases with age. Accordingly, the test is regarded as a true developmental test of motor coordination and is purported to have value as a practical measure of retardation in motor coordination as well as of progress in cases of motor re-education. Norms were developed for boys and girls (N = 540) at each age level, 3 to 12.

Flinchum Study of Motor Ability (Pre-School Children).[21] In a study involving 24 three and four year old nursery school children, Flinchum found six of 12 items satisfactory for multiple correlation with the criterion of judges rating of ability. These were: 35-yard dash, tennis ball throw for distance, horizontal jump, vertical jump, ladder climb, and steps (up and down six steps). The best two batteries were dash and steps (R = .97), and vertical jump and steps (R = .92). Item reliabilities were dash—.88, steps—.78, and vertical jump—.84.

Peacock Achievement Scales in Physical Education (Boys and Girls, 7 to 15 Years).[22] Peacock derived T-score norms of the performance for boys and girls, 7 to 15 years of age, in selected gross motor activities. The items measured were: (1) softball throw for distance (tennis ball for ages 7 to 9)—with one practice trial; (2) soccer punt for distance—best of three trials to the nearest foot after one practice trial; (3) 40-yard run—one trial to the nearest one-tenth of a second; (4) standing broad jump; (5) side stepping—number of center line crossings in 15 seconds on the New York State side step test; and (6) grip strength—one trial on each hand administered as for the Rogers Test. Face validity was claimed for the items, and details regarding reliability and the size and

---

[20] E. A. Cowan and B. M. Pratt, "The Hurdle Jump as a Developmental and Diagnostic Test of Motor Coordination for Children from Three to Twelve Years of Age," *Child Development*, V, No. 2 (June, 1934), 107.

[21] Betty M. Flichum, "A Pilot Study in the Measurement of Motor Ability of the Pre-School Child," Microcard Master's Thesis, Woman's College, University of North Carolina, 1962.

[22] William H. Peacock, "Achievement Scales in Physical Education Activities for Boys and Girls" (Research Council, University of North Carolina, Chapel Hill); as reported with norms in SR 1.

constituency of the normative group are not reported. Accordingly, the test is cited essentially as a resource for test construction.

Olympic Motor Ability Test (High School Girls).[23] Kammeyer adapted the Humiston Motor Aibility Test for use with high school girls by simplifying the test progression and making several changes necessitated by arrangement of equipment in the gymnasium. The test progression involves: run through a maze of 17 chairs, jump over a horse, turn in a circle and continue through barriers, climb and descend a perpendicular ladder, pick up a ball from an assistant, throw ball over a rope and catch it, drop the ball, make a lateral roll on a mat, crawl under a sawhorse, and run 50 feet to the finish line. Satisfactory test validity was established by using two criteria—athletic achievement in a battery of skill tests and athletic participation. Study of reliability disclosed that the better of two trials yields a satisfactorily reliable score. No norms are available.

Larson Motor Ability Test (College Men).[24] Larson developed one of the most valid tests of general motor ability in two forms for college men by means of the factor analysis technique. The indoor battery includes (1) dodging run as for the Cozens Test; (2) bar snap; (3) chinning; (4) dips; and (5) vertical jump (preferably using the Mac-Curdy Vertical Jumpometer; if not, initial height is determined while facing wall and point of jump shown by chalked middle finger). The outdoor battery consists of (1) baseball throw for distance, (2) chinning, (3) bar snap, and (4) vertical jump. The reference contains tables for both tests to change raw scores into weighted standard scores and to determine the classification on the basis of the sum of the weighted scores (index score). In administering the indoor test, the directions stipulate that at least 10 minutes should intervene between chinning and dips. By placing dips first and chinning last in the testing order, the most expeditious use of time will be made; however, this change may affect the applicability of norms. With a testing station for each item, both tests can be given to about 50 to 60 subjects in an hour. The indoor form requires approximately 8 minutes to test a subject, whereas the outdoor test takes about 5 minutes.

Validity coefficients were .97 for the indoor test and .98 for the outdoor form, reliability .86. These tests are purported to measure ability in the basic elements underlying sport performance (total motor ability), and they do not predict sports skills.

---

[23] Shirley J. Kammeyer, "Reliability and Validity of a Motor Ability Test for High School Girls," *Research Quarterly*, XXVII, No. 3 (October, 1956), 310.

[24] Larson, *loc. cit.*

Emory University Test (College Men).[25]   The eight items of an ability classification test used at Emory University were analyzed statistically, resulting in a four-item test with a multiple correlation of .987 with the original test score. This shortened version includes (1) softball throw—better of two throws, single-step throw with opposite foot follow-through; (2) vertical jump—facing board to record initial height, marked with piece of chalk; (3) 60-yard dash; and (4) basketball dribble—dribble the length of an 86-foot court while weaving through four chairs spaced equidistance and alternately 3 feet to right and left of a line between the baskets, make a basket, dribble through chairs to starting end, and make another basket—scored as time to the nearest tenth of a second. The items of the original test that were eliminated are chinning, football throw, volleyball serve, and soccer dribble.

Oberlin College Test (College Men).[26]   At Oberlin College a qualifying test for an elective program in physical education was developed that includes a sampling of the elements generally considered to be encompassed in all-round athletic ability. The test entails the following elements, events, and standards: (1) running—176 yards (2 laps on indoor track), 24 seconds; (2) jumping—running high jump, 4 feet 10 inches; (3) vaulting—low horizontal bar, 47 inches; (4) climbing—20-foot rope from kneeling start, 12 seconds; (5) pulling and lifting—two backward circles on high bar from motionless hanging start for both, no floor contact between; (6) pushing—dips, 10; (7) throwing—baseball throw at 18-inch diameter target from 60 feet, three out of five throws; (8) swimming—100 yards, 1 minute and 45 seconds; (9) tumbling—hand spring; and (10) balancing—handstand confined to 4-foot diameter circle, 10 seconds.

Sigma Delta Psi (College Men).[27]   Sigma Delta Psi, a national honorary athletic fraternity, requires the following achievements for membership: (1) 100-yard dash—11.6 seconds; (2) 120-yard low hurdles —16 seconds; (3) running high jump—height-weight classification; (4) running broad jump—17 feet; (5) 16-pound shot-put—according to weight, 30 feet for a man 160 pounds or over; (6) 20-foot rope climb— 12 seconds, or golf—four of five shots for accuracy; (7) baseball throw —250 feet, or javelin throw—130 feet; (8) football punt—120 feet; (9) 100-yard swim—1 minute and 45 seconds; (10) 1-mile run—6 minutes;

[25] Emery W. Seymour, "Classification of Emory University Male Freshmen in Physical Education Classes," *Research Quarterly*, XXIV, No. 4 (December, 1953), 459.

[26] "Qualifying Test for Elective Program in Physical Education," *Journal of Health and Physical Education*, VII, No. 8 (October, 1936), 512.

[27] *Sigma Delta Psi Handbook*, Sigma Delta Psi, School of Health and Physical Education, Indiana University, Bloomington, Indiana.

(11) front handspring, landing on feet; (12) handstand—10 seconds, or bowling—160 average for three games; (13) fence vault—chin high; (14) good posture—standard B of the Harvard Body Mechanics Posture Chart; and (15) scholarship—eligible for varsity competition. Although the tests are criterion-referenced, as described, the handbook contains national scoring tables for intra- and inter-chapter competition.

GENERAL MOTOR CAPACITY TESTS

Tests of general motor capacity encompass an individual's innate potentiality for all motor skill performance and endeavor to indicate the probable developmental ceiling. One published test dealing specifically with this quality warrants description.

McCloy Motor Capacity Test (Boys and Girls) [28]

McCloy proposed a combination of previously established tests for the measurement of general motor capacity of boys and girls at both elementary and secondary school levels. This includes (1) McCloy Classification Index (size and maturity)—found to be of little value for girls and not included in girls' tests; (2) Sargent Jump—vertical jump measured by sighting height reached by top of head (power, scored in centimeters); (3) 10-second squat thrust (agility); and (4) Iowa-Brace Test (motor educability, expressed as T-score, see page 428). The prediction formulas developed for the different school levels and each sex follows:

Elementary school boys:
$$.181 \text{ CI} + .769 \text{ SJ} + .510 \text{ I-B} + 2.187 \text{ st} - 62$$

Elementary school girls:
$$3.576 \text{ SJ} + 2.20 \text{ I-B} + 19.12 \text{ st} + 29$$

Junior and senior high school hoys:
$$.329 \text{ CI} + 1.446 \text{ SJ} + .926 \text{ I-B} + 3.973 \text{ st} - 202$$

Junior and senior high school girls:
$$3.576 \text{ SJ} + 2.20 \text{ I-B} + 19.12 \text{ st} + 119$$

The total score derived by the formula is known as the *general motor capacity score* (GMCS), a measure of an individual's innate motor potentiality, which is comparable to the raw score on an intelligence

[28] C. H. McCloy, "The Measurement of General Motor Capacity and General Motor Ability," *Supplement to the Research Quarterly*, V, No. 1 (March, 1934), 46; and presented in McCloy and Young, *op. cit.*, chap. 12.

test. By dividing the GMCS by a norm based on the Classification Index for boys and on age for girls, the *motor quotient* (MQ) is computed, which in turn is comparable to the intelligence quotient (IQ). The MQ serves to interpret the GMCS for the individual, since it indicates the motor capacity of a person relative to his size and maturity.

In validating the batteries, a criterion of the T-score sum of 11 test items for boys and 10 for girls was used. The resultant correlations of .969 for boys and .921 for girls were spuriously high. This was largely attributable to the inclusion of the test items as part of the criterion. Studies correlating the batteries with teacher ratings have produced coefficients ranging from .512 to .812. The second reference cited contains a description of the test complete with conversion charts and norms.

GENERAL MOTOR EDUCABILITY TESTS

Tests of general motor educability are meant to disclose an individual's ability to learn *new* motor skills (and by definition should rely heavily upon items that are new to the student).[29] The order of presenting the educability tests follows their chronological development.

Brace Motor Ability Test [30]

Brace pioneered acceptance of the challenge for a scientifically devised battery of motor tests applicable to large groups by developing a test purporting to measure native motor ability rather than acquired ability. While this test was not specifically designed for motor educability and perhaps might be more properly classified as a motor capacity test, it is included here to afford continuity to the development of such tests. The test consists of two batteries of ten events in the nature of easily administered stunts scored on a pass or fail basis, the test score being the total events passed. The items include (those marked by an asterisk are referred to in the description of the Iowa-Brace Test):

1. Heel-toe walking in a straight line.
2. Starting with feet apart, jump into the air, clap feet together, and land with feet apart.
3. Sit up from supine position, arms folded on chest, without raising feet from the floor.

---

[29] D. K. Brace, *Measuring Motor Ability: A Scale of Motor Ability Tests* (New York: A. S. Barnes & Co., 1927).

[30] As a test construction resource, a descriptive list of 37 motor aptitude test items is contained in: A. H. Ismail, J. E. Christian and W. V. Kessler, "Body Composition Relative to Motor Aptitude for Preadolescent Boys," *Research Quarterly*, XXXIV, No. 4 (December, 1963), 462.

4. From standing position with arms folded behind back, kneel on both knees and recover.

°5. Three push-ups.

6. From a squat position on toes with feet together, knees out, and finger tips touching the floor, spring to an erect position on heels, feet about 18 inches apart and arms horizontally to the side. Repeat three times.

°7. Make a full left turn in the air, landing on the same spot.

°8. As in 2, except clap feet together twice.

9. While holding left foot behind right knee, touch left knee to the floor and return.

°10. Jump through loop formed by grasping toes of one foot with opposite hand.

11. Jump and slap both heels with hands behind the body.

12. Kick with right foot so toes come at least to shoulder level.

°13. Stand on left foot, bend forward to place hands on floor, extend right leg behind, touch head to floor, and recover to standing position.

°14. Hold a full-squat position for 5 seconds with arms between and behind ankles, hands clasped in front, and heels together.

°15. As in 7, except turn to right.

°16. Jump to feet from kneeling position.

°17. Standing with arms and legs crossed, sit and recover.

°18. Stand for 10 seconds, eyes closed, on left foot with sole of right foot against inside of left knee and hands on hips.

19. Five-second squat balance.

20. From a standing position, sit down on left heel while right foot is extended forward off the floor and then recover.

Validity coefficients of .68 for boys and .52 for girls were reported with criterion of expert judgment and .80 with results of a decathlon. Considerable criticism has been leveled at the validity of this test because the criteria are doubtful measures of inherent motor skill. Evidence shows that older individuals tend to score better than younger testees and that learning takes place during the test trials and with further practice, which is not characteristic of a true measure of native ability. Upon further study Brace concluded that the test fails to measure motor learning to the extent that it warrants classification as a test of motor educability, even though it appeared slightly better than the Iowa Revision.[31] The reliability ranged from .66 to .82 on individual items—.80 for the whole test.

Norms are available for ages 8 to 18 for both boys and girls and for college women, with no differentiation between age, weight, or sex

[31] D. K. Brace, "Studies in Motor Learning of Gross Bodily Motor Skills," *Research Quarterly*, XVII, No. 4 (December, 1946), 242.

being made. This limits applicability largely to individuals in the middle and lower range of performance ability and suggests construction of local norms. While large groups can be tested in a 40-minute period when subjects score one another, testing in groups of four is advocated for pupils below the fifth grade. To minimize the practice effect, the test is administered to groups by dividing the group into two lines and giving the first ten tests to line 1, followed by the second ten tests to line 2, and then having line 1 do the second tests, followed by line 2 with the first ten tests. Prior to the execution of a given stunt, the correct performance and common faults should be demonstrated and relevant questions answered.

Iowa Revision of the Brace Test [32]

In an endeavor to revise the Brace Test to be a test of motor educability, McCloy excluded those stunts that depend primarily upon strength. After experimentation with 40 different stunts, 21 were retained, 10 of which were in the Brace Test. Items were selected in which the percentage of individuals passing the stunt increased proportionately with age and which manifested low correlation with measures of strength, size, maturity, and power, while giving consideration to greater skill. The items in the Iowa-Brace Test include (items marked by an asterisk represent Brace stunts as numbered above):

1. From side leaning rest position on right side, raise left arm and leg and hold for 5 seconds.
2. Hold a one-knee balance on floor for 5 seconds with arms sideward at shoulder level.
3. From balance position in 2, touch head to floor and recover.
4. Standing on one foot, eyes closed, take five hops backward, maintaining position.
*5. Three push-ups.
6. Jump, swing legs forward, and touch toes with hands, not bending knees more than 45 degrees.
*7. Full left turn.
*8. Double heel click.
9. Move arms in a circle 1 foot in diameter with arms horizontally to the side while bouncing up and down from a full-squat position for 10 seconds.
*10. Loop jump.
11. Standing on the left foot, jump and make a half-turn left.
12. Swing left leg to the side, jump up with right leg, clap feet, and land with feet apart.
*13. Foot-touch-head.

[32] McCloy and Young, op. cit., chap. 11.

*14. Grapevine.
*15. Full right turn.
*16. Kneeling jump.
*17. Crossed leg sit.
*18. Stork stand.
19. Do a Russian dance step by alternately raising legs forward, twice on each side; heel of extended leg may touch the floor.
20. From a sitting position with lower legs flexed and on the floor, arms under knees, and hands grasping ankles, roll as a top onto right knee, right shoulder, back, left shoulder and knee, and recover. The movement is done twice to complete a circle.
21. While squatting on either foot, hands on hips, raise other leg forward and hold for 5 seconds.

Table 11–2 shows the stunts included in test batteries for elementary (grades four to six), junior high (grades seven to nine) and senior high (grades ten to twelve) schools. Two trials are allowed for each stunt; and in scoring, two points are given for successful performance on the first trial, one point on the second trial, and no points for failure on both attempts. T-score tables are given in the reference. In administering the test the group procedure employed by the Brace Test is advocated.

Table 11–2. Stunts Selected for Iowa-Brace Test Batteries

	Elementary School		Junior High School		Senior High School	
	1st Half	2d Half	1st Half	2d Half	1st Half	2d Half
B	4	1	13	1	13	14
O	2	14	5	14	6	5
	11	17	11	9	16	12
Y	6	16	20	16	18	19
S	7	19	8	19	21	10
G	4	13	1	13	14	1
I	15	14	9	11	6	15
R	7	16	12	6	17	16
L	20	12	20	16	19	3
S	6	8	19	21	20	21

Like the Brace Test, this test was validated against a criterion of achievement, not ability to learn. Studies suggest that the Iowa-Brace Test does not represent an improvement over the Brace Test (if anything, the latter is slightly superior), and that neither can be justified as a true test of motor educability.

Johnson Test of Motor Educability (Ages 11 to Adulthood) [33]

Johnson designed a test to measure native neuromuscular skill capacity for use in sectioning classes into homogeneous skill groups, which later studies show is probably the most valid test of general motor educability available. Ten items were selected from a group of 100. All exercises involving pronounced elements of strength, speed, endurance, fear, familiarity, strangeness, or practice were eliminated. The test is performed on 10-ounce canvas, 8 by 20 feet, secured smoothly over 6- by 10-foot gymnasium mats. Special markings are painted on the canvas as illustrated in Fig. 11–2. Each lengthwise lane is 18

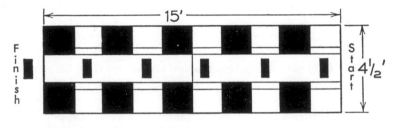

Fig. 11–2. Canvas markings for Johnson Test.

inches wide, and the outside lanes are divided into 18-inch squares. The lines marking the rectangular outline and the three 18-inch lanes are ¾ inch wide and painted black. A special lane 2 feet wide down the center of the canvas has side lines and a halfway cross line painted red. Beginning with the second square from the starting end, alternate squares in the outside lanes are painted black. While the center lane is not marked off in squares, beginning with the first space, alternate spaces in this lane contain a black target 3 by 12 inches; and an additional target lies just outside the finish end of the rectangle.

The test items include:

1. *Straddle jump.* Starting with feet together in the first center target, hands on hips, the subject jumps astraddle to the first

---

[33] Granville B. Johnson, "Physical Skill Tests for Sectioning Classes into Homogeneous Units," *Research Quarterly,* III, No. 1 (March, 1932), 128.

two black squares and returns to feet-together position on the second center target. This procedure is continued across the mat, concluding on the finish target.

2. *Stagger skip.* Starting with feet together in front of the right lane, hands on hips, the subject steps with left foot on the first center target and hops on left foot to the first black square on the left. Then, a step is made onto the second center target with the right foot, followed by a hop on the right foot onto the second black square on the right. This procedure is continued across the mat to the finish target.

3. *Stagger jump.* The subject begins in front of the right lane and, keeping feet together and hands on hips throughout the stunt, jumps obliquely to the first white square on left, to the first black square on right, to the second white square on left, and so forth, finishing in the left lane next to finish target.

4. *Forward skip holding opposite foot from behind.* Starting with feet together in front of either outside lane, the subject steps with the right foot into the first white space, raises left foot behind and takes it behind right thigh with right hand. In this position, a forward hop is made into the first black space, after which the left foot is released so that it can be placed in the second white square while the right foot is held with the left hand behind the left thigh. The subject hops in this position into the second black square and continues this alternating across the mat.

5. *Front roll.* Ignoring all black markings and heeding the red, the subject starts in front of the center lane and performs a forward roll within the limits of the first half of the lane, never touching or overreaching the red lines. In a like manner, a second forward roll is made in the second half of the red center lane.

6. *Jumping half-turns, right or left.* Starting on the first target with feet together and hands free, the subject jumps to the second target while executing a half-turn, right or left. A jump is then made to the third target, turning another half-turn in the same direction with feet continually together. This procedure is followed across the mat, finishing on the final target with subject facing the starting end.

7. *Back roll.* Performing within the red lane, the subject begins in front of the center red lane with back to the pattern and executes a back roll in each half of the lane without touching or overreaching the red side lines.

8. *Jumping half-turns, right and left alternately.* Beginning with feet together on first target and hands free, the subject jumps and executes a half-turn right or left with feet together, landing on the second target. Next, the jump is made to the third

target while a half-turn is executed in the opposite direction from the first half-turn. The subject continues this procedure, alternating direction of rotation, and finishes on the final target facing the starting end.

9. *Front and back roll combination.* Performing within the red lane, the subject starts in front of the center lane and does a front roll in the first half of the lane, finishing with legs crossed at ankles and executing a 2-foot pivot turn, right or left. This is followed by a back roll in the second half of the lane without touching or overreaching the red lanes, as pertains to all rolls.

10. *Jumping full turns.* Starting in front of the first white square in either outside lane, the subject jumps forward with feet together to the first black square while executing a full body turn, right or left. This procedure continues on the black spaces across the mat with rotation in the same direction, concluding on the last black square.

In scoring, each stunt counts ten points, making the maximum total 100 points. One point is deducted from the score for (1) each step, skip, or jump that does not land entirely within square limits; (2) each failure to land simultaneously with both feet on feet-together jump; (3) each time a landing is made on a target without the feet touching the target or with feet touching lane boundaries; (4) failure to maintain a steady rhythm throughout the series of jumps or skips (items 1 to 4); and (5) if position is discontinued somewhere in the exercise. For item 4, one point is deducted for overstepping a square, improper position, or both on each skip. Each roll counts five points with the following deductions: two points for touching or overreaching red side lines, one point for end lines; and five points for failure to do a true roll. In the jump turns, two points are deducted for each jump in which the subject does not land with both feet on target or within square, or turns the wrong way, or both. In addition, for full-turn jumps, two points are subtracted when turns are too far or not far enough, or when balance is lost before the next jump begins. The total points deducted are subtracted from the maximum of 100 to give the subject's score. No norms are available.

The reference includes instructions for each item, including infractions and scoring, to be read to testees after a single perfect demonstration of each stunt. Suggested organization is in groups of ten, wherein each exercise is performed by all testees before the next one is introduced, and subjects perform each stunt in a different order to minimize any advantage gained from watching others perform. This latter point is easily accomplished when the lead subject for an item moves to the rear of the line for the next stunt, and so forth. In a 40-minute period, 20 to 30 students may be tested.

Johnson reported a validity of .69 without describing the criterion. Another study established a validity coefficient of .97 with the criterion of the number of trials required for junior high school boys to learn a series of ten tumbling stunts. Studies of reliability involving high school girls have proved less satisfactory (.61 and .64 to cite two) than the .97 coefficient reported by Johnson for college men.

Metheny Revision of the Johnson Test [34]

After a study of the Johnson Test, Metheny proposed a simplified version derived by reducing the number of stunts without great loss in validity. The four items in the boys' test correlated .977 with the total Johnson score and .934 against a criterion of the number of trials necessary for each boy to learn ten tumbling stunts of varying degrees of difficulty. Using three of these four tests for girls resulted in .868 correlation with the total Johnson score. By eliminating six of the original ten items, Metheny was able to simplify the canvas markings for this revision (Fig. 11–3) on the same size canvas. The lines of the

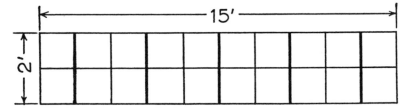

Fig. 11–3. Canvas markings for Revised Johnson Test.

rectangle and the center line dividing it into two narrow lanes are ¾ inch wide. The rectangle is divided into ten equal parts lengthwise by lines drawn 18 inches apart, on center, alternately ¾ inch and 3 inches wide. All lines are black.

The revised test includes items, 5, 7, 8 (front roll; back roll; jumping half-turns, right and left alternately) for boys and girls and also for boys, item 10 (jumping full turns). The same testing procedure, scoring, and directions apply for the revised test, except that the instructions have been changed to correspond with the different canvas markings.

[34] Eleanor Metheny, "Studies of the Johnson Test as a Test of Motor Educability," *Research Quarterly*, IX, No. 4 (December, 1938), 105.

The 3-inch lines are used instead of the targets in the original pattern, and jumping full turns are done in every second space. The time required for test administration has been reduced greatly, and 40 to 60 students can be tested in a 40-minute period. No norms are available. The teacher should recognize that the Metheny revision places undue emphasis on tumbling, or specifically the front and back roll, so that performances may be influenced appreciably by activities practiced in tumbling classes. In the original test 3 of 10 items involved rolls; whereas 2 of 4 (for boys) or 2 of 3 (for girls) entail basic tumbling skills in the Metheny revision.

Adams Sport-Type Motor Educability Test (College Men) [35]

Based upon an analysis of motor educability tests, Adams classified items into two types, stunt and sport, found not to be highly related. He derived a four-item test for college men from a criterion of 49 sport-type learning tests ($R = .79$); reliability .92 and .89 with two groups of 20. The tests include: (1) wall volley—10½-foot wall line and 3-foot restraining line with total score being the sum of 7 trials, each of which is scored as the number of consecutive volleyball volleys up to 10; (2) supine tennis catch—scored as the number of successes in 10 trials in which testee catches with either hand a ball that he has thrown at least 6 feet high, while remaining in a supine position; (3) ball bounce—testee stands in the center of a 6-foot diameter circle and attempts 10 consecutive volleyball volleys on the top end of a softball bat grasped a hand's length from its heavy end, scored as the sum of the volley scores for each of 10 trials; and (4) basketball shooting—number of successful free throws in 20 attempts. The regression equation for raw scores (with factors rounded) is: 7.17 Test 1 + 17.29 Test 2 + 2.70 Test 3 + 19.23 Test 4.

Other General Motor Educability Tests

Age-Height-Weight Classification Indices. As implied previously relative to general motor ability, age-height-weight classification indices may be considered to be indicants of educability for purposes of tentative classification or grouping and in instances where more elaborate or costly methods are impractical. However, these indices fail to approximate the validity of most other tests of educability, as they also fail to do when used for motor ability purposes.

[35] Arthur R. Adams, "A Test Construction Study of Sport-Type Motor Educability Test for College Men," Microcard Doctoral Dissertation, Louisiana State University, 1954.

Harvard Modification of the Brace Test (Children 5 to 9 years).[36] The Brace Test was modified by the Department of Child Hygiene, Harvard School of Public Health to meet the need for a measure of motor ability for young children to relate to other measures of development. This modification was comprised of 16 of the original items with standardized directions designed for comprehension by children 5 to 9 years old. (It should be noted that the directions are structured in a manner that seemingly enhances learning of the stunts rather than being merely descriptive of the task to be performed.) The items on the Brace Test that were eliminated include item 3—sit-ups (a comparable test was part of the orthopedic examination given), item 8— double heel clap, and item 10—jump through loop. The other item changes amounted to combining jump-turn item 15 with item 7 and not stipulating recovery to standing position in item 13. The desirability of having the testee choose the direction to rotate in a jump-turn appears questionable rather than scoring one trial to the right and one to the left. Both directions would seem to be important in assessing one's ability to learn motor skills.

The items were scored on a 6-point scale, since great differences were discernible in the types of failure observed. Scoring deficiencies only as failure (on a pass or fail basis) did not contribute to analysis of individual performance and of probable improvement with age. The rating scale (0 to 5) was made definitive and specific for each item by describing the characteristic of a given rating. For example, performance in holding the stork stand (one-leg balance with eyes shut for 10 seconds) was rated 0—1 second or less, 1—2 to 3 seconds, 2—4 to 5 seconds, 3—6 to 7 seconds, 4—8 to 9 seconds, and 5—10 seconds. No norms are reported.

Carpenter Test of Motor Educability (Primary Grades).[37] Carpenter devised a mat test for motor educability at the primary level using a mat 3 by 10 feet marked according to the Johnson mat design with the squares along each side being 1 foot across and targets 2 by 8 inches placed in the center zone. The test items include (1) left-foot hop, (2) diagonal jump (both feet), (3) right-foot backward hop, (4) left-foot sideward hop, and (5) right-foot sideward hop.

The items are scored like the Johnson Test with one point being deducted from the perfect score of 10 for each violation in performance. Validity coefficients of .89 for girls and .87 for boys are reported

---

[36] V. S. Vickers, Lillian Poyntz, and M. P. Baum, "The Brace-Scale Used with Young Children," *Research Quarterly*, XIII, No. 3 (October, 1942), 299.

[37] Aileen Carpenter, "Test of Motor Educability for the First Three Grades," *Child Development*, XI, No. 4 (December, 1940), 293.

using criterion of total points on a battery of 12 events. Reliability on individual items ranged from .77 to .90. Suggested norms are given for boys and girls which do not consider body-type classification.

TESTS OF PARTICULAR COMPONENTS OF MOTOR PERFORMANCE

McCauliff Agility Components Test [38]

While agility is defined in Chapter 7 as a component of motor fitness, tests of agility exclusively are most appropriately considered in the category of general qualities. McCauliff constructed an agility components test to measure the complex factor of agility as it relates to sports activities which suggest a communality of movement patterns. After deliberative analysis of activities in a total college physical education program, five general patterns of movement were deemed to be most common overall for the sports included. These were: (1) change of level, (2) lateral movement, (3) rotational movement, (4) forward diagonal movement, and (5) change of direction. Tests patterns, labeled agility components, were designed to represent each general movement pattern and arranged in a sequential order so as to incorporate a short form of the test within the total test structure.

The test layout is diagrammed in Fig. 11–4. The test procedure follows.

1. To begin the testee lies supine with heels at the starting line, one arm at the side and the other bent at the elbow to align the forearm vertically. Upon the timer's command to go when ready, the testee slaps the hand on the mat, and the watch is started. Head and shoulders must remain in contact with the mat until the slap occurs.
2. The subject rises quickly, places both feet in square "a" on the mat and leaps forward to square "b" marked on the floor.
3. From "b" the testee leaps laterally (left or right) to square "c' or c'", shuffles laterally to the end of the adjacent rectangle, tags beyond the line with one foot, shuffles back to land in the attached square, "c" or "c'," and leaps laterally to "b." This pattern is then repeated to the opposite side by leaping laterally to "c'" or "c," etc.
4. Next the testee leaps from "b" onto "d" and "e," from where a diagonal step forward is made with either foot to tag the line, after which the foot is returned to "e." The testee then pivots forward a quarter-turn and tags the second line with the same

---

[38] C. Elizabeth McCauliff, "A Test of Selected Agility Components," Microcard Doctoral Dissertation, Springfield College, 1968.

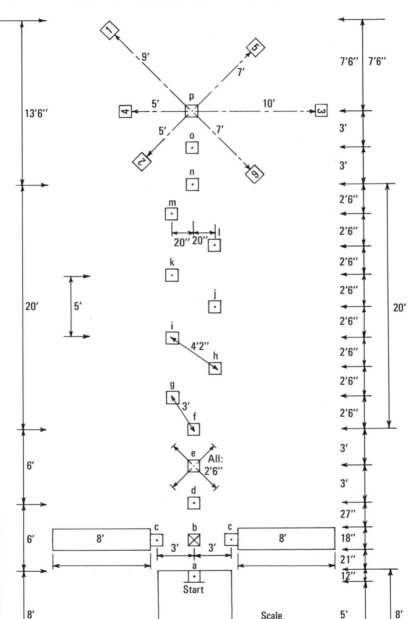

Fig. 11–4. Diagram of markings for McCauliff Agility Components Test.

foot, returns the foot to "e" and continues this procedure until all four lines have been touched.

5. The testee then leaps to "f" and forward in sequence by diagonal leaps to reach square "p" and immediately runs to square "1" to tag it with one foot and return to tag "p" with both feet. This procedure is repeated until squares "2" through "6" have been tagged in numerical order, and the testee faces the start from "p." (This completes the short form.)

6. The testee next leaps forward to "o," and "n" and on through the diagonal leaps to "e" where a diagonal step backward is taken with either foot to tag the first line and the foot is returned to "e." The testee pivots a quarter-turn to the rear and tags the second line with the same foot, and so forth, until all four lines have been tagged.

7. The testee leaps forward on to "d" and "b" to reach "a" and then reaches forward or leaps to a squat, all-fours or prone position to tag the finish line. (This completes the long form.)

8. The score is the time to the nearest one-tenth second on one trial, with a warmup orientation run allowed. The testee is informed immediately of infractions by the tester's response, "No," and is required to correct the error before continuing.

Validation was based on the ability of the instrument to discriminate among the capacities for agile movement of six groups of college men at differing levels of proficiency and participation in sports, ranging from varsity athletes in different sports to non-athletes. The long form was more discriminating than the short form of the test. Reliability coefficients ranged from .87 to .99, and .88 to .96 for the different groups on long and short forms, respectively, with total sample (N = 79) coefficients of .99 on both forms. Norms are not available.

Wyrick Motor Creativity Test (College Women) [39]

Wyrick described four test items devised for each of four motivators—rubber balls, parallel lines, a red hoop, and a low balance beam. These motivators were designed to serve as stimuli for tests capable of differentiating individual ability to produce both number and uniqueness of responses in problem solving tasks of a motor nature. Three tests forms, each measuring a different aspect of motor creativity, emerged from a multiple regression analysis of data from 25 college women; Form O—motor originality; Form F—motor fluency; and Form MC—motor creativity (motor originality and fluency). Alternative form re-

[39] Waneen Wyrick, "The Development of a Test of Motor Creativity," *Research Quarterly*, XXXIX, No. 3 (October, 1968), 756.

liability of .92 was found. The reference constitutes an important resource for test construction of this aspect of motor performance.

SPECIFIC CONSIDERATIONS

In actual fact the teacher should be conversant with general concerns relevant to test selection, construction and administration as well as the specific considerations for physical performance tests as a group and for motor fitness and particular sport skill tests. The following items are, accordingly, applicable to these other two areas but are briefly mentioned as specific considerations in the realm of general qualities.

1. *Reporting scores.* Since the general motor factor is essentially a conglomerate of the specific skills that are defined to constitute it, as appropriate, test results should be expressed both as a profile of specific scores and a composite "general" score.
2. *Ability in proper context.* Attention should be directed to assure that the ability in question is tested in a realistic manner; that is, conforms to the test criterion regarding teaching utility that skills be performed under conditions similar to actual use. The ball-on-a-cord apparatus for batting ability illustrates this concern.
3. *Irrelevant requirements.* Test item directions should not impose requirements that are not an integral part of the task being measured. To illustrate, in the soccer wall volley the stipulation that loose balls be retrieved with the feet introduces a contaminating factor for a test of volleying ability.

RESOLVING THE ILLUSTRATIVE PROBLEM

In order to select a test suitable for junior high school, or any other level and situation, the teacher must realize not only the relatedness and interdependence of the three general qualities of motor performance, but also the particular significance of each and apply this to the particular need involved. Furthermore, the concept of general qualities as "the sum of the desired specifics" must be understood. In reality resolution of the problem entails two steps that may best be carried out concurrently: (1) deciding which of the three qualities will be used; and (2) determining which test, if any, of this particular quality appears most suitable to the situation. In terms of the first step, the teacher must decide *what is important to the teaching situation. Is it the present level of ability?* This looms especially important where the competitive element may be involved—either in a learning situation or intramural activity. *Is it the capacity or potential of the student?* This would be desirable in programs with special stress on individual development or those striving particularly for long-range developmental objectives. *Or is it the educability or ability to learn motor skills,* perhaps including an indication of limits or inherent skill? While basic to all teaching, the significance of this element is accentuated when limitations as to time or large classes dictate making the most out of comparatively little.

This differentiation between the three qualities is intended only to show the separate elements involved and particular use relative to each. Actually, the interrelatedness of these items renders it difficult, if not impossible, to construct a "pure" test of a given quality. Many tests, while classified and intended as a test of one particular element, involve one or both of the other elements to some extent. The test selection may be determined more by the tests available than the quality concerned. Ideally, both would be involved. In deliberation regarding the area of general qualities of motor performance, the teacher should remember that tests in this area provide the basis for grouping students for instruction as well as diagnostic and prognostic information for furthering individual development. In considering the suitability of various tests, it is prudent to bear in mind, without sacrificing immediate needs, the desirability of a test that will have direct applicability itself or will fit in with the testing program in senior high school. In addition to or in lieu of these general qualities the teacher may wish to consider a test of a particular component of motor performance, for example, agility, in light of special emphasis of the physical education program.

For resolution of the problem at hand in the context of overall appraisal, the teacher may decide that the motor fitness test selected for the program contains enough items representative of general motor qualities for use as an indicant of this area. Substantiation for this decision can be readily discerned by analysis of the components encompassed in the New York Physical Fitness Test or by noting the similarity between the items on the AAHPER Fitness Test and the McCloy General Motor Achievement Test. If after use this proves unsatisfactory, consideration as a substitute measure would be given to the Barrow Test for boys and the Newton Test for girls. When program needs and trends warrant further and more specific testing in this area, the Johnson Test will be used. This decision is based on the present appraisal of this test as the best measure of educability and its utilization of different types of test items than other selected tests.

SELECTED REFERENCES

1. BARROW, HAROLD M., and McGEE, ROSEMARY. *A Practical Approach to Measurement in Physical Education.* Philadelphia: Lea and Febiger, 1964.
2. BOVARD, J. F., COZENS, F. W., and HAGMAN, E. P. *Tests and Measurements in Physical Education,* 3d ed. Philadelphia: W. B. Saunders Co., 1949.
3. CAMPBELL, W. R., and TUCKER, N. M. *An Introduction to Tests and Measurement in Physical Education.* London: G. Bell & Sons Ltd., 1967.
4. CLARKE, H. HARRISON. *Application of Measurement to Health and Physical Education,* 4th ed. Englewood Cliffs, N. J.: Prentice-Hall, Inc., 1967.
5. MATHEWS, DONALD K. *Measurement in Physical Education,* 4th ed. Philadelphia: W. B. Saunders Co., 1973.
6. McCLOY, C. H., and YOUNG, N. D. *Tests and Measurements in Health and Physical Education,* 3d ed. New York: Appleton-Century-Crofts, Inc., 1954.
7. SCOTT, M. GLADYS, and FRENCH, ESTHER. *Measurement and Evaluation in Physical Education.* Dubuque: W. C. Brown Co., 1959.

12

Application of Sports Skill Tests

The learning of selected skills comprises the essense and foundation of physical education, and accordingly skills in specific sports and dance constitute a major emphasis in viable programs. This stress on sports skill instruction should certainly be reflected in attention directed to the testing of skills in specific sports activities. The applicability of such skill tests, as described in Chapter 7, is manifold and includes use for diagnostic purposes, equating ability, motivation, and ascertaining achievement and teacher effectiveness. These tests are specific or peculiar to the particular sport concerned. Presently satisfactory tests are not available for all of the many physical education activities. Although few, if any, such tests exist in some sports, notable progress has been made in proper construction of skill tests in several areas since the comparatively recent historical inception of skill tests.

HISTORICAL BACKGROUND

Prior to 1924, certain fundamental sport skill test items were included as part of tests of general qualities of motor performance. But until this time, no attempt had been made to design a battery of test items to determine ability in a particular game. At the height of attention to ability testing in college, McCurdy as Chairman of a National Committee on Motor Ability Tests pointed out the possibilities of extending testing to the various games, particularly the major sports, and set up tests of strength, skill, speed, endurance, and agility in football, soccer, field hockey, basketball and tennis. At this time, 1924, Brace instigated focus on sports skill at elementary and secondary school levels by reporting a battery of six achievement tests in basketball. These tests were revised slightly and published again 3 years later with achievement tests in indoor baseball and soccer.[1] Additional pioneer work in the development of tests of sports skill was done by Beall, who in 1925 devised a test in tennis to measure selected qualities deemed essential for success in playing tennis.[2] In 1927, Bliss included four sport technique tests in basketball and baseball as part of a study concerning skill progression for boys and girls at the junior high school level.[3]

From these beginnings, the development of skill tests picked up in the early 1930's. In 1931, Rodgers and Heath published a scientifically devised achievement test in playground baseball for grades four through six using items derived from teacher analysis of the game.[4] The following year these authors developed an achievement test in soccer for intermediate-grade boys.[5] In establishing scientific authenticity and T-scale norms approximately 1,400 boys were tested. Shortly after these two tests, the momentum increased so that by 1940 skill tests began to appear in many activity areas. Since these beginnings, skill testing has shown steady growth, although perhaps not to the extent deemed desirable. About 1960 the Research Council of the AAHPER undertook a project to develop sport skills tests in 15 different activities, complete with national norms. The first test report and manual, on football, appeared in 1965.

AN ILLUSTRATIVE PROBLEM

Which of the available skill tests, if any, should be selected for the various sports activities included in the junior high school program of physical education? Critical analysis of skill tests to answer this question provides the focus for this and the next chapter. However, as in the other areas of measurement, available tests appropriate for different age levels will be reported to facilitate resolving the problem at any educational level.

[1] David K. Brace, *Measuring Motor Ability* (New York: A. S. Barnes & Co., 1927), pp. 74–84.

[2] Elizabeth Beall, "Essential Qualities in Certain Aspects of Physical Education with Ways of Measuring and Developing the Same," *American Physical Education Review*, XXXIII, No. 10 (December, 1928), 648.

[3] J. G. Bliss, "A Study of Progression Based on Age, Sex, and Individual Differences in Strength and Skill," *American Physical Education Review*, XXXII, No. 1, 2 (January, February, 1927), 11, 85.

[4] Elizabeth G. Rodgers and Marjorie L. Heath, "An Experiment in the Use of Knowledge and Skill Tests in Playground Baseball," *Research Quarterly*, II, No. 4 (December, 1931), 113.

[5] Marjorie L. Heath and Elizabeth G. Rodgers, "A Study in the Use of Skill and Knowledge Tests in Soccer," *Research Quarterly*, III, No. 4 (December, 1932), 35.

SPORTS SKILL TESTS

The emphasis in presenting skill tests herein leans more to the inclusion of many available tests with the references rather than to a comprehensive description of certain tests. The author believes that this resource approach affords more thorough coverage within the limits of practicality. The inclusion of each test herein and its order of appearance implies neither its complete acceptability nor relative importance. As in other areas of measurement, tests are included either for consideration or to indicate the suitability of different types of test items for a given activity, or for both reasons.

In presenting the different tests no further description will be given of basic items contained in Appendix B, except in instances where a difference or modification exists or particular clarification appears desirable. Also, a cross-reference between tests will be made to minimize repetition.

AAHPER Sports Skills Tests

Inasmuch as certain basic characteristics were established for all tests developed as part of the AAHPER Sports Skills Project, these are best described at the outset rather than as part of each test discussion. Each test was designed to measure a single basic skill and regarded as a "practice test" as a means of improving skill as well as reflecting ability at a given time. Content (face) validity was accepted for each test. Reliability standards were established as at least .80 for events scored on the basis of distance and not less than .70 for events scored on the basis of accuracy and form. While test administration directions vary slightly for some of the sports skills, essentially they stipulate organization of squads of 5 to 8 testees for rotation among stations in numerical sequence. The manuals illustrate a suggested arrangement of testing stations, when appropriate.

In collecting test development data the tests were administered in schools in several hundred cities throughout the United States after the students had completed an instructional unit in a particular sport. Percentile norms for each skill test were prepared, based upon 600 to 900 scores for each sex, ages 10 through 18.

Several limitations of the tests in the general context warrant noting. The failure to report reliability coefficients for each test and the intercorrelations between the different items for a given sport deprive the teacher of important resource information. The development of battery norms based on an appropriate standard score scale would be helpful to teachers who desire to utilize the tests as a battery as well as individually for evaluative purposes.

Archery

Hyde Archery Achievement Scales (College Women).[6] On the basis of three experimental studies, Hyde devised scales to evaluate achievement in archery for college women in the Columbia Round and for the 50-, 40-, and 30-yard distances. The scale, presented in the reference, consists of three parts and is applicable only for 24 arrows at each distance, as follows: (1) a scale to evaluate the first Columbia Round ever shot by a beginner; (2) a scale to evaluate the final Columbia Round after unlimited practice, such as the end of a season; and (3) scales for evaluating achievement at each of the three distances. Before taking the first test, a beginner should have shot a minimum of 120 arrows at each distance. The third scale, based on final Columbia Round scores, may be used to measure success at any distance during practice periods. The Columbia Round for women includes 24 arrows shot at each of the three distances in the order given above.

For the test, arrows are shot in ends of 6 arrows each at a 48-inch standard target, centered 4 feet from the ground. One practice end is permitted at each distance. At least one distance should be completed at each session. The target areas from center to the outside are scored as 9, 7, 5, 3, and 1. Based on 1,452 subjects, validity coefficients of .82 for beginners and .96 for advanced archers were obtained at 50 yards and .91 and .93, respectively, at 40 yards.

AAHPER Archery Test (Boys and Girls)[7]

The test developed for archery as part of the Sports Skills Project of the Research Council of AAHPER consists of two ends (total of 12 arrows) with intervening rest from distances of 10, 20, and 30 yards for boys, and 10 and 20 yards for girls. Four practice arrows are allowed at each distance. Standard targets and scoring are used, as described under the Hyde Scales. Percentile norms appear in the reference for each sex at each distance and for the composite of all arrows shot.

Bohn Test (College Men).[8] Bohn constructed an archery test for college men entailing 30 arrows shot at a 30-foot distance. Validity of .93 with the criterion of tournament scores and reliability of .79 were obtained.

---

[6] Edith I. Hyde, "An Achievement Scale in Archery," *Research Quarterly*, VIII, No. 2 (May, 1937), 109. Scale is reproduced in SR (selected reference) 3.

[7] *Skills Test Manual: Archery for Boys and Girls* (Washington: American Association for Health, Physical Education and Recreation, 1967).

[8] Robert W. Bohn, "An Achievement Test in Archery," Microcard Master's Thesis, University of Wisconsin, 1962.

School Archery Standards.[9]   Reichart described four standard rounds, designated by the National Archery Association and appropriate for elementary and secondary schools. She cited the standards of the Camp Archery Association as an illustrative achievement scale.

Badminton

Miller Badminton Wall Volley Test.[10]   Through a study of play in a national amateur championship tournament, Miller found that the finalists, men and women, in singles events consistently used clears more often than any other stroke during all of their games. She then analyzed movies of the various types of clears and designed the test dimensions in light of this analysis. The test requires a wall space of at least 10 feet in width and 15 feet in height with a line marked at a height of 7 foot 6 inches. A floor line is marked 10 feet from and parallel to the wall. Upon signal, the testee puts the sponge-end shuttlecock into play with a legal serve from behind the 10-foot line and continually volleys the rebounds for 30 seconds. Three 30-second trials are given with at least 30 seconds of rest between. A practice period of 1 minute should be given before the first trial. The final score is the total number of hits striking the wall on or above the 7-foot 6-inch line, including "carries" or double hits, and made from behind the floor restraining line. The shuttlecock remains in play regardless of faults. For college girls, a validity of .83 with a criterion of tournament play and reliability of .94 are reported. Illustrative norms are reported for college girls on a smooth cement surface ($\overline{X} = 41.7$, $s = 19.6$, N = 100) and college boys on a smooth brick wall ($\overline{X} = 76.3$, $s = 21.7$, N = 115). But norms should be established for the particular wall surface used.

French Badminton Test (College Women).[11]   French devised two simple test items—serve and clear—to measure badminton playing ability of college women. The serve test involves serving 20 birds (consecutively or in two groups of 10) to a target (Fig. 12–1) in the opposite service court by directing the bird beneath a rope stretched 20 inches above and parallel to the net. Illegal serves are repeated. The radii of the target arcs are 22, 30, 38, and 46 inches, respectively.

The second item, the clear test, consists of returning 20 serves over a rope stretched across the court 14 feet from the net and 8 feet high and onto a target (Fig. 12–2). To receive the serve, the testee stands on the

9 Natalie Reichart, "School Archery Standards," *Journal of Health and Physical Education,* XIV, No. 2 (February, 1943), 81.
10 Frances A. Miller, "A Badminton Wall Volley Test," *Research Quarterly,* XXII, No. 2 (May, 1951), 208.
11 M. Gladys Scott, "Achievement Examinations in Badminton," *Research Quarterly,* XII, No. 2 (May, 1941), 242.

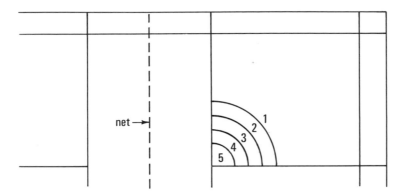

Fig. 12-1. French serve target.

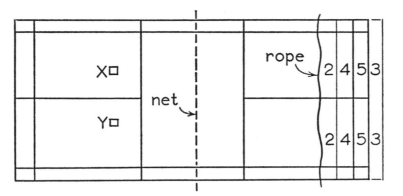

Fig. 12-2. French clear target.

center line between two 2-inch squares marked on the floor 3 feet either side of the center line and 11 feet from the net. An experienced player serves each bird from the intersection of short service and center lines on the target side. The serve must reach the testee and be between the squares, but the testee may move into desired position once the serve is made. The target markings consist of a parallel line 2 feet toward the net from the doubles rear service line and a similar line 2 feet farther from the net than the rear singles service line. Illegal strokes are repeated.

The final score for each test item consists of the total number of points scored by legal hits that passed either below or above the rope, as specified. Coefficients of .85 and from .77 to .98 are reported for validity and reliability, respectively. Scoring tables are available for beginners and advanced players. Ten trials reportedly will suffice for each test, except in the case of the service test for beginners.

French-Stalter Badminton Test (College Women).[12] French and Stalter constructed tests of footwork, wrist action, and smashing ability to supplement the previously validated French test items and form a battery of skill tests in badminton to measure playing ability. Two tests of footwork were proposed—shuttle and diagonal—using the limits of singles side lines, and doubles and short service lines. For illustration, the shuttle test consists of shuttling back and forth between the side lines for 15 seconds while holding a racket—four trials given. To test wrist power, the subject volleys against a wall from behind a 6-foot restraining line for 30 seconds, beginning play with an underhand serve. A 5-minute practice period and four trials are allowed. The wall area should be at least 15 feet high and 12 to 15 feet wide. In the smash test, the subject attempts 20 smashes from her starting position on the short service line into the target area on the opposite side of the net. The bird is put into play by an experienced player who hits it over a rope 7 feet high stretched 2 feet from and parallel to net on the target side. Norms based on 59 college women are available for interpreting performance on individual tests. A four-test battery of serve, clear, wall volley, and shuttle resulted in a validity coefficient of .698. Eliminating the serve gave a three-test battery with a validity of .679.

Lockhart-McPherson Badminton Test.[13] Lockhart and McPherson devised a volleying test for classification purposes with college women. The test consists of three 30-second trials of volleying a shuttlecock against a wall area (10 feet high and 10 feet wide) from behind a 3-foot restraining line after initiating the play from a 6-foot 6-inch starting line. Rests between trials and a 15-second practice period are permitted. The score is the total number of hits above the 5-foot net line on the wall in the three trials. Hits made from in front of the restraining line do not count, but the shuttlecock remains in play. Validity is reported as .71, with criterion of judges' rating, reliability as .90. T-scale norms were obtained with 178 college women, using a wood wall surface. Satisfactory use for college men and junior and senior high school boys and girls has been reported by other investigators.

Scott-Fox Serve Test (College Women).[14] Scott and Fox proposed a long serve test using the rope location in the French clear test and the target markings of the French serve test relocated to the outside rear

[12] Esther French and Evelyn Stalter, "Study of Skill Tests in Badminton for College Women," *Research Quarterly*, XX, No. 3 (October, 1949), 257.

[13] Aileene Lockhart and F. A. McPherson, "The Development of a Test of Badminton Playing Ability," *Research Quarterly*, XX, No. 4 (December, 1949), 402. Norms are also available in SR 1 and 2.

[14] M. G. Scott and Esther French, *Measurement and Evaluation in Physical Education* (Dubuque: W. C. Brown Co., 1959), pp. 147–48.

corner of a singles service court. Validity of .54 with judges' rating and split-half corrected reliability of .77 were reported (N = 45). The reference contains T-scales for this test as well as for short serve, clear, and two volley test items described in other tests.

Baseball

Since little has been reported in the area of baseball testing, the reader is referred also to tests described under softball. An early test suggests elements to consider in testing baseball skills, namely, control and accuracy in pitching, infield throw, batting, and rapid throw.[15] T-score tables are available in the reference but no indicant of scientific authenticity is reported.

Kelson Baseball Classification Plan (Boys 8 to 12 years).[16] Kelson devised a classification plan through a study involving 64 Little Leaguers, ages 8 to 12. The boys were evaluated relative to five abilities deemed essential—batting, throwing for distance, accuracy in throwing, catching fly balls, and fielding ground balls. For validation a correlation of .85 was obtained between a throw for distance test and the composite criterion of the abilities above based on the season's batting average, tests, and judges' evaluation. The test is performed by throwing a Little League baseball from behind a starting line, with a run permitted, to an area with lines marked off at 5-feet intervals from 50 to 200 feet beyond the starting line. The score is the best of three trials recorded to the nearest foot, and it is interpreted as follows: 177 feet and over—superior, 145 to 176 feet—above average, 113 to 144 feet—average ability, 80 to 112 feet—below average, and 79 feet or less—inferior.

Basketball

Edgren Basketball Test.[17] Working with college men, Edgren devised a test of ability in the fundamentals of basketball in individual play that suggests the possible direction for developing a highly valid test, even though the test is not completely standardized. The test items include:

1. *Speed pass.* Make and catch ten passes from behind an 8-foot restraining line.
2. *Accuracy pass.* Execute five passes each with chest push, un-

[15] C. D. Wardlaw, *Fundamentals of Baseball* (New York: Charles Scribner's Sons, 1929).

[16] R. C. Kelson, "Baseball Classification Plan for Boys," *Research Quarterly*, XXIV, No. 3 (October, 1953), 304.

[17] H. D. Edgren, "An Experiment in Testing Ability and Progress in Basketball," *Research Quarterly*, III, No. 1 (March, 1932), 159.

derhand, two-hand shoulder, and one-hand overhead hook passes to a three-zone rectangular target.

3. *Pivot and shoot.* Five pivot and shoot attempts from beyond foul circle.
4. *Speed dribble.* Around four chairs spaced 6 feet apart, beginning 15 feet from starting line and back.
5. *Dribble and shoot.* From one side of basket, out across foul line, to other side, repeating five times.
6. *Accuracy shooting.* Ten free-throw attempts.
7. *Opposition shooting.* Attempt five baskets while guarded.
8. *Ball handling.* Make and catch ten passes moving back and forth laterally.

Scoring tables are not available. Edgren reported a validity coefficient of .77 with ability rating.

Johnson Basketball Ability Test (High School Boys).[18]   An early test of basketball ability for high school boys was devised by Johnson along with a test of potential ability. The latter consists of four items—footwork, jump and reach, dodging run, and Iowa-Brace Test—none of which require ball handling, and resulted in validity of .84 and reliability of .93. The ability test includes:

1. *Field goal speed test.* Upon signal, the subject makes as many baskets as possible in 30 seconds, starting any place under the basket (validity—.73, relaibility—.73).
2. *Basketball throw for accuracy.* Subject makes ten baseball or hook passes at a wall target 40 feet away. The target is a rectangle 60 inches wide by 40 inches high, starting 14 inches from the floor and containing a 40- by 25-inch and a 20- by 10-inch rectangle. The rectangles, including the line, score 1, 2, and 3 points from outside in (validity—.78, reliability—.79).
3. *Dribble test.* Subject starts from right side of a 6-foot-long starting line (12 feet from the first hurdle) and dribbles alternately left then right around four hurdles aligned 6 feet apart and returns in similar manner around starting line and continues for 30 seconds. A point is scored each time a zone (either side of a hurdle or end of the starting line) is passed, making ten possible points in a round trip (validity—.65, reliability—.78).

The three-item scores are totaled to give the battery score, which in the developmental study (N = 183) ranged from 16 to 68 with a median of 42. Coefficients of .88 and .89 were reported for validity (divergent group criterion) and reliability of the ability test, respectively. A serious drawback concerning the use of this test has been its lack of availability.

---

[18] L. W. Johnson, "Objective Tests in Basketball for High School Boys." Unpublished Master's Thesis, State University of Iowa, 1934.

Lehsten Basketball Test (High School Boys).[19]   Lehsten developed an eight-item test that correlated .80 with a jury rating of basketball ability. The test was reduced to five items by selecting the items with the highest validity that were found to correlate .97 as a composite score with the original test. The test items include:

1. *Baskets per minute.* Starting at the foul line, but shots may be taken from any place on the court.
2. *Vertical jump.* Holding a piece of chalk and initial mark made while facing wall.
3. *Forty-foot dash.* Run on the court starting upright.
4. *Wall bounce.* Scored as the number of catches on the fly made in 10 seconds of two-hand passes to a 2- by 4-foot wall target (3 feet off the floor), remaining behind a 6-foot restraining line.
5. *Dodging run.*

T-scales and an achievement scale are available.

Knox Basketball Test.[20]   Knox developed a four-item test that was validated against ability to make a ten-man high school basketball squad for competition in an Oregon district tournament.   The test results showed 89 per cent agreement with squad membership and 81 per cent with winning a starting position. Reliability for the total test was .88. Very satisfactory results have been reported by other investigators in using the test as a classifier for competition or a predictor of ability on both high school and college levels. The test items include:

1. *Speed dribble.* Standing with hands on knees behind starting line where ball is placed, upon signal, the subject dribbles around four chairs, as in the Johnson Test, ending at the starting line. Chairs are placed 15 feet apart, beginning with the first chair, which is placed 20 feet from the starting line. Score is the time in seconds (reliability—.71).
2. *Wall bounce.* Scored as time in seconds to make 15 chest passes from behind a 5-foot restraining line. Test is repeated if any rebound requires subject to take more than one step in recovery (reliability —.78).
3. *Dribble shoot.* From a starting line on right side line of the court, 65 feet from the basket, upon signal, the subject dribbles around three chairs, makes a basket, and returns to the starting line by dribbling around the chairs. The chairs are arranged so as to divide the 65 feet distance into four equal segments. Time in seconds constitutes the score (reliability—.58).

[19] N. Lehsten, "A Measure of Basketball Skills in High School Boys," *The Physical Educator,* V, No. 4 (December, 1948), 103.
[20] R. O. Knox, "Basketball Ability Tests," *Scholastic Coach,* XVII, No. 3 (March, 1947), 45.

4. *Penny-cup test.* Standing backwards behind the starting line, upon signal, the subject turns to run across a "signal line" (8 feet from start) to the finish line (20 feet from start) on which are placed three cups—red, white, and blue—spaced 5 feet apart. At the signal line, the examiner calls out the color of cup into which the testee should drop the penny he is holding. The time elapsed until penny drop is heard represents the score for one trial. The score is the number of seconds to perform four consecutive trials (reliability —.90).

The seconds required to complete each of the four tests constitute the final score.

Friermood Basketball Progress Test (Boys and Men, 12 to 30).[21] Friermood described a battery of tests useful for motivation, although neither scientific authenticity nor norms are available. The items include (1) pass accurately, (2) pivot for efficiency and form (subjective), (3) speed-control dribble, and (4) shoot accurately—free-throw and dribble shot.

Stroup Basketball Test (College Men).[22] At Southern State College, Stroup developed an easily administered basketball test for college men and used scores of competing teams and student opinion for validation. The test items are (1) basket shooting—from any position for 1 minute; (2) wall passing—number of passes in 1 minute, 6-foot restraining line; and (3) obstacle dribbling—subject dribbles for 1 minute alternately to the left and right of seven bottles placed in a straight line at 15-foot intervals and scored as number of bottles passed properly and not knocked down. Tables are provided to convert raw scores to scale scores, which are averaged to obtain a skill score, and to interpret the skill score in terms of a normative distribution.

Albion Basketball Rating Scale (College Men).[23] Voltmer and Watts developed at Albion College a rating scale for evaluating ability of inter-collegiate squad members that might be applied for physical education class purposes. Players are scored during a contest or scrimmage for making a basket or free throw, gaining possession of the ball (such as off the backboard or intercepting a pass), tying up the ball, and gaining possession after a jump ball. Points are deducted for a missed shot, losing

[21] H. T. Friermood, "Basketball Progress Tests Adapted to Class Use," *Journal of Health and Physical Education*, V, No. 1 (January, 1934), 45.

[22] Francis Stroup, "Game Results as a Criterion for Validating Basketball Skill Tests," *Research Quarterly*, XXVI, No. 3 (October, 1955), 353. Tables are reproduced in SR 3.

[23] E. F. Voltmer and T. Watts, "A Rating Scale of Player Performance in Basketball," *Journal of Health and Physical Education*, XI, No. 2 (February, 1940), 94.

possession of the ball, personal foul, his man scores a basket, or he is tied up with the ball. The net score serves to show relative proficiency of players, while an analysis of the scoring chart affords a means of diagnosing individual deficiences. Little evidence is gained on passing and ball handling ability except as reflected in losing possession of the ball. In applying this scale for team selection, the test authors noted that it discloses the "steady" player as well as the erratic individual who may be highly regarded because of an occasional brilliant play.

AAHPER Basketball Test (Boys and Girls).[24] The AAHPER test developed for basketball consists of 9 practice-type items for boys and girls for which one practice shot or trial is allowed. These items are:

1. *Front shot.* Fifteen shots from a spot just behind the free throw line but outside the circle to the left side. Two points are scored for each basket made and one for hitting the rim.
2. *Side shot.* Ten shots taken from each side of the basket near the corner and behind a line 20 feet from the basket; scored as item #1.
3. *Foul shot.* Four series of 5 shots with intervening rest while others shoot. One point is scored for each successful shot.
4. *Under basket shot.* Upon command testee attempts as many lay-up shots as possible in 30 seconds from a position beneath the basket, recovering each shot. The score is the better number of baskets made in two trials.
5. *Speed pass* (wall pass). Ten passes are made as rapidly as possible by any method (push pass is faster) at about head height. Score is the time in seconds and tenths for the better of two trials.
6. *Jump and reach* (vertical jump). Better of two trials to the nearest inch with side to the wall for initial mark and jump, and holding a piece of chalk.
7. *Overarm pass for accuracy.* Ten single overarm passes are made from behind a throwing line to a wall target 35 feet away. Target consists of three concentric circles, 18, 38 and 58 inches in diameter, with lower edge 3 feet above the floor and assigned score values of 3, 2 and 1, respectively.
8. *Push pass for accuracy.* Ten two-hand push or chest passes are made at a target as described in item #7 from behind a line 25 feet away.
9. *Dribble.* Performed alternately right and left around six chairs spaced 8 feet apart, beginning 5 feet from the starting line, with either hand and dribbling the ball at least once in passing each chair. Score is the better of two trials in seconds and tenths.

[24] *Skills Test Manual: Basketball for Boys;* and *Skills Test Manual: Basketball for Girls* (Washington: American Association for Health, Physical Education and Recreation, 1966).

Young-Moser Basketball Test (Secondary School Girls).[25]   Young and Moser developed a five-item test of basketball playing ability for girls involving (1) wall-bouncing speed, scored as total wall hits in two 30-second trials from behind a 6-foot restraining line; (2) accuracy throw at a moving target, ten throws; (3) free jump, highest hanging strip touched, similar to "Latchaw" method (see page 413); (4) Edgren ball handling; and (5) bounce and shoot—scored as baskets made in bouncing and shooting alternately from two prescribed spots at 15 feet and a 45-degree angle from the backboard. A validity coefficient of .86 was obtained with judges' rating of game play. Reliability ranged from .89 to .90. The Wisconsin study found the reliability of items 2 and 5 too low for use as tests of specific skill for individual grading.[26] Norms are available for junior and senior high school girls. Directions call for administration of the test in four parts.

Wisconsin Basketball Test (College Women).[27]   A test was devised at the University of Wisconsin to measure basketball playing ability for grading purposes and was based on critical appraisal of the Young-Moser Test. The items include (1) bounce and shoot—score for each trial represents combined scores of speed and accuracy in taking ten shots alternately from two prescribed spots located 18 feet from the backboard and at a 45-degree angle; (2) zone toss—scored as the time required in the best four of six trials to throw ball over a rope and catch it outside a prescribed zone ten times; and (3) wall speed. In the bounce-and-shoot test, the ball is first taken from a chair to one side of the starting mark and returned after retrieving by a pass to an assistant before going to the opposite side to continue. Time is recorded to nearest tenth of a second, and accuracy is scored as 2 points for a basket and 1 point for hitting the rim but missing the basket. The final score for this item is the sum of the best two of three complete trials given at least two minutes apart. Norms are available, and validity of .66 and item reliabilities of .82, .74 and .89 were reported.

Leilich Test (College Women and Women Majors).[28]   Leilich proposed three tests as reflecting the basic factors of basketball skill disclosed by factor analysis, namely, basketball motor ability, speed, ball handling in-

[25] Genevieve Young and Helen Moser, "A Short Battery of Tests To Measure Playing Ability in Women's Basketball," *Research Quarterly*, V, No. 2 (May, 1934), 3.

[26] R. B. Glassow, V. Colvin, and M. M. Schwarz, "Studies in Measuring Basketball Playing Ability of College Women," *Research Quarterly*, IX, No. 4 (December, 1938), 60.

[27] *Ibid.*

[28] Avis Leilich, "The Primary Components of Selected Basketball Tests for College Women," Microcard Doctoral Dissertation, Indiana University, 1952.

volving passing accuracy and speed, and ball handling involving goal shooting accuracy. These tests are (1) bounce and shoot—as in the Wisconsin Test; (2) half-minute shooting—score is greater number of baskets made in two trials from any position (an attempt counts if ball leaves hands before time expires); and (3) push pass—better of two trials with chest passes for 30 seconds made at a three-concentric circle target from behind a 10-foot restraining line, scored as the cumulative total of points (5, 3, and 1 points awarded for areas described by 10-, 20-, and 30-inch radii, respectively, with lower edge 2 feet from the floor). In a separate study these tests were used to determine achievement levels in basketball skills, reported as T-scores and percentile ranks, based on the performance of 1,812 women physical education majors in 59 institutions throughout the nation.[29]

Schwartz Basketball Test (Senior High School Girls).[30] Schwartz devised a test for purposes of motivation and measuring achievement and utilized critical analysis of experts to validate the items. The items are (1) bounce over a 6-foot area; (2) pass and catch; (3) jump and reach; (4) throw for goal; and (5) pivot, bounce, and shoot. Achievement scales were set up on the basis of performance records of 1,000 girls.

Dyer-Schurig-Apgar Basketball Test (Secondary School and College Girls).[31] Dyer and associates devised a test battery of (1) throw at moving target, (2) Edgren ball handling test, (3) bounce and shoot, and (4) free jump and reach. The reference contains scoring tables and norms and reports satisfactory validity and reliability of .89.

Bowling

No test of bowling per se has appeared; but the score itself serves as an indicant of relative ability and, when a record of scores is kept, a measure of improvement. In addition to the score for a complete game, discrimination between levels of ability can be made by the sum of the first balls in each frame for a game or the score made on four common spare setups in which five balls are bowled at each setup. Two studies have been made to establish norms of bowling achievement relative to ability on the college level.

[29] W. K. Miller, "Achievement Levels in Basketball Skills for Women Physical Education Majors," *Research Quarterly*, XXV, No. 4 (December, 1954), 450. Norms are reproduced in SR 1.

[30] Helen Schwartz, "Knowledge and Achievement Tests in Girls Basketball at the Senior High School Level," *Research Quarterly*, VIII, No. 1 (March, 1937), 143.

[31] J. T. Dyer, J. C. Schurig, and S. L. Apgar, "A Basketball Motor Ability Test for College Women and Secondary School Girls," *Research Quarterly*, X, No. 3 (October, 1939), 128.

Phillips-Summers Bowling Achievement Scales (College Women).[32] Phillips and Summers developed norms and analyzed learning curves in bowling based on 3,634 women students in 22 colleges. In using the norms to determine progress, the steps are (1) find the beginning level of ability by averaging the first 5 lines bowled, (2) average the scores of the first 10 lines of bowling and find the rating for the subject's level of ability, (3) find the rating at the end of 15 lines by averaging the last 5 lines (11–15) and referring to norms at the level of ability, and (4) continue the latter procedure for 20 and 25 lines of bowling. The norms are limited by insufficient number of cases at the extreme levels of ability and, in many cases, after ten games.

Martin Bowling Norms (College Men and Women).[33] Bowling norms to evaluate and classify college men and women at different skill levels were developed by Martin and were based on performances of 704 students in 26 lines of bowling during instructional classes. Students are classified according to ability on the basis of an average score of the first 5 lines of bowling (individuals with no prior experience were automatically classified as beginners) into three ability groups:

	Men	Women
Beginning	120 or under	98 or under
Intermediate	121 to 145	99 to 119
Advanced	146 and over	120 and over

The final cumulative average is computed after 26 lines, and the initial (5-line) average is subtracted from the final average to give the improvement score. Both results are interpreted by use of their respective norm tables according to the initial ability rating. These tables are limited by an insufficient number or lack of cases at the advanced level of ability.

Upon change of the physical education program at UCLA from a required to an elective basis, norms were established for inexperienced and experienced men and women (N = 320).[34] Students who had bowled less than 10 games and had received no formal instruction were classified as inexperienced and were given four to six periods of instruction, while the experienced group bowled for four classes. Norms were based on the average of two games bowled after these orientation periods and the average of the final two games at the end of the semester, during which

[32] Marjorie Phillips and Dean Summers, "Bowling Norms and Learning Curves for College Women," *Research Quarterly*, XXI, No. 4 (December, 1950), 377. Norms are also reported in SR 4.

[33] Joan L. Martin, "Bowling Norms for College Men and Women," *Research Quarterly*, XXXI, No. 1 (March, 1960), 113.

[34] Joan Martin and Jack Keogh, "Bowling Norms for College Students in Elective Physical Education Classes," *Research Quarterly*, XXXV, No. 3, Pt. 1 (October, 1964), 325. Norms are reported in SR 3.

a total of 26 to 39 games were played. The normative scores were categorized as superior, good, average, poor and inferior, with each category encompassing 1.2 standard deviations and the average group centered on the mean. The means and standard deviations of non-experienced men for initial and final scores were 110.3 and 17.9, 133.1 and 19.1; for experienced men—143.4 and 30.7, 151.7 and 23.3. These values for non-experienced women were 89.0 and 22.6, 112.2 and 14.6; for experienced women—121.9 and 19.7, 128.7 and 18.3. While these data are not directly comparable to the earlier study, it was noted that the initial average of non-experienced men was 22 higher for those in the elective program and 15 higher for non-experienced women.

Fencing

Little attention appears to have been directed to the development of tests in fencing. To date two efforts warrant noting for resource purposes.

Safrit Test for Beginning Fencers (College Women).[35]   In an informative study Safrit analyzed two tests—one involving speed of the lunge and designated form checks; the second adding an accuracy component to the content of the first test. With ten trials, reliabilities of .78 and .71 for the respective tests were reported.

Emery Rating Scale for Foil Fencing.[36]   Emery devised a rating scheme dealing with seven aspects of fencing skill and using 1–3 scale (poor, fair, and good categories). The component parts to be considered in rating were delineated under each aspect. Performance standards were included.

Field Hockey

Schmithals-French Field Hockey Test (College Women).[37]   A three-item test of achievement in field hockey skills was constructed by Schmithals and French. The first item combined with a knowledge test is proposed for early season classification. The items include the following.

1. *Dribble, dodge, circular tackle, and drive (ball control).* Standing behind a starting line, the subject upon signal dribbles the ball from the line for 30 feet, keeping to the left of a foul line; performs a dodge around a standard 35 feet from the start; and recovers the ball to execute a circular tackle around a standard 45 feet from the

[35] Margaret J. Safrit, "Construction of Skills Tests for Beginning Fencers," Microcard Master's Thesis, University of Wisconsin, 1962.

[36] L. Emery, "Criteria for Rating Selected Skills of Foil Fencing," *Bowling/Fencing/Golf Guide, 1960–1962*, Division of Girls and Women's Sports, AAHPER, p. 74.

[37] Margaret Schmithals and Esther French, "Achievement Tests in Field Hockey for College Women," *Research Quarterly*, XI, No. 3 (October, 1940), 84.

start; and then drives the ball across the starting line on the right side of the foul line (looking from the start). The score is the average time in seconds of six trials.

2. *Goal shooting.* Upon signal, the subject dribbles 15 feet to a 6-foot 6-inch by 11-foot rectangle from within which a drive is made to a target 36 feet 6 inches straight ahead. The target is 12 feet long and divided into 11 areas that are scored 1 to 6 from the outside inward. After ten trials, a like number is made with the target placed 45 degrees to the right at the same distance, followed by ten trials with the target placed to the left 45 degrees from the rectangle. Each trial is scored as time in seconds to hit or pass over the target. The item score consists of the sum of the two best even numbered trials and two best odd numbered trials on each of the three sets of trials.

3. *Fielding and drive.* Upon signal, the subject runs from behind the goal line to drive a ball from between the foul line (10 feet away) and the restraining line (10 feet further away) to outside the striking circle. The examiner rolls the ball from the striking circle directly toward the subject at a speed of 45 feet in 1.7 seconds. Sixteen trials are given. The score is the sum of the average of the three best even numbered trials and the average of the three best odd numbered trials.

A more definitive description of testing layout is available in the reference. For all items, one practice trial is allowed. Norms are not reported in the original study but are presented by Scott and French.[38] With a criterion of expert judgment, the item validity ranged from .44 to .48, with a multiple correlation of .62. Spearman-Brown formula estimates from split-half reliability for the items ranged from .90 to .92. The best combination of two skill factors was found to be goal shooting left and item 3 (intercorrelation of .22, validity of .60).

Friedel Field Hockey Skill Test (High School Girls).[39] Friedel proposed a test of fielding, control, and drive while moving. The subject runs from the starting end of a 10- by 25-yard rectangle and fields a ball rolled from a corner on the starting end toward a target 1 by 2 yards, centered 15 yards away. After fielding, the ball is dribbled to the end line and driven back across the starting line. Ten trials are given with the ball rolled from the right corner and ten from the left. The elapsed time is totaled separately for each side and then combined for the final score. A validity coefficient of .87 was reported with the Schmithals-French ball

[38] Scott and French, *op. cit.*, pp. 170–72.
[39] Jean Friedel, "The Development of a Field Hockey Skill Test for High School Girls," Microard Master's Thesis, Illinois State Normal University, 1956. Norms are reported in SR 1.

control test. Reliability estimates were .90 and .77 on left and right sides stepped up from split-half coefficients.

Strait Field Hockey Test (College Women).[40] Strait constructed a test consisting of the best time for three trials in a continuous circuit involving dribbling, dodging, driving, receiving and circular tackling. A special equipment layout and somewhat complicated maneuvers are entailed. Because of these disadvantages and the general shortcomings of "conglomerate" tests (that is, combining a number of different skills), the test description is not included.[41] Coefficients of .76 and .86 were reported, respectively, for validity (criterion of judges' rating) and reliability. For the use of judges in rating ability in test validation, Strait developed a five-point scale on which the specific features characterizing each point are delineated.[42] This may well serve as a useful resource for the teacher either for class use or in validation of a teacher-made test.

Illner Field Hockey Test (High School and College Girls).[43] Illner devised a drive test, based on authoritative recognition of it as the most important basic skill in field hockey. The test consists of tapping and then driving a ball from a position 2 yards outside the apex of the scoring quadrant (15 yards in radius) toward the center two of eight flags placed at ½ yard intervals on the arc. Ten trials are taken to the right; ten to the left. The test score is the sum of the mean accuracy score and elapsed time for trials on each side plus a penalty factor for fouls and violations. The flag areas for accuracy scoring are assigned values of 1 for the central area and 2, 3, 4, and 5 points moving outward—right and left. Satisfactory authenticity was established, but norms were not presented.

Field Hockey Achievement Scales.[44] Cozens, Cubberley, and Neilson constructed achievement scales for the following field hockey skill tests: 25-yard dribble, dribble and push pass, obstacle dribble, penalty corner hit for beginners, intermediate corner hit, and advanced corner hit.

[40] Clara J. Strait, "The Construction and Evaluation of a Field Hockey Skill Test," Microcard Master's Thesis, Smith College, 1960.

[41] A succinct description is available in: K. Luttgens, W. D. McArdle, and J. A. Faulkner, "Team Sports Skills Tests," *An Introduction to Measurement in Physical Education,* Vol. 3, H. J. Montoye, (ed.) (Indianapolis: Phi Epsilon Kappa Fraternity, 1970), pp. 68–70.

[42] Cited in: H. M. Barrow and Rosemary McGee, *A Practical Approach to Measurement in Physical Education* (Philadelphia: Lea and Febiger, 1964), pp. 291–92.

[43] Julee A. Illner, "The Construction and Validation of a Skill Test for the Drive in Field Hockey," Microcard Master's Thesis, Southern Illinois University, 1968.

[44] F. W. Cozens, H. J. Cubberley, and N. P. Neilson, *Achievement Scales in Physical Education Activities for Secondary School Girls and College Women* (New York: A. S. Barnes & Co., 1937).

Football

AAHPER Football Test (Boys).[45] The items included in the AAHPER test for football are:

1. *Forward pass for distance.* Best of three trials made from within a 6 foot zone behind the throwing line.
2. *Fifty-yard dash with a football.* Better of two trials.
3. *Blocking.* Upon signal the testee executes a cross-body block on each of three sand-filled bags, driving them to the ground, and runs back across the starting line. Bag 1 is on a line perpendicular to and 15 feet from the starting line; bag 2 is 15 feet from bag 1 on a line parallel to the starting line; and bag 3 is 15 feet from bag 2 on a line at a 45 degree angle from the line between bags 1 and 2, leaving bag 3 about 5 feet from the starting line. Score is the better of two trials.
4. *Forward pass for accuracy.* Testee passes with good speed from behind a 15-yard throwing line at a target of three concentric circles with 2-, 4- and 6-foot diameters and scoring 3, 2, and 1 points, respectively. The bottom of the target is 3 feet above the ground. Scored as the sum of 10 trials, with line hits counting the higher value. Circle lines are 1 inch wide. A taut canvas target suspended from a set of goal posts is described.
5. *Football punt for distance.* Testee punts by taking one or two steps within a 6-foot zone behind the kicking line. Scored as the best of three trials.
6. *Ball changing zigzag run.* Upon signal the testee runs with a football in his right hand and extends the left arm as he passes to the right of a chair 10 feet from the starting line. Continuing, the ball is changed to the left hand and the right arm is extended as he passes to the left of the second chair, and so on around five chairs (all 10 feet apart) and back to the starting line in the same fashion. The score is the better of two violation-free trials, that is, without chair contact and with proper ball and free arm action.
7. *Catching the forward pass.* Upon signal the ball is centered to an expert passer, and the testee runs straight from a point on the scrimmage line 9 feet from the center on the side toward the turning direction. He proceeds to a turning point 30 feet away and then turns to run beyond the passing point, which is marked 30 feet away from the turning point on a line parallel to the scrimmage line. The ball is passed over the passing point above head height, and the testee attempts to catch it. Passes that fail to go over the passing point at a reasonable height are disregarded. One practice run is permitted on each side.

[45] *Skills Test Manual: Football* (Washington: American Association for Health, Physical Education and Recreation, 1965).

8. *Pull-out.* From a set position with hands at the midway point on a line between two goal posts, the testee pulls out on signal and runs around the right hand post. He then turns to run across the finish line located 30 feet from and parallel to the starting line. The score is the better of two trials.

9. *Kick-off.* The ball is placed on a kicking tee with a slight backward tilt; the testee takes a preparatory run and place-kicks for distance. The longest of three trials is the score.

10. *Dodging run* (Appendix B). Carrying a football as preferred; scored as better of two trials (without dropping the ball).

The tests are administered on a suitable smooth grass playing area. One practice trial is allowed, except for item 2. Distance measurement is made perpendicular to the starting line and recorded as the point of initial contact with the ground, taken to the last whole foot. Time events are measured in seconds and tenths.

As a note of interest, item intercorrelations, although not available, would be particularly helpful to establish the actual relatedness of items 6 and 10, and 2 and 8 (indeed among all four). Casual observation suggests that these items may measure essentially the same qualities.

Borleske Touch Football Test (College Men).[46] Upon analysis by 46 experts regarding elements for inclusion, Borleske proposed a test of touch football for college men. The test items include:

1. *Forward pass for distance.* After a 1-minute warmup, the subject takes a pass from center and passes the ball from behind the starting line onto a marked field. The best of three trials is scored as the distance estimated to the nearest yard.

2. *Catching forward pass.* Subject is allowed one fair trial (wherein ball can be touched with reasonable effort) to catch a pass in running each of three prescribed patterns: (a) go down 10 yards and out 90 degrees right, (b) go down 10 yards and cut 35 degrees left, and (c) go down and left 45 degrees to the 15-yard marker and cut 45 degrees right. Ten points are scored for each catch, and no warmup is permitted.

3. *Punt for distance.* Standing at least 7 yards behind the center, subject receives the pass and kicks the ball within 2 seconds onto a marked field. Scored same as the forward pass.

4. *Running, 50-yard straightaway.* After a 1-minute warmup, the subject assumes a backfield 3-point stance 5 yards behind the center and upon snap back takes the ball and runs 50 yards (from stance point) as fast as possible. One trial is allowed, scored to the nearest tenth of a second.

[46] S. C. Borleske, "A Study of Achievement of College Men in Touch Football," *Research Quarterly,* VIII, No. 2 (May, 1937), 73. T-scores are also reported in SR 3 and for a junior high school application in SR 1.

5. *Zone pass defense.* A passing situation is simulated with the passer 10 yards behind center, lined up on edge and just to the left of center facing a rectangle 28 by 24 yards, which is divided into four quadrants. Subject stands in the farther zone on the passer's right and has one trial in each of three plays—with one, two and three receivers entering the subject's zone. The plays are called by huddle in any desired order. The scoring is for knock down or interception as 2 or 4, 6 or 8, and 10 points for either in the case of one, two, or three receivers in the zone, respectively. A trial is repeated in instances where neither defense nor receiver can reach pass. Interference by defense results in one-third deduction of any points scored on that play.

T-score norms are available for the test. For validation the test was found to correlate .93 with an objective criterion comprised of 18 individual tests, which in turn correlated .85 with subjective judgment. A simplified version of the test—items 1, 3, and 4—reduces the time requirements considerably and correlated .88 with the objective criterion. A rating scale is not available for the three-item battery.

Brace Football Achievement Test (College Men).[47] A football achievement test was proposed by Brace to predict likely success of players. The test includes (1) forward pass for distance—2 trials; (2) punting for distance—2 trials; (3) forward pass at a target of 2-, 4-, and 6-foot diameter concentric circles, 15-yard restraining line—3 trials; (4) dodge and run—dodging run with football; (5) 50-yard dash—with football; (6) charging—with harness connected to back and leg dynamometer; (7) pull out—time to run around post 9½ feet to the left and across line 5 yards forward; and (8) blocking—time to knock over three dummies and complete a 15-yard course. One practice trial is allowed for each item except 5. No scoring tables are available. Low but acceptable validity with judgment criterion was reported.

Football Achievement Scales (College Men).[48] Cozens prepared standardized directions and achievement (sigma) scales for college men for the following items: (1) drop-kick for accuracy, (2) pass for accuracy, (3) pass for distance, and (4) punt for distance.

Golf

While the game of golf serves as it own best test, limitations imposed by available time and facilities render it impractical. When using the

[47] D. K. Brace, "Validity of Football Achievement Tests as Measures of Motor Learning and as a Partial Basis for the Selection of Players," *Research Quarterly,* XIV, No. 4 (December, 1943), 372.

[48] F. W. Cozens, *Achievement Scales in Physical Education Activities for College Men* (Philadelphia: Lea & Febiger, 1936).

game score as a test, a nine-hole round is desirable, although a minimum of a five-hole score might be utilized for anyone except a complete beginner; and the score should be supplemented with ratings made during the test holes. Developed tests also serve as desirable means of practice for selected game elements.

Clevett Golf Test.[49]   Clevett developed a pioneer test of golf consisting of four items: tee-shots with brassie and mid-iron, mashie approach shot, and carpet putting. The tee-shots are made in a cage onto a 10-foot-square target, divided into 25 scoring areas and placed 21 feet from the tee. The approach test is made at a spot 15 feet from the nearest point of target. Ten trials are given in each test item. Target scores are taken as the zone where the ball strikes, except in the case of putting. No norms are available, nor are test development statistics.

McKee Golf Test.[50]   McKee scientifically devised a test, purported to be diagnostic, of the full swinging golf shot. The test consists of making ten five-iron shots onto an area 175 by 80 yards and determining the time the ball is airborne; the distance covered in the air along the intended line of flight; and the distance from the line of flight that the ball deviated, measured at right angles. Unless the ball is aloft at least 0.6 second, the trial is repeated. From this information, the range, velocity, angle of impact, and angle of deviation are computed. The test possesses face validity and yielded reliabilities of .95, .89, and .89 for range, velocity, and angle of impact. The angle of deviation proved low in reliability (.60) but valuable as a practice motivator to encourage exercising more care in lining up shots. No norms are available.

A test was also developed with a cotton ball instead of a regular golf ball and using an area 20 by 30 yards. It proved to be a valid and reliable (.88) measure of range in the full-swing shot. The lower validity coefficients for velocity, impact, angle, and deviation suggest use as a supplement for teacher analysis for diagnostic purposes. The advantages of the cotton ball test lie in ease of administering and economy of time.

Vanderhoof Golf Test.[51]   Vanderhoof made a study with college women using plastic practice balls. Two of the tests taken from this study and designed for indoors are drive test with a brassie and five-iron approach. For both tests, the testee is allowed unlimited practice swings, two or three warmup balls, and 15 test trials. The trials are

[49] Melvin A. Clevett, "An Experiment in Teaching Methods of Golf," *Research Quarterly*, II, No. 4 (December, 1931), 104.

[50] Mary E. McKee, "A Test for the Full Swinging Shot in Golf," *Research Quarterly*, XXI, No. 1 (March, 1950), 40.

[51] Ellen R. Vanderhoof, "Beginning Golf Achievement Tests," Microcard Master's Thesis, State University of Iowa, 1956.

taken at a distance of 14 feet from the near edge of the target, which is divided into three zones each 20 feet long and scoring 1, 2, and 3 points, respectively. The drive and approach tests resulted in validity coefficients of .71 and .66 with form rating and reliability of .90 and .84, respectively; when combined a correlation of .78 was obtained with the judgment criterion. The reference contains the five-point scale used in judges' rating.

Brown Golf Skills Test.[52]   Brown devised a five-item test for use with coeducational physical education classes at Southern Methodist University, complete with separate T-scale norms for men and women. The items with validity and reliability coefficients are: (1) chip—15 shots from behind a shooting line to a trapezoidal target, shown in Fig. 12–3, with points scored 3, 2, and 1 according to the area in which ball

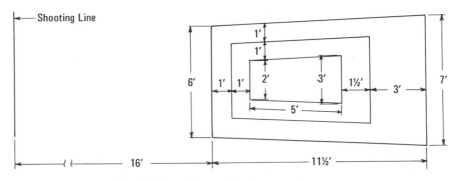

Fig. 12–3. Target for Brown chip test.

first hits the ground (.662, .806); (2) short pitch—15 shots from behind a shooting arc located 65 feet from the center of three concentric circles with radii of 7½, 15, and 22½ feet and scored, 3, 2, and 1, respectively, at point of first ground contact (.847, .631); (3) approach—15 shots on test target for item 2, scored where ball comes to rest (.752, .652); (4) driving—5 shots scored as point of rest on scoring layout shown in Fig. 12–4 (.699 for men, .294 for women, reliability—.511); and (5) putting—12 holes putted on a green of six holes with two 15 feet and four 18 feet in length and situated with one downhill, one uphill, one breaking left, one breaking right, and two level (.790, .711).

The "Best 9 Scores" made by 113 students during six weeks of course play served as the validity criterion, yielding a coefficient of .753 with

[52] H. Steven Brown, "A Test Battery for Evaluating Golf Skills," *Proceedings of the National College Physical Education Association for Men*, 1966, pp. 69–70.

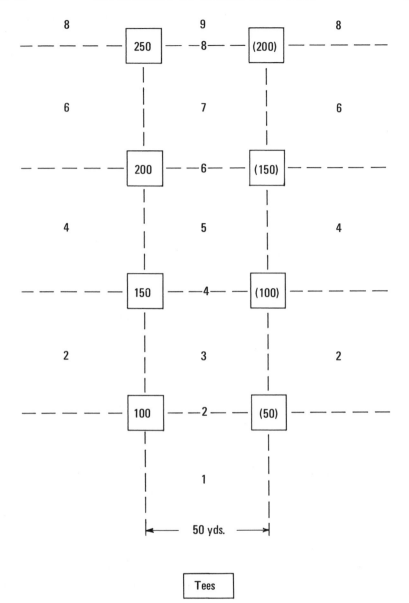

Fig. 12–4. Target for Brown driving test. (Figure in parentheses in yard distance markers applies to women's tests.)

sum of the item scores. The low reliability reported for the driving item indicates the need to increase the number of trials. This test, while warranting some refinement, illustrates that a feasible "component and total game analysis" type of skill assessment may be possible.

West-Thorpe Eight-Iron Approach Test (College Women).[53] To meet the need for a measure of a reduced swinging stroke West and Thorpe devised an approach test with an eight-iron. The testee makes a shot from behind a restraining line 12 yards from the pin. The target consists of six concentric circles with the inner circle having a radius of 1½ yards and the radius for each outward circle is increased by 1½ yards; scoring 7 to 2 points for circles and 1 point outside. Each trial is subjectively rated as 1 to 3 points on vertical projection angle which is added to the accuracy score. The total of 24 trials, 12 on two days, constitutes the test score. Content and divergent group validity was established, and minimally acceptable reliability (.60–.75) was obtained (N = 424).

Davis Five Iron Test (College Women).[54] Davis devised a full swinging five iron test for distance and accuracy for college women consisting of total score on two ten-ball trials with intervening rest onto a target field as shown in Fig. 12–5. A reliability of .80 was estimated from split-half correlation; content (face) validity was claimed. Norms were not prepared.

Benson Golf Test.[55] Clarke describes an unpublished test by Benson in which a different scoring scheme that warrants description for illustrative purposes is utilized in a test using the five iron as an indicant of overall ability. Yardage indicators are placed on a line at 25-yard intervals up to 150 yards. At the 150-yard distance a perpendicular line is extended to either side with deviation signs numbered from 1 to 9 placed at 5-yard intervals. For the test, after 5 practice shots, 20 shots are scored for distance in flight and deviation from the intended line of flight. Reliability estimated from split-half coefficients was .90 and .70 for distance and deviation scores.

---

[53] Charlotte West and Joanne Thorpe, "Construction and Validation of an Eight-Iron Approach Test, *Research Quarterly*, XXXIX, No. 4 (December, 1968), 1115.

[54] C. M. Davis, "The Use of the Golf Tee in Teaching Beginning Golf." Unpublished Master's Thesis, University of Michigan, 1960.

[55] H. Harrison Clarke, *Application of Measurement to Health and Physical Education* (4th ed.; Englewood Cliffs, N. J.: Prentice-Hall, Inc., 1967), pp. 317–318; Cited from unpublished paper by D. W. Benson, "Measuring Golf Ability Through Use of a Number Five Iron Test," Research Section, California Assn. HPER Convention, 1963.

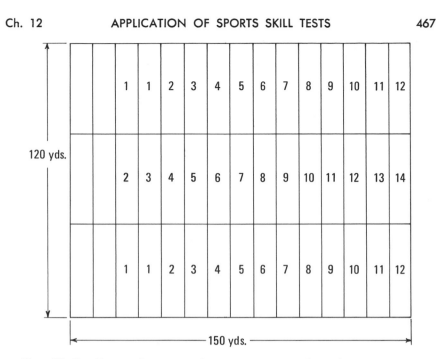

Fig. 12–5. Target layout and scoring zone values for Davis Test.

Gymnastics and Tumbling

To date measurement of ability in gymnastics and tumbling has been largely limited to subjective judgment. The importance of form in this activity renders the development of objective measures difficult. In an effort to provide a sound basis for subjective judgment, Zwarg described guides for evaluating apparatus performance along with an explanation of proposed rules governing apparatus competition.[56] A study made at the 1950 National Collegiate Athletic Association Gymnastic Meet found that the objectivity coefficients of judging different events were reasonably high at this level of competition and judging.[57] A comparable study in 1961 failed to show any improvement in a decade with some decreases and some increases in objectivity coefficients.[58] Parallel bars, tumbling and free exercise reflected disappointingly low objectivity.

[56] L. F. Zwarg, "Judging and Evaluation of Competitive Apparatus for Gymnastic Exercises," *Journal of Health and Physical Education,* VI, No. 1 (January, 1935), 23.
[57] Paul Hunsicker and Newt Loken, "The Objectivity of Judging at the National Collegiate Athletic Association Gymnastic Meet," *Research Quarterly,* XXII, No. 4 (December, 1951), 423.
[58] John Faulkner and Newt Loken, "Objectivity of Judging at the National Collegiate Athletic Association Gymnastic Meet: A Ten-Year Follow-Up Study," *Research Quarterly,* XXXIII, No. 3 (October, 1962), 485.

Larson reported a scheme for testing skill in elementary school gymnastics utilizing a scale from 0 (inability to perform) to 3 (good performance) combined with a difficulty multiplier for each stunt.[59] The description and illustrations constitute a test development resource for the teacher.

Bowers Gymnastic Skill Test (College Women).[60] Bowers devised a rating procedure for beginning to low intermediate gymnastic skills for college women involving uneven parallel bars, balance beam, free standing exercise, side horse vaulting, and tumbling. Along with the scale point description for each item a listing of the most common errors is given. While more definitive reliability and objectivity analysis is desirable, the scale is useful as a resource or for experimental application. The detailed nature of it renders description herein impractical.

Wettstone Test of Gymnastic and Tumbling Potential Ability (College Men).[61] A test of potential ability was constructed by Wettstone to aid coaches in finding students with essential innate capacity in this area. A list of 34 capacities usually possessed by a good gymnast was compiled through a survey of coaches, outstanding gymnasts, and authorities in physical education measurement. Tests were devised for the 15 highest ranking qualities. After a thorough study of 22 gymnasts, a correlation of .79 was obtained between subjective rating of potential ability and three elements—thigh circumference divided by height (t_c/d); strength test (s) consisting of chins, dips and thigh flexion; and Burpee Test (BT) for 10 seconds. The thigh flexion test consists of maximum number of leg raisings to the horizontal while hanging from stall bars. The regression equation for predicting potential gymnastic ability is:

$$PGA = -.355 \left(\frac{t_c}{d}\right) + .260(s) + .035(BT) + 13.990$$

The reference contains a scale for rating beginning with the category, "not quite varsity material."

[59] Robert F. Larson, "Skill Testing in Elementary School Gymnastics," *Physical Educator*, XXVI, No. 2 (May, 1969), 80.

[60] Carolyn O. Bowers, "Gymnastic Skill Test for Beginning to Low Intermediate Girls and Women," Microcard Master's Thesis, Ohio State University, 1965.

[61] Eugene Wettstone, "Tests for Predicting Potential Ability in Gymnastics and Tumbling," *Research Quarterly*, IX, No. 4 (December, 1938), 115.

Handball

Cornish Handball Test.[62]   The first scientifically devised test of hand-ball skill was developed by Cornish. Using a criterion of the difference of points scored by a subject as compared to points scored against him in 23 games and involving 134 different subjects, a validity coefficient of .694 was obtained with a multiple correlation of five skill tests. The tests include the following.

1. *Thirty-second volley.* Subject drops the ball to the floor and strokes it to the front wall from behind the service line for 30 seconds. Ball may be struck from in front of line only when it does not return far enough. Missed balls are replaced immediately by tester. The score is the number of wall hits.

2. *Front-wall placement.* Starting from the service line for each trial, the subject tosses the ball to the front wall below a line 6 feet above the floor. Upon rebound, the ball is hit to the front wall and scored according to the markings as shown in Fig. 12–6. A total of ten trials, five with each hand, are made and points are summed for the test score.

3. *Back-wall placement.* The tester tosses the ball so as to hit the back wall about 3 feet from the floor, whereupon the subject strokes it onto the front wall target (Fig. 12–6). Five strokes are made with each hand, and the total points are recorded as the score.

4. *Power test.* Standing in the service zone, the subject tosses the

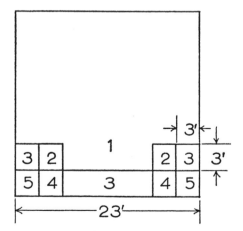

Fig. 12–6. Front wall scoring target for Cornish handball test.

[62] Clayton Cornish, "A Study of Measurement of Ability in Handball," *Research Quarterly*, XX, No. 2 (May, 1949), 215.

ball to the front wall and upon bouncing from the floor strokes it so as to strike the front wall below a line 6 feet from the floor and rebounding into the zoned court. Balls landing ahead of the service line score 1 point. The 23 feet behind the service line (regulation court) is divided equally into four zones, scored as 2, 3, 4, and 5 points going from service line backward, respectively. A trial is repeated when ball strikes front wall above the line or if subject steps into front court. The total points on five trials with each hand are recorded.

5. *Placement service.* The subject makes ten serves, 5 of which are cross-court, with normal serving hand. The total points are recorded, as scored on the back-court markings shown in Fig. 12–7.

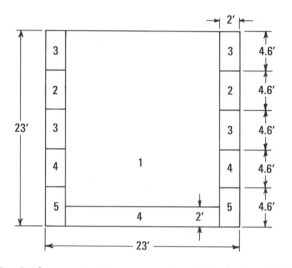

Fig. 12–7. Backcourt scoring target for Cornish handball placement-service test.

Cornish suggests a two-test battery of items 1 and 5, which correlated .667 with the criterion. The power test appears to be the best single test in view of its correlation with the other tests. Neither norms nor reliability are reported. Inasmuch as these tests tend to duplicate game situations, they also comprise good practice for skill development.

Oregon Handball Test.[63] A three-item test was proposed in a study at the University of Oregon from 17 strength, motor ability and handball skill test items administered to 37 male undergraduates using the criterion of average score in a partial round robin tournament. The items

[63] G. G. Pennington, J. A. P. Day, J. N. Drowatzky, and J. F. Hansan, "A Measure of Handball Ability," *Research Quarterly,* XXXVIII, No. 2 (May, 1967), 247.

include: (1) service placement—10 trials to a scoring target as shown in Fig. 12–7); (2) total wall volley—one 30-second trial from behind center of short service line and a 30-second trial using only the nondominant hand, scored as total number of wall hits; and (3) back-wall placement —as Cornish test item 3. The court size (18-foot width) and the ball were peculiar to the game as played at this institution, and the scoring was modified to award a point (15-point game) on every play regardless of server. These items yielded a multiple correlation coefficient of .802 with the criterion. The score form of the regression equation for the test was: Criterion = 1.37 item 1 + 2.27 item 2 + 1.59 item 3 + .29 (with σest = 15.57). The best single item correlation with the criterion was obtained for item 1, r = .711. A multiple correlation of .791 was derived for items 1 and 2 with the criterion. It warrants noting that this two item combination closely approximated the multiple correlation for the three-items and basically consists of the same two items recommended by Cornish as a two-test battery.

DeWitt Handball Tests.[64]   DeWitt describes several tests that, while not scientifically devised, suggest study, namely, (1) service test with back court divided into 15 scoring zones; (2) volley accuracy test to front-wall target; (3) volley speed test for 1 minute; and (4) power test, each trial scored as distance shot lands behind service line.

Ice Hockey

Despite the comparatively early appearance of an unscientifically devised ice hockey test, 1935, progress in this area has been meager, which is largely attributable to the limited use of ice hockey in physical education programs. The reader may derive ideas for test items in addition to those indicated below by analysis of items in other sports skills entailing similar elements, such as controlled dribbling.

Brown Ice Hockey Test (Girls).[65]   As part of a teaching unit on ice hockey for girls, Brown suggests a three-item test entailing (1) dribbling and dodging—subject carries puck over a 30-yard course to the left of a chair at 15 yards and around chair at 30 yards returning in a similar manner to the starting line; (2) goal shooting—subject skates around behind cage and shoots for goal from behind a 5-foot restraining line, taking 5 shots from both sides; and (3) speed skating and dribbling— subject dribbles puck to a line 40 yards away and returns. The test was not analyzed statistically, and scoring tables and norms are not given.

[64] R. T. DeWitt, *Teaching Individual and Team Sports* (Englewood Cliffs, N. J.: Prentice-Hall, Inc.), pp. 231–33.
[65] Harriet M. Brown, "The Game of Ice Hockey," *Journal of Health and Physical Education*, XIV, No. 4 (December, 1943), 372.

DeWitt Ice Hockey Tests.[66] DeWitt briefly describes three skill tests for ice hockey: (1) shooting for accuracy—10 shots taken from 20 feet at a goal-like target divided into 12 scoring areas; (2) dribbling—time for subject to stick-handle puck one lap around rink in path measured 6 feet inward from side boards; and (3) zigzag skating—time to cover one lap of course, alternately dodging 15 obstacles. The tests are not scientifically devised, and no scoring tables are available.

Ithaca Ice Hockey Skill Tests.[67] Merrifield and Waldorf devised six tests to measure selected basic ice hockey skills using 15 members of the Ithaca College Hockey Club. Two tests—shooting and passing—were dropped because of poor reliability, leaving the following items: (1) forward skating speed—over a 120 foot straight-line course; (2) backward skating speed—over above course, starting and skating backward; (3) skating agility; and (4) puck carry—starting from behind a start-finish line on which the puck lies just to the left of an obstacle, the testee skates to the left of this first obstacle and alternately around six other obstacles spaced 30 feet apart and returns similarly to the finish. The obstacles were constructed of wood, 30 inches high on a 2 by 4 inch base. For this latter test item, control of the puck must be maintained throughout, and the test is repeated if two or more obstacles are knocked over.

The pattern for the skating agility item is shown in Fig. 12–8. The skater starts from behind the starting line and skates through the pattern

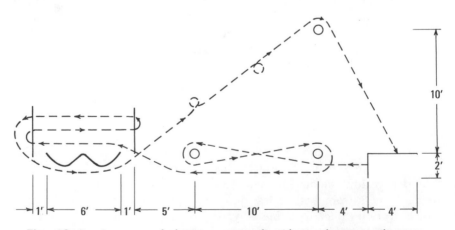

Fig. 12–8. Layout and skating pattern for Ithaca skating agility test.

[66] DeWitt, *op. cit.*, pp. 253–54.
[67] H. H. Merrifield and G. A. Walford, "Battery of Ice Hockey Skill Tests," *Research Quarterly*, XL, No. 1 (March, 1969), 146.

to the further of two 4-foot lines in front of the goal cage. A stop is performed outside the line followed immediately by a start, and this stop-and-start is repeated at the other 4-foot line. In completing the pattern to the finish, a turn to skate backwards, backward skating and a turn to return to forward skating are performed. The score for each item is the better of two trials timed to the nearest tenth of a second as the first skate reaches the finish line. Trials are repeated if a fall occurs. A hockey stick is carried below shoulder level with both hands for all items. For items 3 and 4 half-speed practice trials are allowed. With the criterion of coach's ranking of playing ability, validity coefficients of .83, .79, .75, and .96 were obtained for items 1 to 4, respectively. Spearman *rho* coefficients for reliability were .74, .80, .94, and .93. From the findings the authors inferred that items 1, 4 and either 2 or 3 may be used as measures of ice hockey skills. The puck carry was deemed to be the best single item for determining overall ice hockey ability.

SELECTED REFERENCES

1. BARROW, HAROLD M., and McGEE, ROSEMARY. *A Practical Approach to Measurement in Physical Education.* Philadelphia: Lea and Febiger, 1964.
2. CAMPBELL, W. R., and TUCKER, N. M. *An Introduction to Tests and Measurement in Physical Education.* London: G. Bell & Sons, Ltd., 1967.
3. CLARKE, H. HARRISON. *Application of Measurement to Health and Physical Education,* 4th ed. Englewood Cliffs, N. J.: Prentice-Hall, Inc., 1967.
4. MATHEWS, DONALD K. *Measurement in Physical Education,* 4th ed. Philadelphia: W. B. Saunders Co., 1973.
5. McCLOY, C. H., and YOUNG, N. D. *Tests and Measurements in Health and Physical Education,* 3d ed. New York: Appleton-Century-Crofts, Inc., 1954.
6. MONTOYE, HENRY J. (ed.). *Sports Tests and Evaluation in Dance (An Introduction to Measurement in Physical Education,* Vol. 3). Indianapolis: Phi Epsilon Fraternity, 1970.
7. SCOTT, M. GLADYS, and FRENCH, ESTHER. *Measurement and Evaluation in Physical Education.* Dubuque: Wm. C. Brown Co., 1959.

13

Additional Sports Skill Tests*

Rhythms and Dance

Tests in the area of rhythms and dance began to appear in the early 1930's, but to date they have been primarily instruments of research and not practical for teacher use. Annett concluded that the Seashore Rhythm Test was fairly satisfactory in predicting skill in motor rhythm, based on obtaining a .47 correlation between scores of physical education majors on this test and a criterion of expert judgment of skill in motor rhythm.[1] On the basis of considerable study, Lemon and Sherbon felt that a practical rhythm test can be established specifically for physical education and warrants study.[2] Their illustrative pilot test included having the subject express four different rhythm patterns and then step three specific tempos in a given time (10 seconds).

Shambaugh developed a rather complicated procedure for measuring rhythmic response that proved satisfactory with a small group but is impractical for teacher use.[3] Two parts are involved: one in which time in performing given rhythmic patterns is recorded on a revolving drum located beneath a specially devised platform, and the second entailing comparative measurements between strides made on a flour-dusted floor

* As noted in Chapter 12, no further description is given of basic test items contained in Appendix B, unless a modification exists or clarification appears warranted.

[1] Thomas Annett, "A Study of Rhythmic Capacity and Performance in Motor Rhythm in Physical Education Majors," *Research Quarterly*, III, No. 2 (May, 1932), 183.

[2] Eloise Lemon and Elizabeth Sherbon, "A Study of the Relationships of Certain Measures of Rhythmic Ability and Motor Ability in Girls and Women," *Supplement to the Research Quarterly*, V, No. 1 (March, 1934), 82.

[3] M. E. Shambaugh, "The Objective Measurement of Success in the Teaching of Folk Dancing to University Women," *Research Quarterly*, VI, No. 1 (March, 1935), 33.

in response to tempo set on a record. Early attempts to measure rhythmic response were also made by Buck,[4] McCristal,[5] and Muzzy.[6] In 1960 Ashton summarized developments in rhythm testing and suggested how the teacher might proceed in this area.[7]

Ashton Gross Motor Rhythm Test.[8]   On the basis of considerable study involving college women, Ashton developed a gross motor rhythm test involving simple movement initiated by the student. It consists of three parts: (1) directed walk, run, and skip; (2) musical excerpts in which subject performs movement to fit the music; and (3) derived or combined dance steps wherein the step is identified (as either polka, waltz, or schottische) for the student to perform. The use of this test, together with the rating scale (0 to 4) described in the reference was found satisfactory in instances when varied forms of dance must be judged within one class period and without extensive staff training. Two groups of three students can be tested every 15 minutes. Reliability of .86 was reported, and standardized instructions were prepared.

Benton Dance Movement Capacity Test.[9]   Working with college physical education majors, Benton devised a test to disclose ability in performing modern dance movements, recognizing that the dance movement is not entirely rhythm but entails other elements such as agility, motor educability, strength, and balance for which adequate tests are available. The test was composed of a weighted battery of five Johnson-type items, six Brace-type stunts, Bass Static Balance Test (crosswise), McCloy Physical Fitness Index, Seashore Series A Rhythm Test, and Seashore Motor Rhythm Test. Using a criterion of expert judgment, validity coefficients ranging from .77 to .93 were obtained for five regression equations with various combinations of the test item scores.

Waglow Social Dance Test (College).[10]   Waglow developed a test of social dance ability using a specially prepared record in which a melody was played in the rhythm of waltz, tango, slow fox trot, jitterbug, rumba, and samba. Four of the basic steps are performed from and

---

[4] Nadine Buck, "A Comparison of Two Methods of Testing Response to Auditory Rhythms," *Research Quarterly,* VII, No. 3 (October, 1936), 36.

[5] K. J. McCristal, "Experimental Study of Rhythm in Gymnastics and Tap Dancing," *Research Quarterly,* IV, No. 2 (May, 1933), 63.

[6] Dorothy M. Muzzey, "Group Progress of White and Colored Children in Learning a Rhythm Pattern," *Research Quarterly,* IV, No. 3 (October, 1933), 62.

[7] Dudley Ashton, "Action Research in Rhythmic Testing," *Journal of Health and Physical Education,* XXXI, No. 8 (November, 1960), 37.

[8] Dudley Ashton, "A Gross Motor Rhythm Test," *Research Quarterly,* XXIV, No. 3 (October, 1953), 253.

[9] Rachel J. Benton, "The Measurement of Capacities for Learning Dance Movement Techniques," *Research Quarterly,* XV, No. 2 (May, 1944), 137.

[10] I. F. Waglow, "An Experiment in Social Dance Testing," *Research Quarterly,* XXIV, No. 1 (March, 1953), 97.

about a specific starting point. Low validity and reliability are reported; the objectivity coefficient was .792. The test appears practical and does not consume undue time, but revision of the scoring is indicated in an endeavor to yield satisfactory validity and reliability.

Coppock Test of Rhythmic Motor Response.[11] As a measure of the rhythmic element in dance, Coppock devised a test with 92 college women consisting of 23 patterns of walking-type movements in a designated area. The patterns included measures of 3/4, 4/4, and 5/4 meters, as tape recorded at 84 beats per minute using a drum. Tests were given individually and took 15 minutes. In scoring, one point was awarded for correct movement rate for meter and the same for tempo on two identical measures for each pattern. A practice trial was given on the first two patterns. Validity coefficients of .49 to .51 for meter, tempo, and combined scores were obtained with the criterion of judges' ratings and .52 to .69 with the Gordon Rhythm Imagery Test. The stepped-up split-half correlation estimates of reliability were .91 for meter and .90 for tempo. The basic statistics for the test group are reported. The author observed that the meter method of scoring appeared preferable.

Riding

Crabtree Riding Test.[12] The only resource test available for riding is an eight-item score chart for judging riding ability. The items with their point allocations (which sum to 40 for the total test) are: mounting (3); dismounting (3); walk (5); trot—collected and extended (14); canter—collected and extended (11); and general horsemanship (4).

Skiing

Street Skiing Test.[13] To enhance administrative simplicity Street proposed a time score as the sole basis for measuring skiing performance over a long and short course. Validity coefficients with judges' rating for men and for women over both courses ranged from .62 to .94; reliability coefficients from .67 to .93.

Soccer

An early and inclusive test of soccer skill for girls was described by Vanderhoof which, while not scientifically devised, covered important

---

[11] Doris E. Coppock, "Development of an Objective Measure of Rhythmic Motor Response," *Research Quarterly*, XXXIX, No. 4 (December, 1968), 915.

[12] Helen K. Crabtree, "An Objective Test for Riding," *Journal of Health and Physical Education*, XIV, No. 8 (October, 1943), 419.

[13] Richard H. Street, "Measurement of Achievement in Skiing," Unpublished Master's Thesis, University of Utah, 1957.

elements of soccer, including dribble; trapping; place kick for accuracy; dropped ball kick for distance; volley for distance with forehead, shoulder, hip, or knee; throw-down (securing ball from opponent within a 6-yard circle); tackling; corner kick; and goalkeeper's test.[14] The test description includes a suggested scoring graph to facilitate analyzing an individual's ability and to afford a basis for assigning team positions.

The first scientifically devised soccer skill test was constructed by Heath and Rodgers for fifth- and sixth-grade boys and girls based on teacher analysis of the game.[15] The test items include (1) dribble—over a course of four chairs spaced on a line 3 yards apart, beginning 5 yards from the starting line; (2) throw-in—ten trials to 2- and 4-foot diameter target centered 6 yards away; (3) place kick for goal—10 trials from 12 yards; and (4) kicking and rolling ball—five trials on ball rolled from each side of goal. T-scales are available for fifth- and sixth-grade boys. Coefficients of .60 and .62 for the two grades were obtained with teacher judgment. Reliability was reported as .72 to .74 for composite scores.

Two other early resource tests of soccer were mentioned in describing the historical background of skill tests (Chapter 12). Cozens and his associates devised a test for high school and college girls involving place kicking for distance, punting, dribbling, the throw-in, and the goal kick.[16] T-score tables are available, and satisfactory validity and reliability are reported. Neilson and Cozens describe four soccer tests—dribble, kick for distance, place kick for accuracy, and throw-in for distance—complete with achievement scales for boys and girls in elementary and junior high school.[17]

Bontz Soccer Test (Fifth and Sixth Grades).[18] Bontz constructed what has proved to be an interesting test and practice technique for children in fifth and sixth grades, consisting of a series of skills administered in consecutive order. To administer the test:

1. Mark the area as shown in Fig. 13–1 with a 6-foot-long starting line drawn opposite to, 55 yards from, and centered on the 18-foot wide

[14] Mildred Vanderhoof, "Soccer Skill Tests," *Journal of Health and Physical Education,* III, No. 8 (October, 1932), 42.

[15] M. L. Heath and Elizabeth G. Rodgers, "A Study in the Use of Skill and Knowledge Tests in Soccer," *Research Quarterly,* III, No. 4 (December, 1932), 35.

[16] F. W. Cozens, H. J. Cubberley, and N. P. Neilson, *Achievement Scales in Physical Education Activities for Secondary School Girls and College Women* (New York: A. S. Barnes & Co., 1937).

[17] N. P. Neilson and F. W. Cozens, *Achievement Scales in Physical Education Activities for Boys and Girls in Elementary and Junior High Schools* (New York: A. S. Barnes & Co., 1934).

[18] Jean Bontz, "An Experiment in the Construction of a Test for Measuring Ability in Some of the Fundamental Skills Used by Fifth and Sixth Grade Children in Soccer," Unpublished Master's Thesis, State University of Iowa, 1942.

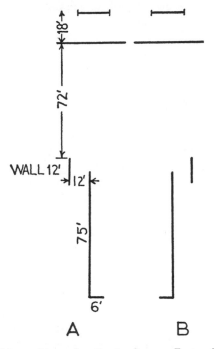

Fig. 13–1. Field markings for Bontz Soccer Test. A, right-foot kick; B, left-foot kick.

goal. A restraining line is marked from the left end of the starting line for 25 yards toward the goal line. A 12-foot wall area is placed 12 feet to the left of and parallel to the restraining line, centered on the end of the restraining line. The area is also laid out with a wall on the right side.

2. Upon signal, the subject dribbles the ball from the starting line to the right of the restraining line to a point where it is kicked with the right foot diagonally against the wall, as though passing to another player. After recovery, the ball is dribbled and kicked for a goal before crossing the 6-yard line.

3. Four trials are given with the right-foot kick on the left-hand wall, and four with the left-foot kick on the right-hand wall. Two practice trials are given with each foot. If an error occurs, the trial is repeated. Each trial is scored as time to the nearest half-second, and the total time consumed in eight trials comprises the test score.

Validity is reported as .92 with subjective criterion, and reliability is .93 by odd-even method. The ranges and medians for the study group are reported.

Shaufele Soccer Test (Ninth- and Tenth-Grade Girls).[19] Shaufele devised the following soccer tests for ninth- and tenth-grade girls.

1. *Volleying.* Subject volleys a ball for 1 minute against a wall target (15 by 10 feet) beginning 15 feet from the wall and thereafter from anywhere within a 30-foot square on the floor. Score is the number of target hits made in the better of two trials given on different days. A 30-second practice trial is allowed. (Validity—.57 subjective, .68 with other tests; reliability—.67.)

2. *Passing and receiving.* Subject passes and receives ball on rebound from a wall three times in 10 seconds over a 55-foot span while staying outside a restraining line 8 feet from the wall. The ball must be touched twice between each recovery and pass. The score is the number of completed recoveries made; but in order for the third recovery to count, the finish line must also be crossed. One practice trial is given, and the score consists of a total of two trials from each end. (Validity—.50 subjective, .68 with other tests; reliability—.56 odd-even.) The test involves difficult skills and is a good practice activity.

3. *Judgment in passing.* Staying outside of a restraining line drawn 4 feet inside the right goal post and perpendicular to the goal line, subject dribbles ball from a 12-yard line, passes the 6-yard line, and kicks for a goal within 4 seconds. A bench is placed 4 feet from and parallel to the goal with its left end centered on the goal. Five legal trials are given from each side, with restraining line and bench changed for turns from the left. Score is the total goals scored. (Validity—.34 subjective, .65 with other tests; reliability—.69 odd-even.)

McDonald Soccer Test (College Men).[20] McDonald proposed a soccer wall volley test to predict game efficiency. Subject stands on or behind a 9-foot restraining line and volleys the ball for 30 seconds against a backboard, 30 feet long and 11½ feet high. Balls may be retrieved with hands or feet. Two spare balls are placed 9 feet behind restraining line. The sum of fair kicks on the best three of four allowed trials constitutes the score. Against the criterion of coaches' judgment of playing ability, validity coefficients of .94 for varsity players, .63 for junior varsity players, .76 for freshmen varsity players, and .85 for the combined groups (53 men) were obtained.

[19] Evelyn F. Shaufele, "The Establishment of Objective Tests for Girls of the Ninth and Tenth Grades to Determine Soccer Ability," Unpublished Master's Thesis, State University of Iowa, 1940. T-scale for volleying test is reported in SR (selected reference) 1.

[20] L. G. McDonald, "The Construction of a Kicking Skill Test as an Index of General Soccer Ability," Unpublished Master's Thesis, Springfield College, June, 1951.

Mitchell Modification of McDonald Soccer Test (Fifth and Sixth Grade Boys).[21] The McDonald Test was adapted by Mitchell for fifth- and sixth-grade boys by: reducing the backboard size to 8 feet wide and 4 feet high; moving the restraining line to a distance of 6 feet; using boundary lines from 3 feet outside each target to join a line parallel to and 12 feet from the target; not permitting use of hands by testees in retrieving balls; providing retrievers who are aligned along the boundary line to place the ball on the line in front of them upon retrieving it; and using one practice trial and the sum of three consecutive 20-second trials as the score. A kick made just before time expires counts if it strikes the target. One point was deducted for a hand infraction and, when appropriate, the use of head or other legal body parts was permitted to propel the ball. For validation, rho = .84 and r = .76 were obtained with the criterion of judges' ranking and rating, respectively (N = 192); for reliability, same day test-retest rho = .93. T-scale is available in the reference as well as the descriptive criteria with which judges rated ability and which entailed: general soccer ability, kicking ability, ball control techniques, and game knowledge.

Johnson Soccer Test (College Men).[22] Johnson devised a soccer wall-volley test with college men at the University of British Columbia using a goal-sized target board (24 by 8 feet) and a restraining line at a distance of 15 feet. A box of spare balls was centered on the target, 30 feet away. To put the rubber soccer ball into play, it is dropped from waist level and kicked before or after striking the ground. The score is the total number of balls that rebound across the restraining line in three 30-second trials, less any infractions for illegal play. The study group entailed five groups of 15 players representing various ability levels, viz., varsity first, second, and third teams, physical education majors, and required program students. Validity coefficients of .58, .84, .81, .94 and .98 were derived for the respective sub-groups with the criterion of ability ranking; a composite group correlation of .86 was obtained. Inter-trial reliability for trials two and three was .80. The norm chart for interpreting scores was reported as: 42 and over—superior; 37–41—good; 31–36—average; 25–30—below average; and 24 and below—poor.

Crawford Soccer Test Battery (Women Physical Education Majors).[23] From a study involving 30 women majors in physical education, Crawford

[21] J. Reid Mitchell, "The Modification of the McDonald Soccer Test for Upper Elementary School Boys," Microcard Master's Thesis, University of Oregon, 1963. T-scale is reported in SR 1.

[22] Joseph R. Johnson, "The Development of a Single-Item Test as a Measure of Soccer Skill," Microcard Master's Thesis, University of British Columbia, 1963.

[23] Elinor A. Crawford, "The Development of Skill Test Batteries for Evaluating the Ability of Women Physical Education Major Students in Soccer and Speedball," Microcard Doctoral Dissertation, University of Oregon, 1958.

constructed a battery of soccer skill tests yielding a multiple correlation of .80 with the criterion of judges' rating. The tests are:

1. *Dribbling.* The subject dribbles to the right of the first obstacle, placed 5 yards from the start-finish line, and alternately around four other obstacles spaced 5 yards apart; returning in the same manner. Score is the sum of three trials timed to nearest second, following one practice trial.

2. *Foot passing and receiving.* The course consists of five contiguous 12-foot wide wall areas; a 4-foot start-finish line perpendicular to the wall at either end of the course, beginning at a point 7½ feet outside the target areas and 6 feet from the wall; a 6-foot restraining line, 75 feet long, connecting the two start-finish lines; and a boundary line 75 feet long and 16 feet from the wall. Upon signal the testee dribbles from behind the starting line on the left and makes and receives passes into each of the five wall areas consecutively from within the playing zone. The trial is completed when testee and ball cross the finish line. Then a trial is taken in the return direction with the left foot; followed by second trials. The score is the sum of the faster time to the nearest second for each foot.

3. *Passing and trapping.* The ball is passed onto a 12-foot wide wall area and trapped from behind a 8-foot restraining line that extends 17 feet in length and within boundaries formed by side lines drawn from the target sides through the ends of the restraining line to meet the ends of a back boundary line, 22 feet long and parallel to the wall at a distance of 16 feet. A trial consists of the number of traps of legally passed balls that is made within 30 seconds. The score is the best of three trials, taken after one practice trial.

For tests 2 and 3, retrievers are stationed along the boundaries to return stray balls to the line. The respective coefficients for validity and estimated reliability from split-half correlations were: (1) .73, .89; (2) .58, .84; and (3) .45, .88. As noted, the best single test was the dribble test. The multiple regression equation for the battery was: 1.5 test 1 + test 2 + 1.8 test 3 − 132. T-scales were computed for the study group. Two other tests were studied and yielded low validity, namely, the Shaufele volley test; and goal kicking, five trials from each of three points 36 feet from the goal center.

Warner Soccer Test.[24] Warner proposed a test of the fundamental skills of soccer based upon evaluation of items by soccer coaches relative to their importance and learning difficulty. The test items include: kicking for distance, right and left foot; corner kick; heading; throw-in for

[24] Glenn F. H. Warner, "Warner Soccer Test," *Newsletter of the National Soccer Coaches Association of America,* VI (December, 1950), 13. A description of distance kicking and dribble items with norms for high school boys is reported in SR 1.

distance; penalty kick; and speed dribble. No reliability data are reported. The test constitutes a good test development resource for the teacher.

Softball

An excellent beginning in the development of softball skill tests, as well as other team sports, is attributed to Rodgers and Heath.[25] They devised a test involving the following elements: softball pitch for accuracy, batting, catching fly balls, catching grounders, and hit and run. T-scales were set up for fifth and sixth-grade boys. Low validity and reliability afforded a challenge to controlled conditions for further study.

O'Donnell Softball Test (High School Girls).[26] A test of basic skills for high school girls was proposed by O'Donnell as a means of classification and a measure of softball playing ability. The items include:

1. *Speed throw.* Subject throws a ball from behind restraining line (65 feet from the wall) upon signal to the designated wall. The time elapsed until the ball hits the wall is recorded. Subject may step over the line after ball is released. The score is the best of three trials taken to the nearest tenth of a second.
2. *Fielding fly balls.* From behind a restraining line 6 feet from the wall, the subject throws a ball upon signal to the wall on or above a 12-foot line, catches it on the fly, and repeats the procedure for 30 seconds. One practice throw is allowed. The score is the number of legal catches made in one 30-second trial. Balls may be caught ahead of the restraining line, but all throws must be made from behind it.
3. *Throw and catch.* From behind a starting line, which is directly beneath a rope stretched 8 feet above the floor, the subject throws a ball over the rope and runs to catch it on the fly. The purpose is to cover maximum distance and catch the ball. The score is the best of three trials, recorded as the distance to the heel of the front foot measured to the nearest foot. One practice is allowed.
4. *Repeated throws.* Upon signal the testee picks up a ball from the 15-foot restraining line and throws it from behind this line to a wall on or above a 7½-foot line, catches the rebound and throws again, repeating this procedure for 30 seconds. The score is the number of legal hits in one 30-second trial.
5. *Fungo batting.* The subject stands in the batter's box, tosses the ball into the air, and bats it. A ball landing in the outfield counts

[25] E. G. Rodgers and M. L. Heath, "An Experiment in the Use of Knowledge and Skill Tests in Playground Baseball," *Research Quarterly*, II, No. 4 (December, 1931), 113.

[26] Doris J. O'Donnell, "Validation of Softball Skill Tests for High School Girls," Unpublished Master's Thesis, Indiana University, 1950.

5 points; infield, 3; and a foul ball, 1 point. The score is the sum of points on ten trials. The batter must swing at the tossed ball to constitute a trial.

6. *Overhand accuracy throw.* The subject throws a ball from behind a 45-foot restraining line to the target drawn on a wall with its center 3 feet from floor. The concentric circles of the target have radii of 33, 21, 11, and 3 inches, scoring as 1, 2, 3, and 4, respectively. The score is the total points scored on ten trials.

Equations are given for three simplified batteries to evaluate playing ability: six-test battery and three-test (items 3, 4, and 6) and two-test (items 3 and 4) batteries. Reported validity of all batteries is .912 or above with six-test battery being most valid. The softball playing ability scores for the six-test battery = .6 item 2 + .3 item 3 + .6 item 4 + .1 item 5 + .4 item 6 − .3 item 1. Norms based on 50 subjects are available for individual items and the three batteries.

Fringer Softball Skill Tests (High School Girls).[27] Fringer devised the following tests for high school girls: (1) fly ball—total catches in three 30-second trials of throws made above a 10-foot high wall line, with the first throw only made from behind a 30-foot restraining line; (2) fielding grounders—number of wall target hits in two 45-second trials; and (3) throw for distance, with one step. For test 2 the target is a 5-foot diameter circle with lower edge 4 feet above the floor. Upon signal the testee runs from the starting point (centered on the target and midway between two bases 20 feet apart and 30 feet from the wall) and places one foot on a base and throws at the target, retrieves the ball and repeats the procedure from the other base, and so on. Using the criterion of repeated throws (scored as total of six trials) the multiple correlation for these tests was .83 and with items 1 and 2, .80.

Shick Defensive Softball Test Battery (College Women).[28] Shick devised a battery of defensive softball skills tests with 59 college women consisting of: (1) repeated throws—sum of four 30-second trials with 10-foot wall and 23-foot restraining lines; (2) field test—sum of four 30-second trials of throwing from behind a 15-foot restraining line and fielding a ball on rebound from a wall on or below a 4-foot wall line; and (3) target test—score is total points on wall and floor targets compiled in two trials of 10 throws made from behind a 40-foot restraining line to the wall target for rebounding onto the floor target, as shown in Fig. 13–2. The

[28] Jacqueline Shick, "Battery of Defensive Softball Skills Tests for College Women," *Research Quarterly*, XL, No. 1 (March, 1970), 82.

[27] Margaret N. Fringer, "A Battery of Softball Skill Tests for Senior High School Girls," Unpublished Master's Thesis, University of Michigan, 1961. Norms are reproduced in SR 1 and 2.

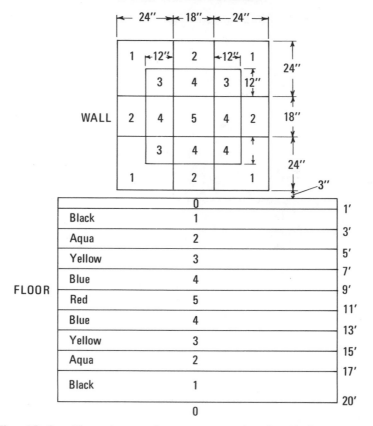

Fig. 13–2. Dimensions and target areas for the Shick target test.

coefficients for validity (judgment criterion) and reliability for the respective tests were: (1) .69, .86; (2) .48, 89; (3) .63, .88; and for the battery, .88, .75. Although the battery can be completed in one period, it is recommended that half of each test be given during each of two class periods to take into account the possible day-to-day variations in score.

Fox-Young Batting Test.[29] Fox and Young constructed a test of batting distance using a batting tee. The subject takes three practice hits from the tee, making necessary adjustments. Then five swings are taken, and the distance covered by the ball in the air is recorded to the nearest foot. The total distance covered in the five trials represents the score. Coeffi-

---

[29] Margaret G. Fox and Olive G. Young, "A Test of Softball Batting Ability," *Research Quarterly*, XXV, No. 1 (March, 1954), 26.

cients of .87 and .64 are reported for reliability and validity, respectively. Experience and practice with the batting tee should be a prerequisite for this test. The O'Donnell item 4 was modified by scoring it as the total hits in six trials.

Selected Softball Tests (College Women).[30] Scott and French describe, complete with T-scales, tests of repeated throws, distance throw, and batting tee similar to those noted herein. In addition this reference includes a fielding test that requires two wall surfaces perpendicular to each other with a base located at a right angle to the target on the forward wall and 20 to 40 feet from the left wall. The target is centered 48 inches above the floor and consists of concentric circles 3, 12, 21, 30, and 39 inches in radius. With a foot on the base the testee throws the ball to the left wall, then fields and throws it quickly at the target. The total of elapsed time and target score for 10 trials constitutes the test score. Low validity and reliability are reported.

Cale Study of Selected Softball Test Items (College Women).[31] Based on a study of selected softball test items involving 100 college women, Cale found three to be reliable and practical measures. These items and their reliabilities were: repeated throws—.81 (sum of four 30-second trials using 13-foot high wall line and 10-foot restraining line); distance throw—.91 (best of three throws to furthest 5-yard marker passed); and batting tee—.96 (scored as total yardage in 20 trials, after 5 practice, with each trial measured to nearest yard). Fielding grounders, fielding fly balls, and batting a pitched ball yielded poor reliability and were not deemed valuable as skill test items. The need for further study of the throw for speed and accuracy test was indicated. The importance of adjusting the wall and restraining lines in the repeated throws test for different rebounding surfaces was cited.

AAHPER Softball Test (Boys and Girls).[32] The AAHPER test for softball consists of the following items for boys and girls:

1. *Throw for distance.*
2. *Overhand throw for accuracy.* Testee throws overhand with both feet behind a 65-foot throwing line at a target of three concentric circles with 2-, 4- and 6-foot outside diameters and scoring 3, 2,

---

[30] M. G. Scott and Esther French, *Measurement and Evaluation in Physical Education* (Dubuque: W. C. Brown Co., 1959), pp. 199–211.

[31] Audrey A. Cale, "The Investigation and Analysis of Softball Skill Tests for College Women," Microcard Master's Thesis, University of Maryland, 1962.

[32] *Skills Test Manual: Softball for Boys;* and *Skills Test Manual: Softball for Girls* (Washington: American Association for Health, Physical Education and Recreation), 1966.

and 1 points, respectively. The lower target edge is 3 feet above the ground.

3. *Underhand pitching.* Legal underhand pitches are made with one foot in contact with the pitching line to a target consisting of two concentric rectangles assigned score values of 2 and 1 points for inner and outer areas, including the lines. The pitching line is 46 feet from the target, which is placed with the lower edge 18 inches above the floor. The inner rectangle is 17 inches wide and 30 inches high; the outer rectangle is 12 inches wider and longer. The score is the sum of 15 trials.

4. *Speed throw.* Fifteen overhand throws are made and caught from behind a 9-foot throwing line to a wall area at least 8 to 10 feet wide and high. The score is the better of two trials timed in seconds and tenths.

5. *Fungo hitting.* Subject stands behind home plate, tosses the ball up and attempts to hit a fly ball into right field, and then alternates hitting to left and right fields. Two consecutive misses count as a trial. Fly balls and grounders that reach the designated field beyond the base line are awarded 2 and 1 points, respectively. The score is the sum of 20 trials, 10 to each field.

6. *Base running.* Upon signal the subject takes a complete swing at an imaginary ball from the right hand batter's box, drops the bat and runs around the bases, touching each one. The score is the better of two trials timed in seconds and tenths.

7. *Fielding ground balls.* A rectangular area 17 by 60 feet is marked on the field with cross lines 25 and 50 feet from the throwing end. A test assistant throws the ball to strike the ground within the side lines and before the 25-foot line. The testee starts back of the 50-foot line and moves to field the ball cleanly and hold it momentarily. The thrower releases a ball at 5-second intervals until 20 trials are completed. After the first trial begins the testee may field anywhere back of the 25-foot line. The score is the number of correctly fielded balls.

8. *Catching fly balls.* GIRLS. A thrower stands in a restraining zone 5 feet behind home plate and throws the ball over a rope 8 feet high, located 5 feet in front of home plate, and into a 60-foot square zone centered on second base. Throws are varied so that approximately the same number are thrown into the middle and outside thirds of the zone. The player stands at second base and moves into position to catch each ball. The score is the number of successful catches in two series of 10 trials. BOYS. This test requires a two story building or the equivalent, rendering it impractical for general consideration.

One practice trial is permitted for items 4, 6, 7, and 8; one or two for item 2; and trials to either side for item 5.

Speedball

Buchanan Speedball Tests (High School Girls).[33] As a measure of basic speedball skills, Buchanan proposed the following:

1. *Lift to others.* From a 6-foot restraining line on a specially marked area, the subject lifts and passes a soccer ball with either foot diagonally across a net 2½ feet high and into a 3-foot square. Score is the number of successful attempts in five trials with each foot.
2. *Throwing and catching.* Wall pass with a soccer ball with a 6-foot restraining line for 30 seconds. Score is the average number of catches in five trials.
3. *Dribbling and passing.* Upon signal, the subject dribbles from the starting line alternately to right and left of five Indian clubs aligned 10 yards apart and upon reaching the last club passes to the left into the goal. The goal line, like the starting line, is located 10 yards from the end club. The goal is 6 feet wide, beginning 4 feet to the left of the projected line of clubs. After five trials beginning to the right of the first club, five are performed on the opposite side, with goal likewise on the opposite side. Three scores are derived, namely: (1) total of ten time scores measured to nearest second, (2) number of accurate passes made in ten trials, and (3) combined score obtained by subtracting (2) from (1).
4. *Kick-ups.* Starting behind a line marked 4 feet from a corner of a 2-foot square, subject runs as the ball is released by the thrower so as to land in the square. The testee attempts to kick up and catch the ball. The ball is thrown from overhead at a distance of 3 feet from side of the square to the right of the testee. The score is the number of successful attempts in five trials with each foot.

Validity coefficients range from .57 to .88 with a criterion of combined teacher rating of playing ability. Norms are available. To predict playing ability, the best combination of tests was found to be:

$$PA \text{ Score} = \text{Throwing-and-catching} + 3 \text{ (passing)}$$

This short battery is suggested when time limitations exist.

Smith Speedball Tests (College Women).[34] Smith constructed three speedball tests for college women with relatively low validity using a

[33] Ruth E. Buchanan, "A Study of Achievement Tests in Speedball for High School Girls," Unpublished Master's Thesis, State University of Iowa, 1942.

[34] Gwen Smith, "Speedball Tests for College Women," Unpublished Study, Illinois State Normal University, 1947.

subjective criterion. The tests include (1) kick-up to self—subjects throws ball from behind a 7-foot restraining line and kicks it up to catch and repeats for 30 seconds, scored as successful kick-ups in six trials (validity .54, reliability .81); (2) wall pass—the number of throws from behind a 7-foot restraining line in four 15-second trials (validity .51, reliability .75); and (3) foot pass to wall—the ball is kicked from behind a 7-foot restraining line diagonally against wall and retrieved on the other side of a center 6-foot neutral zone marked off behind the restraining line, this procedure is repeated to alternate sides for 30 seconds. The score for test 3 is the total wall hits made by legal kicks in six trials (validity .30, reliability .46). Test 3 includes elements common to soccer also.

Crawford Speedball Test Battery (Women Physical Education Majors).[35] As part of a study to develop a soccer test for women physical education majors, Crawford constructed a battery of speedball skill tests which gave a multiple correlation of .81 with a judgment criterion. The tests include (1) dribbling and (2) foot passing and receiving, as described for the soccer test, and (3) lift to teammate (validity, .46; estimated reliability, .82). For test 3 the subject lifts the ball to a wall target consisting of two concentric squares (8- and 24-inch sides scored as 3 and 1 point values) with the bottom 2 feet above the floor. Three practice and five test trials are taken from a spot 6 feet from the wall on a line perpendicular to the right edge of the target, followed by the same number of trials from the same spot on the left target edge. The score is the sum of points for ten trials. T-scales were derived for the study group. The multiple regression equation was: 1.5 test $1 + 1.3$ test $2 +$ test $3 - 123$. Three other tests were studied: kick-up to self, as Buchanan test, poor validity and reliability; 15-second target wall pass; and punting.

Squash Racquets

While no scientifically constructed tests exist for squash racquets, DeWitt[36] suggests three for consideration. They are:

1. *Service.* Subject serves into the proper service court, which is divided into six scoring zones (see Fig. 13–3). Score is total points on five trials.
2. *Rally accuracy.* Subject serves ball that rebounds legally and then hits the ball to the target zones on the front wall, as shown

[35] Crawford, *loc. cit.*

[36] R. T. DeWitt, *Teaching Individual and Team Sports* (Englewood Cliffs, N.J.: Prentice-Hall, Inc.), pp. 334–36.

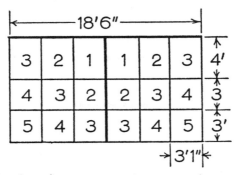

Fig. 13–3. Squash racquets service test scoring zones (floor).

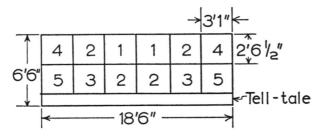

Fig. 13–4. Squash racquets rally accuracy scoring zones (front wall).

in Fig. 13–4. Score is total points on five trials. The teacher might consider a more controlled manner of initiating play.

3. *Rally speed.* Subject serves ball and then goes behind short line to play the ball for 1 minute. The number of legal front-wall hits constitutes the score.

The scoring values presented in the figures here represent one-half the value suggested by DeWitt, and in Fig. 13–4 the outside zones have been increased one point. Other suggested revisions for teacher consideration are (1) allow five trials into each service court, ten in all, on service test; and (2) specify a more definite manner of putting the ball into play for the rally accuracy test.

Swimming and Diving

While the literature contains evidence of considerable study and varied forms of suggested tests in swimming, the number of scientifically constructed tests remains meager. Also, few have undertaken to establish scale scores by which the value of a swimming performance might be judged. Certainly by its basic nature, swimming poses problems in constructing scoring tables that differ from those applicable to other activities. Hopefully this will afford a challenge, not a deterrent, to continued development of swimming tests. However, this fact does explain why the preponderance of tests have been empirically rather than scientifically devised to measure various levels of swimming ability.

A study of published material on swimming tests reveals general use of test items involving form, speed, endurance, safety skills (e.g., treading water), stunts, and lifesaving techniques. Parkhurst gave direction to the development of swimming tests through an article in which earlier tests were described briefly and categorized on the basis of two scoring schemes —one allowing for varying degrees of perfection in scoring (rating scale approach) and the second scoring only satisfactory performance.[37] Parkhurst then presented a definitive plan for grading as developed for women at the University of Texas, which lists the activities comprising a chart for beginner, intermediate, advanced, and advanced swimming and lifesaving levels. Each specified activity is assigned a difficulty rating expressed as the number of points to be awarded when the item is completed satisfactorily, such as jellyfish float for 15 seconds—5 points. The number of points scored on the achievement chart is used for grading purposes in accordance with established standards.

The instructional program of the American National Red Cross utilizes a definitive and empirically derived test of ability from beginning to advanced skill that has seen considerable usage in schools.[38] The three aquatic items of the original AAHPER Youth Fitness Test represent an appraisal of level of basic ability or fitness to handle oneself in water.[39]

As an early instigator of scientific development of swimming tests, Cureton undoubtedly laid much of the foundation for the scientifically oriented tests described below. His initial work, which led to the National YMCA Aquatic Tests, consisted of an array of 25 items correlated with the criterion of teacher judgment and reflected satisfactory reliability.[40] Cozens and his associates developed some speed swimming scales of secondary school girls and college women for freestyle, breast stroke, and racing back stroke at 20, 30, 40, 50, and 60 yards that are

[37] Mary G. Parkhurst, "Achievement Tests in Swimming," *Journal of Health and Physical Education*, V, No. 5 (May, 1934), 34.

[38] *Instructor's Manual: Swimming and Water Safety Courses* (rev. ed., Washington: The American National Red Cross, 1968).

[39] *AAHPER Youth Fitness Test Manual* (Washington: American Association for Health, Physical Education and Recreation, 1958).

[40] T. K. Cureton, *Standards for Testing Beginning Swimming* (New York: Association Press, 1939). Digested in *Research Quarterly*, X, No. 4 (December, 1939), 54.

of interest but of little value in view of the great strides made recently in instructional swimming programs.[41]

Hewitt High School Swimming Achievement Scales.[42] Hewitt constructed achievement scale scores for high school boys and girls based on tests given to 1,093 California students. The tests (with validity and reliability coefficients) are:

1. *50-yard crawl for time.* Subject uses a racing dive start; the time is recorded to the nearest tenth of a second (.65, .92).
2. *25-yard flutter kick for time with polo ball.* Start is made by a regulation push-off beginning from a position in the water with one hand on the gutter. Time to nearest tenth of a second is recorded when ball touches pool end (.60, .89).
3. *Glide and relaxation ability for 25 yards in three swimming styles.* To determine the minimum number of strokes to cover 25 yards. Only one leg action and one arm action allowed per stroke, and score is the number of strokes used plus one for the push-off.
   a) *Elementary back stroke.* Start is made in water by a regulation push-off in glide position with arms at side. Frog kick is used. Arms must remain in the water at all times and may be moved above the shoulders for the recovery phase (.88, .96).
   b) *Side stroke.* Start is made in water by a regulation push-off in glide position resting on under arm extended overhead. Both arms must remain in the water at all times (.94, .90).
   c) *Breast stroke.* Start is made in water by a regulation above-water push-off in glide position with arms extended overhead (.77, .93).

In lieu of an external criterion of swimming ability, the individual items were correlated with the criterion of total scores in all events to give the reported validity coefficients. The reference contains separate achievement scales for boys and girls. If a single best measure of high school swimming ability is desired, the side stroke is suggested in view of its .94 correlation with the total test (composite) score.

Hewitt College Swimming Achievement Scales (Men).[43] Hewitt worked out swimming achievement scales on tests given to over 4,000 college men, including the tests used for wartime scales [44] with the

---

[41] Cozens, Cubberley, and Neilson, *loc. cit.*

[42] Jack E. Hewitt, "Achievement Scales for High School Swimming," *Research Quarterly*, XX, No. 2 (May, 1949), 170.

[43] Jack E. Hewitt, "Swimming Achievement Scales for College Men," *Research Quarterly*, XIX, No. 4 (December, 1948), 282.

[44] Jack E. Hewitt, "Achievement Scales for Wartime Swimming," *Research Quarterly*, XIV, No. 4 (December, 1943), 391.

addition of 25- and 50-yard sprints. The tests (with validity and reliability coefficients) are:

1. *20- and 25-yard underwater swim.* Subject uses a regulation start,
   swims entire distance, and finishes underwater. Any style is acceptable. Score is recorded as time in tenths of seconds, but no
   score is given if any part of the body surfaces (.88, .94).
2. *15-minute endurance swim.* Swimmer uses regulation start and
   any style of swimming and turns. Each swimmer counts his own
   lengths, which are converted into yards for scoring; over half a
   length at finish is credited as a length. No score is given for
   swimming less than 15 minutes (.72, .89).
3. *25- and 50-yard sprint swims for the crawl* (.67, .90), *breast* (.54,
   .89), *and back* (.57, .91) *stroke.* Either 25- or 50-yard distance is
   selected. Subject uses a regulation start. Score is in tenths of
   seconds.
4. *50-yard glide relaxation ability for the elementary back* (.90, .95),
   side (.93, .91), *and breast* (.75, .92) *strokes.* Administered as a
   25-yard test for high school with no arm or leg action allowed on
   push-offs. Scored as number of push-offs plus the number of
   strokes for each event.

The composite score constituted the validity criterion. The 25- and
50-yard sprint tests in each stroke were given to the standard group with
resulting intercorrelations of .90 or above. For classifying students when
time is limited, a combination of the 25- or 50-yard crawl plus the three
gliding strokes is suggested, inasmuch as it correlated .87 with the
criterion of total score.

Cureton Test of Endurance in Speed Swimming.[45]   Cureton proposed
a test of endurance in speed swimming to disclose information as to the
relative perfection of a swimmer's speed and endurance condition. To
determine a swimmer's rating in a 20- or 25-yard pool the procedure is:
(1) record the time to sprint at full speed one lap, starting in the water
with feet on the wall and one hand grasping the gutter; (2) after at
least 15 minutes' rest, the swimmer is timed for 100 yards including time
for each lap, doing the first lap at full speed so as to be within $\frac{1}{5}$ of a
second of the trial lap time (subject may be stopped and tested again
when he can swim first lap in desired time); (3) compute the dropoff
times for each successive lap and note if these intermediate times gradually increase (if not, subject must repeat test since he did not "go the
limit"); (4) compute the dropoff index by subtracting the first lap time
from that for the fourth lap; (5) enter performance scale to derive percentile ranks for speed and endurance.

[45] T. K. Cureton, "A Test for Endurance in Speed Swimming," *Supplement to the
Research Quarterly,* VI, No. 2 (May, 1935), 106.

The performance scale includes both 20- and 25-yard pools. The time for the 100-yard swim can be predicted very closely for the 20-yard course from the formula:

Time (100 yards) = 5 (time 20-yard sprint) +

2.25 (dropoff index) + 5.5

The formula for the 25-yard pool (approximate, as derived from the above) is:

4 (time) + 2.6 (index) + 5.5

Reliability is satisfactory for speed (.99) and low for endurance (.77), but the test should prove satisfactory for secondary schools if students are motivated to their best performance.

Fox Swimming Power Test (College Women).[46]   An objective test of swimming power was developed by Fox for both side stroke and front crawl and appears applicable to back crawl, breast stroke, and elementary back stroke. The test consists of measuring the distance covered in five complete strokes and glides. To start, the subject assumes a proper floating position for the stroke involved with the ankle supported at malleoli level by a weighted rope held 1 foot below the surface and 2 feet from the pool end. The pool deck is marked by tape in 5-foot intervals from the starting line. The line is dropped for the start and when the sixth stroke is initiated the distance at the point of the malleoli is read to the nearest foot. T-scores were computed for the side stroke and crawl strokes with 97 college women. Face (content) validity was assumed, and reliability coefficients were reported as .95 for crawl and .97 for side stroke.

Rosentowieg revised the Fox test to obviate certain administrative shortcomings.[47] The revisions were: (1) use of a partner to support legs with forearms at the start; (2) distance was determined at the point of the shoulders; and (3) six arm stroke cycles were taken. The better of two trials constituted the score. Slightly lower reliability coefficients were reported—.89 for front crawl, .91 for side stroke (N = 184)—than for the original test.

Connor Swimming Skill Tests (Elementary School Children).[48]   Two swimming tests for elementary school boys and girls were proposed by

[46] Margaret G. Fox, "Swimming Power Test," *Research Quarterly*, XXVIII, No. 3 (October, 1957), 233. T-scores are also available in SR 3.
[47] Joel Rosentowieg, "A Revision of the Power Swimming Test," *Research Quarterly*, XXXIX, No. 3 (October, 1968), 818.
[48] Donald J. Connor, "A Comparison of Objective and Subjective Testing Methods in Selected Swimming Skills for Elementary School Children," Microcard Master's Thesis, Washington State University, 1962.

Connor; namely: (1) 50-yard prone swim—start with a push-off in the water; and (2) 50-yard combined swim—start with a push-off, swim 25 yards prone, turn over and swim 25 yards on the back. The tests and scoring methods for the different ages: *Girls*—5 to 9 years, test 1 for time or test 2 for stroke count, and 10 to 12 years, test 1 for time or stroke count; and *Boys*—5 to 9 years, test 1 for time, and 10 to 12 years, test 2 for stroke count.

Kilby Study of Stroke-Count Testing.[49]　In a study with college women (N = 148) Kilby found that the stroke-count method was a more valid measure of swimming ability for elementary back and side strokes with advanced swimmers (r's = .68–.78) than for those of intermediate ability using the criterion of ability rating. Reliability coefficients ranged from .71 to .80. Consideration of performance errors enhanced correlation with the validity criterion more for intermediate than for advanced swimmers.

Durrant Synchronized Swimming Rating.[50]　Durrant developed an analytical method of rating seven synchronized swimming stunts that proved consistent with both experienced and inexperienced judges. This method elicits performance rating in relation to correct execution of a stunt rather than by comparing subjects. For the study three experienced and three inexperienced judges rated 24 girls and women ranging from beginner to advanced levels in ability. The rating sheet for each stunt was divided into columns showing each component part and its point value. The part ratings (to tenth of a point, permitted) were totaled to give the score for that stunt. The correlations between judges' ratings were higher and showed less variation among judges for the four stunts with higher point values (r's = .75–.96) than for the other stunts (r's = .47–.94). The reference contains a table of point values for component movements of stunts and figures illustrating the component parts and their point values for each stunt.

Diving.　To date, only one scientifically devised diving test has been developed, as described below. For the most part, teachers use or adapt the competitive diving scoring procedure for class needs. According to NCAA rules,[51] a dive is judged on a scale from 0 to 10 using points and half-points as follows:

---

[49] E. J. Kilby, "An Objective Method of Evaluating Three Swimming Strokes," Microcard Doctoral Dissertation, University of Washington, 1956.

[50] Sue M. Durrant, "An Analytical Method of Rating Synchronized Swimming Stunts," *Research Quarterly*, XXXV, No. 2 (May, 1964), 126.

[51] Vic Gustafson (ed.), *Official Collegiate-Scholastic Swimming Guide*, 1973 (Phoenix: National Collegiate Athletic Association, 1972).

Excellent .... 9–10 points
Very good .... 8–8.5 points
Good .... 7–7.5 points
Satisfactory .... 5–6.5 points
Deficient .... 3–4.5 points
Unsatisfactory .... .5–2.5 points
Completely failed .... 0 points

In competitive scoring, each dive is assigned a difficulty rating, ranging from 1.2 to 3.0, by which the judges' award is multiplied to derive the score for a given dive. For teacher use, a 0 to 5 rating may be used, preferably in conjunction with a list of elements of a good dive.

As a matter of resource interest herein, Foster conducted a study utilizing a part method of judging diving wherein each judge was assigned to rate one of three parts, viz.: approach and take-off; height and mechanics of the dive; or alignment and entry.[52] This method was compared to the conventional procedure in collegiate dual and championship meets, both men and women. The part method gave very close relative ranking, higher total scores, and greater range of scores. Additionally, the part method was found to be valuable both as a diagnostic teaching tool and as an educational tool for training officials.

Bennett Diving Test.[53] To meet the need for a test of diving ability for a beginning class, Bennett developed a test of more than 50 items ranging from simple stunts to difficult dives, arranged empirically. The final score for the test is the number of items passed according to the standards described for each item. An unlimited number of trials is allowed for each item, and the subject need not pass an item before going to the next. The test was established on the basis of 26 cases. A validity coefficient of .94 was obtained with the criterion of diving points scored on eight dives with three judges according to competitive rules at the end of the semester. In addition to being scientifically authentic —reliability .90 (estimated from split-halves), objectivity .93—this test appears to have value as a teaching progression check list.

Table Tennis

Mott-Lockhart Table Tennis Backboard Test (College Women).[54] A table tennis test was constructed by Mott and Lockhart using a center-

[52] John T. Foster, "Alternate Procedures for Judging and Scoring Competitive Diving," Microcard Master's Thesis, State University of Iowa, 1956.

[53] L. M. Bennett, "Diving Ability on the Springboard," *Research Quarterly*, XIII, No. 1 (March, 1942), 109.

[54] J. A. Mott and Aileene Lockhart, "Table Tennis Backboard Test," *Journal of Health and Physical Education*, XVII, No. 9 (November, 1946), 550. T-scales are also available in SR 1, 2 and 3.

hinged table with one-half of the table supported vertically at right angles to the remaining test half of the table. A net line (6 inches high) is drawn on the backboard, and a small box holding two balls is attached to the side of the table. The test consists of dropping a ball to the table upon signal and then rallying it with the paddle against the vertical surface for 30 seconds. A hit does not count if the ball is volleyed, the player's free hand is placed on the table in making or recovering from the play, or the ball strikes the backboard below the chalk net line. Any number of bounces on the horizontal surface are permitted; and when control of a ball is lost, another ball is put into play immediately. The test score is the best number of legal backboard hits in three trials, given with a short rest intervening. A practice period is recommended. The reference contains T-scores for college women. The reported coefficients are .84 for validity and .90 for reliability. Purportedly the test has a threefold use: practice and motivating device, indicate achievement, and classify tournament players. Obviously, the test does not afford analysis of the strokes and game elements.

Tennis

As the result of a study of the elements in skillful tennis and possible tests, Beall contributed to the development of such tests by concluding that (1) to measure tennis coordination, a test must be based on the specific elements comprising the various strokes, not general coordination; and (2) the quality of accurate knowledge of strokes can be measured.[55] In reporting available tests, the two tests that first received recognition are presented at the outset along with a study comparing the two.

Dyer Backboard Test (College Women).[56] A test of tennis ability was proposed by Dyer entailing a backboard or wall about 10 feet high and 15 feet wide. A net line is drawn, 3 inches wide, across the backboard with the top edge 3 feet from the floor. For the test, the subject stands behind a restraining line 5 feet from the wall and upon signal puts the ball into play by bouncing it on the floor and hitting it with any stroke. The ball is stroked to the wall repeatedly for 30 seconds. It may bounce any number of times on the floor or be volleyed. The subject begins the test holding two balls, and additional balls are placed in

[55] Elizabeth Beall, "Essential Qualities in Certain Aspects of Physical Education with Ways of Measuring and Developing the Same," *American Physical Education Review*, XXXIII, No. 10 (December, 1928), 648.

[56] Joanna T. Dyer, "The Backboard Test of Tennis Ability," *Supplement to the Research Quarterly*, VI, No. 1 (March, 1935), 63; and "Revision of Backboard Test of Tennis Ability," *Research Quarterly*, IX, No. 1 (March, 1938), 25. Scoring table is also available in SR 3.

a box on the restraining line at the side. The score is the total number of legal hits (above net line and stroked from behind restraining line) made in three trials. Scoring tables were prepared (1938) by Dyer for college women, and Miller published T-scores and percentile norms for women physical education major students.[57] Validity correlation of .92 was obtained with a criterion of tournament standings, and satisfactory reliability was reported. Specific skills are not measured by this test.

Broer-Miller Forehand-Backhand Test (College Women).[58] Broer and Miller devised a test of tennis ability with college women utilizing a regulation court and forehand and backhand strokes. The court markings, as shown in Fig. 13–5, consist of chalk lines and numbers indicating

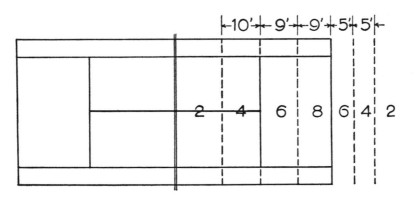

Fig. 13–5. Court markings for Broer-Miller Forehand-Backhand Drive Test.

the point value for each zone. A rope is stretched across the court 4 feet directly above the top of the net. For the test the subject stands behind the baseline on the unmarked side; bounces the ball; and hits it between net and rope, aiming for the back 9 feet of the opposite court. Fourteen trials are given with both forehand and backhand strokes. A let ball is taken over, but a ball missed on the bounce constitutes a trial. Balls that go over the rope are scored as half the zone value, and line balls score the higher value. Scoring tables are not available. The results based on small groups yielded validity coefficients of .85 for the intermediate group and .61 for beginners with the criterion of judges'

[57] Wilma K. Miller, "Achievement Levels in Tennis Knowledge and Skill for Women Physical Education Students," *Research Quarterly*, XXIV, No. 1 (March, 1953), 81.

[58] Marion R. Broer and Donna M. Miller, "Achievement Tests for Beginning and Intermediate Tennis," *Research Quarterly*, XXI, No. 3 (October, 1950), 303.

rating. Reliability coefficients of .80 were reported for both groups. The test authors suggest further study in light of its promise as a practical and useful objective grading device as well as a means of classifying.

Fox Study of Dyer and Broer-Miller Tests.[59] A subjective scheme for rating tennis performance was devised at the University of Washington for use at the end of a beginners' course in conjunction with the Dyer and Broer-Miller Tests. Four judges rated all players in a doubles match at the same time, utilizing this scheme that included serving ability as well as forehand and backhand drives. The findings reveal that:

1. Dyer and Broer-Miller Tests have relatively low correlation, indicating they do not measure the same thing.
2. Correlation with rating (.79) indicates that, unlike the Dyer Test, the Broer-Miller Test can be used with a fair degree of confidence (.79) as a measure of beginners' ability to use basic strokes and serve in a game situation when backboard practice was included in the course.
3. An insignificant improvement in correlation (.81) was noted when Dyer and Broer-Miller Tests were combined and correlated with ratings.
4. Since neither the Dyer nor the Broer-Miller Test measures serving ability as included in the judges' rating, the validity coefficient was accordingly lower. This suggests the need for a supplemental scientifically authentic test of serving ability to result in a true and inclusive measure of tennis ability.

Ronning Wall Test (College Men).[60] Ronning studied wall tests consisting of the sum of three trials of 30- and 60-seconds each with the restraining line at distances of 5, 15, 25, and 35 feet. Two study groups were involved; 42 college men enrolled in a beginner's class in the physical education service program, and 8 varsity players. The best test combination for both groups proved to be 60-second trials with the 35-foot restraining line. Validity coefficients of .90 and .97 were obtained with tournament ranking for the class group and coach's ranking with the varsity players, respectively. Divergent group validity was also established. A reliability coefficient of .92 was derived for the class group.

Hewitt Revision of the Dyer Test (College).[61] Hewitt revised the Dyer Test by: moving the restraining line behind which all shots are

[59] Katharine Fox, "A Study of the Validity of the Dyer Backboard Test and the Broer-Miller Forehand-Backhand Test for Beginning Tennis Players," *Research Quarterly*, XXIV, No. 1 (March, 1953), 1.

[60] W. E. Ronning, "Wall Tests for Evaluating Tennis Ability," Microcard Master's Thesis, State College of Washington, 1959.

[61] Jack E. Hewitt, "Revision of the Dyer Backboard Tennis Test," *Research Quarterly*, XXXVI, No. 2 (May, 1965), 153.

made to 20 feet from the wall; using a serve to put the ball into play; begin timing each 30-second trial when the first serve strikes the wall; and using the mean of three trials as the score. A 2-minute warm-up period on an auxiliary wall was allowed. With the criterion of ability ranking four beginners' groups yielded correlation coefficients ranging from .12 to .43 for the original Dyer Test and from .68 to .73 for the Hewitt revision. Two advanced groups yielded validity coefficients of .84 and .89 with ability ranking. Reliability coefficients of .82 for beginners and .93 for advanced players were obtained.

Hewitt Tennis Achievement Test (College).[62]   To evaluate three basic tennis skills at the university level Hewitt constructed tests of: (1) forehand drive; (2) backhand drive; (3) service placement; and (4) speed of service. For tests 1 and 2 the testee stands at the center of the baseline in readiness to receive balls hit by the instructor across the net from the intersection of the center and service lines. After five practice trials, 10 trials are taken with each stroke; the subject choosing any ten balls to return. The ball is driven across the net where the backcourt is zoned into four zones 4½ feet deep beginning at the baseline and assigned point values of 5, 4, 3, and 2; the forecourt scores 1 point. Balls passing over a restraining rope stretched 7 feet above the net are given one-half value. All net balls are repeated. The court layout for tests 3 and 4 is shown in Fig. 13–6. Test 3 consists of ten good serves below the restraining rope and into the right service court. Net balls are repeated. For test 4 each of the ten good serve placements in test 3 is scored as the zone into which the second bounce falls. This scheme was adopted after experimentation indicated that the distance a served ball bounces upon hitting the service court is a good indicator of its speed.

Reliability coefficients for tests 1 to 4 were .75, .78, .94, and .84. Validity coefficients ranged from .52 to .93 for beginner, advanced, and varisity groups with the criterion of ability ranking. Achievement norms are reported for each of the groups. These respective groups were tested on the Hewitt revision of the Dyer test with resulting validity coefficients of .73, .84, and .87. Hewitt concluded that the revised Dyer test is probably the best test (especially for non-beginners), because of administrative feasibility. However, the most valid of the achievement tests were test 3 for varsity players (.93) and test 4 for beginners (.89).

Hewitt Classification Tests (College).[63]   Hewitt devised two simple tennis tests for gross classification of university students into ability

---

[62] Jack E. Hewitt, "Hewitt's Tennis Achievement Test," *Research Quarterly,* XXXVII, No. 2 (May, 1966), 231.

[63] Jack E. Hewitt, "Classification Tests in Tennis," *Research Quarterly,* XXXIX, No. 3 (October, 1968), 552.

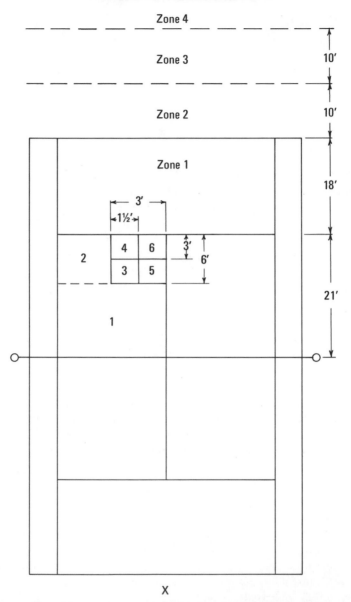

Fig. 13–6. Court markings for Hewitt service tests.

groups. The tests may be descriptively termed (1) court bounce and (2) air volley. For test 1 the subject bounces a tennis ball on the court to a height of hip level or above with forehand grip. For test 2 the subject hits the ball to or above shoulder level with backhand grip and subsequently alternates forehand and backhand in keeping the ball in the air; the racket must be kept below shoulder level and the ball must reach at least shoulder level to score. For both tests a 15-second practice is allowed, and the best number of legal hits in three 30-second trials constitutes the score. Trials are initiated by hitting the ball out of the hand. Reliability of test 1 was computed as .88; test 2, .83 (N = 114). Validity coefficients with the criterion tournament ranking were derived for nine different groups varying in size from 9 to 16 students and ranged from .56 to .88 for test 1 and from .23 to .88 for test 2. The reference contains ability scales for these tests and also for the Dyer test and the Hewitt revision of the Dyer test. Evidence supports the preferential use of the wall test.

Kemp-Vincent Rally Test (College).[64] Kemp and Vincent constructed a rally test with university students to overcome criticisms of available tests which include: failure to simulate game conditions, and necessitate special equipment or markings and considerable time for administration. For this test two players of similar ability take opposing positions on a singles court. Upon signal one testee bounces and puts a ball into play with a courtesy stroke from behind the baseline. The players keep the ball in play for 3 minutes. If a ball is hit into the net, or otherwise goes out of play, another ball is put into play as initially. In scoring the hits for both players are totaled, disregarding the outcome of the hit and including courtesy strokes. From this figure the number of errors committed by each player is subtracted to find the final rally score for each testee. Errors involve failure to legally hit the ball into the opposite singles area or to put a new ball into play properly from behind the baseline. Out-of-bounds balls may be played at the discretion of the testee to save time. A trial test period is given for orientation.

Using the validity criterion of tournament ranking, coefficients of .84 and .93 were obtained for 24 men and women in a beginners instructional class and 30 in an intermediate level class, respectively. Reliability coefficients were .86 and .90 for beginners and intermediate players. A correlation of .80 was derived with the Iowa Modification of the Dyer Test (27½-foot restraining line) for 362 men and women ranging from beginner to advanced levels of ability. As an evaluative note, the teacher should recognize the contingency of test performance upon the ability of the playing partner.

Tennis Tests of Achievement (College Men).[65] DiGennaro constructed the Tennis Test of Achievement (TTA) for novice tennis players

[64] Joanne Kemp and M. F. Vincent, "Kemp-Vincent Rally Test of Tennis Skill," *Research Quarterly*, XXXIX, No. 4 (December, 1968), 1000.

[65] Joseph DiGennaro, "Construction of Forehand Drive, Backhand Drive, and Service Tennis Tests," *Research Quarterly*, XL, No. 3 (October, 1969), 496.

based on 64 college men in a beginning tennis course. The tests are: (1) forehand drive; (2) backhand drive; and (3) service test. Five practice and 20 test trials are allowed for each test. To administer the tests, in addition to the court markings shown in Fig. 13–7, a restraining rope is

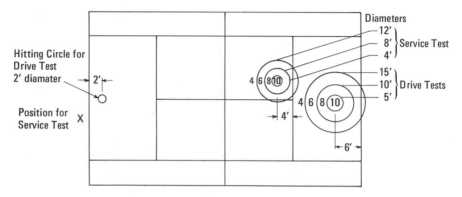

Fig. 13–7. TTA testing station layout.

stretched 3 feet above the net, and a scorer stands 2 feet behind the target area. For tests 1 and 2 the subject stands behind the hitting circle, facing the net with the racket held in front. The tester drops a tennis ball into the circle from about 6 feet above it. After it bounces, the subject attempts to drive the ball over the net and under the restraining rope, aiming for the center of the drive target. Balls landing outside the circular target but within the backcourt count 4 points; those landing in the forecourt, 2 points. For test 3, legal overhead serves are executed from the marked position on the baseline, 4 feet to the right of the center-line. The score for each test is the sum of 10 trials, and balls that do not go beneath the restraining rope score half of the value of the area in which they hit.

Content validity was established, and reliability coefficients of .67, .66, and .80 were obtained for tests 1, 2, and 3. Additionally as an aspect of validity, using the criterion of the number of successful drives and serves during a round robin tournament, correlation coefficients of .40, .78, and .66 were obtained for the respective tests. Drive tests subsequently administered with a ball-boy machine resulted in scores that correlated .48 for forehand and .60 for backhand drives. Percentile norms are reported for the study group.

Track and Field

Extensive use has been made of track and field events as items of tests of motor fitness, general qualities of motor performance, and certain skill areas. Norms are available for interpreting many of these individual test items, and several of the available achievement scales contain a number of track and field events. However, concerted effort has not been directed to the development of a battery of track and field tests.

UCLA Fall Decathlon (College Men).[66] A fall decathlon for college track squads was developed at UCLA to stimulate all-round competition and evaluate scientifically individual abilities. The decathlon was designed for administering in 3 days as follows: (1) 75-yard dash, 12-pound shot-put, standing hop, step and jump, and 330-yard run; (2) 120-yard low hurdles, running high jump, and 660-yard run; and (3) running broad jump, discus throw, and 1,320-yard run. The pole vault was eliminated because of the danger involved for those unfamiliar with the event; and the standing hop, step, and jump was substituted. The scoring scheme, based on a 1,000 point maximum, was constructed by using the increase increment principle. Equivalent scoring tables found in the reference were derived for each event from the performance records of two previous decathlons and of men in track and field classes over a period of years and from the results of five intramural track meets.

Volleyball

All of the available tests of volleyball skill have one thing in common, since they employ some version of the wall volley (see Appendix B), which has acceptably high validity and reliability. Considerable study has been directed to testing in this sport, especially for girls and women.

French-Cooper Volleyball Test (High School Girls).[67] As an inclusive test of skill elements in volleyball, French and Cooper devised four items—repeated volleys, serving, set-up and pass, and recovery from the net. The best combination of measures for girls, grades nine to twelve, was repeated volleys and serving test items, yielding a validity coefficient of .81 with ability rating, item intercorrelation of .39, and satisfactory reliability. Only these two items are described below, inasmuch as the others utilize the now illegal practice of setting the ball up to oneself.

1. *Repeated volleys.* Subject tosses a volleyball underhand to a wall and volleys it for 15 seconds from behind a 3-foot restraining line and above a net line 7½ feet from the floor. The score is the total number of legal wall hits made in the best five of ten trials (validity–.72, reliability–.78).

2. *Serving.* Subject attempts ten legal serves. Let serves do not

[66] F. W. Cozens, "A Fall Decathlon for Track Squads," *Research Quarterly,* IX, No. 2 (May, 1938), 3.

[67] E. L. French and B. I. Cooper, "Achievement Tests in Volleyball for High School Girls," *Research Quarterly,* VIII, No. 2 (May, 1937), 150.

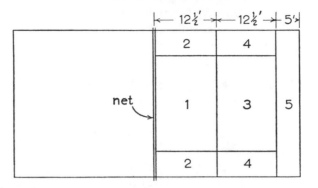

Fig. 13–8. Court markings for French-Cooper Serve Test.

count and are repeated. Two practice trials are given. Score consists of the total values hit in ten trials, as shown in Fig. 13–8. Line balls score the higher value, validity–.63, reliability–.68).

Scott and French present T-scales for these tests.[68] For repeated volleys, scales are also given for the best of three trials for high school and the best three of five trials for college women.

Russell-Lange Volleyball Test (Junior High School Girls).[69] The French-Cooper Test was adapted to grades seven to nine by Russell and Lange. The repeated volleys test was scored as the best number of legal volleys in three 30-second trials. The serving test was scored as the best of two trials of ten serves each. Scoring tables appear in the reference, and the sum of the scaled scores for both tests constitutes a measure of volleyball playing ability. Reliability of .87 and .92 for the respective tests and combined validity of .77 were reported.

Lamp Volleyball Test (Junior High School).[70] A four-item volleyball test for junior high school boys and girls was devised by Lamp with scientific authenticity comparable to the other tests. The items appear useful for practice of game elements. Figure 13–9 illustrates the court markings and test position. Jumping standards (x) with a crossbar or rope at a height of 7 feet 6 inches are placed on the 6-foot line. The test items include:

1. *Serve.* Subject serves ball with underhand motion and open hand into left-hand court, scoring 2 or 1 points if successful.

[68] Scott and French, *op. cit.*, pp. 232–33.
[69] Naomi Russell and Elizabeth Lange, "Achievement Tests in Volleyball for Junior High School Girls," *Research Quarterly*, XI, No. 4 (December, 1940), 33. Norms are available in SR 1, 2, 3 and 6.
[70] Nancy A. Lamp, "Volleyball Skills of Junior High School Students as a Function of Physical Size and Maturity," *Research Quarterly*, XXV, No. 2 (May, 1954), 189.

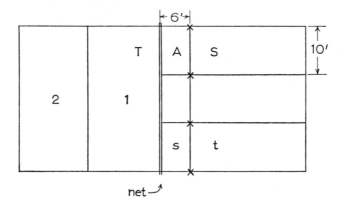

Fig. 13–9. Court markings and positions for Lamp Test.

2. *Setup.* Tester (T) tosses ball over net and crossbar to subject (S), who attempts to set it up over crossbar into area A (2 points). Balls hitting lines or crossbar score 1 point.
3. *Net pass.* Tester (t) tosses ball over crossbar to subject (s) with back to net, who attempts to pass it over the net.
4. *15-second volley.* 3-foot restraining line and 7-foot 6-inch net line.

Ten trials are scored for items 1 to 3, and one trial for item 4. Scoring tables are not available.

Wisconsin Volleyball Test (College Women).[71]   A test consisting of serving and volley items for women was developed at the University of Wisconsin. For the service test, the subject serves 15 balls to a specially designed target placed in the far left corner of the service court and 15 balls to the target when placed in the right corner. The target consists of four concentric squares, 16-, 12-, 8- and 4-foot, placed so that two sides of the 8-foot square coincide with the end and side lines of the court. The target areas are scored as 7, 6, 5, and 4 points; and 2 points are given for an in-bounds serve not hitting the target and 1 point for an out-of-bounds serve. A wire may be placed 3½ feet above the net, and balls passing beneath it score an additional point. This wire can be eliminated without affecting the reliability and validity. In the volley test, the subject must stand behind a 6-foot line only when tossing the ball into play. The score is the number of legal wall hits in three 30-second trials. A tin strip 2 inches wide and 12 feet long is advocated for placement on the wall, with the lower edge 7½ feet from the floor to indicate the legality of borderline hits. Coefficients of .79 and .51 with ability rating and .84

[71] Gladys Bassett, Ruth Glassow, and Mabel Locke, "Studies in Testing Volleyball Skills," *Research Quarterly*, VIII, No. 4 (December, 1937), 61.

and .89 for reliability were reported for the respective tests. Norms are not available. The serving test alone suffices to predict a player's ability in the game of volleyball.

Liba-Stauff Volleyball Pass Test (College Women and Junior High School Girls).[72] Liba and Stauff devised a test to assess ability to execute a volleyball chest pass based on a preferred height and distance of 15 and 20 feet for college women and 13 and 12 feet for junior high school girls. The test task consists of attempting to make a chest pass over two ropes onto a target strip. The score for each trial is derived by multiplying the height score by the distance score. A table of reliability estimates was prepared for varying trials on 1 to 4 days, and content validity was claimed.

Brady Volleyball Test (College Men).[73] As a test of volleyball skill for college men, Brady devised a repeated volley test using a target formed on a smooth wall by a horizontal chalk line 5 feet long and 11½ feet from the floor with vertical lines extending upward toward the ceiling at either end. The number of legal wall hits within the target in 1 minute constitutes the test score. Validity established with subjective judgment was .86; reliability was .93. Brady stated that the test is not as accurate with individuals below college level or those with very inferior ability. When used to measure improvement, he suggests that the difference between scores made on the first and last test be added to the last test score.

Variations of Repeated Volleys. A variation of the wall volley with 7½-foot net-line and 6-foot restraining line was developed by Crogen for high school girls in which the player volleys repeatedly for 10 (25 or 30) hits; it is scored by subtracting the number of fouls from the number of volleys made.[74] Reported reliability is .70, .74, and .77 for 10, 25, and 30 hits, respectively. Validity is based upon ability to win a round-robin tournament of repeated volleys. Scores were noted to improve with practice and to reflect playing experience.

For college women, Mohr and Haverstick presented evidence of the apparent superiority of a 7-foot restraining line over lines 3 or 5 feet from the wall in the repeated volleys test (7½-foot net-line).[75] Height of the player was found to be related to volley performance at the 3-foot line

[72] Marie R. Liba and M. R. Stauff, "A Test for the Volleyball Pass." *Research Quarterly*, XXXIV, No. 1 (March, 1963), 56.

[73] G. F. Brady, "Preliminary Investigations of Volleyball Playing Ability," *Research Quarterly*, XVI, No. 1 (March, 1945), 14.

[74] Corinne Crogen, "Volleyball Classification Tests," *The Physical Educator*, IV, No. 3 (October, 1943), 34.

[75] Dorothy P. Mohr and M. J. Haverstick, "Repeated Volley Tests for Women's Volleyball," *Research Quarterly*, XXVI, No. 2 (May, 1955), 179; and "Relationship Between Height, Jumping Ability, and Agility to Volleyball Skill," XXVII, No. 1 (March, 1956), 74.

but not at 7 feet. Reliability of volleys was almost the same at 3-, 5-, and 7-foot lines—.81, .81, and .83. The evidence disclosed suggests that the repeated volleys test should consist of three trials at the 7-foot line, using a regulation net line on the wall; and if time is limited, either two trials at the 7-foot or one trial each at the 5- and 7-foot lines should be used.

In a similar study with 136 high school girls, Camp also found the 7-foot line preferable.[76] Coefficients for 3-, 5- and 7-foot restraining lines were .92, .89 and .88 for reliability, and .60, .66 and .66 with judges' ratings. A slight relationship between height and test scores was found (r's $= .32-.39$) with the 7-foot line being the least.

Clifton experimented with three 30-second trials and restraining lines at 5 and 7 feet with college women (N $= 45$) and found that the best coefficients of validity (.70) and reliability (.83) were obtained using the sum of legal volleys made on or above the 7½-foot wall line from behind the 7-foot restraining line in two trials.[77] A rest interval of at least 2 minutes was allowed between trials.

Cunningham and Garrison eliminated the restraining line to better approximate a game situation and constructed a high wall volley test for college women (N $= 111$) consisting of the better of two 30-second trials using a wall target 3 feet wide and 10 feet above the floor.[78] The small target area requires accurate placement of the volley. Coefficients of .87 for reliability and .72 for validity with judges' ratings were derived. This validity was significantly greater than that determined for the Liba-Stauff Pass Test (.60) with the same study group.

The Brady test was adapted by Kronqvist and Brumbach for high school boys (N $= 71$) by placing the 5-foot wall line 11 feet above the floor and scoring the best two of three 20-second trials.[79] One practice-trial and at least a 30-second rest between trials were allowed. Coefficients of .77 with ability rating and .82 for reliability were obtained.

AAHPER Volleyball Test (Boys and Girls).[80] The AAHPER test for volleyball is comprised of the following items for boys and girls:

1. *Volleying.* Score is the number of legal volleys (maximum of 50) executed in 1 minute to a target line 5 feet long and 11 feet above the floor with a 4-foot vertical line extending upward at each end.

[76] Billie A. Camp, "The Reliability and Validity of a Single-Hit Repeated Volleys Test in Volleyball and the Relationship of Height to Performance on the Test," Microcard Master's Thesis, University of Colorado, 1963.

[77] Marguerite Clifton, "Single Hit Volley Test for Women's Volleyball," *Research Quarterly*, XXXIII, No. 2 (May, 1962), 208.

[78] Phyllis Cunningham and Joan Garrison, "High Wall Volley Test for Women's Volleyball," *Research Quarterly*, XXXIX, No. 3 (October, 1968), 486.

[79] R. A. Kronqvist and W. B. Brumbach, "A Modification of the Brady Volleyball Skill Test for High School Boys," *Research Quarterly*, XXXIX, No. 1 (March, 1968), 116.

[80] *Skills Test Manual: Volleyball for Boys and Girls* (Washington: American Association for Health, Physical Education and Recreation, 1969).

2. *Serving.* Ten legal serves are taken to a court marked as shown in Figure 13-10. Net balls count as trials but do not score. For subjects under age 12 a 20-foot serving line is used.

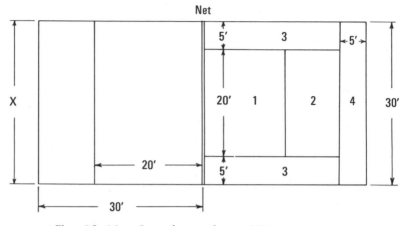

Fig. 13—10. Court layout for AAHPER serving test.

3. *Passing.* Subject (S) stands as shown in Figure 13-11 and receives a high throw from test assistant (T) and passes the ball over the 8-foot high rope onto the target area, alternating trials to the right and left. Twenty trials are taken with one point scored for each pass that goes over (without touching) the rope and lands directly on any part of the target area.

4. *Set-Up.* Subject (S) stands on the court layout where shown in Figure 13-12 and receives a high throw from test assistant (T) and executes a set-up so that it goes over the rope onto the target area without touching the rope or net. Ten trials are taken to the right and 10 to the left, with each successful trial scoring one point.

Unlike the other AAHPER tests, the directions do not mention practice trials. The teacher will note the similarity in the task for items 3 and 4, consequently, item intercorrelation would appear desirable to afford justification for utilizing both items. In critique, attention is drawn to shortcomings of the volleying item both in terms of extended duration of trial and the stipulation of a maximum, as noted under specific considerations.

SPECIFIC CONSIDERATIONS

Intelligent selection, construction and administration of sports skills tests necessitates an understanding of the important characteristics that

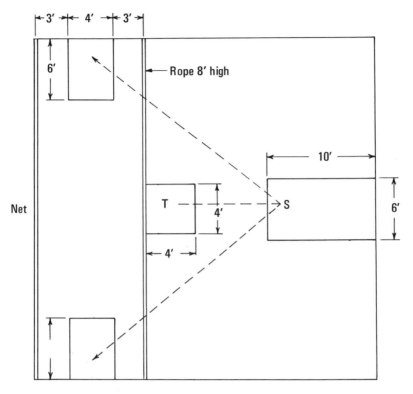

Fig. 13–11. Court layout for AAHPER passing test.

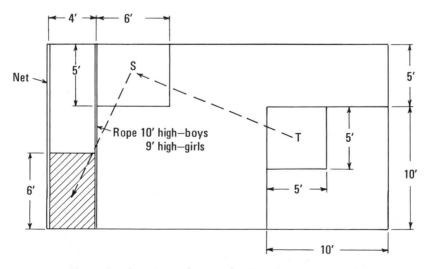

Fig. 13–12. Court layout for AAHPER set-up test.

are peculiar to this area of measurement and the particular sport activity, as well as the specific application of the general test considerations to physical performance tests. In addition to cognizance of these pertinent considerations discussed in Chapters 3, 4 and 6, the teacher should pay heed to the specific concerns for tests of motor fitness and general qualities of motor performance in the quest for factors relevant to sport skill areas. The following specific considerations for sports skills tests include those applicable to two or more different sport skill areas as well as those peculiar to one area.

1. *Test scope.* Scope encompasses breadth and depth. The test purposes determine the number of items for inclusion. For classification or as an indicant of overall achievement, one or two items may suffice, whereas performance on various skill components is important when definitive analysis and diagnosis of learning difficulty and achievement is desired. The test should reflect appropriate sampling of content (sport skills) both in terms of what to and what not to include. Overemphasis on some skills and omission of important other ones should be avoided. The Borleske Touch Football Test illustrates this problem, wherein the items involve only ball handling skills, no other game aspects. Another prevalent oversight is failure to ascertain the intercorrelation of test items in a test to insure that complemental information is maximized and supplemental minimized.

2. *Test item content contamination.* Except as noted below, the teacher should avoid including two or more different skills in a test item whereby the eventual score becomes a conglomerate that defies interpretation and analysis as to which aspect may require more instruction and practice. For example, a poor score on a dribble and shoot test in basketball may be attributable to poor ability in either dribbling or shooting, or both. This is not to infer that combined speed and accuracy are not desirable in test items, such as softball throw or basketball shoot, for such a combination reflects the reality of the skills in actual use. Conglomerate (or multi-skill) tests may be useful as an overall indicant of ability in some instances. Examples of this type are the dribble-dodge-circular tackle-drive item and the Strait "continuous circuit" test in field hockey.

3. *Performance as a validity criterion.* The actual validity of many skill tests for which the criterion of ability rating is used remains questionable. This problem can be obviated by the use of game statistics (such as batting averages, fielding averages, or shooting percentages) as the criterion where appropriate. In reality these statistics are easier to obtain in many instances than competent judging, and they eliminate the time and various diffifficulties entailed in the rating procedure.

4. *Multi-trial tests.* When more than one trial is given, the teacher is faced with the question whether to use the sum (or mean) of trials as the score or the best score obtained in any of the allowed trials. While sometimes the desired test information or necessary computation suggest the latter, generally better reliability results when the sum or mean of trials is used, as substantiated previously in Chapter 4. Using the sum of legal wall hits for all trials in a wall pass or volley for skill test in basketball, soccer, tennis, or volleyball illustrates the recommended procedure. As indicated, exceptions may be warranted in instances such as when the teacher prefers to know the maximum achievement each testee can attain for one of two or more trials on a wall pass or volley, or when time to the nearest tenth of a second is the score, posing a computational problem. Another concern to be resolved with multi-trial items is the provision of adequate rest between trials that involve more than 20 seconds in duration, including volley or throw items. To illustrate, based on the study of softball items cited earlier, Cale advocated a minimum interval of two minutes.

5. *Testing set-up.* The use of apparatus and markings in testing set-ups presents a difficult problem, namely, provide a setting to judge performance objectively and yet avoid including performance cues or facilitators that assist the testee in approximating the desired performance. As described in the discussion of suggestions for test administration and scoring in Chapter 6, the lesser skilled individuals are benefited particularly by the presence of a guide which does not exist in the game context. The use of rope stretched at a specified height over a playing court illustrates this concern. A test asistant can be positioned with sighting points to judge the height variable in such items, to cite one means of overcoming this limitation.

6. *Undesirable test characteristics.* Three concerns represent prevalent limitations in available sports skill tests that should be avoided. First, trials of volleying or throwing in excess of 20 or 30 seconds in duration (depending upon age level) are contraindicated. Beyond this time, muscular and cardiovascular endurance (physical condition) begin to exert an effect, and a "pure" measure of skill is no longer assured. The volleying item in the AAHPER volleyball test (one-minute trial) exemplifies an item that entails more than volleying ability per se, but the testee's capability for prolonged activity as well. This test also illustrates the second concern, wherein a maximum of 50 is scored. The imposition of a maximum on performance prevents gaining the complete picture of performance capability and knowledge of the actual limits of exceptional attainment. While admittedly not many testees will exceed the maximum for this particular test, the need for it is unwarranted with a specific time limitation. The principle of test design whereby

all testees are able to register their performance on the scale should be followed. Third, relatively few of the available skill tests present item scores of the type that are comparable for different skills in a profile context and combinable to afford a composite test score. Accordingly, the teacher should plan to develop suitable scale scores necessary for skill tests that are selected or constructed.

7. *Rebounding tests.* Considerable use is made of ball rebounding in tests for many sports activities. The teacher should recognize the possible need to adjust the distance of the restraining line from the wall and/or the height of the wall target line, when applicable, for different walls. This pertains to every testing situation, since variation in wall surface, structure and composition can account for appreciable differences in rebound distance.

8. *Swimming strokes-for-distance tests.* More accurate scoring is possible when the distance covered by a specified number of strokes is measured, as compared to determining the number of strokes to cover a specified distance. Obviously, distance can be measured more readily and precisely than a swimming stroke can be fractionated.

RESOLVING THE ILLUSTRATIVE PROBLEM

Critical analysis of the sports skill tests described herein relative to the particular needs of a teaching situation discloses the scarcity of appropriate tests in many areas. Nevertheless, much valuable resource information is contained in these tests, either as certain test items that may be used individually as well as in conjunction with other teacher selected items or as items that may be revised to render them suitable. The teacher should realize the generally existing need to establish norms for the local situation, since in many instances norms do not exist for the level concerned or are not suitable due to "out-of-dateness" or other reasons. The value of reviewing the available tests for resource purposes in test construction appears obvious. Not only does such review suggest types of test items, but it also affords evidence of the efficacy of many items.

A serious drawback in the development and refinement of suitable tests, especially in "dearth" areas (e.g., riding, skiing) has been the failure of teachers to disseminate many of the findings of experimentation in skill testing. While graduate research studies constitute an important source of test development, an invaluable resource exists in the vast amount of information accruing from "on the job" teacher experimentation. The tremendous need is to encourage teachers to share their experience and findings and for the profession to afford feasible and ready means of such dissemination.

Basic to determining the suitability of a specific skill test looms the matter of intended purpose for the test—is it to provide a general indicant of present ability, such as for classifying, or is it to afford a more inclusive and definitive picture of ability to measure achievement? A number of the tests presented may serve admirably as an indicant of ability prior to a unit of instruction but indicate little, if anything, relative to an objective measure of achievement upon completion of the unit. Perhaps the teacher would like to use the same test before and after. And taking this one step further, the teacher may wish to have the test consist of items involving game elements that can be practiced by themselves to improve game skill during the unit of instruction, as the AAHPER tests are intended.

In resolving the illustrative problem in Chapter 7 concerning the proposed approach in organizing a junior high school testing program in physical education, it was decided to include first skill tests of achievement in soccer, tumbling, and tennis. The immediate concern then becomes whether a satisfactory test is available in these activities. For soccer, both the Bontz and Shaufele Tests may be applicable; but the latter permits a more definitive analysis of skill. In tumbling, presently no published test exists. Evidence suggests that the Broer-Miller Tennis Test is more suitable than the Dyer Test for measuring achievement, although both were devised for college women. The teacher must decide whether the most suitable tests, Shaufele and Broer-Miller, provide satisfactory measure of achievement for this situation. If not, it will become necessary for the teacher either to revise and/or supplement these tests with other items or to construct the type of tests desired. In constructing the tumbling test, the teacher may derive some help from the Johnson Test of motor educability.

As the need for selection of tests in other sport areas develops, these two chapters should serve as the source list of available tests and test items.

SELECTED REFERENCES

1. BARROW, HAROLD M., and McGEE, ROSEMARY. *A Practical Approach to Measurement in Physical Education.* Philadelphia: Lea and Febiger, 1964.
2. CAMPBELL, W. R., and TUCKER, N. M. *An Introduction to Tests and Measurement in Physical Education.* London: G. Bell & Sons, Ltd., 1967.
3. CLARKE, H. HARRISON. *Application of Measurement to Health and Physical Education,* 4th ed. Englewood Cliffs, N. J.: Prentice-Hall, Inc., 1967.
4. McCLOY, C. H., and YOUNG, N. D. *Tests and Measurements in Health and Physical Education,* 3d ed. New York: Appleton-Century-Crofts, Inc., 1954.
5. MONTOYE, HENRY J. (ed.). *Sports Tests and Evaluation in Dance (An Introduction to Measurement in Physical Education,* Vol. 3). Indianapolis: Phi Epsilon Kappa Fraternity, 1970.
6. SCOTT, M. GLADYS, and FRENCH, ESTHER. *Measurement and Evaluation in Physical Education.* Dubuque: Wm. C. Brown Co., 1959.

14

Knowledge Testing

Tests in the previous chapters of this part have been concerned with the basic type of learning referred to as "technical learning"—broadly conceived to entail not only skill performance but also the physical qualities (such as strength and agility) that influence it. Attention is now directed to the second basic type of learning, associated learning— knowledge and understanding. The scope of tests of associated learning (cognitive domain), as described in Chapter 7, encompasses information ranging from that basic to all physical education experiences to that peculiar to a particular activity. It might be expressed concisely as learning the *why, when,* and *how* of physical education. Generally stated, this includes knowledge and understanding of the need for physical activity and its effect on the individual in addition to the history, technique, and strategy of specific sports. Tests of knowledge and understanding possess value for determining both beginning level and achievement as well as to motivate learning by disclosing the interrelatedness of associated learning and activity performance. In affording overall appraisal, tests of associated learning are not only intricately but in reality also inextricably tied up both in technical and concomitant learnings.

HISTORICAL BACKGROUND

Knowledge testing represents one of the later developments in physical education measurement, originating in 1929 with the publication of a basketball test by Bliss. A year later, Knighton published the first soccer test. A pioneer baseball test with reported reliability was presented by Rodgers and Heath in 1931. In the next several years, the first tests in a number of different activities appeared, such as: girls' basketball officiating and several sports information tests for high school boys in 1932; golf and rhythms in 1933; field hockey in 1934; tennis and comprehensive tests in selected activities in 1935; and high school girls' basketball in 1937.

From these beginnings, other tests in the same and different activities emerged. As an analysis of the tests described below shows, until relatively recently the contributions in knowledge testing had been made largely by women, little by men, and involved the college level in the main. Recently tremendous impetus to knowledge testing has evolved from the identification of a body of knowledge in physical education. This not only has begun to exert a profound influence on the content and conduct of physical education programs in schools and colleges but also has divulged the need for knowledge testing and for satisfactory and appropriate tests. The AAHPER Committee on Understandings and Knowledge in Physical Education proposed the categorization of this body of knowledge into three areas: activity performance, the prime area; the "why" or effects of activity; and factors modifying activity and their effects.[1] Subsequently, three AAHPER Cooperative Physical Education Tests were developed and nationally normed within this context for each of three grade classifications—4–6, 7–9, and 10–12. This development and other indications suggest that scientifically devised knowledge tests will improve in quality and quantity as the increasing importance of knowledge testing becomes realized.

AN ILLUSTRATIVE PROBLEM

The focus of this chapter resides in ascertaining what tests are available and an indication of suitability for a junior high school physical education program. It should be recognized that in most instances where a test is desired, the specific emphasis and content of the program as a whole or particular activity units afford the final basis of appropriateness. With this in mind, the question is: What knowledge tests are suitable for junior high schools? The presentation of tests will be inclusive so that this question may be answered for any educational level.

The knowledge tests will be presented by including the source in the text along with an annotation containing the basic descriptive information. The sources and basic description of available tests herein should prove of value not only in locating desirable tests but also as guides for the teacher who is interested in constructing better tests. The latter concern entails suggested test content and item construction and also the

[1] *Knowledge and Understanding in Physical Education* (Washington: AAHPER, 1969), p. ix.

procedure to follow in test construction. Because of the variability of teaching emphasis regarding content in a given activity, this second use of the test listing below will perhaps assume greater importance. Notwithstanding, the advantage of selecting appropriate standardized tests over poorly constructed teacher-made tests lies in the scientific authenticity and mode of construction.

To afford a basis for informative consideration of available tests, the reader should become fluent with the characteristics and concerns pertaining to the selection and construction of knowledge tests as depicted in Chapters 3 to 5. This will assure a sounder analysis of tests and better comprehension of assets and undesirable aspects of different tests. Approaching the problem in this manner will also contribute to construction of teacher-made tests by disclosing items that are effective and those that do not appear to function well.

SELECTED KNOWLEDGE TESTS

In reviewing tests of physical education knowledge, it should be realized that items dealing with rules or the basic aspects of a particular sports activity that may be altered by rule changes may become out of date with any revisions affecting the rules. Also, facts relating to the nature and effects of physical activity may change with important implications for participation. Consequently, selected items of even recent tests may need modification to render them appropriate. In describing the tests, reference to the need for revision in accordance with the changing concepts of the game involved, particularly with older tests, and factors relating to participation in physical activity is presumed to be implied throughout.

Knowledge tests in physical education divide themselves naturally into two categories: comprehensive physical education or sports knowledge, and tests in specific activities. The first category may entail tests of two forms: those comprised of general information pertaining to all activity and perhaps some items specific for particular activities blended into a single test; and those consisting of separate sections devoted to specific activities, i.e., a series of individual tests.

Comprehensive Physical Education Knowledge Tests

AAHPER TESTS (Grades 4–12). AAHPER COOPERATIVE PHYSICAL EDUCATION TESTS (Princeton, New Jersey: Educational Testing Service, 1970). Tests at each of three levels (grades 4–6, 7–9, 10–12) were constructed in two alternate forms of 60 MC items each, involving working time of 40 minutes, and based upon the body of knowledge contained in the

AAHPER manual, *Knowledge and Understanding in Physical Education*. The tests are designed to cover the facts and concepts entailed in three content areas—activity performance, effects of activity, and factors modifying activities. The interrelatedness of content in the tests and the use of a single converted score scale is intended to provide a program of evaluation that monitors student progress over a span of school years. The tests represent the cooperative endeavor of Educational Testing Service, an advisory committee of AAHPER, and selected specialists. Test development involved 14,000 students throughout the country. Content validity was established; reliability coefficients ranged from .72 to .82. Norms for the different grades are based on 1200–1800 students. Specimen sets for consideration by teachers and testing materials are available from ETS, Box 999, Princeton 08540. Appropriate answer sheets for several scoring machines are also obtainable.

Two questions are cited below as illustrative of both content and continuity of coverage on two different level tests in the same content domain—Effect of Activities. The AAHPER knowledge manual lists 24 concepts in this domain under the sub-heading: Immediate Effects—Physiological Responses.

The first concept explains, "When a person is active the heart rate increases." For Grades 7–9 the relevant question is:

The increase in heart rates during exercise results in

A. better circulation to the muscles.
B. hastening the onset of fatigue.
C. a noticeable shortness of breath.
D. a longer recovery period after exercise.

The last concept in the same content domain states, "As a person starts exercise after being inactive there is increased relaxation and freer movement." For grades 10–12 the related question is:

In order to be relaxed and have freer movements at the beginning of his tennis game, a player should

A. start to play immediately.
B. take a warm shower before the game.
C. have a massage before the game.
D. volley the ball for a while before starting to play.

HEMPHILL INFORMATION TESTS (High School Boys). Fay Hemphill, "Information Tests in Health and Physical Education for High School Boys," *Research Quarterly*, III, No. 4 (December, 1932), 83. Describes construction of information tests concerned with the following phases of a physical education program: major athletic activities (baseball, football, basketball); minor sports (soccer, tennis, handball, volleyball); health related to physical education; self-defense (boxing, wrestling); and recreational sports (golf, hiking, fishing and hunting, swimming, boating and canoeing, riding and horsemanship, camping and picnicking, horseshoes). The tests contain 751 TF (true and false) and MC (multiple choice) items. Sample test questions of different categories are included along with tentative norms, grades eight to eleven. Validity and reliability was established; coefficients for the latter ranged from .67 to .88.

HENNIS KNOWLEDGE TESTS (College Women). Gail M. Hennis, "Construction of Knowledge Tests in Selected Physical Education Activities for College Women," *Research Quarterly*, XXVII, No. 3 (October, 1956), 301. A definitive description of test construction and statistical analysis. Tests consist of four-option MC items, ranging from 32 to 37 items on the following: badminton, basketball, bowling, field hockey, softball, tennis, and volleyball. Tests not included in the reference; obtainable through the author, University of North Carolina at Greensboro. Tests conform to table of specifications showing percentage distribution of course content. Reliability coefficients ranged from .72 to .81.

MINNESOTA KNOWLEDGE TESTS (College Women). Catherine Snell, "Physical Education Knowledge Tests," *Research Quarterly*, VI, No. 3 (October, 1935), 78; VII, No. 1 (March, 1936), 73; and VII, No. 2 (May, 1936), 77. The first reference describes construction of the following tests at the University of Minnesota: fundamentals of physical education (50 items), archery, field hockey, hygiene (90 items), volleyball, soccer, basketball, baseball, tennis, golf, and horseback riding. Validity and reliability was established. Reliability coefficients ranged from .51 (riding) to .93 (hockey) and for baseball, soccer and volleyball were .85 or .86. All tests consist of 45 five-response MC items unless otherwise noted above. First reference contains first four tests; second reference contains volleyball, soccer, and basketball tests; and the last reference presents the remaining four tests.

WALKER TEST (College). William P. Walker, "The Development of a General Knowledge Inventory Test and a Resource Syllabus for a Foundation Course in Physical Education for College Freshmen," Microcard Doctoral Dissertation, Florida State University, 1965. A test of two 90-item non-equivalent forms involving five categories: physiological principles of exercise and movement; kinesiological and mechanical principles; sports knowledge; physical education objectives; safety and first aid; and motor learning. Content validity was established, as were reliabilities of .64 (Form A) and .66 (Form B). Reference contains both test forms, a rating scale for each test category, and a thorough review of literature on physical education knowledge testing.

Mood Physical Fitness Knowledge Test (Professional Students). Dale Mood, "Test of Physical Fitness Knowledge: Construction, Administration and Norms," *Research Quarterly*, XLII, No. 4 (December, 1971), 423. Two essentially parallel forms of a test consisting of 60 four-option MC items constructed to measure the physical fitness knowledge of senior physical education majors. Content validity was established by categorizing current written physical fitness materials into 10 topical areas and utilizing weightings derived from a survey of the Research Council, AAHPER. Reliabilities were .74, Form A, and .77, Form B. T-scores were based on tests of 2,226 senior majors. Percentile ranks of T-scores for 15 normative groups were computed for men and for women in four categories—freshmen, senior and master's students in physical education, and non-major seniors (N = 4,167 in 150 institutions). Tests and norms are not reported but available from the author.

Stradtman-Cureton Physical Fitness Knowledge Test (Secondary School Boys and Girls). A. D. Stradtman and T. K. Cureton, "A Physical Fitness Knowledge Test for Secondary School Boys and Girls," *Research Quarterly*, XXI No. 1 (March 1950), 53. A test of 100 MC items designed to ascertain the amount of knowledge about desirable practices in physical fitness possessed by the students, including the more common psychological and physiological implications of activities of various kinds. Validity was established, and reliabilities of .94 (boys), .96 (girls), and .96 (combined) were reported. Scoring tables prepared but not included. Test not included, other than 11 illustrative questions.

Cowell Test of Principles (Professional Students). Charles C. Cowell, "Cowell Test of Ability to Recognize the Operation of Certain Principles Important to Physical Education" (Cincinnati: Tri-State Offset Company, 817 Main St., 1961). A 50-item five-option MC test designed to evaluate the general background of professional physical education students and their ability to recognize the operation of certain principles and generalizations from disciplines from which basic principles of physical education are derived. The content areas include scientific method, philosophy of education, sociology, human biology, growth and development, social psychology, psychology of learning, mental hygiene, curriculum planning and develpment, educational methods, physiology of activity, cultural anthropology, and evaluation and measurement. Validity and reliability ($r = .78$) were established. Six-sigma scales and classification norms were derived for senior and graduate men and women, and also for freshmen men and women. Its suggested uses include: one basis for selection of undergraduate and graduate students; pre- or post-test for certain courses; and as part of a general comprehensive examination.

RHODA TEST OF VOCABULARY (Professional Students). William P. Rhoda, "The Construction and Standardization of a Test of Technical Vocabulary in Selected Areas of Physical Education for Senior and Graduate Levels," Microcard Doctoral Dissertation, University of Oregon, 1951. A test of 90 five-option MC items covering three areas; physiological sciences, measurement and evaluation, and restricted and corrective. Textbook content analysis afforded the basis of validity. Total test reliabilities were .90 for graduate (N = 295) and .85 for senior (N = 417) levels with acceptable sub-test coefficients. T-scores and percentile norms are reported based on 14 colleges and universities.

FRENCH PROFESSIONAL KNOWLEDGE TESTS (College Women). Esther French, "Construction of Knowledge Tests in Selected Professional Courses in Physical Education," *Research Quarterly*, XIV, No. 4 (December, 1943), 406. Tests on 16 activities—badminton, basketball, body mechanics, canoeing, field hockey, folk dancing, golf, recreational sports (aerial darts, bowling, deck tennis, handball, shuffle board, table tennis, tetherball), rhythms, soccer, softball, stunts and tumbling, swimming, tennis, track and field, and volleyball. Used for diagnostic purposes at State University of Iowa. Two forms were constructed: long, average number of items being 53; and short, entailing 20 to 26 questions. Validity established. Reliabilities ranged from .70 to 88—long form; .62 to .88—short form. Norms given for short form. Tests not included in reference; available only as testing service from the State University of Iowa Examination Service.

Other Educational Testing Service Programs (Princeton, N.J., 08540). THE UNDERGRADUATE PROGRAM FOR COUNSELING AND EVALUATION— Field Test in Physical Education. A 150-item test, one of 25 two-hour field tests designed to measure progress in a college student's major field of study. Useful both for academic counseling after the sophomore year and for senior comprehensive examinations. The program also includes: modular tests in certain fields; area tests in humanities, natural science, and social science; and an aptitude test.

TEACHER EDUCATION EXAMINATION PROGRAM—Teaching Field Test in Physical Education. One of 15 teaching field tests designed for use as an aid in evaluating competence for teaching in specific fields. The program also includes a second group of tests, the General Professional Examinations, dealing with general knowledge and abilities deemed essential for all prospective teachers.

NATIONAL TEACHER EXAMINATIONS—Teaching Area Examinations in Physical Education. A separate test for men and women, two of 25 teaching area examinations, designed to provide independent measures

of the academic preparation of prospective teachers for elementary a
secondary school teaching. Common Examinations include: Professio
Education; Written English Expression; Science and Mathematics; a
Social Studies, Literature and the Fine Arts. These tests are utilized
local school districts to assist in selection and assignment of teachers,
as an element in teacher certification by some states.

SCHOOL PERSONNEL RESEARCH AND EVALUATION SERVICES—Speci:
Examination in Physical Education. One of 20 speciality examinati
this test is designed to measure familiarity with the skills and knowle
needed to teach men's or women's physical education. The Com
Examinations are adopted from the National Teacher Examina
(NTE) to assess general and professional education. This examin
program constitutes a supplement to the NTE for use by schools,
leges, and agencies to assess cognitive achievement of teachers fo
service education, professional guidance, and evaluative purposes. U
the NTE, the examinations are not intended for certification of s
personnel and special local administrations can be arranged as de

Tests in Specific Sports Activities

In looking for tests pertaining to a particular activity, the reader :
also refer to the tests given above.

Badminton. HOOKS TEST (College Men). Edgar W. Hool
"Hooks Comprehensive Knowledge Test in Selected Physical Edu
Activities for College Men," *Research Quarterly*, XXXVII, No. 4 (I
ber, 1966), 506. Describes contruction of 50-item MC badminton
college men. Acceptable validation was described; reliability, .8
tional percentile norms were developed (N = 2,832). Test is not in
in the reference but is available from the author at East Carolina
(Greenville, North Carolina) along with manual containing t
specifications, and district and national norms.

PHILLIPS TEST (College Women). Marjorie Phillips, "Standar
of a Badminton Knowledge Test for College Women," *Researc
terly*, XVII, No. 1 (March, 1946), 48. A description of constru
100-item badminton test (TF and MC) for college women i
difficulty and validity rating of all items and norms for begin
intermediates based on 1,471 papers from 30 colleges. Scoring
ber MC correct plus TF right minus wrong increased reliabi
.86 to .92. Test is not included.

SCOTT TEST (College Women). M. Gladys Scott, "Achieve
aminations in Badminton," *Research Quarterly*, XII, No. 2 (Ma
242. A test developed through the Research Committee of th

Association of Physical Education for College Women, consisting of 47 MC and 33 TF items. Discriminatory power and difficulty rating given for each item. Validity established; reliability—.79 for MC and .72 for TF items. Test and suggested grading plan included.

WASHINGTON TEST (College Women). Katharine Fox, "Beginning Badminton Written Examination," *Research Quarterly*, XXIV, No. 2 (May, 1953), 135. A test for beginners in badminton developed at the University of Washington. Includes 106 items (61 TF, 37 short answer, 8 identification). Validity established; reliability—.88. Reference contains test and score sheet, complete item analysis, but no norms.

Basketball. SCHWARTZ TEST (High School Girls). Helen Schwartz, "Knowledge and Achievement Tests in Girls' Basketball on the Senior High School Level," *Research Quarterly*, VIII, No. 1 (March, 1937), 143. Consists of 50 TF, 20 MC, 15 completion, and 15 pictorial questions covering rules, team play, strategy, fundamental techniques, and positions of players with their duties. Validity established but reliability or scoring tables not given. Test is scaled with the companion skill test. Pictorial questions represent interesting innovation wherein stick figures and diagrams illustrate a choice of play situations. Test included.

SCHLEMAN OFFICIATING TEST (College Women Majors). Helen B. Schleman, "A Written-Practical Basketball Officiating Test," *Journal of Health and Physical Education*, III, No 3 (March, 1932), 37. Not scientifically devised but cited for originality since test consists of actual scrimmage with competent players and two officials in which planned violations are set up in 90-second situations. Testee identifies the obvious violation that the official failed to call or incorrect action taken by the official in the given period. A sample test sheet and a test composed of 17 situations are given.

SCOTT TEST FOR OFFICIALS. M. Gladys Scott, "Written Test for Basketball Officials," *Journal of Health and Physical Education*, VIII, No. 1 (January, 1937), 41. Describes use of an illustrated chart for recording response to simulated game situations as a test and the development of a written examination with sample questions.

Field Hockey. DEITZ-FRECH TEST (High School Girls). Dorthea Deitz and Beryl Frech, "Hockey Knowledge Test for Girls," *Journal of Health, Physical Education and Recreation*, XI, No. 6 (June, 1940), 366. A test of 77 items (completion, alternate response, and MC), for use with girls, grades nine to twelve. Validity and reliability not reported. Test is given along with results derived from 172 girls.

GRISIER TEST (Women). Gertrude J. Grisier, "The Construction of an Objective Test of Knowledge and Interpretation of the Rules of Field

Hockey for Women," *Supplement to the Research Quarterly,* V, No. 1 (March, 1934), 79. Describes construction of three equivalent forms of a test with established validity and reliability, r's = .88, .88, and .92. No tests given. Form A was used by U. S. Field Hockey Association during 1933 season.

KELLY-BROWN TEST (College Women Majors). Ellen D. Kelly and J. E. Brown, "The Construction of a Field Hockey Test for Women Physical Education Majors," *Research Quarterly,* XXIII, No. 3 (October, 1952), 322. Definitive description of a carefully devised test of 88 five-response MC items, including consideration of non-functioning items, discriminatory power, and difficulty rating. Validity and reliability (.94) established. Test not included but obtainable from Dr. Kelly, Illinois State Normal University at Normal.

Golf. MURPHY TEST. Mary A. Murphy, "Criteria for Judging a Golf Knowledge Test," *Research Quarterly,* IV, No. 4 (December, 1933), 81; and "Grading Student Achievement in Golf Knowledge," *Research Quarterly,* V, No. 1 (March, 1934), 83. First reference describes a carefully devised test comprised of 50 TF, 10 completion, and 30 matching items. Test and grading scales included. Validity and reliability (r = .86) established, but item analysis is not reported. T-score table presented in second reference.

FLORIDA TEST (College Men). I. F. Waglow and C. H. Rehling, "A Golf Knowledge Test," *Research Quarterly,* XXIV, No. 4 (December, 1953), 463. Describes development of 100-item TF test at University of Florida. Test is included with answers, difficulty rating, discriminatory power, and notations for items in need of revision. Validity established; reliability—.82.

Gymnastics. GERSHON TEST (Professional Men). Ernest Gershon, "Apparatus Gymnastics Knowledge Test for College Men in Professional Physical Education," *Research Quarterly,* XXVIII, No. 4 (December, 1957), 332. A description of a test of apparatus gymnastics for college men in professional physical education. Test consists of 100 TF and MC items, given to 940 men in 40 colleges and universities throughout the country to derive national norms. Validity and reliability (r = .72) established. A copy of the test, directions, scoring key, and evaluation schedules obtainable by qualified instructors from the author at Wisconsin State College in LaCrosse.

Soccer. HEATH-RODGERS TEST (Fifth- and Sixth-Grade Boys). M. L. Heath and E. L. Rodgers, "A Study in the Use of Knowledge and Skill Tests in Soccer," *Research Quarterly,* III, No. 4 (December, 1932), 33. A test of 100 TF items dealing with game rules and maneuvers and developed in conjunction with a skill test. Validity established; reliability—.90. Test included along with T-scales.

WINN TEST (College Men). Jerome E. Winn, "Soccer Knowledge Test for College Men," Microcard Doctoral Dissertation, Indiana University, 1957. A 100-item (60 TF, 40 four-option MC) test of soccer knowledge for college men was developed along with two 65-item equivalent form tests (40 TF, 25 four-option MC). Validity was established, and respective Spearman-Brown reliability coefficients were .94, .81, and .81. T-scale norms are reported for long test (N = 828) and Forms A and B (N = 326) based on selected colleges and universities.

KNIGHTON TEST (Women). Marian Knighton, "Soccer Questions," *Journal of Health and Physical Education,* I, No. 8 (October, 1930), 29. A test, not scientifically devised, on soccer rules as compiled by the Women's Committee and intended to give beginners a better understanding of the game. Test included; consists of 25 TF, 5 MC, and 5 completion items.

Softball. RODGERS-HEATH TEST (Fifth- and Sixth-Grade Boys). E. L. Rodgers and M. L. Heath, "An Experiment in the Use of Knowledge and Skill Tests in Playground Baseball," *Research Quarterly,* II, No. 4 (December, 1931), 113. A test of 100 TF statements on game rules and maneuvers, developed in conjunction with a skill test and involving 1,800 pupils. Validity and reliability (r = .89) established. Test given along with T-scale.

HOOKS TEST (College Men). Edgar W. Hooks, Jr., "Hooks Comprehensive Knowledge Test in Selected Physical Education Activities for College Men," *Research Quarterly,* XXXVII, No. 4 (December, 1966), 506. Describes construction of 50-item MC softball test for college men with acceptable validation, reliability of .77, and national percentile norms (N = 3,513). Source of test materials is stated under Hooks badminton test.

FLORIDA TEST (College Men). I. F. Waglow and Foy Stephens, "A Softball Knowledge Test," *Research Quarterly,* XXVI, No. 2 (May, 1955), 234. A test consisting of 60 TF, 25 completion, and 5 fair-or-foul questions and 10 ball-in-play or dead-ball situations, as developed at the University of Florida. Validity and reliability (r = .78) established. Test included with answers, item difficulty rating, and discrimination indices for each item. Norm table and T-scales presented.

Swimming. SCOTT TEST (College Women). M. Gladys Scott, "Achievement Examinations for Elementary and Intermediate Swimming Classes," *Research Quarterly,* XI, No. 2 (May, 1940), 100. A test developed through the Research Committee of the Central Association of

Physical Education for College Women covering swimming and water safety and consisting of two forms—beginners (56 MC and TF items) and intermediate (58 MC and TF items); reliabilities of .89 and .87, respectively. Validity established and discriminatory power and difficulty rating given for each item. Test and grading scale included.

Tennis. HEWITT TEST (College). Jack E. Hewitt, "Hewitt's Comprehensive Tennis Knowledge Test—Form A and B Revised," *Research Quarterly*, XXXV, No. 2 (May, 1964), 147. A revision of a test (*Research Quarterly*, 1937) for men and women consisting of two forms each with 50 items—TF, MC, diagrammatic, and matching. Table of specifications covers game fundamentals, rules, playing situations, history of the game, and equipment. Validity was established, including .89 correlation with playing experience; reliability was .89. Both test forms are given along with scoring keys and grading norms.

HOOKS TEST (College Men).—Edgar W. Hooks, Jr., "Hooks Comprehensive Knowledge Test in Selected Physical Education Activities for College Men," *Research Quarterly*, XXXVII, No. 4 (December, 1966), 506. Describes construction of 50-item MC tennis test for college men with acceptable validation, reliability of .81, and national percentile norms (N = 2,740). Source of test materials is stated under Hooks badminton test.

MILLER TEST (College Women Majors). Wilma K. Miller, "Achievement Levels in Tennis Knowledge and Skill for Women Physical Education Major Students," *Research Quarterly*, XXIV, No. 1 (March, 53), 81. Designed for college women majors in physical education, consisting of 100 items—30 TF, 30 three-response, and 40 MC items. Comprehensive coverage of game. Validity established; reliability—.93. Norms are included based on 612 subjects. Test not given but obtainable by qualified instructors from the author at Ohio University, Athens.

SCOTT TEST (College Women). M. Gladys Scott, "Achievement Examinations for Elementary and Intermediate Tennis Classes," *Research Quarterly*, XII, No. 1 (March, 1941), 40. A test developed through the Research Committee of the Central Association of Physical Education for College Women consisting of two forms—elementary (66 MC and TF items) and intermediate (51 MC and TF items); respective reliabilities of .87 and .78. Does not test same content as Hewitt Test. Validity established, and discriminatory power and difficulty rating given for each item. Test and grading scales included.

WASHINGTON TEST (College Women). Marion B. Broer and Donna M. Miller, "Achievement Tests for Beginning and Intermediate Tennis," *Research Quarterly*, XXI, No. 3 (October, 1950), 303. A description of a comprehensive test developed at the University of Washington in conjunction with a skill test. Comprised of 128 items—TF, MC, identification, completion, and matching. Validity established; reliability coefficients of .82 for beginner and .92 for intermediate tests. Test included with difficulty rating and discriminatory power of each item.

WAGNER TEST (College Women Beginners). Miriam W. Wagner, "An Objective Method of Grading Beginners in Tennis," *Journal of Health and Physical Education*, VI, No. 3 (March, 1935), 24. Gives 10 sample questions of a test to illustrate appropriate type of questions for beginners; not scientifically devised.

Volleyball. HOOKS TEST (College Men). Edgar W. Hooks, Jr., "Hooks Comprehensive Knowledge Test in Selected Physical Education Activities for College Men," *Research Quarterly*, XXXVII, No. 4 (December, 1966), 506. Describes construction of 50-item MC volleyball test for college men with acceptable validation, reliability of .73, and national percentile norms (N = 4,140). Source of test materials is stated under Hooks badminton test.

LANGSTON TEST (College Men Majors). Dewey F. Langston, "Standardization of a Volleyball Knowledge Test for College Men Physical Education Majors," *Research Quarterly*, XXVI, No. 1 (March, 1955), 60. A description of construction of a volleyball test for men physical education major students; composed of 70 TF and 30 MC items covering all phases of game from its history to officiating. Established validity and reliability (TF—.90, MC—.82). Questions coded for IBM scoring. National norms presented. Test not included but obtainable by qualified instructors from the author at New Mexico University, Portales.

Special Purpose Test

The following test is not a test of physical education knowledge in either the general or specific context, but deals with the application of a special subject (statistics) that is essential in graduate study and research in physical education. Hence, it is categorized as a special purpose test.

BURKHARDT STATISTICAL COMPREHENSION TEST (Graduate Professional Students). Edward Burkhardt, D. R. Casady, and R. A. Forsyth, "Statistical Comprehension for Graduate Students in Physical Education: Test and Norms," *Research Quarterly*, XLII, No. 3 (October, 1971), 235. Two closely parallel forms of a test of 50 four-option MC items designed to measure statistical comprehension of graduate students in physical education. Content validity was established, entailing involvement of 32 members of the Research Council, AAHPER. Reliability was reported as intercorrelation of Forms A and B, $r = .73$. Norms were constructed for all examinees ($N = 1,013$) and males and females at 51 institutions and also for 11 categories representing different levels of graduate work completed. Test copies and norms are not presented but obtainable from E. Burkhardt.

RESOLVING THE ILLUSTRATIVE PROBLEM

In appraising the appropriateness of published tests many of the specific considerations for knowledge test construction presented in Chapter 5 have particular relevance. Especial heed should be paid to the prevalent shortcomings in physical education tests, wherein: rules of play and facts are overemphasized; understanding, application and interpretation questions are neglected; and relevance of test item content is minimal at best. In essence the compatibility of a test for a given situation is a function of the specificity and relevance of test content for the instructional program content that it is intended to sample. Expectedly, the table of specifications (test "table of contents") may render many tests inappropriate in their entirety in terms of teacher needs and indeed, totally usable tests may be hard to find. Notwithstanding, critical review of published tests affords a valuable resource of test items for teacher-made tests. In addition to the tests described herein, for other tests to be reviewed in the quest for desirable tests and test items the teacher should consult: (1) later issues of the professional periodicals that have been cited; (2) physical education activity handbooks; [2] (3) national association guides, such as those of the Division of Girls and Women's Sports (DGWS), AAHPER; (4) the annual AAHPER publication, *Completed Research in Health, Physical Education, and Recreation*, containing abstracts of many theses and dissertations and a bibliography of pertinent research articles; and (5) the listing of microform theses and dissertations. [3] Regardless of the sources consulted, the teacher should at least find some potentially good test item suggestions but should anticipate that many of the items themselves will be poorly constructed and necessitate careful overhaul. In many instances the test item idea may be suitable but adjustment will need to be made to the specific situation.

[2] Illustrative of these is: George B. Dintiman and Loyd M. Barrow, *A Comprehensive Manual of Physical Education Activities for Men*, and *Instruction and Evaluation Manual for Teachers of a Comprehensive Manual of Physical Education Activities for Men* (New York: Appleton-Century-Crofts, 1970). Tests comprised of TF, MC, and matching items are included, along with recommended skill test items.

[3] Microform Publications, School of Health, Physical Education, and Recreation, University of Oregon, Eugene, Oregon 97403. In 1972 the publication format was changed from microcard to microfiche.

Thus, analysis of the available tests of physical education knowledge, irrespective of specific areas involved in the problem, will not only afford the answer as to the suitability of any tests but also provide insight into effective suggestions to incorporate and other factors to avoid in constructing a test. Certainly, the limited number of tests available for consideration at different grade levels points to the fact that in many instances construction represents the only immediate solution.

Turning to the specific problem, what knowedge tests are appropriate for junior high school, as for skill tests, the practical approach appears to consider soccer, tumbling, and tennis—the first activities to be included in the testing program. In all three instances, no test is available. The Heath-Rodgers Soccer Test or the soccer test of the Hemphill Test series might serve as valuable resource material for adaptation, although the former is comprised only of TF items. No test exists for tumbling, and the tennis tests are not designed for this level. However, a tennis test such as the Hewitt Test might be adapted; or all the available tests might be used as suggestive material for constructing a tennis test. Actually, as analysis reveals, no tests of knowledge in specific activities have been devised for the junior high school level. The AAHPER Cooperative Physical Education Tests, Forms 3A and B, for junior high school might well be administered in one form at the beginning of grade 7 and in the alternative form at the end of grade 9 to provide a basis for planning and evaluating instruction and learning directed toward the body of knowledge in physical education. In using this test the teacher should compute local norms to supplement the national norms for the particular grade involved. Utilization of blanket tests (i.e., including a number of different grades—7–9) of any type should be made in light of the implicit limiting factors. The vocabulary difficulties encountered and varying intellectual concepts and psychological characteristics at different age levels tend to reduce the validity and reliability of such blanket tests. While a concern at all levels, the problem is especially noteworthy at the elementary level.

The admonitions concerning blanket tests and the scarcity of knowledge tests in physical education confirm the previously stated value of this chapter for resource purposes in test construction. The available tests suggest some desirable features and items together with the undesirable and particular areas of needed attention. Coupled with the understanding of test construction developed through Chapters 4 and 5, the teacher now should be equipped to design a test for a given situation. The selected references for those chapters include suggested reading to indicate what comprises a well-constructed test of associated learning and how to proceed to devise such a test.

SELECTED REFERENCES

1. BARROW, HAROLD M., and McGEE, ROSEMARY. *A Practical Approach to Measurement in Physical Education*, 2d ed. Philadelphia: Lea and Febiger, 1971.
2. BUROS, OSCAR K. *Tests in Print*. Highland Park, N. J.: Gryphon Press, 1961.
3. BUROS, OSCAR K. *The Seventh Mental Measurement Yearbook*. Highland Park, N. J.: Gryphon Press, 1972.
4. *Knowledge and Understanding in Physical Education*. Washington: AAHPER, 1969.
5. MEHRENS, WILLIAM A., and LEHMANN, IRVIN J. *Standardized Tests in Education*. New York: Holt, Rinehart and Winston, Inc., 1969.

15

Measuring Attitudes and Behavior

Measurement related to the third type of learning—concomitant—is often overlooked or belittled in terms of importance, largely because of the intangible aspect of the quality concerned and the uncertainty and difficulty inherent in determining what exists. However, such should not be the case. In reality, the attitude and practice of an individual present a vital concern, since neither skill nor knowledge possession reflects the influence on shaping one's pattern of living as made by attitudes, and behavior.

Concomitant learning (affective domain) not only determines efficiency, efficacy, quality, and quantity of technical and associated learnings but also goes hand in hand with these two other types of learning. In other words, technical and associated learning per se will not achieve their fullest potential and influence unless they are planned with concomitant learning in mind. For example, the attainment of considerable proficiency and understanding in an activity generally predicates and would be unlikely without positive attitudes toward the activity as evinced by the perseverance to practice continually and devotedly. The reader should refer to Chapter 7 to gain fuller realization of the significance of concomitant learning and the relationship to overall appraisal. Sight should not be lost of the fact that physical educators, in addition to many other teachers and administrators, recognize the tremendous potential in personality and social development that may be realized through physical education. Notwithstanding, concerted effort must be made to discover and utilize the best practical means of teacher appraisal to corroborate the aforementioned suppositions in a given situation by showing the "measurable extent" to which physical education is contributing to desired personality and social development. This will engender program support and also meet the fundamental need for information to complete the overall appraisal of students.

It appears prudent to reiterate the teacher's twofold concern in concomitant learning so as to contribute fully to all-round development of the individual, namely, the development of desirable attitudes and behavior through participation in physical education activities, including favorable disposition toward such participation while remaining alert to facilitate their transfer to other situations to the extent possible. Since a person may reveal different attitudes and behavior when exposed to different situations coupled with the varied experience situations confronted in physical education, practically every facet of a student's personality is open to the physical education teacher for inspection, study, and diagnostic teaching. The challenge for the teacher is to select and utilize effectively appropriate tools to divulge these facets of personality implicit in concomitant learning.

HISTORICAL BACKGROUND

The development of tools for appraising concomitant learning has the most recent origin of the three types of learning. Shortly after 1920, attention was directed to the measurement of attitudes of various kinds. The questionnaire or inventory method appeared first, followed soon after by arbitrary rating scales. The development of these basic techniques has continued as illustrated by the relatively recent modification of an earlier scale to render possible the measurement of a large number of attitudes using a single scale. Two other tools appropriate for use in this area first appeared in the middle 1930's and have since undergone considerable refinement, namely, sociometry and anecdotal records. The pioneering effort in applying tools of concomitant learning to physical education is credited to McCloy.[1] He proposed a behavior rating scale that served as the basis for scales developed subsequently by two other researchers. From these beginnings in physical education, tools of the aforementioned types have been developed by using applicable techniques, modifying other techniques to render them suitable, and designing tools specifically for physical education.

THE TOOLS FOR APPRAISING CONCOMITANT LEARNING

The tools for evaluating concomitant learning may be arbitrarily classified as rating scales, self-report instruments (inventories and attitude

[1] C. H. McCloy, "Character Building in Physical Education," *Research Quarterly*, I, No. 3 (October, 1930), 42.

scales), sociometry, and anecdotal records. In considering the various tools and their use, the reader should consult Chapter 5 wherein many basic concerns are described relative to the construction and use of these tools and, in particular, rating scales and self-report instruments. Needless to say, this information should serve as an invaluable guide in ascertaining the appropriateness of available instruments.

A rating scale is primarily a device for recording observations, intended to assist the teacher or rater to recognize what is being looked for, and to describe more precisely the degree to which the quality under examination actually exists. The behavior frequency rating chart represents a variation of the rating scale in which the number of times a behavior appears is recorded.

Self-report instruments invoke student response—written or oral—to questions pertaining to his typical behavior or reaction in specific situations. These tools find use in situations wherein the rating technique is impractical or not applicable to the characteristic in question. To differentiate between self-report instruments, as arbitrarily defined in Chapter 5, "scale" refers to a measure of attitude (or behavior) and "inventory" denotes personality assessment. The inventory, attitude scale and the rating scale may be designed for concomitant learning expressed in general social behavior or as related specifically to physical education situations.

Sociometry represents a technique for assessing social development and may be described as a scientific method of studying a group and the interrelationships between the individuals comprising it. Briefly stated, it is based on student response to a question or questions dealing with names of other students with whom one would like to be associated for a specific purpose.

The anecdotal record constitutes cumulative notations of observed behavior of a given individual over a period of time. Unlike other techniques of noting behavior, the anecdotal report is intended to be a record of actual behavior rather than impressions or interpretations, and as such may be viewed as an overall summation of behavioral performance.

These tools of concomitant learning find use in revealing attitudes, appreciations, behavior, interest, personality qualities, and social adjustment. The fact that these characteristics in the main may be expressed in non-verbal behavior or verbal (symbolic) behavior accounts for the different types of tools employed. The importance of establishing proper rapport for administering these tools, and especially the self-report type, cannot be overemphasized. The teacher should recognize that student response may be distorted from reality by the desire for social acceptance and likelihood of individual bias, either consciously or unconsciously. Desirable rapport will tend to eradicate conscious distortion of facts.

Upon such rapport, then, depends the honest response necessary for validity.

In teacher use of measures of concomitant learnings, the approach should be positive, not negative. The teacher should apply these tools to determine the degree of adjustment existing, not maladjustment. This dictates avoidance of methodology that is clinical in nature, such as projective techniques. A word of admonition in teacher application of these tools concerns not looking upon the results as infallible. Instead, the findings should be viewed as aids in discovering needs to be met in fostering desirable social and personality adjustment.

AN ILLUSTRATIVE PROBLEM

Are there any available measures of concomitant learning appropriate for use with a junior high school physical education program? This chapter presents different instruments for measuring attitudes and behavior. for possible consideration in resolving this question as stated or for any other educational level.

The description of each instrument is not definitive but intended to disclose the basic characteristics. As in the case of knowledge tests, this information should serve as an invaluable guide for the teacher in the construction or modification of tests for a specific situation and also as a resource list of tests, some of which may be appropriate as published. The order of presentation is not meant to imply relative importance but is arbitrary, based primarily on chronological development.

ATTITUDES AND BEHAVIOR REFLECTING PERSONAL AND SOCIAL ADJUSTMENT

Rating Scales

McCloy Behavior Rating Scale.[2] The first device to evaluate behavior in physical education was proposed by McCloy. This behavior rating scale lists 37 specific traits, grouped into nine categories (see Blanchard scale below). Each specific trait is rated relative to frequency of observation on a 5-point scale (never—1, seldom—2, fairly often—3, frequently —4, extremely often—5) with 5 exemplifying good behavior. For each trait, the rater also notes the assurance upon which the rating is based, expressed as a mere guess (0), slight inclination (1), fair assurance (2), or positive assurance (3). Scientific authenticity is not reported.

[2] *Ibid.*

O'Neel Behavior Frequency Scale.[3]   O'Neel patterned a scale after McCloy's, using 18 behavior frequencies found to be most valid and reliable of 50 studied and categorized under McCloy's nine components. Because of low reliability of test items, the author does not propose this scale as a reliable measure of character.

Blanchard Behavior Rating Scale.[4]   Blanchard constructed a scale, which essentially represents a modification of the McCloy scale, intended to serve as a measure of character and personality for counseling purposes.   This scale was derived from analysis of a pilot administration of 45 traits and entails 24 trait actions classified in nine groups suggested by McCloy.   McCloy's 5-point frequency rating scheme is employed, but the rater's assurance column was eliminated.   Internal validity and reliability were established.

The trait categories with the first trait action listed under each follow:

Leadership—1.   He is popular with classmates.
Positive active qualities—4.   He quits on tasks requiring perseverance.
Positive mental qualities—8.   He shows keenness of mind.
Self-control—10.   He grumbles over decisions of classmates.
Cooperation—12.   He is loyal to his group.
Social action standard—15.   He makes loud-mouthed criticisms and comments.
Ethical social qualities—17.   He cheats.
Qualities of efficiency—19.   He seems satisfied to "get by" with tasks assigned.
Sociability—22.   He is liked by others.

Cowell Social Adjustment Index.[5]   A social adjustment index was devised by Cowell to provide a quantitative indicant of social adjustment and to disclose individuals warranting especial help through physical education.   Ten acceptable pairs of behavior trends were developed, consisting of good and poor adjustments in specific behavioral responses.   The positive expression of behavior trends is called "Trend Index Form A," whereas Form B contains the negative statement of the ten behavior trends.   The subject is rated as to the presence of each trend on a 4-point scale from "not at all" (0) to "markedly" (3), with a plus sign for each

---

[3] F. W. O'Neel, "A Behavior Frequency Rating Scale for the Measurement of Character and Personality in High School Physical Education Classes for Boys," *Research Quarterly*, VII, No. 2 (May, 1936), 67.

[4] B. E. Blanchard, "A Behavior Frequency Rating Scale for the Measurement of Character and Personality in Physical Education Classroom Situations," *Research Quarterly*, VII, No. 2 (May, 1936), 56. The scale also appears in SR (selected reference) 4 and 5.

[5] C. C. Cowell, "Validating an Index of Social Adjustment for High School Use," *Research Quarterly*, XXIX, No. 1 (March, 1958), 7. Available from Tri-State Offset Co., 817 Main Street, Cincinnatti, Ohio. The index also appears in SR 1 and 4.

value on Form A and a minus sign on Form B. Thus, a well-adjusted individual will score high on Form A and receive a near-zero score or low negative score on Form B, resulting in a high plus score. Contrariwise, a minus score indicates poor social adjustment.

Two of the ten statements of behavior trends appear below as given on each form:

Form A	Form B
1. Enters heartily and with enjoyment into the spirit of social intercourse.	1. Somewhat prudish, awkward, easily embarrassed in his social contacts.
2. Frank, talkative and sociable, does not stand on ceremony.	2. Secretive, seclusive, not inclined to talk unless spoken to.

The reference contains norms involving 222 junior high school boys based upon the observations of three teachers checking observations on both the positive and negative forms at different times, i.e., six ratings for each individual. The internal consistency of the instrument was verified by factor analysis, and divergent group validity and reliability (.82) were established.

Cowell Personal Distance Scale.[6] Based on the premise that one's degree of belonging or being accepted as a member of his own social group represents an important criterion of adjustment to the group, Cowell developed a scale derived from a student ballot. Each student in a class indicates the personal distance at which he prefers to hold each of his classmates by checking (1) into my family as a brother, (2) as a very close pal, (3) as a member of my gang or club, (4) on my streets as a next-door neighbor, (5) into my class at school, (6) into my school, or (7) into my city. The distance value of each category coincides with the order of listing; for instance, the maximum distance value is 7. The index of acceptance is determined by totalling all the weighted scores, dividing by the number of ratings to the nearest hundredth, and multiplying by 100. The lower the index, the lower the degree of acceptance given by the group. The reference contains norms based on 151 high school boys. This scale can be applied to either the same or opposite sex. Validity was established and satisfactory reliability (.88–.93) reported.

Moore-Falls Physical Performance Scale (Grades 5 and 6).[7] Moore and Falls devised an extreme modification of the Cowell Personal Distance Ballot to give a paper and pencil rating of physical performance

---

[6] *Ibid.*
[7] G. C. Moore and H. B. Falls, "Functional Classification for Physical Education in the Upper Elementary Grades by Peer Assessment," *Research Quarterly*, XLI, No. 4 (December, 1970), 519.

for use as a classification measure. Fifth- and sixth-grade boys and girls (N = 538) were asked to rate each of their classmates (regardless of sex) on the assumption that they had to choose a team to play on, in physical education, for the entire year in all types of games. The point scale was: 5—star for your team, very good in sports; 4—regular for your team, good in sports; 3—substitute for your team, poor in sports; 2—too poor for your team, poor in sports; 1—too poor for class, cannot play. Another category, "Do not know well enough to rate," was provided, but it was not included in computations. The sum of the ratings divided by their number comprised the scale score of each student. Divergent group validity was established using the criterion of mean T-score for four AAHPER fitness test items. PPS scores correlated .58 for boys and .51 for girls with fitness test scores. Test-retest reliability of the PPS was .81 for fifth-grade (N = 163) and .88 for sixth-grade (N = 144) students. Thus, the PPS affords a means to assist the teacher in identifying who possess high or low levels of motor fitness in situations where it is not practical to administer a motor fitness test.

Winnetka School Behavior and Attitude Scale (Nursery School Through Sixth Grade).[8] Van Alstyne described a device designed to rate the emotional and social aspects of the personality of children from nursery school through the six grade in terms of five general categories or traits—cooperation, social consciousness, emotional security, leadership, and responsibility. The scale consists of 13 situations with varying levels of response as derived from analysis of actual classroom occurrences. To illustrate, one of three situations categorized under "cooperation" appears below (decile scores are indicated in parentheses).

Situation I. When taking turns with apparatus or materials or in a group discussion:

1. Waits patiently for a turn (10)
2. Takes turn willingly (9)
3. Needs occasional reminder to be patient (5)
4. Is impatient while waiting turn (2)
5. Is unwilling to wait turn (1)
6. Is unwilling to wait turn and interferes with other children's activities (1)

Validity is established, and retest reliability is reported as .87. The reference contains a table showing the distribution, decile scores, and grade medians for the 13 situations involving 1,128 Winnetka school

[8] Dorothy Van Alstyne, "A New Scale for Rating School Behavior and Attitudes in the Elementary School," *Journal of Educational Psychology*, XXVII, No. 9 (December, 1936), 677. Test published by Winnetka Educational Press, Winnetka, Illinois.

children. Suggestions pertaining to use of this scale include: (1) at least 2 months' observation of the child by the teacher should precede rating, (2) scale should be employed for analysis of individual differences within a grade rather than between grades, and (3) a profile graph of results will portray assets and limitations among the five general traits. The scale appears to be of value in disclosing instances of poor adjustment during the formative years for habit patterns.

Cassidy Class Experience Check List.[9] A class experience check list, as described by Cassidy, warrants mention for illustrative and suggestive purposes, even though it is not reported as being scientifically devised. The check list (Fig. 15–1) contains 24 items considered to be definite tangible experiences in physical education. The items are divided into four groups, and the observer encircles the appropriate rating for each item. When viewed from top to bottom, the completed check list affords a picture of overall behavior, wherein the majority of students will score as "always" or "usually"—7 to 10. With the list turned on its side, the ratings reveal a graphic portrayal of the groups. The illustrative ratings in Fig. 15–1 disclose no definite pattern of consistency in behavior-response and show low ratings except in the second area pertaining to athletic abilities. This expression of the rating in profile form might be applied for both teacher construction of scales and adaptation of available scales.

Inventories

As depicted in Chapter 7, ideally the physical education teacher will obtain desired information in the area of psychological tests from the school guidance office along with a technical interpretation of the findings. The general personal and social adjustment inventories described herein, when necessary, can be administered by the teacher and suggest items for inclusion to reveal various characteristics. The listing below also includes inventories designed for use in a specific physical education situation.

Bell Adjustment Inventory (High School Through Adults).[10] Bell devised an inventory in two forms—for high school and college students, and for adults. The student form (published in 1934 and revised in 1962) has six scores: home, health, submissiveness, emotionality, hostility, and masculinity. The adult form (published in 1938) also provides six scores: home, occupational, health, social, emotional, and a total score.

---

[9] Rosalind Cassidy, *Counseling in the Physical Education Program* (New York: Appleton-Century-Crofts, Inc., 1959), pp. 89–91.

[10] Hugh M. Bell, *The Adjustment Inventory* (Palo Alto: Consulting Psychologists Press, Inc., 1963).

CLASS EXPERIENCE CHECK LIST

(Student)	Physical Education				
Experience	Always	Usually	Frequently	Seldom	Rarely

Meeting mechanical and roll-call expectations:

Experience	Always	Usually	Frequently	Seldom	Rarely
Arrives at class on time	10 9	8 7	(6) 5	4 3	2 1
Is in proper uniform	10 9	8 (7)	6 5	4 3	2 1
Is dressed on time	10 9	8 7	(6) 5	4 3	2 1
Lines up for roll call	10 9	8 7	6 (5)	4 3	2 1
Maintains order at roll call	10 9	8 7	6 5	(4) 3	2 1

Meeting athletic and squad experience expectations:

Experience	Always	Usually	Frequently	Seldom	Rarely
Participates in exercises	10 9	8 7	6 5	(4) 3	2 1
Is responsive to demonstrations	10 9	8 7	(6) 5	4 3	2 1
Participates in relays and drills	10 9	8 (7)	6 5	4 3	2 1
Participates in squad games	10 9	(8) 7	6 5	4 3	2 1
Participates in individual activity	10 9	(8) 7	6 5	4 3	2 1
Participates in test activity	10 9	(8) 7	6 5	4 3	2 1

Meeting social and emotional expectations:

Experience	Always	Usually	Frequently	Seldom	Rarely
Displays cooperative attitude	10 9	8 7	(6) 5	4 3	2 1
Displays loyalty to squad and leaders	10 9	8 7	(6) 5	4 3	2 1
Displays leadership in class	10 9	8 7	6 5	4 (3)	2 1
Displays adherence to class regulations	10 9	8 7	6 5	(4) 3	2 1
Displays friendliness	10 9	(8) 7	6 5	4 3	2 1
Plays and works well with others	10 9	8 (7)	6 5	4 3	2 1
Displays interest and enthusiasn	10 9	8 7	(6) 5	4 3	2 1
Attempts to better himself in activities	10 9	8 (7)	6 5	4 3	2 1
Displays dependability	10 9	8 7	6 5	(4) 3	2 1
Displays good humor	10 9	(8) 7	6 5	4 3	2 1

Meeting definite class standards:

Experience	Always	Usually	Frequently	Seldom	Rarely
Has skills for satisfactory class work	10 (9)	8 7	6 5	4 3	2 1
Has regular attendance	10 9	8 7	6 (5)	4 3	2 1
Showers regularly	10 9	8 7	(6) 5	4 3	2 1

Fig. 15–1. Cassidy class experience check list.

The inventory contains 200 items answered Yes, No, or ?, requires about 30 minutes to complete, and is basically self-administrable. The manual contains interpretative guidelines and geographically biased student norms. Satisfactory reliability is reported (r's > .80).

Washburne Social Adjustment Inventory (Above Eighth Grade).[11] To determine social and emotional adjustment, Washburne constructed a group test of 123 questions for all ages above the eighth grade. It requires 30 to 40 minutes to administer. The score purportedly indicates overall adjustment along with a separate measure of development in different traits found to be highly correlated with social and emotional adjustment but very slightly correlated with intelligence. The traits or subtests include truthfulness, happiness, alienation, sympathy, purposes, impulse judgment, control, and wishes. Reported validity (.90) and reliability (.92) resulted from test and item revision over an extended period involving over 10,000 individuals.

Guilford-Zimmerman Temperament Survey (Grades Nine to Sixteen).[12] This inventory resulted from extensive factor-analytic studies of items typically appearing on personality inventories. It consists of 300 items covering ten traits or factors with responses, Yes, No, ?. Evidence on scientific authenticity is limited, but subtests approach length necessary for satisfactory reliability.

Thurstone Temperament Schedule (Grades Nine to Sixteen, Adults).[13] Thurstone constructed this test based on the responses of normal individuals to measure seven factors which were found by factor analysis to account for the variance of the 13 factors in some of the scales developed by Guilford. The test contains 20 items for each trait and is self-administrable with responses, Yes, No, ?. Scale reliabilities vary from .45 to .86; validity data relative to educational decision making are not available.

California Test of Personality.[14] The California Test of Personality provides scores relating to 12 personality characteristics, subtotal scores for social and personal adjustment, and a total adjustment score. Items are answered on a "Yes–No" basis. Two forms are available covering five different levels: primary (K–3); elementary (grades 4–8); intermediate (grades 7–10); secondary (grade 9-college); and adult, comprising 180 items. The characteristic low reliability of trait sections with but 5 to 15

[11] John N. Washburne, *Washburne Social Adjustment Inventory* (New York: Harcourt, Brace & World, Inc., 1940).

[12] *Guilford-Zimmerman Temperament Survey* (Beverly Hills: Sheridan Supply Co., 1949).

[13] *Thurstone Temperament Schedule* (Chicago: Science Research Associates, Inc., 1953).

[14] L. P. Thorpe, W. W. Clarke, and E. W. Tiegs. *California Test of Personality,* Revised Form (Los Angeles: California Test Bureau, 1953).

items renders only subtotal and total scores satisfactorily reliable. It warrants noting that on many items in these inventories the testee is asked how he feels about certain things, which tends to produce more valid results than asking whether or not he does these things.

The Sixteen Personality Factor Questionnaire (Ages 15 and over).[15] R. B. Cattell at the Institute for Personality and Ability Testing has been instrumental in the development of four different personality questionnaires to extend systematic continuous personality measurement from adulthood down to six years of age. These different inventories are designed to measure the main dimensions of personality as revealed by factor analysis. The *16 PFQ* is applicable to individuals ages 15 and older and yields the most comprehensive profile of personality available in a single test. Equivalent Forms A and B consist of 187 items, with 10 and 13 items assessing each of the various factors. Norms are available for college students and high school seniors, general adult population, and selected occupational groups. Validation is based on factor analysis, although some other evidence suggests that reduction to a smaller number of basic factors is possible. The reliability of the various scales is low, which is characteristic of the relatively small number of items comprising them. Notwithstanding, the *16 PFQ* has seen considerable and seemingly effective use in physical education research.

Related IPAT Questionnaires (Ages 6 to 18).[16] The three other inventories published by the Institute for Personality and Ability Testing contain dimensions that parallel those of the *16 PFQ*. The IPAT *High School Personality Questionnaire* (1953-60), authored by R. B. Cattell, H. Beloff and R. W. Coan, covers ages 11 to 18; the IPAT *Children's Personality Questionnaire* (1959-60), authored by R. B. Porter with R. B. Cattell, ages 8 to 12; and the IPAT *Early School Personality Questionnaire* authored by R. W. Coan with R. B. Cattell, ages 6 to 8 years.

California Psychological Inventory (13 years and over).[17] The California Psychological Inventory (CPI) was constructed to afford a multidimensional assessment of the personality of normal individuals in various settings; psychopathological characteristics are not assessed. It consists of 480 true-false items which constitute 18 different scale scores bearing titles depicting more or less socially desirable aspects of behavior, such as dominance, sociability, and self-control. The CPI is essentially self-

---

[15] R. B. Cattell and H. W. Eber, *The Sixteen Personality Factor Questionnaire*, Revised 1962. (Champaign, Ill.: Institute for Personality and Ability Testing, 1962).

[16] Published by the Institute for Personality and Ability Testing, Champaign, Illinois.

[17] Harrison G. Gough, *California Psychological Inventory* (Palo Alto: Consulting Psychologists Press, Inc., 1960).

administrable and untimed. Retest reliabilities were .65 for males and .68 for females. Norms are available for 6,000 males and 7,000 females from 30 states, including separate mean profiles for high school and college students of each sex. Based on its careful construction, support by empirical evidence, and reported intercorrelations with other widely used personality tests, the CPI is regarded as one of the best personality inventories for use with normal individuals of age 13 or more.

The Eysenck Personality Inventory.[18] The EPI is an inventory designed to measure two main personality factors; viz., Extraversion-Introversion (E), and Neuroticism (N) or stability-instability. It contains an 18-item lie scale and has two parallel forms. The inventory resulted from extensive research, and the items are worded to facilitate comprehension and response by subjects of below average education or intelligence. Retest reliabilities at one-year interval varied from .84 to .94 on E and N sections; Spearman-Brown prophecy formula estimated reliability was .86 for E and .90 for N sections. Norms are available on several thousand British subjects, normal and abnormal in personality. The EPI has seen considerable use in British physical education studies and limited use in American research.

Mooney Problem Check List (Junior High School through Adults).[19] The Mooney Problem Check List is available in four levels: junior high school (grades 7–9), senior high school (grades 9–12), college, and adult. The items consist of brief statements of personal problems derived from analysis of written statements of problems from over 4000 students, and from adults and other sources. To complete the check list the individual checks all the problems that apply to him, underlining those of greatest concern. The senior high school and college forms consist of 330 items in 11 areas; the junior high school form has 210 items in seven areas; and the adult form covers nine areas. The problems involve health, home adjustment, sexual problems, financial concerns, religious difficulties, social relations, and others. Since it is not a test in the conventional sense, validity and reliability data are not available; neither are normative data. For each level provision is made for the respondent to indicate whether and, if so, with whom he would like to discuss his problems.

SRA Inventories (Grades Four to Twelve).[20] Two inventories have

[18] H. J. Eysenck and S. B. G. Eysenck, *Manual of the Eysenck Personality Inventory* (London: University of London Press, Ltd., 1964). Available from Educational and Industrial Testing Service. P. O. Box 7234, San Diego, California.

[19] Ross L. Mooney, *Problem Check List* (New York: The Psychological Corp., 1950).

[20] H. H. Remmers and R. H. Bauernfeind. *SRA Junior Inventory* (1957); and H. H. Remmers and B. Shimberg, *SRA Youth Inventory* (1960, Chicago: Science Research Associates, Inc.).

been devised to disclose problems that cause the most worry for boys and girls. *SRA Junior Inventory* (grades four to eight) samples problems in five areas: about myself, about me and my school, about me and my home, getting along with other people, and about things in general. It is highly regarded among adjustment inventories for this level. *SRA Youth Inventory* (grades seven to twelve) covers problems of youth categorized into eight areas.

Billet-Starr Youth Problems Inventory (Junior and Senior High School).[21] This inventory, BSYPI, was designed to help school personnel quickly identify the self-acknowledged problems of students in grades 7–12. It has two levels: junior high school (grades 7–9) containing 432 problems; and senior high school (grades 10–12) with 441 problems. Eleven areas are identified with 9 to over 80 problems occurring in each of the different areas. Area and total scores are determined. Students indicate their personal response to each item as: NP—no problem, S—somewhat of a problem; or M—much of a problem. Geographically biased percentile norms ($N = 8675$) for each sex are available. The limitations relating to validity and reliability that are characteristic of other check lists apply, but BSYPI has as yet not seen as extensive use as other check lists to have proven its validity.

The Adjective Check List (College).[22] The Adjective Check List affords a convenient assessment of desirable personality characteristics of college men and women. It consists of 300 adjectives descriptive of personality attributes and can be used for self-assessment or rating by others. The instrument is organized into 24 scales and is presently advocated only for research use.

Link Inventory of Activities and Interests (Ages 10 to 20).[23] Link developed an inventory applicable to children and youth, 10 to 20 years of age, to measure social initiative or aggressiveness, self-determination, and adjustments to the opposite sex. A personality quotient is derived from a weighted combination of the scores on these traits. Reliability of test parts ranged from .70 to .88.

Dawley-Troyer-Shaw Inventory (Grades Three to Six).[24] The authors describe the construction and application of a problem-situation test for

[21] I. S. Starr and R. O. Billett. *Billett-Starr Youth Problems Inventory* (New York: Harcourt, Brace and World, 1961).

[22] H. G. Gough and A. B. Heilbrun, *The Adjective Check List Manual* (Palo Alto: Consulting Psychologists Press, Inc., 1965).

[23] Henry C. Link, "A Test of Four Personality Traits of Adolescents," *Journal of Applied Psychology*, XX, No. 5 (October, 1936), 527.

[24] D. J. Dawley, M. E. Troyer, and J. H. Shaw, "Relationship Between Observed Behavior in Elementary School Physical Education and Test Responses," *Research Quarterly*, XXII, No. 1 (March, 1951), 71.

grades three to six consisting of 15 problem situations and 90 test items to be answered yes or no. An anecdotal summary was developed for use in conjunction with the inventory for corroboration of a subject's written response by his overt behavior. The reference contains a sample question and summary sheet with anecdotes. The authors noted that pupil response was not corroborated by observed behavior to a satisfactory extent.

Thune Inventory (Weightlifters).[25] A 108-item inventory was constructed and applied to YMCA men by Thune in a study of the personality of weightlifters. Two related inventories and several standard personality inventories comprised the source for deriving the questions. The inventory was divided into four categories: present health, self-confidence, manly—individualistic, and miscellaneous. The reference includes 25 of the items as part of tables showing a summary of the most significantly differentiating responses to the first three categories.

Flanagan Inventory (College Men).[26] Flanagan devised a 123-item inventory derived from parts of available tests to study personality traits as related to voluntary participation in six different physical education activity groups—fencing, basketball, boxing, swimming, volleyball, and badminton. The test sections include (1) items of factor M (masculinity-feminity) from Guilford-Martin Inventory, (2) Allport Ascendance-Submission Scale, (3) Guilford Introversion-Extroversion Scale, and (4) emotional stability section of Smith Human Behavior Inventory.

Sociometry

Succinctly stated, sociometry entails a study of group organization by objectively identifying the social forces within the group for the purpose of arranging the most harmonious and productive combinations within the group. The application of this field to educational endeavor was pioneered by Jennings, whose work gave direction to its use in physical education.[27] The potential of sociometry in physical education lies not only in its value in indicating social development of individuals, but also in facilitating better understanding and planning for social outcomes in the program and affording a basis for group organization that will engender interpersonal acceptance. In instances where sociometric techniques have been used to determine group constituency in physical education, generally three results accrue: greater socialization,

---

[25] John B. Thune, "Personality of Weightlifters," *Research Quarterly*, XX, No. 3 (October, 1949), 296.

[26] Lance Flanagan, "A Study of Some Personality Traits of Different Physical Activity Groups," *Research Quarterly*, XXII, No. 3 (October, 1951), 312.

[27] Helen H. Jennings, *Sociometry in Group Relations* (Washington, D. C.: American Council on Education, 1948).

more mutual attachments between individuals, and a decrease in negative feelings.

The sociometric test, used to detect the amount of organization shown by social groups, consists of determining who would like to be with whom for a specific purpose, such as playing a game. An illustrative application of the sociometric test involves having each student place his name on a 3- by 5-inch card and under it list in order of choice the names of three individuals whom he or she would like to have as a fellow squad member for physical education class activity. On the bottom of the card may be listed the name of any individual with whom association as a squad member is not wanted. In eliciting choices the teacher should encourage complete freedom and spontaneity of expression. To attain this the following assurances must obtain: the choice has interest and meaning for the individual, the expressed wishes will be taken into account, and the responses will be kept confidential. To prevent any adverse effect on response, care must be exercised so as not to use the term "sociometric test," which is apt to hold frightening connotations for many students.

While the teacher may study the cards to discern readily apparent group patterns and popular and unpopular individuals, the use of a tabulation form appears more feasible. Using such a form, as shown in Fig. 15–2, permits efficient and expeditious tabulation of results to provide a simple graphic picture.

The choices on each card are transposed by finding each student's name in the left-hand column of the form and then noting as 1, 2, and 3 the choices under the appropriate names listed across the top margin. Any rejections are recorded as "R." The number of choices used may be noted in the right marginal column. Upon completion of the tabulation, the number of times each individual is selected as first, second, and third choice is indicated below and the overall total is computed. If desired, an acceptance score to show comparative popularity may be computed by weighting each first choice as 3, second choice as 2, and third choice as 1.

The analysis of the data is furthered by using another sociometric instrument, the sociogram, to render visible the patterns of group organization and the position of each individual relative to every other individual. To construct a sociogram, as illustrated in Fig. 15–3, a symbol represents each individual; and the choices are drawn as recorded on the tabulation form. Both plotting and comprehension are facilitated by placing the more popular students in the center and the less popular around the outside. Analysis of the sociogram can be simplified by directing attention to one individual and studying the interrelationships shown by the lines leading to and from this case. The teacher should apply the following criteria in analyzing the sociogram:

1. The fewer the isolates (unchosen and without choices) and rejections, the better.
2. The greater the number of reciprocated or mutual choices, the better.
3. With improved group organization, the number of overchosen decreases and the choices become shared by all. (This is reflected in less range in acceptance scores with all scores tending to hover closely about the mean. In Fig. 15–2, improvement would see the acceptance scores approach the mean score of 6.)
4. With group maturation, the structural analysis of the group reveals a more highly differentiated and all-pervading network tending toward complex integration.

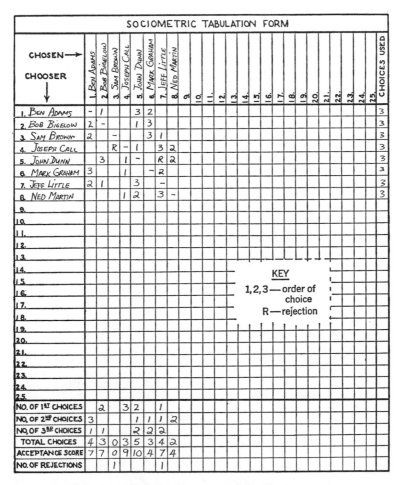

Fig. 15–2. Sociometric tabulation form.

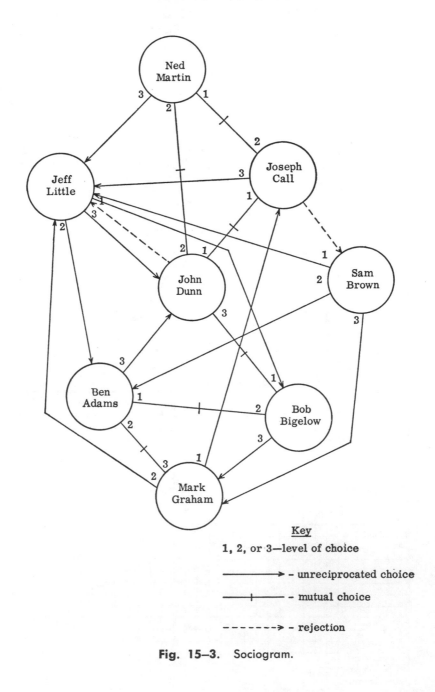

Key

1, 2, or 3—level of choice

———————▶ - unreciprocated choice

———————┼——— - mutual choice

- - - - - -▶ - rejection

Fig. 15–3. Sociogram.

On the basis of the sociometric test and the sociogram, the teacher may make assignments in light of considerations suggested by Jennings.

1. Give each unchosen or seldom chosen individual his first choice. These individuals have the greatest need for security. Highly chosen individuals are usually secure and aid others.
2. If there is a pair relationship, give each individual his highest reciprocal choice.
3. If the individual only receives choices from persons he has not chosen, give him his first choice.
4. Be sure no individual is put with persons who have rejected him.
5. Be sure to give each individual [at least] [28] one of his choices.[29]

Applying these guides to the sociogram in Fig. 15–3, to divide the group, one possible arrangement would place John, Joe, Ned, and Bob in one squad and Jeff, Sam, Mark, and Ben in the other. The prime concerns are allowing Sam, not chosen by anyone, his first choice and insuring that Sam is not placed with Joe and Jeff is not teamed with John. The latter two instances involved rejections.

Two other supplemental procedures may possess value for the physical education teacher. The first is the *Acquaintance Volume Test* that measures the expansiveness of each individual within a given time period. For example, at the start of a semester or unit of instruction, each class member lists the names of individuals known to him or her. This procedure is repeated at the end of the time period; and the comparative results divulge the number of new acquaintances made and, accordingly, provide an indicant of the amount of social interaction. The second supplemental measure consists of a class check list by means of which each student indicates his feelings for every other class member by checking in the proper column as "like," "dislike," or "indifferent."

Another sociometric application is the use of the *Guess Who?* or *Who's Who in My Group?* peer-rating technique which employs the approach of asking students directly how they feel about other students. Two variations are used. The student may be asked to note in writing the group member who: (1) is the best all-round athlete in class games; (2) tends most to pick on and annoy others; (3) follows directions best; and so on. Alternatively, group members may be requested to write the names of any individuals in the group who: (1) have outstanding ability in games; (2) seem to be friendly with everyone; (3) never get mad when anything goes wrong; and similarly. Regardless of the variation chosen, the scale should include traits that are desirable as well as others that are not; and the scoring for each individual is the number of

[28] Brackets represent the author's addition.
[29] Jennings, *op. cit.*, pp. 45–46.

times his or her name appears for a desirable characteristic, less the number it appears for undesirable items. Thus a picture of peer-perception for a particular group on the characteristics included is afforded the teacher.

The validity and reliability of the sociometric test have been found quite satisfactory in terms of what they attempt to measure. This is substantiated by the fact that the children most frequently selected generally exhibit many more socially desirable assets than do those seldom chosen. However, rapport must be good and the situation meaningful for desirable scientific authenticity to obtain. Remmers [30] has presented a definitive description of the sociometric test and other methods of analyzing sociometric data which constitutes a valuable resource for the teacher desiring further information.

For further description of sociometry and its application to physical education, several sources exist that should prove both interesting and helpful to the reader.[31] The teacher should realize that, in addition to the testing values inherent in sociometry, definite implications exist for teaching per se, inasmuch as the basic premise of sociometric grouping holds that people do their best when associated with those they like.

Anecdotal Records

An anecdotal record may be defined as an objective verbal description by the teacher of significant occurrences or behavior incidents in the life of a student that reveal meaningful information about the individual. When employed properly, this instrument provides a record of actual behavior and represents a most valuable measurement device for concomitant learning, particularly in terms of social development. Its use is not limited to concomitant learning, however. While considerable confidence can be placed in properly constructed and carefully used tests of technical and associated learnings, as well as concomitant, such instruments will not reveal everything to the extent desired. Careful and systematic observation will often afford a measure of existence of certain traits or qualities that the aforementioned tests and devices seldom, if ever, furnish. Such observation may also serve as a means of validating the findings of inventories and skill tests. These observations should be recorded in an organized and meaningful manner so as to facilitate pe-

[30] H. H. Remmers, "Rating Methods in Research on Teaching." In N. L. Gage (ed.), *Handbook of Research on Teaching* (Chicago: Rand McNally & Co., 1963), Chap. 7.

[31] Patricia W. Hale, "Proposed Method for Analyzing Sociometric Data," *Research Quarterly*, XXVII, No. 2 (May, 1956), 152; Hilda C. Kozman (ed.), *Group Process in Physical Education* (New York: Harper & Bros., 1951), pp. 194–212; and Frances Todd, "Sociometry in Physical Education," *Journal of Health–Physical Education–Recreation*, XXIV, No. 5 (May, 1953), 23.

riodic analysis and interpretation of notations. And finally, realization of the potential value of this procedure will be consummated only when results are used in constructive appraisal. Hence, proper application of anecdotal records to accomplish the desired purpose encompasses four steps: (1) observe conduct, (2) record observations, (3) periodically analyze and summarize anecdotes, and (4) use the results.

The observation upon which each anecdote is based should be made carefully and governed by the same conditions that prevail for rating, as described in Chapter 5 under performance rating and rating scales. Given an accurate observation of a meaningful situation, the anecdotal record will be valid and reliable to the extent that it actually reproduces whatever was observed. Actually, the best anecdotal record is a sound motion picture. Since this is impractical, the teacher should endeavor to create a "motion picture image" in recording anecdotes. The following characteristics of proper anecdotal records represent guides for the teacher.

1. Record what is actually seen or heard. If inferences, guesses, or assumptions are included, they should be so labeled.
2. Put anecdotes on a record form suitable for intended use; either a separate card for each anecdote or a multiple anecdote form. Figure 15–4 illustrates the latter.
3. Establish a plan of periodic observation and recording and adhere to it to make the record cumulative. This may vary from noting every instance of conduct that attracts the teacher's attention or seems characteristic of the individual to planning for one anecdote on each student in a given period of time.
4. Choose words and phrases whose meaning is clear and, so far as possible, unequivocal.
5. Use words and phrases that are definable in terms of things rather than words. Concrete statements are preferable to abstract ones. To illustrate, "He refused to join his squad group," not "He did not cooperate."
6. Avoid words and phrases with strong emotional connotations, such as love, hate, insolent, courteous, loyal, dishonest, and the like.
7. Do not use words and phrases that express the observer's judgment or opinion rather than his perception. Some frequently encountered "judgmental" terms include well-behaved, delinquent, aggressive, didn't try, industrious, nervous, and happy.
8. For each incident, when appropriate, note any interpretative comments, including background information, relevant to it and, as a separate or distinguishable entry, record any suggestions or recommendations that appear warranted.

Anecdotal records possess great value only when made cumulative by the addition of new anecdotes as meaningful situations arise and are

Name _____

Directions

Under incident below, record observations that bear on the student's physical, mental, and social development opposite the appropriate grouping of technical, associated or concomitant learning. Do not evaluate, but describe. Avoid vague words such as good, strong, shy, etc. Enter statements of what happened or what you saw, as "Did three push-ups and couldn't do any more," "Cried and started fighting when he was called out in kickball."

Date and sign each entry. And as appropriate, alongside the incident record any relevant background and other interpretative information, as well as any suggestions or recommendations.

Incident	Interpretation and Suggestions	Date	Signature

T L
e e
c a
h r
n n
i i
c n
a g
l

A L
s e
s a
o r
c n
i i
a n
t g
e
d

C L
o e
n a
c r
o n
m i
i n
t g
a
n
t

> In a class volleyball game, John had two attempted spikes blocked by Andrew and Charles on successive points that ended the game. Whereupon, John grabbed the ball, threw it vigorously in apparent disgust at Charles' feet and stalked off the court. This behavior is out of character for John and may be related to the fact that he has a new and sickly baby brother (his only sibling) which has drastically altered the attention he receives at home. It might be desirable to encourage John to become involved in some after-school activities.
> — C. R. Meyers, 1/7/74

Fig. 15–4. Multiple anecdotal record for physical education.

recorded. And logically their value increases with the number of observations that are noted. Especial heed should be paid to minimizing the use of high-level abstractions in notations in order to obtain an "operational description" of behavior that gives anecdotal records their real significance.

In maintaining logical and well-organized anecdotal records, it becomes necessary to devise a method for systematically recording and compiling this information to facilitate its review and effective use. The anecdotal record system should be designed to allow for anecdotes by different teachers over a period of time. Periodically, the material recorded for each student should be reviewed, summarized, and interpreted so as to disclose such concerns as patterns of behavior, degree of social adjustment, and areas in which individual guidance appears indicated. It is this summary statement for each period of review (such as six months or a year) that renders fullest meaning for the cumulative record. Accordingly, it would appear that the specific anecdotes might well be destroyed after summarization to avoid prejudicial interpretation by other teachers and administrators who may view a few specific anecdotes out of the summarized context. Particular emphasis should be made to insure that this periodic analysis, summary and interpretation of anecdotes is done carefully so as to present a realistic, undistorted picture of the individual.

Two particular concerns dealing with the interpretation of anecdotes and their periodic summarization warrant mention as admonitions. It is most important that a clear line of demarcation be recognized between anecdotal facts and opinion, since any intermixing simply contaminates the facts per se and defies meaningful and accurate interpretation. And in summarizing, teachers (or observers in general) should avoid the tendency to overgeneralize on the basis of striking rather than typical incidents, which is also distorting.

In the last step in the procedure, use of the results, lies the justification for keeping anecdotal records. Anecdotal records demand considerable teacher time and are warranted only on the basis of application made of the findings. As already indicated, such records possess considerable value and may be employed to the extent permitted by teacher time. The importance as a resource for meaningful teacher notations for parents on report cards should be obvious. Even under severe time limitations, the teacher may find it possible to note salient occurrences relative to selected individuals and thereby contribute to a more complete understanding of these students requisite to individual guidance.

As a final note attesting to the importance of anecdotal records, it should be pointed out that the anecdotal record summaries might well comprise an integral part of the cumulative record of each individual, as described in Chapters 7 and 16, showing the profile of test results in the various areas of measurement as they contribute to overall appraisal of the individual. Conceivably, these records afford a means of tying together in a cohesive bond various particulars of an individual's cumulative record and render it more meaningful.

ATTITUDES AND BEHAVIOR TOWARD PHYSICAL EDUCATION AND PHYSICAL ACTIVITY

Behavior Scales

Cowell Check Sheet of Sports Outcomes.[32] Cowell proposed an evaluative check sheet for self-appraisal regarding the outcomes of sports participation for boys that could be easily adapted for girls. The device consists of 20 desired behavior characteristics revealed in sports participation. For example, the first statement questions the extent to which the subject learned "to sacrifice my own personal 'whims' or desires for the good of the group or team." The subject checks the existence of each item as (1) not at all, (2) very little, (3) somewhat, (4) a great deal, and (5) a very great deal. Total scores approximating 100 represent desirable behavioral outcomes. The check sheet itself serves as a compilation of values obtainable through learning experiences in physical education.

Johnson Sportmanship Attitude Scales (Junior High School).[33] Johnson definitively describes the development of two alternate scale forms of 21 different items each from an initial set of 152 items representing descriptions of ethically critical sportsmanship behavior from the content universe of football, basketball and baseball. Intrinsic validity was established through the scale-discrimination technique, an eclectic method of scale development proposed by Edwards and Kilpatrick and later clarified by Edwards. Items were written according to the criteria cited by Edwards. The scale development study involved 500 junior high school boys and girls. Coefficients of .86 for reliability and .81 and .86 for reproducibility for Forms A and B, respectively, were obtained. The scales are not included in the reference but available from the author at Southeastern Louisiana College, Hammond.

Action-Choice Tests for Competitive Sports Situations (College).[34] Using a professional jury, Haskins developed 60 items dealing with ethical conduct in sports situations, as accumulated by Betty G. Hartman

[32] Charles C. Cowell, "Our Function is Still Education," *The Physical Educator,* XIV, No. 1 (March, 1957), 6. Check sheet is reproduced in SR 1 and 4.

[33] Marion L. Johnson, "Construction of Sportsmanship Attitude Scales," *Research Quarterly,* XL, No. 2 (May, 1969), 312. The scales are reproduced in SR 1.

[34] Mary J. Haskins, "Problem-Solving Test of Sportsmanship," *Research Quarterly,* XXXI, No. 4 (December, 1960), 601.

of MacMurray College in a previous study. Twenty items were eliminated on the basis of an item analysis of a trial administration to college
men and women (N = 200). Two alternate 20-item forms of the test
were devised which compared favorably with the 40-item test on validity
and reliability, and were deemed satisfactory in that regard. The use
of two sociometric instruments for validation was described. The tests
were published by Haskins and Hartman and are available from the
former at Ohio State University.

Attitude Scales

Wear Attitude Inventory.[35] Wear carefully constructed with the
Likert technique an inventory of 120 items for measuring attitudes of
college men toward physical education as an activity course. Validity
and reliability were established. Response is on a five-choice basis. A
40-item short form was derived through item analysis of the long form,
with reliability of .97 (N = 272). The reference cited contains the short
form of the inventory along with directions and normalized T-scores,
and also statistical data on both forms. The reading ability level was
determined by the Forbes-Cottle readability formula as being twelfth
grade.

To meet the need for equivalent tests of attitudes in ascertaining
change, Wear subsequently developed two alternate scale forms of 30
items each.[36] These forms, A and B, yielded reliability estimates of .94
and .96 and a correlation of .96 between them. They both differentiated
well between divergent groups as a verification of validity. Wear advocates use of these alternate forms to determine even short-term changes
after brief experiences such as viewing a film. The reference contains
both equivalent forms, but the reader is referred to the original reference
(footnote 35) for directions.

Application of the 40-item inventory to a particular situation is illustrated by a study of attitude toward physical education for women at
the University of Michigan.[37] The instrument appears in the reference
and consists of three parts: I, as check list response to informational
questions pertinent to subject's background; II, questions based on the
objectives of physical education; and III, the 27 items of the 40-item
Wear Inventory which for purposes of this study were classified into
areas of contribution as social, physical health, or mental health.

Numerous other applications have been made involving the different

[35] Carlos B. Wear, "The Evaluation of Attitude Toward Physical Education as an
Activity Course," *Research Quarterly*, XXII, No. 1 (March, 1951), 114.

[36] Carlos B. Wear, "Construction of Equivalent Forms of an Attitude Scale," *Research Quarterly*, XXVI, No. 1 (March, 1955), 113.

[37] Margaret Bell, *et al.*, "Attitudes of Women at the University of Michigan Toward Physical Education," *Research Quarterly*, XXIV, No. 4 (December, 1953), 379.

inventory forms. Broer used the 40-item inventory and found it to be a valid and reliable instrument for administration to college women.[38] Moyer and associates used the 40-item inventory with college women as modified by the addition of ten statements that applied specifically to the program at Northern llinois University.[39] A reliability coefficient of equivalence of .83 was determined (N = 43). In a study of 199 college men Campbell concluded that short form A of the attitude scale is a reliable and valid instrument and can be used to measure the attainment of attitudes according to expressed objectives of physical education.[40] Subsequently, Campbell confirmed the appropriateness of scale form A for use with junior high school boys (N = 770).[41] Keogh affirmed the validity of scale form A as applied to college men and women (N = 226).[42] Other illustrative uses of scale form A have included determining the attitudes of entering college freshmen men, effect of a special conditioning class for college men, and the relationship of attitude of college women and success in physical education.

Adams Physical Education Attitude Scales (College).[43] From an initial lot of 150 statements Adams developed two alternative sets of 20-statement Thurstone-Chave-type scales to investigate the attitudes of New Zealand teachers college students toward college subjects. Either set may be used, or both for greater reliability, as a Thurstone-Chave-type test. Or, with the exception of 8 items, the statements on the two sets may be given as a Likert-type test. Validation was established between the two types of scales and against a cumulative self-rating scale. Reliability coefficients were .89 for Likert-type scale, .71 for one set of Thurstone-Chave-type scale, and .84 for both sets. The reference contains the statements and their Thurstone weightings for scoring, as well as appropriate test directions for both types of scales.

Kenyon Physical Activity Attitude Inventory (College).[44] Kenyon noted that past research in attitudes toward physical activity has re-

[38] Marion R. Broer, "Evaluation of a Basic Skills Curriculum for Women Students of Low Motor Ability at the University of Wisconsin," *Research Quarterly*, XXVI, No. 1 (March, 1955), 15.

[39] L. M. Moyer, J. C. Mitchem, and M. M. Bell, "Women's Attitudes Toward Physical Education in the General Education Program at Northern Illinois University," *Research Quarterly*, XXXVII, No. 4 (December, 1966), 515.

[40] Donald E. Campbell, "Student Attitudes Toward Physical Education," *Research Quarterly*, XXXIX, No. 3 (October, 1968), 456.

[41] Donald E. Campbell, "Wear Attitude Inventory Applied to Junior High School Boys," *Research Quarterly*, XXXIX, No. 4 (December, 1968), 888.

[42] Jack Keough, "Analysis of General Attitudes Toward Physical Education," *Research Quarterly*, XXXIII, No. 2 (May, 1962), 239.

[43] R. S. Adams, "Two Scales for Measuring Attitudes Toward Physical Education." *Research Quarterly*, 34:1:91–94 (March), 1963. The scales are also available in SR 5.

[44] Gerald Kenyon, "Six Scales for Assessing Attitudes Toward Physical Activity," *Research Quarterly*, XXXIX, No. 3 (October, 1968), 466.

vealed several shortcomings. These are: (1) characterization has been confined to restricted domains such as physical education, team game competition or sport, rather than being directed to physical activity in its broadest sense; (2) instruments were seldom based upon a thorough application of acceptable test construction procedures and, when used, data were derived for relatively small samples; and (3) the likely multi-dimensionality of the domain in question has not been accounted for when scaling procedures have been used. In an endeavor to overcome these inadequacies he proposed a conceptual framework accruing from a logical analysis of the function allegedly served in contemporary society by physical activity.

The model was characterized as consisting of six dimensions or subdomains as follows:

1. *Physical activity as a social experience.* A characterization of activities in which the primary purpose is to provide a medium for social intercourse, that is, to meet new people and perpetuate existing relationships.
2. *Physical activity for health and fitness.* A characterization of activities in which participation is intended to improve health and physical fitness.
3. *Physical activity as the pursuit of vertigo.* A characterization of activities or experiences providing, with some risk, an element of thrill and excitement through such media as speed, acceleration, sudden change of direction, or exposure to dangerous situations, and with the participant remaining in control.
4. *Physical activity as an aesthetic experience.* A characterization of activities regarded as possessing beauty or certain artistic qualities such as ballet, gymnastics, or figure skating.
5. *Physical activity as catharsis.* A characterization of activities that provide, through some vicarious means, relief from tension precipitated by frustration.
6. *Physical activity as an ascetic experience.* A characterization of activities that are conceived as necessitating long, strenuous and often painful training and stiff competition, and that demand a deferment of many other gratifications.

Within the context of this model Kenyon constructed relatively independent univocal scales for determining attitudes toward physical activity. For each of the six subdomains he identified and defined a universe of content and then developed seven-alternative Likert-type attitude statements deemed to be representative of each dimension. After evaluation by judges, these statements were incorporated into two separate but similar inventories for college men and women. The present inventory, Form D, reflects refinement of earlier forms and consists of 59 statements for men (Form DM) and 54 for women (Form

DW).[45] For Form DM each scale consists of either 9 or 10 items, and the number of statements on Form DW ranges from 8 to 11. The different items were evaluated on the basis of factor and item analysis and have generated reliability coefficients ranging from .72 to .89 for the six scales using Hoyt's analysis of variance approach to internal consistency.

Instrument stability was verified by comparative measures of central tendency, variability and reliability between two similar populations. Validity of the scales was established except for the catharis scale. The criterion was the differentiation between strong and weak preference groups. Kenyon admonishes that the use of these scales should be restricted to research purposes. Alderman applied these scales, using 8 items for each scale, to Canadian champion male and female athletes.[46]

Richardson Physical Fitness and Exercise Attitude Scale (College).[47] Using modified Thurstone-Chave techniques, two equivalent forms ($r = .87$, N = 300) of an equal-appearing-intervals attitude scale were constructed by Richardson to appraise the attitude of college students toward physical fitness and exercise. Each form consists of 19 scaled attitude statements, and the individual notes those items with which he agrees. The attitude score becomes the median value of the items noted. Validity and reliability (.83) were established. The reference contains both forms and directions.

McPherson Physical Activity Attitude Inventory (Men).[48] Using high school teachers as subjects, McPherson developed an attitude inventory that appears to be sensitive in detecting the direction and intensities of attitudes that men have toward exercise and physical activity. The inventory consists of 50 statements to which response is obtained on a five-point Likert-type scale. Divergent group validity was established and the reliability coefficient of equivalence was .92 (N = 25 physical education teachers).

[45] Form D of the ATPA scales with instructions is available as document number 9983 from ADI Auxiliary Publications Project, Photoduplication Service, Library of Congress, Washington, D. C. 20540.

[46] Richard B. Alderman, "A Sociopsychological Assessment of Attitude Toward Physical Activity in Champion Athletes," *Research Quarterly,* XL, No. 1 (March, 1970), 1.

[47] C. E. Richardson, "Thurstone Scale for Measuring Attitudes of College Students Toward Physical Fitness and Exercise," *Research Quarterly,* XXVI, No. 4 (December, 1960), 638.

[48] B. D. McPherson, "Psychological Effects of an Exercise Program for Post-Cardiac and Normal Adult Men," Unpublished Master's Thesis, University of Western Ontario, 1965; and described in: B. D. McPherson and M. S. Yuhasz, "An Inventory for Assessing Men's Attitudes Toward Exercise and Physical Activity," *Research Quarterly,* XXXIX, No. 1 (March, 1968), 218.

Lakie Competitive Attitude Scale (College Men).[49] Lakie developed a scale to reveal the extent to which the "win-at-any-cost" philosophy of athletics is supported. A 55-item scale was administered to 60 college men students and, based upon item analysis and review by a jury, 22 items were selected for inclusion in the final scale. Both favorable and unfavorable statements were included and scored appropriately on a 1–5 scale, with 5 indicating the strongly favored response. Reliability of the scale was determined as .81 (Kuder-Richardson) and deemed satisfactory for differentiating between groups. The reference contains the final scale statements.

Edgington Physical Education Attitude Scale (High School Freshman Boys).[50] Beginning with a preliminary form of 125 statements for jury evaluation, and after two trial administrations, Edgington developed the final form of a 66-item six-point attitude scale for use with high school freshman boys. Construct validity was established through application of the Likert technique and affirmed by divergent group analysis. Reliability was estimated as .92 by the Spearman-Brown prophecy formula (N = 105). The reference contains the complete scale.

The six-point scale employed by Edgington entails a choice from three favorable and three unfavorable graded responses, with no neutral choice. The neutral or undecided category was eliminated in the belief that high school freshman boys might be inclined to choose it too freely. However, this elimination necessitates a definite decision on each statement, whether or not the individual can justifiably respond on an agree–disagree basis. Thus, the scoring does not permit an undecided or neutral choice, even though it may be the only valid response. Accordingly, use of a five- or seven-point scale would permit a valid response to each statement, and the provision of a clear and appropriate direction will minimize any tendency to use the undecided or neutral choice unless entirely warranted.

Kappes Attitude Inventory (College Women).[51] Kappes described an attitude inventory composed of statements regarding physical education and the services offered students by a physical education department. The actual instrument includes two parts. Part I lists 31 activities for rating by the individual on a 5-point scale as to enjoyment

---

[49] William L. Lakie, "Expressed Attitudes of Various Groups of Athletes Toward Athletic Competition," *Research Quarterly*, XXXV, No. 4 (December. 1964), 497.

[50] Charles W. Edgington, "Development of an Attitude Scale to Measure Attitudes of High School Freshman Boys Toward Physical Education," *Research Quarterly*, XXXIX, No. 3 (October, 1968), 505. The scale is reproduced in SR 1.

[51] Evelina A. Kappes, "Inventory To Determine Attitudes of College Women Toward Physical Education and Student Services of the Physical Education Department," *Research Quarterly*, XXV, No. 4 (December, 1954), 429.

in the activity, instruction desired, and skill estimate. Part II is comprised of a series of 54 statements about physical education, one's likes and dislikes, throughout which are dispersed 20 items concerning attitude measurement; rating is on a 5-point scale. The reference contains the inventory, statistical analysis, and description of established validity and reliability (.94) for attitude statements. This inventory attempts to disclose attitude toward physical education while surveying opinions toward organizational and administrational services offered by a department.

Mista Modification of Plummer Attitude Inventory (College Women).[52] To develop an instrument to assess the attitudes of college women toward their high school physical education programs, Mista modified the original 48-item Plummer Inventory [53] by adding 10 items. Based on divergent group analysis of a pilot administration (N = 127), the 30 items that displayed the best discriminatory power were selected for the final inventory, for which reliability of .90 was established. This inventory proved satisfactory in a study with 1,146 college women. The inventory is not included in the reference.

Smith-Bozymowski Warm-Up Attitude Inventory (College Women).[54] Smith and Bozymowski devised an attitude inventory to study the attitude of college women toward warm-ups. The final inventory consists of 34 of the 42 original statements formulated according to the criteria summarized by Edwards (see Chapter 5) and that yielded satisfactory discriminatory power based on Flanagan's technique with upper and lower 27 percent groups. The reliability coefficient of equivalence was .94. The reference contains the final inventory items, which are scored on a 1–5 point scale, from strongly disagree to strongly agree.

McCue Competitive Attiude Scale (College Women).[55] A scale for evaluating attitudes toward intensive competition in team games was constructed by McCue. Although designed for college women, the scale was intended to be applicable at various age levels with slight revision. The scale consists of 77 items to which the subject responds on a five-choice basis ranging from strongly agree to strongly disagree.

[52] Nancy J. Mista, "Attitudes of College Women Toward Their High School Physical Education Programs," *Research Quarterly*, XXXIX, No. 1 (March, 1968), 166.

[53] Tomi C. Plummer, "Factors Influencing the Attitudes and Interests of College Women in Physical Education," Unpublished Doctoral Dissertation, State University of Iowa, 1952.

[54] J. L. Smith and M. F. Bozymowski, "Effect of Attitude Toward Warmups on Motor Performance," *Research Quarterly*, XXXVI, No. 1 (March, 1965), 78.

[55] Betty F. McCue, "Constructing an Instrument for Evaluating Attitudes Toward Intensive Competition in Team Games," *Research Quarterly*, XXIV, No. 2 (May, 1953), 205.

The areas covered include personality development, human relationships, public relations, physical development, skill development, recreation, and safety. Validity and reliability were established, although the adequacy of the latter determination may be questioned. The use of a 3-point scale (-1 to $+1$) resulted in a correlation of .93 with the 5-point scale results. The reference contains the scale items and instructions for the student.

Kneer Adaptation of Wear Attitude Inventory (High School Girls).[56] Kneer revised the 40-item Wear Physical Education Attitude Inventory to adapt it to high school girls. This was accomplished by clarification of statements that tended to be ambiguous for high school girls and by adjusting the reading level from twelfth grade or above to eighth grade, as measured by the Forbes-Cottle readability formula. For validation, the Kneer Inventory correlated .84 with the Wear version and .87 with graphic self-ratings. Reliability was estimated as .95 by the Spearman-Brown prophecy formula.

Mercer Adaptation of the Galloway Attitude Inventory (High School Girls).[57] Mercer adapted the Galloway Attitude Inventory, designed for college women, to render it suitable for use with high school girls. The inventory consists of 40 statements to which response is obtained on a 1–5 point scale. A correlation of .74 was derived with a self-rating scale; reliability was .92.

Carr Physical Education Attitude Scale (High School Freshman Girls).[58] A self-inventory was developed by Carr to measure attitudes of freshman high school girls as related to physical education. The reference contains the 84 statements included in the scale listed in order of decreasing desirability, showing item analysis results. Forty-two statements were found to be highly significant relative to success in physical education and usable for a short form of the attitude-rating scale. Validity was established on the basis of divergent group analysis for the criterion of success in physical education. No evidence of reliability is reported.

[56] Marian E. Kneer, "The Adaptation of Wear's Physical Education Attitude Inventory for Use with High School Girls," Microcard Master's Thesis, Illinois State University, 1956. The inventory is reproduced in SR 1.

[57] Emily L. Mercer, "An Adaptation and Revision of the Galloway Attitude Inventory for Evaluating the Attitudes of High School Girls Toward Psychological, Moral-Spiritual, and Sociological Values in Physical Education Experiences," Microcard Master's Thesis, Women's College, University of North Carolina, 1961. The inventory is also available in SR 1.

[58] Martha G. Carr, "The Relationship Between Success in Physical Education and Selected Attitudes Expressed in High School Freshmen Girls," *Research Quarterly*, XVI, No. 3 (October, 1945), 176.

Drinkwater Attitude Inventory (High School Girls).[59] Using Likert's technique Drinkwater developed two equivalent forms ($r = .87$) of an attitude inventory to determine attitudes of high school girls toward physical education as a career for women. Validity and reliability (.96) were established. Statements were subjected to statistical analysis to eliminate ambiguous items or those with poor discriminatory power. The reference contains both forms of 36 items each and a description of inventory construction.

Seaman Physical Education Attitude Inventory for Physically Handicapped (High School).[60] Seaman devised an inventory to sample attitudes toward physical education of orthopedically and neurologically handicapped secondary school students. The inventory consists of 40 statements (28 favorable, 12 unfavorable) to which response is given on a five-point Likert-type scale. Validity was established in light of self-ratings and participation in physical activities. Reliability was estimated as .96 by Spearman-Brown prophecy formula (N = 50). The inventory proved to be effective in a subsequent study (N = 115) by Seaman. The scale is not included in the reference.

RESOLVING THE ILLUSTRATIVE PROBLEM

In determining the suitability of available measures of attitudes and behavior the reader should be alert to the relevant aspects of the many considerations for construction of rating scales and self-report instruments presented in Chapter 5 as well as the implications of those relating to performance rating scales in Chapter 4. For rating scales one finds that matters pertaining to factors affecting rating, use of raters, and errors in rating all have implications for instrument suitability. For self-reports, however, the response format and attention to establishing rapport represent important concerns. Particular attention to several concerns relating to instrument suitability appears warranted at this point.

Preference should be accorded to a response format designed to make the extreme categories or choices appear less extreme, so as to encourage their use. This is essential in order to minimize the common error of central tendency. The feasibility of using a degree of assurance scale (such as for the McCloy Behavior Rating Scale) should be given careful thought. In essence, the assurance scale gives an indication of the

---

[59] Barbara L. Drinkwater, "Development of an Attitude Inventory To Measure the Attitude of High School Girls Toward Physical Education as a Career for Women," *Research Quarterly*, XXXI, No. 4 (December, 1960), 575.

[60] Janet A. Seaman, "Attitudes of Physically Handicapped Children Toward Physical Education," *Research Quarterly*, XLI, No. 3 (October, 1970), 439.

judge's familiarity with the student, and its use poses the problem of how to interpret the scores. This is perhaps best resolved by avoiding use of assurance ratings and, instead, having judges rate a trait action only if they are familiar with the subject or have an opportunity to observe him for a reasonable time before the rating is rendered.

Two other concerns bear on appraisal of attitudes and behavior and instrument appropriateness. Basic to the decision as to whether to include behavior rating, let alone which instrument to use, the attendant benefit of such rating should be recognized, namely, motivation. Generally, a student strives to do better when aware of the rating and, if informed as to the traits being observed, he tends to evince growth toward specific goals. Further, with tactful apprisal of ratings the student receives valuable aid in self-analysis. And lastly, as consideration is given to self-report devices, it should be realized that even under the most ideal conditions it is desirable to supplement attitudes determined by self-report methods with evidence obtained from direct observation.

A review of available tests of attitudes and behavior indicates that considerable progress has been realized in developing effective means of measuring these so-called "intangibles." Regardless of educational level, the teacher should find a test suitable for use in a given situation or capable of being adapted easily. Certainly, many suggestions for constructing such tests can be gleaned from the available resource instruments.

To focus on what is available for junior high school physical education, the teacher might logically begin by utilizing the findings of the psychological testing as noted on the guidance records to appraise the needs and development of students. As a measure of social adjustment, the Cowell Personal Distance Scale would provide a peer appraisal that can be made each year to reveal status and change. Either the Cowell Social Adjustment Index or a teacher adaptation of the Cassidy Class Experience Check List would provide for teacher appraisal at such time that further emphasis on this aspect is desired. Turning to attitudes and behavior relating to physical education, apparently it may be necessary to construct an attitude inventory specifically for this school level, using the Wear Inventory as a pattern, so that a valid reading can be obtained to give direction to the physical education program. The development of equivalent forms of the attitude inventory would facilitate a retest later during the junior high school experience to ascertain change. This decision regarding the need to construct an inventory should be based upon a study of the discrepancy between the findings of Campbell and Kneer. Campbell concluded that the short form A of the Wear Inventory was appropriate for junior high school boys, whereas

Kneer found modification necessary to render the 40-item inventory suitable for high school girls.

This analysis of available tests of attitudes and behavior completes the presentation of all areas of measurement covering the characteristics of measurement in each area together with a delineation of available tests. The interrelatedness of tests of attitudes and behavior with those involving knowledge and areas of technical learning as they all contribute to overall appraisal of the individual should remain paramount in the teacher's mind.

SELECTED REFERENCES

1. BARROW, HAROLD M., and McGEE, ROSEMARY. *A Practical Approach to Measurement in Physical Education*, 2d ed. Philadelphia: Lea and Febiger, 1971.
2. BUROS, OSCAR K. *Tests in Print*. Highland Park, N. J.: Gryphon Press, 1961.
3. BUROS, OSCAR K. *The Seventh Mental Measurement Yearbook*. Highland Park, N. J.: Gryphon Press, 1972.
4. CLARKE, H. HARRISON. *Application of Measurement to Health and Physical Education*, 4th ed. Englewood Cliffs: Prentice-Hall, Inc., 1967.
5. MATHEWS, DONALD K. *Measurement in Physical Education*, 4th ed. Philadelphia: W. B. Saunders Co., 1973.
6. MEHRENS, W. A., and LEHMANN, I. J. *Standardized Tests in Education*. New York: Holt, Rinehart and Winston, Inc., 1969.
7. OPPENHEIM, A. N. *Questionnaire Design and Attitude Measurement*. London: Heinemann (New York: Basic Books), 1966.

Part III

APPLICATION OF
MEASUREMENT

The full potential value attributable to measurement will not be obtained unless concerted effort is made to insure its effective and appropriate application. This Part deals with fundamental considerations to be heeded so that the desired benefits may be realized. Attention will be directed to the application of measurement as it pertains to the individual student, the physical education program, and the physical education profession.

16

Measurement Applied

As "the proof of the pudding is in the eating," so does the success of the testing program become contingent upon purposeful application of measurement. The reader will recall from the discussion of the function of measurement in Chapter 1 that it affords the bases for such purposes as determining status or progress, classification, diagnosing difficulty and predicting educability, motivation, guidance, research, disclosing teacher and program efficacy, and interpreting physical education. Certainly, with so much to be gained, concerted attention to ways and means of effectively applying measurement appears warranted. Furthermore, the focus of this chapter is intended to encompass the last of the six points that the teacher should understand in the quest to be more effective in teaching, as delineated in Chapter 1. This point pertains to understanding the application of the results of measurement in teaching physical education and the need for interest and desire to apply it and to foster continued development of the scientific approach in physical education.

Throughout Part II of this book, the problem of developing a testing program for a junior high school physical education situation within the pervading context of overall appraisal has served as the focus to engender both continuity and understanding. This frame of reference affords the basis for discussion and desired comprehension of the application of measurement.

EXAMPLES OF MEASUREMENT APPLIED

Implicit throughout this book has been the situational or local application of measurement, employing tests to serve specific purposes for a

565

particular program. As individuals differ in their constituency, goals, and purposes, so do physical education programs. What is best for one may be partially or totally inappropriate for another. With a view toward emphasizing the individuality of testing programs designed for particular situations, the author has chosen to describe several testing programs.

These programs were selected not for examples to be duplicated or for any especial alleged merit. Rather, they were chosen to illustrate two points: (1) how testing programs emanate from a physical education program, are obviously tailor-made for it, and comprise an integral part of the physical education program; and (2) the teacher can find within his or her own proximity illustrations of the application of measurement to meet local needs. The reader should avoid any appraisal of the adequacy of the programs described, inasmuch as such is possible only in light of the objectives of each program and the peculiar characteristics influencing it. Furthermore, such is not the intent of this description. In the instances cited, as should be the case in any truly progressing physical education program, the present testing program does not represent a final entity. But rather it represents a stage in the ever continuing process of test development and will be subjected to modification and amplification as needs may suggest.

The first two of the illustrative programs were developed in school systems located approximately 10 miles apart. One program serves the suburban community of Kenmore, New York, with about 105,000 people. The other serves an industrialized urban community, Niagara Falls, with an approximate population of 104,000. A central New York city of 35,000, Auburn, is cited as a third example.

Testing Program for Kenmore, New York [1]

The development of a testing program for physical education in the public schools of Kenmore-Town of Tonawanda, New York began in 1944. This testing program reflects two basic concerns: (1) to represent ability in selected aspects of the physical education program—speed, strength, endurance, and coordination; and (2) to provide a relatively simple and practical record. A series of physical achievement tests was developed to afford an indicant of individual student, class, school, and school district status at particular grade levels in terms of significant aspects of the physical education program.

Initially the tests were designed for boys, grades ten to twelve, with scores expressed in profile form and percentile norms established. About eight years later, a study was made of the test as applied to junior high

[1] Grateful acknowledgment is accorded to Robert W. Lucia, Supervisor of HPER, for assistance in preparing this description.

school boys, and norms were prepared for test items selected for grades seven to nine along with revised high school norms.

As part of the developmental plan, a study of selected tests was begun in 1960, leading to the establishment of tests and percentile norms covering grades three to twelve, boys and girls. Figure 16-1 shows the record card with the test items for grades seven through nine for boys. (The reverse side of the record card contains space for other test scores and comments.) To these items is added the rope climb—time to ascend 18 feet from a standing start—for boys, grades nine to twelve. For boys in grades three to six, the items consist of 50-yard dash, leg thrust (treadmill) for 30 seconds, pull-ups, sit-ups for 30 seconds, and softball target throw (10 trials to a 2-foot diameter target from 25 feet). For girls in grades three to six these items are the same except that 40 yards is the dash distance, push-ups are substituted for pull-ups, and the softball throw distance is changed to 12 feet for third grade and 15 feet for fourth grade. For girls in grades seven to nine the items are 75-yard dash, leg thrusts for 45 seconds, modified pull-ups, sit-ups for 45 seconds, softball throw at 30 feet, and 25-yard swim. These items are used for senior high school girls except that the softball throw is from 35 feet and the swim is for 50 yards.

In recent years the four-item New York State Physical Fitness Screening Test has also been administered annually in response to a state-wide emphasis. The other remaining aspect of the overall testing program in the Kenmore public schools is the application of six swimming tests for junior and senior high school that are used in conjunction with the instructional program. However, teachers are encouraged to use additional testing as may be desirable in a particular teaching situation. Presently, a two-year moratorium has been declared on utilization of the prescribed testing program to permit teachers to use and evaluate different tests and resolve questions relative to appropriateness of different tests and the desired structure and content of a system-wide testing program. Also, the record keeping system is being studied to permit utilization of EDP (electronic data processing) to the extent feasible. Here then in the Kenmore schools is illustrated various stages in the evolvement and refinement of a testing program to ascertain individual status and development simultaneous with appraising program efficacy.

Testing Program for Niagara Falls, New York [2]

The physical education testing program for the public schools of Niagara Falls, New York developed under the directorship of Harold Herkimer largely from the impetus provided by New York State War-

[2] Grateful acknowledgment is accorded to J. Kenneth Rowe, Director of HPER, for assistance in preparing this description.

KENMORE PUBLIC SCHOOLS

BOYS' PHYSICAL ACHIEVEMENT TESTS

NAME _____ _____
Last First

SCHOOL _____ BIRTHDATE _____

LOCK COMB. _____ SERIAL NO. _____ LOCKER NO. _____

GD.	PERC.	7 GD. P.E. CLASS HGT. ___ WGT. ___						8 GD. P.E. CLASS HGT. ___ WGT. ___						9 GD. P.E. CLASS HGT. ___ WGT. ___					
		100 Yd. Dash	880 Yd. Run	Pull Ups	Sit Ups 60 S.	Basket Ball 60 S.	50 Yd. Swim	100 Yd. Dash	880 Yd. Run	Pull Ups	Sit Ups 60 S.	Basket Ball 60 S.	50 Yd. Swim	100 Yd. Dash	880 Yd. Run	Pull Ups	Sit Ups 60 S.	Basket Ball 60 S.	50 Yd. Swim
A+	91–100 Act. Scr.	+ 14.0 −	− 3:04 −	+ 10 −	+ 36 −	+ 24 −	− 38.9 −	− 13.4 −	− 2:54 −	+ 11 −	+ 37 −	+ 26 −	− 37.9 −	− 12.5 −	− 2:48 −	+ 13 −	+ 39 −	+ 28 −	− 34.7 −
	A.S.																		
A	71–90 Act. Scr.	14.1 14.5	3:05 3:21	9 6	35 31	23 18	39.0 44.9	13.5 13.9	2:55 3:11	10 8	36 32	25 22	38.0 43.7	12.6 13.2	2:49 3:01	12 9	38 34	27 24	34.8 37.6
	A.S.																		
B	31–70 Act. Scr.	14.6 16.2	3:22 3:52	5 4	30 24	17 8	45.0 55.0	14.0 15.5	3:12 3:44	7 4	31 25	21 10	43.8 51.0	13.3 14.8	3:02 3:30	8 5	33 27	23 13	37.7 46.0
	A.S.																		
C	11–30 Act. Scr.	16.3 17.2	3:53 4:24	3 2	23 19	7 6	55.1 65.9	15.6 16.9	3:45 4:23	3	24 20	9 8	51.1 56.9	14.9 16.0	3:31 4:03	4 3	26 21	12 10	46.1 52.3
	A.S.																		
D	0–10 Act. Scr.	17.3 + −	4:25 + −	1 −	18 −	5 −	66.0 + −	17.0 + −	4:24 + −	2 −	19 −	7 −	57.0 + −	16.1 + −	4:04 + −	2 −	20 −	9 −	52.4 + −
	A.S.																		

Fig. 16–1. Kenmore physical achievement record.

time Tests in 1944 for grades seven to twelve and by the Kraus-Weber tests a decade later for the elementary grades. The evolution of the latter warrants definitive description.

The idea of an elementary physical education testing program for Niagara Falls originated with the elementary physical education specialists all of whom "took the bull by the horns" and spent two years in developing the tests. At the outset of the test development project, these teachers outlined the following considerations to guide the design.

1. Tests be suitable for all elementary school facilities in the city.
2. A number of tests might be practiced at home.
3. Tests for boys and girls be as nearly similar as possible.
4. Battery include tests of game skills and rhythm work as well as strength, speed, and endurance.
5. Include credit for ability to swim as especial incentive to entice pupils in schools without pools to participate in after-school swim programs.
6. Tests be appropriate for initiation at fourth-grade level and continuing through the sixth grade.
7. No order of progression be prescribed but left to needs of individual and the class.
8. Ease in administering and scoring.
9. One test be left for each teacher to include something of his or her choice.
10. Provide an award system as an incentive, such as inexpensive buttons.

These suggestions were embodied in the final selection of 20 criterion-referenced tests, that is, described as standards of performance to be attained. In 1969, a slight revision of these tests was made, including some adjustment in performance criteria. Seventeen of the tests are administered identically for boys and girls, although in ten of these the performance criterion varies for boys and girls. The test items include the following (standards are noted as appropriate): *50-yard dash*—boys (8 seconds), girls (8.2 seconds); *chinning*—boys (4), girls (2) *or flexed arm hang*—girls (13 seconds); *push-ups*—boys (10), girls (5); *bent-knee sit-up*—boys (30 in 1 minute), girls (16 in 30 seconds); *volleyball serve* —boys (4 of 5), girls (3 of 5); *basket shooting*, 30 seconds—boys (5 goals), girls (4 goals); *kicking*—football punt or place kick for boys (30 yards), soccer dribble for girls; *softball catch and throw*—fielding for boys, wall throw for girls; *ball handling*—a routine; *primary swimmer's button; rope skipping; rhythmic activity*—gymnastics, polka, or square dance; *balance beam; cartwheel; headstand* (5 seconds); *standing broad jump*—boys (68 inches), girls (66 inches); *high jump*—boys (42 inches), girls (38 inches); *vertical jump*—boys (13 inches), girls (11 inches);

endurance—600-yard run-walk (boys, 139 seconds; girls, 159 seconds) or squat thrust, 30 seconds (boys, 15; girls, 12); and *teacher test.*

Pupil achievement is motivated and acknowledged by a three-button award scheme. A blue "primary fitness" button is awarded upon passing any eight tests, completing seven more tests brings a silver "advanced fitness" button, and completion of all tests wins the gold "superior fitness" button. A testing manual including test directions and suggested forms has been prepared.

Just prior to the physical ability tests, a swimming progress award scheme was devised for use in the elementary school swimming program.[3] Called the "traffic lights of water safety," this scheme employs red, yellow, and green buttons to signify the "danger, caution, and go" levels of swimming ability. The buttons read primary, junior, and skill swimmer, respectively.

Additionally, for grades four to six, as well as seven to twelve, teachers administer annually either the New York State Fitness Screening Test or the AAHPER Youth Fitness Test. At the secondary level, grades seven to twelve, the testing program is left to the discretion of the teachers for boys and girls, other than for the motor fitness test. Previously required performance tests have been suspended to allow for flexibility and teacher experimentation to ascertain those tests that appear most relevant and appropriate for individual students. Teachers are encouraged to find and utilize feasible and effective means of assessing realization of objectives for their own students and programs. Some teachers of secondary girls' programs are using knowledge tests along with skill tests in particular teaching units.

Testing Program for Auburn, New York [4]

The testing program for the public schools of Auburn, New York begins in grade four and covers all grades through the secondary school, where it entails all three areas of learning (that is, physical performance, knowledge, and attitudes). The Auburn public schools are organized in a K-5, 6-8, and 9-12 grades pattern. The four-item New York State Physical Fitness Screening Test is administered in the fall in grades four and five using a team testing approach and involving eight elementary schools. (As an aside, this approach affords a valuable orientation for new physical education teachers and enables them to become familiar with the different elementary schools, their facilities, etc.) A retest is given in the spring by the physical education teacher in each

---

[3] Pools are located in 9 of 18 elementary schools in Niagara Falls.

[4] Grateful acknowledgment is accorded to Henry M. Vetter, Director of Physical Education, for assistance in preparing this description.

school. In this retest the emphasis is motivational and compares each individual with his or her own previous performance in order to ascertain improvement, rather than comparison with others. Above grade five the same test is administered once annually in the spring.

In the upper elementary grades the physical education teacher also administers a rough posture screening and refers students with poor posture to the school nurse. The nurse, in turn, commonly uses the Skan-A-Graf to obtain a record of postural deviations as a basis for a letter to parents describing observed problems and recommendations. In addition, teachers in grades four and up my choose to use other physical performance tests, such as for skills related to instructional units. Generally, knowledge tests are developed by each physical education teacher to cover the activities presented in each of the seasons—fall, winter, and spring—beginning at the fifth-grade level. Beginning in 1972, the Kenyon Physical Activity Attitude Inventory is administered at the secondary level to disclose prevalent student attitude toward physical activity. The use of EDP for compilation and analysis of test results is in the initial stages of implementation.

The testing program at Auburn is under continual review to insure inclusion of the most appropriate measures for determining student progress and program effectiveness within feasible time constraints.

PROFICIENCY AND COMPETENCY TESTING

One particular application of measurement has already had, and from all indications will increasingly have, profound influence upon physical education program content and organization. Reference is to proficiency and competency testing. Mention was made of proficiency testing in the discussion of the specific measurement objectives relating to motor skill achievement in Chapter 1. Succinctly, *proficiency testing* involves ascertaining the performance level of individuals in a particular motor skill or sports activity, or achievement level of knowledge in a particular content area. While the application of this concept is relatively recent in physical education, it has proceeded to a stage of considerable refinement and use in the conventional academic content areas.

The Educational Testing Service (Princeton, New Jersey) has several examination programs of the proficiency type. Its College Entrance Examination Board has developed Advanced Placement Examinations for able students who have done exceptional work in a selected subject matter area in secondary school and wish to demonstrate readiness for courses more advanced than the usual introductory freshman-year college courses. The College Board of ETS has also established the College-Level Examination Program (CLEP) in various subjects to enable individuals who have attained the college level of education outside the classroom to demonstrate their achievement and use the test results in seeking college credit or placement. The New York State Education Department has a College Proficiency Examination Program that presently offers 23 different examinations, none of which duplicates examinations available in the national CLEP series. When CLEP introduces an examination in a new area, the New York program drops any duplicating examination and use of the CLEP examination is recommended. Recently, the New York program introduced three health examinations covering the spectrum and content deemed essential for initial teacher certification in health education.

Application of the proficiency concept has proved effective at secondary and collegiate levels and in the preparation of physical education teachers. Proficiency examinations in skill and knowledge in selected physical education activities afford the basis for classification, satisfying activity distribution requirements, and exemption or waiver of specific courses in secondary school and collegiate physical education programs. The practice of enabling students to meet program requirements through proficiency examinations maximizes both student satisfaction and attainment of program objectives encompassing a variety of activities. Students need not be stifled in courses where they possess proficiency but rather enabled to broaden their experience by electing new activities or advanced courses in activities in which they possess basic proficiency as the program requirements permit.

Proficiency examinations can serve an important function as a prerequisite for activity courses in the professional education programs of prospective physical education teachers. Obviously, students who wish to enroll in a program of teacher preparation in physical education should possess a certain desirable level of entering performance or proficiency in selected activities in order to (1) assure their ability to cope with the minimal performance demands and (2) insure the integrity of the course offerings rather than introducing the impeding influence of students in need of remedial instruction. The use of some form of physical proficiency testing requirement near the terminal phase of a teacher education program in physical education has long been favored by recognized professional leaders who are responsible for such programs.

Competency testing is sometimes regarded as being synonymous with proficiency testing, but for purposes herein the two are differentiated. *Competency testing* is perceived as encompassing overall performance that involves a number of qualifications or, simply, relates to composite performance; that is, competency relative to a task such as teaching physical education. In comparison, proficiency is distinguishable in that it connotes skill or expertise in a particular aspect or quality. In this context it will be noted that proficiency testing is used to satisfy requirements in different skill and knowledge areas embodied in a given program. Whereupon, competency testing is directed to a composite performance in a task or job; one which may well involve evidence of proficiency in selected activity areas as well as other qualities implicit in the task.

Considerable attention has been directed to the competency concept in the preparation of teachers. Some collegiate institutions are experimenting with teacher education programs designed to develop specific teacher competencies that are identified, rather than assuming that successful completion of certain courses and field experiences will automatically assure satisfactory teacher competency. Attention in teacher certification, as is the case for the New York State Education Department, is now being accorded to "field testing" of competency for certification rather than the "courses passed" route. The challenge for the development of effective competency testing programs is apparent. The State University of New York at Buffalo (formerly the University of Buffalo) has for several decades successfully utilized comprehensive examinations pertaining to performance and knowledge in selected physical education activities near the completion of the undergraduate professional physical education program to attest to competence in the major field.[15] Plans call for giving increased emphasis to teaching as well as skill performance and knowledge in the continued refinement of these examinations.

The competency approach to teacher education is envisioned as focusing on the desired end of the process rather than on the means of attainment; thus affording flexibility in the means with assurance of competence. The Educational Testing Service has developed a Teacher Education Examination Program consisting of two groups of tests dealing with those aspects of competency that can be assessed by written tests. General Professional Examinations comprise the first group and are designed to measure general knowledge and abilities considered essential for all prospective teachers. These tests include: social, philosophical, and historical bases of education; learning and instruction; written English expression; cultural background; and basic concepts and principles of science and mathematics. The second group of TEEP tests consists of 15 Teaching Field Tests, one of which is in physical education. Three other ETS examination programs contain field or specialty tests, described in Chapter 14, that are used for competency assessment in physical education, namely, Undergraduate Program for

[5] Carlton R. Meyers, "Comprehensive Examinations," *Journal of Health–Physical Education–Recreation*, XXXVII, No. 2 (February, 1966), 37.

Counseling and Evaluation, National Teacher Examinations, and School Personnel Research and Evaluation Services.

On the application of proficiency and competency tests the matter of establishing the score criterion must be dealt with and can be resolved in several ways. The normative scores, desired level of attainment of program objectives, characteristics of the typical groups involved, and other influential concerns in a particular setting all warrant consideration. In most proficiency tests, by definition, only one score is involved. In competency tests several alternative methods of scoring are possible. A criterion score for each component may be established; a total composite score for all components may prove satisfactory; or a combination of these two may be most appropriate, whereby a criterion score must be attained for each component as well as a composite score that reflects better than just minimum scores in all of the components.

In a sense, the trend to proficiency testing that has been manifested will lead to a long-needed goal in physical education, namely, the definition of desired performance standards in physical education activities for children and youth at the various age or grade levels. But equally important, proficiency testing affords a means of vitalizing physical education programs while enhancing both the satisfaction of students and the diversification and intensity of their skill and knowledge acquisition.

MEANINGFUL RECORDS AND REPORTS

A carefully devised system of meaningful and appropriate records and reports is essential for proper application of measurement. It paints the picture of the testing program, thereby revealing what exists. Meaningful records and reports facilitate the utilization of the results of measurement while fostering their interpretation and enhancing comprehension of their significance. Records and reports should not be envisioned as a lot of busy-work. But rather the system of records and reports will be inclusive to the extent deemed desirable in a given situation and designed in a streamlined fashion so as to afford realization of full benefits from results of the testing program. The intent of such record-keeping should be to compile important information in readily understandable and usable form. As conceived herein, "record" refers to systematic notation of findings ostensibly for teacher use, whereas "report" consists of a summarization of findings designed for dissemination to others.

The implementation of electronic data processing has not only removed the tedious, time-consuming chores involved in compiling records and reports but has virtually assured accuracy and added the dimension of timeliness through speed of processing. The application of EDP is discussed in Chapter 6 in the perspective of organization and administration of a testing program. The reader is referred to that presentation for matters relating to records and reports, along with the application of EDP in the total measurement context.

Records

Records suggested for teacher consideration include cumulative records, self-appraisal forms, class records, and program records. The latter three represent tools that the teacher might find helpful and desirable in a given situation. The first, cumulative records, constitutes the backbone of a testing program, as conceived herein, in the context of overall appraisal of the individual.

Cumulative Records. The physical education cumulative record consists of an inclusive longitudinal account of information pertaining to the quantity and quality of development in various areas and organized so as to afford a means of appraising an individual's overall development. It is not intended to duplicate the cumulative guidance record, which the teacher may consult for supplementary as well as complementary information. A concise description of the importance of and concerns in a physical education cumulative record appear in the summation of Chapter 7.

Permeating the design of the cumulative record should be the intent to engender synthesis of the findings noted for various areas of measurement into the whole relationship for overall appraisal. The graphic presentation or profile of results renders analysis and interpretation easier. The cumulative record may appear on both sides of a 5- by 8-inch card, as Fig. 16–1; or the teacher may prefer an open-end envelope with the cumulative record on the outside. The latter enables the teacher to file certain test forms and supplementary material within a single record. Also, the envelope is generally made larger than the card —about standard paper size proves satisfactory—thereby making the form less crowded and allowing more room for notations.

An illustrative cumulative record is contained in Fig. 16–2 based on the problem, as resolved throughout Part II, involving the development of a junior high school testing program. The basic form is intended to be suggestive and is designed to be adaptable to changes in the testing program and to a variety of programs. As the illustrated program grows, the form can be easily modified. The profile is drawn according to the color legend. For example, a red line signifies seventh-grade findings. In the event the form is to be employed for grades ten to twelve, these

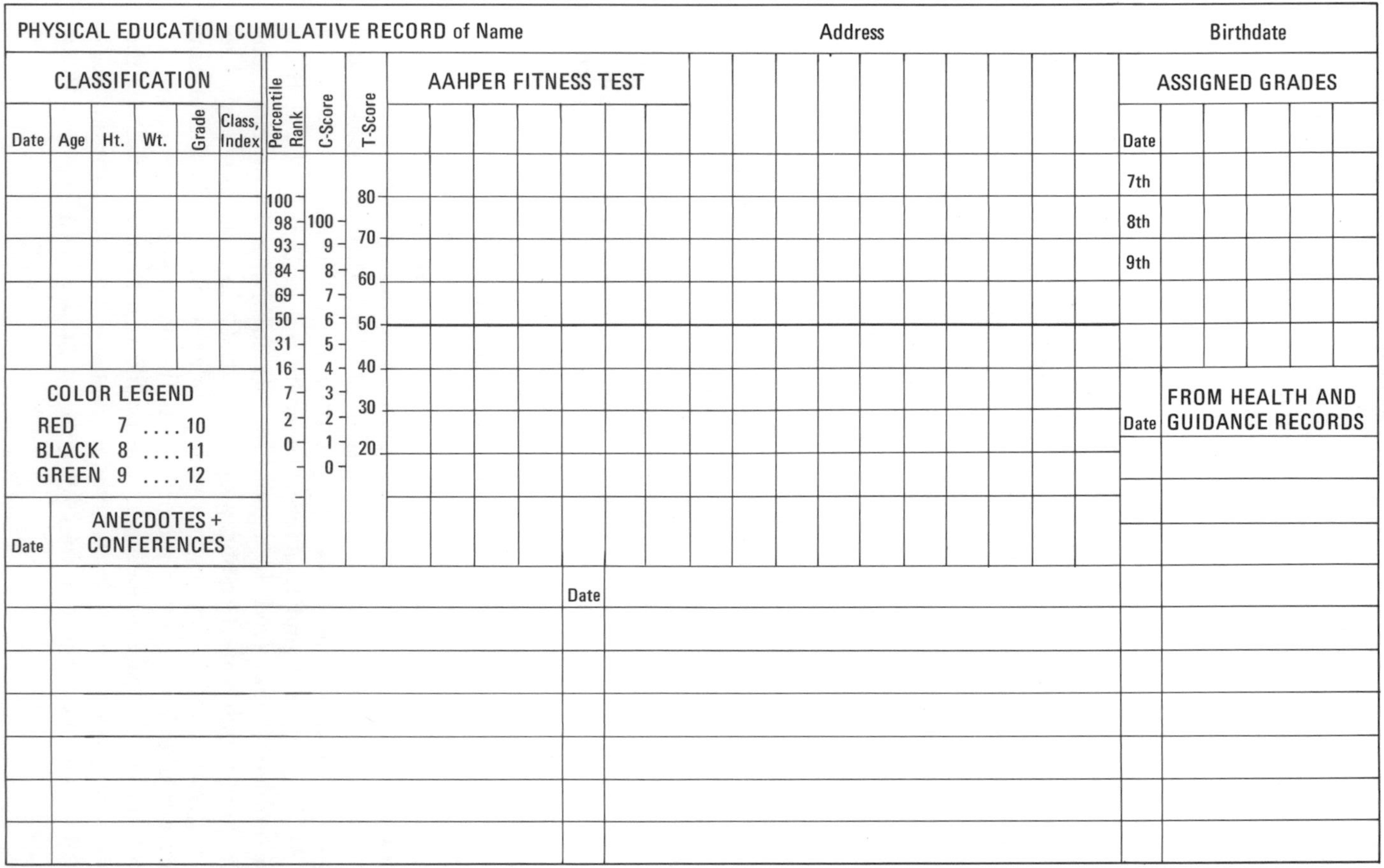

Fig. 16–2. Physical education cumulative record.

later profiles may be drawn with dotted lines. Noting the profile points can be simplified if the teacher records seventh-grade scores in the left side of each column, eighth grade in the middle, and ninth grade toward the right side. Following this procedure lends the record to photocopying, wherein colors are reproduced as black, should this prove desirable.

At this point, brief mention is accorded to the value of drawing a profile of performance or status on selected components, be it as part of a cumulative record or a single report. The ultimate in evaluation is to view the measurement data in an additive and complemental context to afford a basis for judging the general pattern and overall level of a student's development. The pattern described by the profile of development permits the identification of strong and weak aspects and of relationships among the different specific areas of development. The simplicity of construction and ease of interpretation have made the profile a popular method of summarizing and synthesizing the results of measurement in a number of areas. Where available, the digital computer can be programmed to produce profile reports.

Returning to the illustrative cumulative record, the reverse side of the card provides for a record of the skill and knowledge test scores, both general and in specific activities, according to grade level. These scores afford basis for the single expression of skill and knowledge reported annually for the profile on the face of the card. A record of sports participation is also included on the back of the card, and more space may be provided as well for anecdotes. And finally, the raw and scale scores of general tests appearing on the face are noted on the reverse side. In the illustrated record, the same general tests are utilized for boys and girls as shown on the front, whereas the reverse side will reflect the varied programs.

In designing a record form or adapting the illustrated form, the teacher should insure the following provisions that characterize desirable cumulative records: (1) based on objective evidence and accurate behavioral descriptions, (2) indicate measures in comparable and meaningful terms, (3) graphic type designed to facilitate visualization and rapid generalization, and (4) organized into annual divisions to show developmental progress and trends.

Other Records. SELF-APPRAISAL FORMS. The teacher may desire to prepare a form on which each student can note the results of selected tests for a personal record, preferably as a profile graph. It may be patterned after the profile chart on the cumulative record and is intended to stimulate interest in and provide incentive for personal development in the various areas of measurement. On the reverse side of this self-appraisal form might appear a self-rating chart comprised of a series of personality inventory questions designed for physical education and providing for annual or semiannual rating of each item on a 1 to 5-point scale. The Cowell Check Sheet of Sports Outcomes (see page 552) might be consulted to indicate suggestive items for inclusion in such a list. A profile effect can be obtained by an arrangement such as the Cassidy Experience Check List (see page 537) and using the color legend suggested for the cumulative record. Then, the student in the seventh grade would encircle the number (1 to 5) representing his reaction to each question with a red pencil and connect all answers with a red line. Turned on its side, this rating would present a profile for later comparison with the eighth-grade profile made in black.

The value of such a personal record lies in encouraging critical self-analysis with a view to incite improvement in the different qualities through, and as reflected in, physical education experiences. This record is conceived as the personal possession of the student and not for teacher reference except at the pleasure of the student. If desired, the teacher may have a copy of the self-rating chart submitted as part of the student's record. However, it should be recognized that even with desirable rapport the frankness of response may be tempered somewhat when removed from the realm of "strictly personal"; and, hence, therewith would go the full import of the self-appraisal form.

CLASS AND PROGRAM RECORDS. Mention of class and program records is made not with a view toward describing the many and varied forms that they may take, but rather to depict the importance of such records in the application of measurement. The teacher should plan for systematic organization of the results of tests for each class, each grade level, and all grades in the program. Simplicity and essentiality should characterize the keeping of class and program records. These records should contain only basic information necessary to present a picture of performance for the particular group or groups involved. Such information when properly noted affords the basis for interpreting the suitability of available norms and also for devising and revising local norms.

Provision for class and program records makes accessible in systematic form material vital to appraising aspects of physical education at class, grade, or program level without any appreciable delay and the accompanying inconvenience. Generally, interest in a particular question runs high at the time it is posed. Consequently, the chances of favorable action appear greater when facts can be presented immediately or with little time elapsing. As still another important function, these records provide source material for the different reports cited below and exert a telling influence on the caliber of reports made. This in itself constitutes justification for class and program records.

Reports

Inherent in a report resides the matter of evaluation, inasmuch as a report esentially represents a presentation of facts about a given concern in light of which appraisal can be rendered. Hence, by citing the direct and influential relationship to evaluation, coupled with the obvious importance and potential value as a public relations tool, the need for accurate and meaningful reports becomes readily apparent. The concerns of the teacher in developing meaningful reports will be discussed as related to the student, program, and profession. Since prime attention will be centered on reports pertaining to the student, the remaining two areas will be considered first.

Program Reports. Wherein need exists, and it appears ubiquitous, the teacher should devise a report to disclose significant facts indicating how effectively the program is attaining its avowed objectives. The report should represent reality and not be designed expressly to extol virtues and belittle shortcomings. It should be structured simply, include only vital particulars, and be devoid of extraneous and distracting details.

No attempt will be made to develop a sample program report. For purposes herein, it will suffice to recognize certain salient considerations and stress the individuality of such a report, geared to the need it is to meet. Embodying comparative data pertaining to the previous year or years imparts meaning by indicating the direction and degree of development in various aspects of the program. The report need not be confined to the program as a whole but may compare different aspects of the physical education program with other aspects at the present time or with themselves in previous years. Obviously, the report may also compare selected experimental phases of the program with controlled or conventional elements.

The teacher should realize the potential value inherent in program reports before deciding what to do in a given situation. Certainly, the teacher should not be content with any report as required by the school administration unless it is deemed to cover the program adequately and appropriately as the teacher would have it. Instead, the teacher should furnish a supplemental report to a required report. Information derived from measurement relating to all phases of learning—technical, associated and concomitant—should be presented. Particular heed should be directed to evaluation of attitudes and social development, inasmuch as measurement of physical performance and knowledge is usually obtained and the former sometimes neglected, despite the tremendous importance of what it can disclose regarding program efficacy. Discreet use of carefully devised, simple, yet inclusive reports should be made to engender support for the physical education program both from school administrators and faculty and from the public.

Reports to the Profession. Certainly, the growth of a profession reflects the quantity and quality of reports emanating from measurement. Little doubt exists that many significant results of and valuable ideas accruing from physical education programs as disclosed by testing fall by the wayside due to failure to utilize reporting media properly, if at all. It should behoove every dedicated teacher to disseminate such "fruits of labor" to fellow teachers and the profession as a whole. This dissemination may take any one or more of several forms, namely, publication in professional journals, participation in formal conference programs and workshops, joining in an idea-swap-shop or cracker-barrel session, inservice and collegiate courses and informal meetings. Regardless of the media of reporting, the approach should be straightforward, down to earth, "see how we do it" so as to enhance both interest and comprehension. This informative approach to reports, assuming it derives from sound testing procedures, should conceivably lead to teaching-oriented research being done by the teacher that in turn will lead to the teacher doing research-oriented teaching. This represents the Utopia for which this book strives.

Student Reports—Grading. Inasmuch as the student represents the reason for which the physical education program exists, especial importance should be attached to reports about the student, addressed to the student. Granted, there may be supplementary or special reports about students that will be made to responsible people associated with the educational process. But the discussion herein will deal with the prime concern—the student and reporting to him.

Student reports include individual test record forms and an indicant of relative sucess in physical education experiences as given by grade reports. The former represent attempts to present and interpret effectively the results for a student in a basic test of the program, such as the AAHPER Youth Fitness Test or a posture test. The matter of grades in physical education is conceived as an inclusive report of student performance in the acquisition of technical, associated, and concomitant learnings in physical education. It pertains to presenting this information in a meaningful manner.

The intent herein is not to describe and justify the need for grading or delve into the principles of grading, but rather to depict various methods of grading. This description purports to illustrate ways in which the teacher may effectively inform the student as to how fully he or she is attaining the objectives strived for in the program. Grades may be viewed as an attempt to interpret symbolically the success in realizing definite goals in physical education as revealed by the application of measurement. This implies recognition of the objectives by teacher and student in order for the grade to be meaningful. Further, it necessitates determination of the measurable elements that reflect attainment of the objectives and the appropriate weighting of each elemen in terms of its contribution. The grading scheme adopted by the teacher should obviously conform to the school policy. Preferably, the grade should be included on regular report cards. Separate report cards in physical education tend to increase rather than eradicate the feeling of separateness or aloofness of physical education from other curricular areas.

Since the grade report often consists of a composite single grade the teacher must insure that students understand the bases for the grade if meaningfulness is to ensue. Whenever feasible, listing grades in different sports activities or other aspects comprising the final grade engenders its significance. The practice of listing the grade or constituent score for each of the various components or dimensions of the composite grade is referred to as dimensional grading. The various bases used for grading are shown in the illustrated methods of grading. Coupled with determining the bases for grading is the weighting of each basis, that is, the comparative importance. The proportion of the grade assigned to each basis should reflect the importance attached to it in the objectives and the resultant time apportioned each in teaching.

Voltmer and Esslinger [6] suggest the following:

Basis of Awarding Grades	%	or	%	or	%	%
1. Attainment in physical aspects	50		45		40	?
2. Attainment in social aspects	30		35		35	?
3. Attainment in mental aspects	20		20		25	?

Moriarty cites the following example of ascertaining a letter grade (A—5, B—4, C—3, D—2, E—1) according to weightings assigned for the different factors.[7]

Factors	Weighting	Average	Points
Achievement	3	B	$3 \times 4 = 12$
Potential ability	2	A	$2 \times 5 = 10$
Knowledge	1	C	$1 \times 3 = 3$
Attitude	1	C	$1 \times 3 = 3$
Total	7		28

[6] E. F. Voltmer and A. A. Esslinger, *The Organization and Administration of Physical Education* (3rd ed.; New York: Appleton-Century-Crofts, Inc., 1958), p. 346.

[7] Mary J. Moriarty, "How Shall We Grade Them?" *Journal of Health, Physical Education and Recreation*, XXV, No. 1 (January, 1954), 27.

Since the total of 28 points resulted from a total of 7 weighting exponents, dividing 28 by 7 gives the final grade—4 or B.

Cowell and Schwehn [8] proffer the example below, showing provision for plus and minus and using different basis factors.[9]

Excellent	Good	Fair	Poor	Fail
	B+ 4.3	C+ 3.3	D+ 2.3	F+ 1.3
A 5.0	B 4.0	C 3.0	D 2.0	F 1.0
A− 4.7	B− 3.7	C− 2.7	D− 2.7	

Factors	Weighting	Grade	Points
Performance—demonstrated skill	2	4.3	8.6
Knowledge of rules, strategy, techniques	1	2.7	2.7
Attitudes (cooperativeness, sportsmanship, effort, regularity, neatness, leadership)	1	4.0	4.0
Posture and interest in improving physique or figure	1	4.0	4.0
Total	5	5	19.3

Final Grade 3.8 or B—

An illustrative scheme for letter grades to fit the junior high school testing program developed earlier in Part II might utilize the plus and minus rating scale as follows:

Factors	Weighting	Grade		Points
Technical learning	5	(B+)	4.3	21.5
Associated learning	3	(C−)	2.7	8.1
Concomitant learning	2	(B)	4.0	8.0
Total	10		10	37.6

Final Grade 3.7 or B—

Generally speaking, the grade reported for each factor (e.g., C− for associated learning) will represent a combination of several test scores, possibly even involving a different weighting for different tests. For example, the knowledge grade expressed above may be comprised of three quizzes and a final examination.

[8] C. C. Cowell and H. M. Schwehn, *Modern Principles and Methods in High School Physical Education* (Boston: Allyn & Bacon, Inc., 1958), p. 108.

[9] For additional illustrative grading schemes, the reader is referred to Helen M. Barton, "A Grading Plan for Physical Education," *Journal of Health–Physical Education–Recreation*, XX, No. 8 (October, 1949), 512—college women; I. F. Waglow, "Marking in Physical Education," *Journal of Health–Physical Education–Recreation*, XXV, No. 5 (May, 1954), 48—college men; and C. A. Boyd and I. F. Waglow, "The Individual Achievement Profile," *Physical Educator*, XXI, No. 3 (October, 1964), 117.

	Weighting	Grade	Points
Quiz Number 1	1	(B+) 4.3	4.3
Quiz Number 2	1	(D) 2.0	2.0
Quiz Number 3	1	(C) 3.0	3.0
Final examination	3	(D+) 2.3	6.9
Total	6		6 | 16.2

Grade 2.7 or C—

Another method of averaging letter grades, which apparently finds considerable teacher application, utilizes the following point values.

	+ 12		+ 9		+ 6		+ 3		
A	11	B	8	C	5	D	2	F	0
	− 10		− 7		− 4		− 1		

The teacher may find this point value scheme easier to work with, but its use of higher numbers appears to minimize somewhat the effect of a failing grade. Consequently, a slightly higher average may result as compared to the 1 to 5 scale, especially when weighting factors are employed.

While the raw scores may be combined by converting to letter grades first, as done above, the preferable technique (as described in Chapter 2) is to derive T-scores or similar transformed standard scores for the raw scores so as to render them comparable and combinable in a most equitable manner. (As described in Chapter 2, and noted as an admonition here, percentile ranks cannot be used as a basis for combining raw scores.) The categorization of raw scores into 5- or 13-letter grade groupings as shown above obviously results in an appreciable loss of precision in contrast to T-scores, and this loss becomes accentuated when the assigned grades are weighted and/or combined. T-scores maintain their characteristic precision through weighting and combining until the point at which they are converted into the appropriate grading scheme in final form.

And lest it not be overlooked, the importance of proper handling of scores cannot be overemphasized. All good intentions of grading and the plan for it can be undone or invalidated, regardless of their quality, if scores are improperly handled.

Factors	Weighting	T-Score	Points
Technical learning			
Motor fitness	2	67	134
Sport and motor skills	3	61	183
Associated learning	3	46	138
Concomitant learning	2	58	116
	10		10 | 571

Final Grade 57.1 (Mean T-Score)
or B—

Regardless of whether grade computations are made using letter grades or T-scores, when two or more components are combined the teacher should be cognizant of the influence of what is commonly referred to as the "regression effect." This denotes simply that when a student has a high score or grade on one test or component, combining it with another score or grade results in a composite (or mean) that falls closer to the overall group mean (that is, T-score of 50) than the single high score. Contrariwise, this regression effect tends to raise a low score on one item when combined with other scores for the same student, causing the composite to move toward the overall group mean. Most teachers have observed this phenomenon, whereby a lesser number of clear-cut A and F grades occur as the number of grades averaged together is increased. Adjustments may have to be made if a reasonable spread of scores is desired. Obviously, this bunching toward the overall mean becomes more acute as the number of scores combined is increased. The teacher can arbitrarily lower and raise the cut-off points occurring above and below the mean, respectively, to counteract the regression effect. Or more properly, with T-scores it is possible to compute a new T-score based on the composite score, and this will give a desirable proportion of grades in categories on both sides of the mean.

For the sample T-scores above, either the composite or mean T-score can be used to compute the final distribution for grading. Using the composite makes it unnecessary to compute the mean T-score, thereby eliminating a possible source of error.

Before discussing matters relating to grade determination, the inappropriateness of working with raw scores should be explained. The infeasibility of adding raw scores for standing broad jump in inches and 50-yard dash in seconds is obvious, as mentioned in Chapter 2, as is combining raw scores for push-ups and sit-ups. For such purposes T-scores are indispensable. With knowledge tests, combining raw scores on different tests is likewise inappropriate because of the variability of scores, except in rare instances, but this fact is not as obvious as in the case of technical learning tests. If the standard deviations of the different tests to be combined are not the same, those tests with larger standard deviation values will be accorded more weight in the combination, rendering the combination inequitable. By converting raw scores to T-scores, or a similar score based upon the standard deviation and the mean, this shortcoming can be obviated with no loss in precision.

The conversion to letter grades can also be used, but loss in precision is generally appreciable for most cases. When the teacher utilizes a number of knowledge tests, the thorny problems relating to combining letter grades from separate tests can be avoided by basing grades on the percentage of items correct on the final summed scores or a statistical analysis of the final scores. When this is done, the students should be informed that the number of correct answers on all tests will be summed to arrive at the grade and that no grades are to be given for the separate tests.

To determine a letter grade for raw scores or cumulative totals of different test scores, it is recommended that the teacher follow a definite system or utilize the evident natural division points in the score distribution. The percentage scheme based upon the normal probability curve is advocated, whereby the distribution is divided so as to give 7 per cent A, 24 per cent B, 38 per cent C, 24 per cent D, and 7 per cent F. Other distribution divisions that have been proposed by educational measurement authorities include 7–23–40–23–7 and 10–20–40–20–10. A percentage system should serve only as a guide for grading and not as a rigid rule; teacher judgment based on relevant situational characteristics should not be ignored. Essentially, the applicability of such a system depends upon whether the test score distribution is representative of large groups (assuming, of course, a discriminative test). Consequently, it should not be applied to small and select groups. In such distributions the teacher should base the grading on reasonable expectation and natural grouping.

The suggested percentage distribution (7–24–38–24–7) is derived by assigning C to the scores falling .5 standard deviation above and below the mean, which constitutes 19.15 per cent of the scores on either side of the mean or 38.30 per cent altogether in the middle standard deviation of a normal probability distribution. Then B and D grades are assigned to the scores falling within the next standard deviation (24.17 per cent) above and below the C limits, respectively. The tails of the distribution are assigned A and F. Figure 16–3 shows this relationship and includes a comparative scale containing z scores, T-scores, letter grades, and the per-cent-numerical grades often associated with letter grades. It should be noted that the per-cent-numerical grades are based upon the mastery concept that pervaded teacher grading practices for many years and, as such, differs from norm-referenced interpretation, that is, relative performance of testees within a group. In some situations the passing per-cent-numerical grade on a 100 per cent basis has been 60 per cent instead of 65, and the letter grades have been assigned as from 60 to 70 for D and so on, leaving 90 to 100 as A.

The recommended approach to grading herein is, to the extent practical, to use T-scores for conversion to letter grades in final form according to the points of demarcation shown in Fig. 16–3, where T-scores of 35 to 44 are assigned to D grade, and so on. This scale affords the basis for interpretation of T-scores in the letter grade context; with due

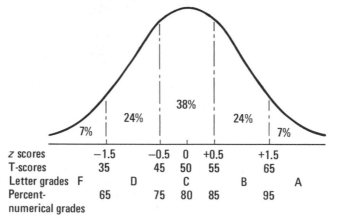

z scores		−1.5		−0.5	0	+0.5		+1.5	
T-scores		35		45	50	55		65	
Letter grades	F		D		C		B		A
Percent-numerical grades		65			75	80	85		95

Fig. 16–3. Normal curve as basis for grading with comparative scale of grade types.

recognition of the regression effect when a number of component scores are combined and the need to make adjustments as appropriate.

Two additional methods of grading merit mention, representing opposite ends in practicality as meaningful reports. Some teachers have utilized a pass or fail, S (satisfactory) or U (unsatisfactory) designation to indicate performance relative to minimum standards only, such as for criterion-referenced tests. The most meaningful method of grading consists of a series of descriptive sentences relating to student progress and limitations. This last method consumes considerable time, but its use has been justified in some elementary school physical education situations.

Attention should be drawn to one item, namely attendance, that is often used as a factor in grading but not included above. The author contends that unless attedance represents one of the objectives to be attained in physical education, it does not warrant inclusion as a determining factor. Attendance is presumed in a grade, and lack of attendance will take from it. In this vein, the teacher should prepare a scale, based on school policy, by which poor attendance will detract from a grade proportional to the number of absences. Some teachers may choose to consider attendance as an index of attitude and incorporate it into concomitant learning.

The teacher should be cognizant of some of the particular concerns and admonitions relating to assesment of concomitant learning—attitudes and social development, especially in reference to grading. Whatever scheme that is adopted, it should be recognized that:

1. Teacher rating should rely on objective data and peer assessment to avoid inaccuracies, bias, and resultant unjustness that tends to characterize subjective judgment.
2. A low grade is not likely to effect a positive change in an anti-social student; it may have the opposite effect.
3. Many of the class administrative details sometimes included in behavior assessment, such as soiled uniforms and punctuality, should be subject to disciplinary procedures rather than incorporated into the grading scheme.
4. A poor attitude can be expected to affect a student's grade in other aspects without a multiple penalty with a grade on attitude as well.
5. To be valid a grade must reflect what exists, and attitude grading tends to encourage conformity and undesirable fawning to gain favorable grades.

Adoption of grading schemes that avoid the above and similar pitfalls will lend credence to the results. Obviously, to engender the validity in grading concomitant learning, the concerns entail both what is assessed and how it is assessed.

Whereas the illustrations of grade derivation have all included some attention to aspects of concomitant learning, it should not be implied that this realm must be included in grading. Some authorities maintain that only three areas lie primarily within the domain of physical education and, accordingly, should constitute the basic factors of grading. These encompass the development of: physical and motor fitness; motor and sport skills; and a body of knowledge in physical education (concerning physical activities and their effects). This is not to suggest that concomitant learning does not constitute an important component of total program evaluation. Admittedly, a program that fails in the development of favorable attitudes and behavior has a serious indictment against it. However, needed evaluative procedures for concomitant learning need not lead to or derive from grades per se.

Inasmuch as grades represent one means of interpreting results and progress of students in physical education, it behooves the teacher to recognize the value of the grading scheme as a public relations tool. Hopefully, the teacher will not resort to minimize the importance of grades but rather seek for and emphasize ways in which they may be rendered more meaningful to students in light of the acknowledged goals in physical education. If grades are considered inaccurate, invalid, or meaningless, the resolution of the matter lies not in deemphasizing grades, but rather in a more careful derivation and assignment of them so that they more truly reflect the extent of important achievements. Properly done, grading in physical education need not be something to be tolerated and defended but will become a significant and influential element in fostering student and parental appraisal and understanding of the student's development as revealed in physical education experiences.

THE SCIENTIFIC APPROACH IN PHYSICAL EDUCATION

The application of measurement as a teaching-learning tool should evolve from the scientific approach in physical education, which should characterize all aspects of teaching. This approach should constitute the teacher's everyday attack on the educational problems confronted and encompass what has been previously described as "teaching-oriented research"; research being a systematic search for knowledge. Teaching-oriented research is conceived to include both findings emanating from the solution of teaching problems and research designed for its immediate implications for teaching, although not necessarily conducted in a teaching situation. Thus, an inclusive conception of the scientific approach may be summarized as an ever-searching problem-solving procedure that should permeate all aspects of teaching.

Many teachers solve problems by accepting judgment of others without any check upon its validity or by deriving the answer from previous experience that may reflect inaccurate observation or interpretation of facts. Also, oftentimes the teacher may recognize a problem, manifest interest in its solution, but not know how to proceed. Perhaps in no other aspect of the school curriculum has there been more practice based largely, if not entirely, on opinion than in physical education. Using the scientific method, the solution of educational problems reflects careful, systematic planning and design and affords sounder basis for operation of the physical education program. Actually, the most effective learning ensues from the organization of experience around problems. That is why problem-solving is generally conceded to comprise the core of the teaching-learning process.

The scientific method in planning for the solution of educational problems is comprised of (1) identifying and defining the problem, (2) choosing a suitable scheme to solve it, (3) choosing or developing means of collecting data, (4) choosing or devising tools to analyze results, and (5) generalizing and interpreting the results of the analysis.

The elements or steps involved in the scientific method may be concisely delineated as:

1. Sensing, identifying, and defining the problem.
2. Review the literature and study the situation for pertinent facts.

3. Formulate hypotheses (proposed solutions).
4. Collect valid data.
5. Analyze the data collected.
6. Propose tentative conclusions.
7. Verify the tentative conclusions by further investigation.
8. Derive final conclusions.
9. Generalize and interpret the results.

Thus, the scientific approach begins when the teacher recognizes a problem and wants to solve it, examines the situation carefully, and studies literature related to the problem. Then the teacher makes some guesses as to the possible solution prior to delving into a thorough search for data (such as exposing one of two similar groups to a variable). Next, the best guess is selected and checked to verify its acceptability more definitely. If the findings verify the guess, the final conclusion is drawn and generalizations made. If not, a new "best guess" is made and checked and the process continued in search of the solution. Obviously, in most occasions, the process will entail several checks of a "best guess" to produce a tenable solution.

Inherent in the scientific approach to physical education resides the dissemination of pertinent findings to the profession as described in the discussion of reports to the profession. Such pooling of information through the media suggested will serve not only to assist other teachers in the solution of similar or related problems but also to enhance the scientific advancement of the physical education profession as a whole. Through the scientific approach and rendering the findings available to the profession, the teacher will contribute to research that is truly teacher-oriented and teacher-assimilable. This should lead to research-oriented teaching and complete the self-perpetuating cycle, reflecting the scientific approach from which it emanates. Associated with this self-perpetuating cycle, the teacher should develop analytical ability and increased understanding relative to any research that may have implications for physical education.

The author allegedly designed the presentation in this book of physical education measurement for the teacher in a way to foster the scientific approach to physical education. By applying measurement in the context of overall appraisal of the individual through this approach, the teacher should contribute to the three-fold betterment of the student, the teacher's program and the profession. Proper teacher utilization of measurement affords a challenge leading to the greatest possible attainment of the avowed objectives of physical education. It should behoove all teachers to meet this challenge.

SELECTED REFERENCES

1. COWELL, C. C., and SCHWEHN, H. M. *Modern Principles and Methods in Secondary School Physical Education,* 2d ed. Boston: Allyn and Bacon, Inc., 1964.
2. GUSTAFSON, WILLIAM F. "A Look at Evaluative Criteria in Physical Education." *Physical Educator,* XX, No. 4 (December, 1963), 172.
3. LIBA, M. R., and LOY, J. W. "Some Comments on Grading." *Physical Educator,* XXII, No. 4 (December, 1965), 158.
4. MATHEWS, DONALD K. *Measurement in Physical Education,* 4th ed. Philadelphia: W. B. Saunders Co., 1973.
5. MONTOYE, HENRY P. (ed.). *Principles and Operational Practices (An Introduction to Measurement in Physical Education,* Vol. 1). Indianapolis: Phi Epsilon Kappa Fraternity, 1970.
6. SOLLEY, W. H.. et al. Grading in Physical Education." *Journal of Health–Physical Education–Recreation,* XXXVIII, No. 5 (May, 1967), 34.
7. THORNDIKE, R. L. "Marks and Marking Systems." *Encyclopedia of Educational Research,* 4th ed. (Robert L. Ebel, ed.) New York: The Macmillan Co., 1969, pp. 759–766.

APPENDIX

Commonly Used Terms in Measurement and in Research Reports

ABSOLUTE GRADING—Assigning grades solely on the basis of performance or attainment. (*See also* Relative Grading.)

AGE NORMS—Scores or values representing typical or average performance for individuals of different age groups.

ANALYSIS OF VARIANCE—The total variation of given measures for a group of individuals may be attributable to variations among the individuals with respect to other factors. To illustrate, the variation in motor ability of a group of students may be due to their variations in age, cultural background, socioeconomic status, and the like. By analysis of variance, the statistical significance of the effect of each factor is tested, indicating the extent to which chance variation might have produced the same effect.

ARITHMETIC MEAN ($\overline{X}$ or M)—The sum of a set of scores divided by the number of scores.

ASSUMED (OR GUESSED) MEAN—The mid-point of the class interval in which it is "guessed" that the arithmetic mean will fall.

AVERAGE—A term applied in general to measures of central tendency of which the most commonly used are arithmetic mean, median, and mode.

BAR GRAPH—A graphic presentation utilizing bars of various length to symbolize differences in quantity, size, or other measures.

BATTERY—A group of several tests of which the results have value individually, in combination, and/or totally. When the tests are standardized on the same population, the results are directly comparable, and the norms are usually termed "integrated."

BIMODAL—A distribution of scores with two foci of central tendency rather than one.

BISERIAL r—A correlation coefficient for two variables, wherein one is a continuous normal distribution while the other is dichotomized (consisting of two parts). For example, a biserial r would be used to disclose the correlation between motor ability (a continuous variable) and honesty or dishonesty (a dichotomized variable).

CEILING—The upper limit of ability measured by a test.

COMPOSITE SCORE—A single value representing the results obtained from several different measures.

CORRECTION FOR GUESSING—A reduction of test score for wrong answers that is sometimes applied to true-false or multiple-choice questions in an attempt to indicate more accurately true knowledge in a written test and to discourage guessing. The conventional formula is $R - W/0-1$, where $0 =$ number of options. For true–false the formula becomes $R - W/2-1$ or $R - W$.

CORRELATION—Relationship or "going-togetherness" between two scores or measures for the same individuals.

CORRELATION COEFFICIENT (r)—A measure of the degree to which two measures go hand-in-hand, that is, are related. It ranges in value from $+1.00$ for perfect positive relationship through 0.00 for none or pure chance to -1.00 for perfect negative relationship. The most common coefficient is Pearson product-moment r; other examples are Biserial, and Tetrachoric.

CRITERION—A specified standard or mode of judgment used as a basis for evaluating a test. The criterion is that which a test is constructed to predict.

CRITERION-REFERENCED MEASUREMENT—A test designed to identify an individual's performance in relation to specified performance standards.

CRITICAL RATIO (CR)—The difference between two statistics divided by the standard error of this difference—used as an indication of the significance of the difference.

CURVILINEAR RELATIONSHIP—A relationship between two variables that is portrayed by a curve, that is, other than a straight line; wherein a change in one variable does not consistently, if at all, accompany a like or inverse change in the other.

DECILE—Any one of the nine points that divide a ranked distribution into ten parts, each containing one-tenth of all cases; every tenth percentile. The first decile is the 10th percentile.

DECILE RANK—The rank order of the 10 decile divisions, wherein the first decile rank is that below the first decile point, and so on.

DERIVED SCORE—A score that has been converted from a qualitative or quantitative mark on one scale into the units of another scale. Commonly used to refer to any scale score derived from raw scores.

DIFFICULTY RATING (VALUE)—The per cent of a specified group who answer a test item correctly.

DISCRIMINATORY POWER—The ability of a test item to differentiate between contrasting groups (for example, good students from poor students), generally expressed as an index of discrimination.

DISTRACTER—The incorrect choices listed in multiple-choice and matching type items; also called alternative, decoy, or foil.

EQUIVALENT (ALTERNATE OR PARALLEL) FORM—Any of two or more forms of a test that are very similar in terms of the nature of the content and the difficulty of items included and that yield approximately the same average scores and measures of variability for a given group.

FACE VALIDITY—Refers to the acceptability of a test and test situation by the tester in terms of apparent use to be made of a test. A test has face validity when it seemingly measures the variable in question.

FACTOR ANALYSIS—Any of several methods (centroid, grouping, principal components) of analyzing the intercorrelations among a set of variables such as test scores. Factor analysis attempts to account for the interrelationships in terms of some underlying "factors," preferably fewer in number than the original variables; and it reveals how much of the variation in each of the original measures arises from, or is associated with, each of the hypothetical factors.

FREQUENCY DISTRIBUTION—A tabulation of scores from high to low (or low to high) showing the number of scores that fall in each score (or class) interval.

FREQUENCY POLYGON—A line graph of a particular frequency distribution.

FUNCTIONING OF RESPONSES—Extent to which various responses are chosen in multiple-choice, multiple-response, and matching items.

GRADE NORM—The average test score obtained by pupils of given grade placement.

HISTOGRAM—A vertical bar graph of a frequency distribution.

HULL SCORE—A standard score scale of values from 0 to 100 with a mean of 50 and extending 3.5 standard deviation units above and below the mean.

INDEX OF DISCRIMINATION—A computation to indicate the degree to which respective test questions discriminate between individuals possessing different levels of the characteristic involved in the test.

INTERCORRELATION—A term describing each of the correlations among a group of tests. Intercorrelations are generally shown in tables giving the correlation of each test with each of the other tests.

ITEM ANALYSIS—The process of evaluating single test items by one of several methods, generally involving determination of the difficulty rating and the discriminatory power of the items and in many cases its correlation with a criterion.

KUDER-RICHARDSON FORMULA(s)—Formulas for estimating the reliability of a test from information about the individual test items or from the mean, standard deviation, and number of test items. These formulas permit estimation of reliability from a single administration of a test without the necessity of dividing the test into halves.

LEVEL OF CONFIDENCE—A statistical term to indicate the degree of confidence that may be placed upon an interval estimate, generally shown by a probability percentage, such as being 95 per cent certain.

LEVEL OF SIGNIFICANCE—A statistical term describing the percentage that defines the likelihood of concluding that a difference between two means, percentages, or other comparable measures exists when in reality it does not. To illustrate, if the difference in mean scores of boys and girls is reportedly significant at the .01 level, this means that there is only a 1 in 100 chance that a sample difference as large as or larger than the one observed would occur by chance sampling error if there is in reality no difference between the mean of the population of boys and the mean of the population of girls.

LINEAR RELATIONSHIP—A relationship between two variables that is portrayed by a straight line; as one variable increases or decreases, the other does likewise or inversely.

MEAN ($\overline{X}$ or M)—(See Arithmetic Mean.)

MEDIAN (MD)—The middle score in a distribution; the 50th percentile. It divides the group into two equal parts.

MODE (MO)—The score or value occurring most frequently in a distribution.

MULTIPLE CORRELATION (R)—The correlation between a dependent or criterion variable and the sum of a number of independent variables, which are weighted so as to give a maximum correlation.

N—The symbol commonly used to represent the number of cases in a distribution or group.

NORMAL DISTRIBUTION—A distribution of scores or measures that in graphic form has a distinctive bell-shaped appearance and is known as a normal probability curve. Scores are distributed symmetrically about the mean with as many cases at various distances above the mean as at equal distances below it, and with cases concentrated near the average and decreasing in frequency the farther one departs from the average, according to a precise mathematical equation.

NORMALIZED SCORES—Applicable to each type of standard score and derived by computing the percentile ranks for raw scores and then determining the equivalent standard score for each percentile value based on the normal curve table, thus avoiding the effects of skewed distributions.

NORM-REFERENCED MEASUREMENT—A test designed to identify an individual's performance relative to that of others on the same measure.

NORMS—Summarized statistics that describe the test performance of specified groups, such as pupils of various ages or grades in the standardization group for the test. Norms are descriptive of average, typical, or mediocre performance and do not constitute standards or desirable levels of attainment Grade, age, T-score, and percentile are the most common types of norms.

OBJECTIVITY—The extent to which a test is consistent in measuring what it measures when administered by different individuals.

OGIVE—A graphic representation of a cumulative frequency distribution.

PARTIAL CORRELATION—The correlation between two variables with the influence of one or more other variables being eliminated.

PERCENTILE (P)—A point (score) in a distribution below which fall the per cent of cases indicated by the given percentile. "Percentile" has no relation to the per cent of correct answers made on a test. Also referred to as centile (C).

PERCENTILE RANK—The per cent of scores in a distribution equal to or lower than the score indicated by the given rank.

PHI (Φ) COEFFICIENT—A product-moment correlation coefficient computed from a fourfold table (double dichotomy). Frequently the dichotomy is between passing or failing a test item and is interpreted as the discrimination effectiveness of an item.

POWER TEST—A knowledge test designed to determine level of performance without concern for speed of response so that only generous, if any, time limits are imposed.

PROBABLE ERROR (P.E.)—A value obtained by multiplying the standard error by .6745. A range of one P.E. on either side of the mean of a normal distribution includes exactly 50 per cent of the cases. Two P.E. units give 82 per cent, 3—95.7 per cent, and 4—99.3 per cent of the cases.

PROFILE (OR PROFILE GRAPH)—The plotting of derived scores, usually connected by a line, to show results on different tests for an individual or group, thus giving an overall picture of performance.

QUARTILE—One of three points dividing the cases in a distribution into four equal groups. The three quartiles (Q_1 Q_2 and Q_3) coincide with the 25th, 50th, and 75th percentiles.

QUARTILE DEVIATION (Q)—One-half of the interquartile range (Q_3–Q_1), used as an measure of variability in conjunction with the median.

RANDOM SAMPLE—A sample of the members of a population drawn in such a way that every member of the population has an equal chance of being included, that is, drawn in a way that precludes the operation of bias or selection. Since a random sample is "representative" of its total population, use of such a sample renders possible generalization of sample findings to the population.

RANGE—The number or spread of scores encompassed in a distribution; determined by adding one to the difference between the lowest and highest scores.

RANKING (RANK NUMBERS OR RANK ORDER)—Arranging the constituents of a group in order in terms of some measure. Rank numbers disclose the relative position of the constituents.

RANK ORDER CORRELATION (RHO)—A method of determining the relationship between scores on two different items in rank order, that is, by assigning ranks to each pair of scores; suitable with a relatively small number of cases.

RATING SCALE—A descriptive, numerical or graphic scheme (or in combination) used in recording impressions or ratings of the extent to which an individual possesses a certain quality or trait.

RAW SCORE—The first quantitative result obtained in scoring a test.

REGRESSION—The tendency for observations showing a high deviation from the mean and a low degree of variability among themselves in terms of one trait generally to display wider variability and markedly less deviation from the mean in a second trait. For example, if a number of adult males taller than 6 feet 6 inches are compared as to weight, they will be found to deviate less from the average weight of adult males than from the average height of adult males.

RELATIVE GRADING—Assigning grades on a relative basis, such as either in terms of achievement in reference to potentiality or in light of overall performance of the group.

RELIABILITY—The extent to which a test is consistent in measuring what it measures. It is usually estimated by some form of reliability coefficient or by the standard error of measurement. Several types of reliability coefficients exist: (1) *Coefficient of internal consistency* refers to a measure based on internal analysis of data obtained or a single test trial, for example, split-half method; (2) *Coefficient of equivalence* refers to a correlation between scores from two forms given at essentially the same time; (3) *Coefficient of stability* refers to a correlation between test and retest with some period of time intervening.

SAMPLING ERROR—Errors due to the chance factors in random sampling, generally estimated statistically by the standard error.

SCATTERGRAM—A two-dimensional chart affording a basis for computing a correlation coefficient for two variables or scores. Pairs of value are tallied on the chart, giving a visual picture of the relationship between the variables.

SCORE (OR CLASS) INTERVAL—The divisions of a frequency distribution bounded by upper and lower score values.

SIGMA (σ)—Designation for standard error and most frequently applied to standard deviation.

SIGMA SCORE—A standard score scale of values from 0 to 100 with a mean of 50 and extending 3 standard deviations above and below the mean.

SKEWNESS (SK)—The tendency of a distribution to depart from symmetry or balance around the mean.

SPEARMAN-BROWN FORMULA—A formula giving the relationship between the reliability of a test and its length. It permits estimation of the reliability of a test lengthened or shortened by any amount from the known reliability of a test of specified length. Its most common application is split-half reliability correlation.

SPLIT-HALF COEFFICIENT—A reliability coefficient obtained by correlating scores on one-half of a test with scores on the other half—generally consisting of odd versus even numbered items.

STA-ELEVEN (C-SCALE)—A standard scale of values 0 to 10, mean of 5, wherein each value (except the extremes) has a band-width of .5 standard deviation; differs from stanine only in addition of another scale value at either end, 0 and 10.

STANDARD—A level or degree of attainment in a quality or characteristic deemed desirable for a certain purpose or function.

STANDARD DEVIATION (s)—A measure of the variability or dispersion of a set of scores. The closer the scores cluster around the mean, the smaller the standard deviation. It is obtained by computing the square root of the mean of the squares of the deviations from the mean of a distribution.

STANDARD ERROR (S.E.) of Measurement—An estimate of the magnitude of the "error of measurement" in a score, that is, the amount by which an obtained score differs from a hypothetical true score. The chances are 2 to 1 that an individual score will lie within the standard error either above or below the true score (68.26 per cent) or 19 to 1 that it is not more than twice the standard error from the true score. The larger the standard error of a score, the less reliable the measure.

STANDARD SCORE—A general term referring to different scores (T-score, z-score, stanine) formed by linear transformation of raw scores to permit comparability and ease of interpretation. The score is expressed as a deviation from the mean in terms of the standard deviation of the distribution (raw score minus the mean, divided by the standard deviation). Use of such standard scores does not affect the relative standing of the individuals in the group or change the shape of the original distribution. (*See also* z-score.)

STANDARDIZED TEST—A test that is composed of empirically selected materials; has definite directions for administration, scoring, and use; data on reliability and validity; and has adequately determined norms.

STANINE (STANDARD-NINE)—A standard scale of values 1 to 9, mean of 5, in which each value has a band-width of .5 standard deviation, except for the ends.

STATISTICAL SIGNIFICANCE—A term applied to a difference when only a slight probability exists that the difference was due to chance variation. (*See* Level of Significance.)

STRATIFIED SAMPLE—A sample selected to represent proportionally different components of a population; such as rural, suburban and urban subjects, geographical regions, or sex.

t-RATIO—The numerical value of the critical ratio and interpreted to test significance as the CR for large N and by use of a special table for small N.

T-SCORE—A standard score with a mean of 50 and one standard deviation equal to 10 score units. This linearly transformed score is sometimes referred to as Z-score to obviate confusion with McCall's (normalized) T-scale.

TEST-RETEST COEFFICIENT—A type of reliability coefficient (stability) obtained by readministering a test to a group of individuals after a short interval and correlating the sets of scores from the two administrations.

VALIDITY—The extent to which a test measures what it is intended to measure, specific to the purposes for which the test is used. The basic types are: *content validity,* which describes the adequacy of the sampling of instructional content or skill performance involved; *cri-*

terion-related validity, indicating the degree to which the scores agree with (concurrent) or predict later performance on (predictive) a given criterion measure; and *construct validity,* which indicates the extent to which certain explanatory constructs or conceptualizations account for performance on the test.

VARIABILITY—The spread or dispersion of scores indicated by such computations as standard deviation, quartile deviation, range of 90–10 percentile scores, and others.

X (OR Y)—The symbol used in measurement to designate a raw score.

z-SCORE—The basic standard score in which a raw score is expressed as the number of standard deviation units that it falls above (+) or below (−) the mean.

Description of Basic Test Items for Strength, Motor Fitness, and Performance

A description of items common to different tests is contained in this appendix in order to permit more concise presentation of tests and avoid needless repetition in Chapters 8 to 13, and to facilitate reference usage. If a particular test contains a modification or in any way varies from this basic item description (for example, an alternative scoring method), this is specifically noted in the textual descriptive material. The descriptions primarily reflect either a pioneer test or the most popular usage; in many instances they are specific for a particular age or age range. Also, since the items are derived from cited tests, in some instances a different method of scoring or testing set-up may be preferable or better. The reader should remain alert to these facts and make suitable adaptations for different age or grade levels as appropriate or for improving the scoring and administration.

These basic descriptions have been arbitarily categorized by purpose as follows:

Dynamic Strength	Explosive Power	Speed and/or Agility
Dips	Standing long jump	Shuttle run
Flexed-or bent-arm hang	Vertical jump	Dodging run
Leg lifts		Dashes
Pull-ups		Quarter-mile run
Push-ups		
Bent-knee sit-ups		
Sit-ups		
Squat jumps		
Squat thrusts		

Ball Events
  Alternate hand wall toss
  Softball throw
  Basketball throw
  Medicine ball put
  Football punt
  Wall pass
  Soccer wall volley
  Volleyball wall volley

Coordination, Balance and Flexibility
  Bar snap
  Cable jump
  Balance stand
  Extent flexibility
  Dynamic flexibillity

DYNAMIC STRENGTH

Dips.

PURPOSE: *To test the strength and endurance of the muscles involved in arm extension.*

Dips are performed on either the regular parallel bars or the wall parallels. The former are preferred, since they may be readily adjusted in width as well as height. In the starting position, the subject supports himself with a straight body by straight arms. The movement is executed by lowering oneself through controlled elbow flexion until the angle at the elbow is 90 degrees or less and immediately returning to full elbow extension. The tester should hold his hand so that it contacts the subject's shoulder when the bent-arm position is satisfactory. The subject performs as many dips as possible. Only fully completed movements count. Repetitions must be continuous with no intervening pause. The trunk and legs should be kept straight, and no supplementary action such as kicking or jerking should be permitted.

Flexed- or Bent-Arm Hang.

PURPOSE: *To test the strength and endurance of the muscles involved in arm flexion and depression.*

The flexed- or bent-arm hang is performed on a horizontal bar or special chinning bar approximately 1½ inches in diameter. The height of the bar should approximate the testee's standing height. The subject uses a forward (overhand) grasp and with the aid of a stool or testing assistants assumes a hanging support position with the elbows flexed, chin above the bar, and chest close to it. The testee holds this position as long as possible. The score is the time to the nearest second that the chin is held above the bar with the head in normal position. The watch is stopped when the chin touches or falls below the bar, and if the head tilts backward to keep the chin above the bar level. Extraneous body movements are not permitted during the test itself, and one trial is allowed.

Leg Lifts.

> PURPOSE: *To test the strength and endurance of the abdominal and hip flexor muscles.*

In the starting position the subject lies supine, hands clasped behind the neck, and elbows held on the floor by an assistant kneeling by the subject's head. The leg lift is performed by raising straight legs to the vertical and returning to the starting position. The test consists of doing as many repetitions as possible within 30 seconds and is scored as the number of times the legs are raised to the vertical position in one trial.

Pull-ups (or Chins).

> PURPOSE: *To test the strength and endurance of the muscles involved in arm flexion and depression.*

Pull-ups are generally performed either on a bar—horizontal bar, overhead ladder, or special chinning bar—or, when specified for a particular test, from rings that are attached to a bar. For girls, the rings may be attached to one of the parallel bars. The subject assumes a hanging support position and pulls himself up until his chin reaches the level of the bar and then returns to a hanging support with full elbow extension. The forward or overhand grasp (palms facing forward) is used in gripping the bar, unless otherwise specified. The test consists of performing as many repetitions of the movement as possible, and the chin must reach above bar level to count. The action must be continuous with no pauses. Kicking, jerking, or otherwise attempting to assist the pulling action is not allowed.

The hanging support position differs for boys and girls. For the boys, the bar should be high enough to permit the subject to be suspended without touching the floor. In instances where this is impossible for tall subjects, the subject's knees must be flexed to prevent contact with the floor. For the *Modified Pull-up* for girls, the bar should be adjusted to the lower level of the sternum (nipple level) while standing. A mat may be laid on the floor to prevent slipping. The subject assumes the hanging support by placing her heels in such a position that the angle between the arms and the body when held straight is a right angle. It may be desirable to provide additional means of preventing foot slippage such as by the tester placing his foot sideward against soles of the subject's feet.

Push-ups.

> PURPOSE: *To test the strength and endurance of muscles involved in arm and shoulder extension.*

For the starting position for boys, the subject assumes a front leaning rest position in which the body is kept in a straight line and supported on the palms of the hands and the base of the toes. The hands are placed directly below or slightly outside of the shoulders with fingers pointing forward. Elbows are straight, feet together. The test movement consists of lowering the body by bending the elbows until only the chest touches the floor and then returning to the starting position. This action is repeated as many times as possible. Only completed movements count, and pauses should not occur between repetitions. The head, trunk, and legs should be kept in a straight line throughout.

The *Modified* (or Bench) *Push-up* may be employed for girls and younger boys. The basic push-up position is altered slightly by use of a stall-bar bench, or a similar bench 13 inches high by 20 inches wide, which is placed on a mat. The subject assumes a front leaning rest position, grasping the outer edges of the bench at the near corners. The angle between the arm and the plane of the body should be 90 degrees. The chest should touch the bench on the down movement.

The *Knee Push-up* for girls varies only in the lower point of support, using bent knees rather than the feet. The subject assumes a front leaning knee rest support with knees flexed 90 degrees upon a mat or padding. A straight head-to-knee alignment should be maintained throughout. When possible, such as if the norms for a published test are not appropriate or of no concern, an alternative method of positioning can be utilized to facilitate the proper body position and movement pattern. For it the subject lies prone, places the hands on the floor beneath the shoulders, and flexes the knees. The elbows are then extended to assume the "up" position and count as one push-up. Considerable difficulty in attaining and maintaining proper hip alignment can thus be obviated.

Bent-Knee Sit-ups.

> PURPOSE: *To test the strength and endurance of the abdominal muscles.*

In the starting position the subject lies supine with shoulders on the floor, hands clasped behind the neck, knees bent to an angle of approximately 45 degrees, with feet as close to the buttocks as comfortable and held flat on the floor by a partner or assistant. The sit-up is executed by rolling up into a sitting position to touch both elbows to the knees. The movement is completed by returning to the starting position. The test consists of performing as many repetitions as possible and is scored as the number of knee-touches within the prescribed time limit. Hand-neck contact must be maintained to count. Only the shoulders must touch the floor before continuing, and pauses are permitted. To maintain the starting position of the legs and feet throughout the test, the partner should kneel straddling the testee's feet and place his hands on the back of the testee's legs, just beneath the knees.

Sit-ups.

PURPOSE: *To test the strength and endurance of the abdominal and hip flexor muscles.*

In the starting position, the subject lies supine, hands clasped behind the neck with elbows retracted (on the floor), legs straight, and ankles held down and about one foot apart by an assistant to maintain heel contact with the floor. The sit-up is executed by rolling up into a sitting position and then twisting the trunk slightly to touch one elbow to the opposite knee with no more than a slight knee bend. The movement is completed by return to the starting position with elbows on the floor. The test consists of performing as many repetitions as possible without pausing, while alternating elbow touches, right and left. The score is the number of knee-touches to the maximum allowed by test directions or time limit. Bouncing, premature twisting to use lateral muscles to assist the sit-up action, failure to maintain hand-neck contact, excessive knee bending, and similar infractions should be disallowed.

Squat Jumps.

PURPOSE: *To test the strength and endurance of the leg and hip extensor muscles.*

To start, the subject stands with the feet 4 to 6 inches apart, the heel of one foot in line with the toes of the other foot, and hands clasped on top of the head. The movement consists of dropping to a full squat on the heel of the rear foot and then springing up immediately with vigorous leg and hip extension and interchanging foot position prior to landing. Upon landing, the subject drops immediately to a full squat and continues, interchanging the feet each time. The trunk should remain erect, and the movement is continuous throughout the test. The subject does as many jumps as possible. Each jump completed satisfactorily counts one.

Squat Thrusts.

PURPOSE: *To test large muscle speed, coordination, and endurance.*

To perform a squat thrust, the subject starts from an erect standing position and moves to a squat rest position by fully flexing the knees and hips and placing the hands on the floor alongside and outside of the legs directly below the shoulders with the fingers pointing forward and elbows straight. Then the hips and legs are fully extended to assume a front leaning rest position. The subject returns to the squat rest position and then to a straight standing position. The action should be continuous, and only movements completed fully and satisfactorily in each aspect should be counted for the score. The subject executes as many squat thrusts as possible in the allotted time.

EXPLOSIVE (MUSCULAR) POWER

Standing Long (Broad) Jump.

PURPOSE: *To test the ability of the body to develop power relative to its weight.*

The testee stands with his toes on, but not over, the starting line and jumps from both feet simultaneously with a free arm swing. The best jump made in three trials is measured to the nearest inch at right angles from the nearest edge of the takeoff line to the closest point of contact of foot or body part with the mat or jumping pit. Any jump in which the jumper's foot goes over the starting line is disallowed. The jumps may be done either on a mat, which is preferably marked with lines to indicate distance, on the floor or into a jumping pit.

Vertical Jump (Jump and Reach).

PURPOSE: *To test the ability of the body to develop power relative to its weight.*

The subject stands facing the wall or jumping board. Keeping both feet flat on the floor, he reaches as high as possible with the fingers of both hands on the board to note the standing reach. Then the subject chalks the fingers of the touch hand and stands sideways a comfortable distance from the board, with reaching arm toward the board. Swinging both arms upward, the subject jumps vertically to the fullest extent and marks the high point on the board with the chalked fingers. Wetting the touch fingers is sometimes preferred to chalk. The jump must be taken without any preliminary foot movement, such as hopping or stepping. The best of three trials is recorded; the score is the distance between the standing reach and the high point to the nearest half-inch. The scoring may be done by measuring the distance directly with a yardstick, using a lined board with height markings and a wet sponge for chalk erasures, or other variations suggested by the author of a given test.

The accuracy and speed of measurement can be enhanced considerably by an adjustable yardstick on a lined jump board [1] or a sliding jump board that is lined and scaled in inches.[2] The testee pushes the yardstick or jump board up to the full extent of the standing reach position, where it is secured. Thus the measuring scale is aligned at the zero mark for the trials and the high point is read directly on the scale. The sliding jump board is housed within a frame that can be mounted on the wall, basketball backboard, or a portable stand. It has the further advantage of being lowered to facilitate score determination.

SPEED AND/OR AGILITY

Shuttle Run.

PURPOSE: *To test speed and agility.*

In a shuttle run, upon command, "Ready—Go," the subject runs from a starting line to a restraining line, returns to the starting line, and repeats this procedure a specified number of times. The subject may be required to run around a marker, touch an object or line at either end, or move objects (for example, 2- × 2- × 4-inch blocks) from one end of the course to the other; the basic intent of so doing is to insure that the specified distance is covered. The score is reported as the elapsed time to the nearest tenth of a scond. In some tests more than one trial is allowed.

The *Potato Race*, a varied pattern shuttle run, is run over a course defined by three 1-foot diameter circles, as shown in Fig. B–1, and requires two 2- × 2- × 4-inch wood blocks. The testee runs from a standing start: (a) to circle two and takes the block from it back to be *placed* in circle one; (b) next to circle three to take the block in it back to be placed in circle one; (c) then taking the first block from circle one to place it back in circle two and return to circle one; and (d) finally taking the remaining block from circle one to place it back in circle

---

[1] B. E. Phillips, "The JCR Test," *Research Quarterly*, XVIII, No. 1 (March, 1947), 12.

[2] J. R. Leighton, "Simplified Scoring in the Jump-Reach," *Journal of Health–Physical Education–Recreation*, XXXVII, No. 8 (October, 1966), 57.

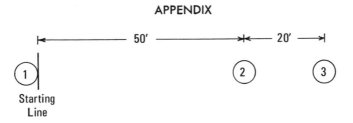

Fig. B–1. Course layout for the potato race.

three and race across the starting line. One trial is given, scored to the nearest second and, for multiple stations, as counted aloud by the starter.

Dodging Run.

PURPOSE: *To test speed, shiftiness, and ability to change direction.*

The dodging run requires the subject to run a prescribed course around obstacles or markers. The score is the time of one trial recorded to the nearest tenth of a second. The course originally devised by Cozens is described for illustration. Five 3-foot track lanes are laid out adjacently and are 11 yards in length. Five regulation low hurdles constitute the obstacles and are placed as follows: A, representing the start and finish, at the end of lane 1; B, 5 yards down lane 2; C, 7 yards down lane 4; D, 9 yards down lane 3; and E, 11 yards down lane 5. The prescribed route begins and finishes on the inside edge of A and runs to the left of B, right of C, left of D, right of and around E, and returning to A in exactly the same path. The test consists of making two complete trips around the course, passing around A after the first trip.

Dashes.

PURPOSE: *To test speed.*

Dashes may be conducted in one of two ways: for a set distance (for example, 50 yards) or for a set time (for example, 4 seconds). The latter provides an expeditious method of group testing, whereas the first way is the conventional race against time and posseses greater accuracy. In both cases the race is run over a straight course on a running track or other suitable area.

DASH FOR SET DISTANCE. The subject sprints a specified distance and the score is the time recorded to the nearest tenth of a second. One trial is allowed. Without a gun, the starter should accompany "Go" with a downward arm sweep to signal the timer.

Dash for a Set Time. Upon signal, the subject sprints for a specified number of seconds down a course that is divided into zones. A whistle is blown to mark the finish, and the score is recorded as the number of the zone in which the subject was running when the whistle sounded. One trial is allowed. The course is marked off in numbered 1-yard zones. For example, in a 4-second dash, 30 to 35 1-yard zones would be marked off and numbered beginning 10 yards from the starting line.

Quarter-Mile Run.

Purpose: *To test speed and endurance.*

On a quarter-mile running track, the subject upon signal runs one lap as fast as possible. One trial is given and is scored to the nearest second to permit group testing by counting aloud the elapsed time in seconds.

BALL EVENTS

Alternate Hand Wall Toss.

Purpose: *To test bilateral eye-hand coordination and skill in throwing and catching.*

The subject stands behind a restraining line 6 feet from a wall (at least 6 feet wide) with a tennis ball in the right hand; extra balls are placed in a container alongside the right foot. Upon command the ball is tossed underhand against the wall and the rebound is caught in the left hand; whereupon it is thrown with the left hand and caught in the right, and so on. The score is the sum of successful catches made in two trials of 30 seconds. Loose balls are replaced from the container. Trapping the ball against the body and crossing the restraining line are not permitted. Brief practice is allowed.

Softball Throw.

Purpose: *To test arm and shoulder-girdle strength and coordination.*

From within a restraining zone formed by two parallel lines 6 feet apart, the subject makes three overhand throws for distance with a regulation (12-inch inseam) softball. The score is the distance to the nearest foot for the best trial as measured perpendicular to the throwing line. A suggested field layout consists of an area 220 feet long, marked off in

10-foot intervals, and 150 feet wide. A line 6 feet before the throwing line defines the throwing area.

A study of alternative throwing methods with college men included the above stride throw as well as feet-in-place and knees-in-place throws.[3] Intercorrelations were quite high, .81–.85, as were reliability coefficients, .91–92. The knees throw proved easier to administer—less time, testing area and illegal throws. The feet-in-place method resulted in more violations and required more testing time. Most violations in the stride throw were due to trials not falling in the testing area.

Basketball Throw.

PURPOSE: *To test arm and shoulder-girdle strength and coordination.*

The subject throws a regulation basketball for distance from behind a throwing line employing any technique. A running approach is permissible. Score is the best of three trials measured to the nearest foot. No warmup throws are permitted. A throwing area of at least 120 feet for boys and 80 feet for girls should be provided and marked lengthwise by lines at 5-foot intervals beginning 15 feet from the throwing line, which should be about 8 feet from the end of the area.

For the *Sitting Basketball Throw* the subject uses an overhand bent-arm motion to throw a regulation basketball for distance with the preferred arm, while sitting behind a restraining line with legs straight and apart, heels kept on the floor. The score is the better of two trials measured to the nearest foot. Straight arm lobs and warmup throws are not permitted. The throwing area should be 10 feet wide, 75 feet long, and marked at one foot intervals beginning 25 feet from the restraining line.

Medicine Ball Put.

PURPOSE: *To test arm and shoulder-girdle strength and coordination.*

The subject puts a 6-pound medicine ball from behind a restraining line using a running approach, if desired. The best of three trials is recorded to the nearest half-foot, and no warmup throws are permitted. A line 15 feet behind the restraining line designates the area limited to the run.

[3] C. J. Cotten and E. Chambers, "A Comparison of Three Methods of Administering the Softball Throw," *Research Quarterly*, XXXIX, No. 3 (October, 1968), 788.

Football Punt.

PURPOSE: *To test arm- and foot-eye coordination and kicking power.*

The subject punts three times, and the furthest distance is recorded as estimated to the nearest yard. No warmup punts are permitted. Any number of steps prior to punting may be taken within a 15-foot restraining area. A suggested kicking area would be a field 120 yards long and 55 yards wide, marked lengthwise by numbered 10-yard lines with intermediary 5-yard lines.

Wall Pass.

PURPOSE: *To test skill in ball handling and control.*

Standing with both feet behind a restraining line 9 feet from a solid smooth wall, the subject upon signal passes a regulation basketball against the wall in any manner as many times as possible in 15 seconds. The subject must retrieve missed rebounds and return to the line before continuing. Three practice throws are allowed. The score is recorded as the number of wall hits in the time allotted.

Soccer Wall Volley.

PURPOSE: *To test ability and accuracy in repeatedly kicking a soccer ball from a specified distance.*

Upon signal, the subject kicks a regulation soccer ball from behind the restraining line, aiming for the target area on a wall; retrieves the ball; and repeats this procedure for 15 seconds. The ball must be retrieved with the feet only when in the rectangular area in front of the restraining line; otherwise, hands are permitted in retrieving the ball. A successful kick is one made from behind the line and hitting the target between the boundary lines. After a 15-second practice trial, four 15-second trials are given; and the total successful kicks are noted for each trial. The score is the best of four trials. The target areas is marked on a flat wall, 4 feet wide and 2½ feet high extending from the floor. A similar rectangular area is marked on the floor extending 2½ feet from the wall and 4 feet wide. The outer floor boundary line is extended 1 foot in either direction, parallel to the wall, to constitute the restraining line.

Volleyball Wall Volley.

PURPOSE: *To test ability and accuracy in repeatedly volleying a volleyball (from a specified distance).*

Standing in any desired position behind the restraining line, upon signal, the subject throws a regulation volleyball against the wall in the target area, volleys the rebound to the target, and continues. Missed balls are retrieved and put into play as initially from behind the restraining line. To be counted, a volley must fall inside, not on, the boundary line of the target area and must be legally executed—not pushed or caught and thrown. Initial throws do not count—only volleys. After one 10-second practice trial, four 15-second trials are given; and the total successful volleys are noted for each trial. The score is recorded as the best of four trials. A marked area 8 feet wide by at least 4 feet high at a distance of 3 feet from the floor represents the target area. The restraining line, 8 feet long, is drawn on the floor parallel to and 4 feet from the wall.

COORDINATION, BALANCE AND FLEXIBILITY

Bar Snap.

PURPOSE: *To test body coordination, agility, and control.*

With the bar set at 4 feet 6 inches above the floor, the subject stands close to and grasps the bar. The action is begun by swinging underneath the bar and shooting the feet close to the bar, up and out. The back is arched as the feet are thrust away from the bar. The hand-push away from the bar finishes propulsive action, and landing is made on both feet. Two warmup trials are permitted. The best of three trials is recorded as the distance to the nearest inch from the bar to the nearest point where a part of the body touches the floor.

Cable Jump.

PURPOSE: *To test the ability to coordinate the action of body parts in a gross movement.*

The subject holds a 24-inch length of rope in front with one hand grasping each end in such a way that the rope is not taut but hanging in the middle. The test consists of jumping over the rope, through the arms, landing on the feet without (1) hitting the rope with the feet, (2) losing hold of the rope during the jump, or (3) losing balance upon landing. The score is the number of correct jumps in five trials.

Balance Stand.

PURPOSE: *To test the ability to maintain bodily equilibrium while standing with eyes closed.*

The subject stands with hands on hips and the preferred foot aligned along the long axis of the balance rail. The test consists of balancing on the preferred foot with eyes closed as long as possible to a 20 second maximum. It begins when the subject attains a balanced position, closes his eyes, and says "Go." It ends when the eyes are opened, one or both hands are removed from the hips, the floor is touched by any part of the body, or 20 seconds elapse. One practice trial is given with the eyes open, after which two trials are administered. Each trial is scored as the number of seconds elapsing between "Go" and any one of the terminating conditions. The two trials are added for the total score. The balance apparatus consists of a wood rail, ¾ × 1½ × 24 inches, mounted on a base board.

Extent Flexibility (Twist and Touch).

PURPOSE: *To test the ability to flex or stretch the trunk, back, arm and shoulder muscles in a lateral movement.*

The right-handed subject stands with left-side toward the wall so that the fist can just touch it when the left arm is held side horizontal. The feet are together and perpendicular to, with toes touching, a line drawn at right angles to the wall. To assume the starting position the right arm is raised side horizontal with palm down and fingers extended together, and an assistant or partner places a foot alongside the testee's right foot to prevent movement. From this position the subject twists clockwise reaching back around as far as possible to touch the wall scale momentarily with the right hand. One practice trial is given, followed by one test trial which is scored as the farthest point held at least two seconds and measured to the nearest inch. The wall scale is 30 inches long, marked in half-inch intervals, and of sufficient width to accommodate varying heights of testees. The scale is aligned horizontally so that the 12-inch mark is directly above the floor line. The test action and set-up, as shown in Fig. B–2, is reversed for left-handed subjects.

Dynamic Flexibility (Bend-Twist-Touch).

PURPOSE: *To test the ability to repeat rapid flexing and twisting movements of the upper body.*

The subject stands with feet shoulder-width apart and back close to the wall, allowing sufficient space to bend down without touching it. An "X" is put on the wall (chalk or tape) at shoulder height on the body mid-line; another "X" is on the floor on the body mid-line just in front of the feet. Upon command, "Go," the subject bends down to touch the floor "X" with both hands and immediately rises, twisting to the left, to touch the wall "X" with both hands. This constitutes one cycle, and the next cycle is performed by twisting to the right. The

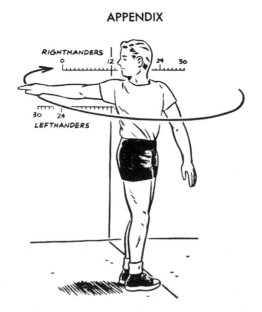

Fig. B–2. Markings and action pattern for extent flexibility test.

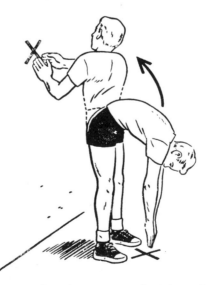

Fig. B–3. Markings and action pattern for dynamic flexibility tests.

score is the number of cycles to alternate side completed in 20 seconds. The test set-up and action pattern is shown in Fig. B–3. The demonstration should include three cycles, emphasizing speed, to illustrate the action pattern.

Normative Data
for Selected Tests

Table C–1. Basic Statistics for New York State Physical Fitness Test *

Test	Grade	Boys			Girls		
		Mean	Std. Dev.	SE_M	Mean	Std. Dev.	SE_M
Posture	5	56.2	5.0	1.0	57.9	4.2	1.1
	8	53.0	5.9	0.8	52.8	7.2	0.7
	11	55.8	5.4	0.9	52.6	7.2	1.0
Target throw	5	7.5	3.7	1.8	3.3	2.7	1.4
(accuracy)	8	9.6	3.9	1.8	6.9	3.6	1.7
	11	11.8	3.8	1.5	7.9	3.6	1.7
Pull-up or	5	15.7	10.2	3.1	8.6	6.9	2.5
modified push-up	8	5.9	4.0	1.1	31.4	15.5	5.8
(strength)	11	9.5	4.4	1.3	22.1	9.6	4.5
Sidestep	5	13.5	2.2	1.1	13.0	2.5	1.3
(agility)	8	15.6	2.0	1.2	15.3	3.1	1.7
	11	18.2	2.9	1.4	15.2	2.9	1.4
50-yard dash	5	8.7	0.7	0.4	8.8	0.8	0.4
(speed)	8	7.5	0.6	0.2	8.2	0.9	0.3
	11	6.8	0.5	0.2	8.2	0.7	0.3
Squat stand	5	7.6	10.1	3.5	10.6	16.3	8.6
(balance)	8	21.3	22.7	5.1	6.0	6.9	2.0
	11	27.3	23.2	5.2	8.7	16.4	2.3
Treadmill	5	51.7	14.5	7.5	45.4	18.2	6.3
(endurance)	8	93.5	25.3	7.1	52.1	15.1	5.4
	11	98.8	24.8	10.5	49.9	10.1	4.0
Total	5	30.2	6.3	2.1	31.6	5.7	2.1
without	8	31.6	6.3	2.2	32.3	7.3	2.3
posture	11	31.2	7.2	2.4	30.5	6.3	2.1
Total	5	35.3	7.2	2.1	37.3	6.2	2.0
with	8	35.6	7.2	2.3	36.4	8.2	2.4
posture	11	36.2	8.2	2.4	34.5	7.0	2.1

*Based on 841 pupils in six public schools in 1963. (At grades 5, 8, and 11, respectively—N = 147, 150, 127 for boys; and 144, 123, 150 for girls.)

Table C–2. Basic Statistics for New York State Physical Fitness Screening Test *

| Test | Grade | Boys | | | Girls | | |
		Mean	Std. Dev.	SE_M	Mean	Std. Dev.	SE_M
Sidestep	5	12.7	2.2	0.9	12.4	2.1	0.9
(agility)	8	15.6	2.1	1.0	14.4	2.0	1.0
	11	17.9	2.3	0.9	15.7	2.5	0.9
Sit-up	5	25.4	6.0	1.7	20.5	5.5	1.6
(strength)	8	49.9	12.4	3.3	22.3	6.1	2.4
	11	54.8	10.9	2.9	22.7	5.8	1.8
Dash	5	11.9	0.8	0.3	12.2	0.9	0.3
(speed)	8	23.4	1.8	0.8	16.0	1.3	0.3
	11	29.6	1.9	0.4	15.7	1.1	0.4
Squat-thrusts	5	15.4	3.2	1.2	12.7	3.7	1.3
(endurance)	8	27.9	5.9	2.4	13.3	2.6	0.8
	11	30.5	7.6	1.5	14.2	2.3	1.0
Total	5	20.1	4.0	1.3	19.3	4.7	1.4
	8	20.1	5.4	1.5	20.3	5.1	1.4
	11	20.8	5.1	1.2	22.9	4.7	1.5

*Based on 1,043 pupils in seven public schools in 1963. (At grades 5, 8, and 11 respectively—N = 166, 186, 166 for boys; and 174, 177, 174 for girls.)

Table C–3. Basic Statistics for CAHPER Fitness-Performance Test—Boys

Test		Age										
		7	8	9	10	11	12	13	14	15	16	17
Speed	$\overline{X}$	19.8	23.5	26.4	27.3	30.2	29.7	32.5	32.9	33.4	34.9	34.1
sit-up	s	9.4	8.9	9.4	9.5	9.6	10.1	10.3	9.9	10.9	9.7	10.2
	N	300	584	584	499	483	485	446	373	354	286	259
Standing	$\overline{X}$	44	48	52	54	58	60	64	70	74	79	82
broad	s	7.0	7.4	7.1	7.2	7.9	8.5	9.7	10.2	9.7	10.0	9.0
jump	N	300	583	581	502	484	484	442	370	353	286	259
Shuttle	$\overline{X}$	14.12	13.50	12.97	12.78	12.47	12.32	11.99	11.55	11.26	10.94	10.76
run	s	1.29	1.27	1.23	1.18	1.25	1.18	1.18	1.09	1.03	0.93	0.93
	N	297	575	575	490	470	476	441	368	352	285	258
Flexed-	$\overline{X}$	22.9	28.4	31.4	32.8	34.9	37.5	41.0	47.1	49.6	53.2	52.6
arm hang	s	18.3	20.3	18.9	20.1	20.4	20.8	21.4	21.8	20.4	19.9	18.8
	N	308	589	584	503	485	477	442	369	351	285	255
50-yard	$\overline{X}$	10.21	9.69	9.23	8.88	8.57	8.45	8.11	7.67	7.32	7.09	6.99
run	s	1.1	1.0	0.84	0.80	0.80	0.85	0.79	0.79	0.72	0.61	0.93
	N	309	590	581	499	480	474	440	367	350	282	251
300-yard	$\overline{X}$	85.8	80.5	76.7	73.8	71.9	69.2	66.0	62.5	60.0	57.8	56.2
run	s	11.2	9.3	9.1	8.7	10.2	7.6	7.2	6.8	6.0	4.9	4.1
	N	307	588	579	493	477	472	437	366	348	280	250

Table C–4. Basic Statistics for CAHPER Fitness-Performance Test—Girls

Test		7	8	9	10	11	12	13	14	15	16	17
							Age					
Speed	$\bar{X}$	17.2	18.8	20.2	22.4	24.8	23.1	22.7	20.1	22.2	22.5	19.9
sit-up	s	9.3	9.5	9.6	10.2	10.2	10.4	9.4	10.1	9.7	9.5	9.6
	N	364	632	576	500	477	435	354	369	340	301	176
Standing	$\bar{X}$	43	46	49	52	55	56	58	59	61	62	60
broad	s	6.4	7.9	8.2	7.3	8.1	8.5	8.8	10.4	9.5	8.2	7.6
jump	N	364	631	578	500	476	438	354	371	340	301	177
Shuttle	$\bar{X}$	14.84	14.12	13.81	13.28	13.04	13.01	12.77	12.65	12.57	12.52	12.61
run	s	1.46	1.26	1.34	1.23	1.32	1.27	1.19	1.19	1.16	1.17	1.09
	N	362	618	570	491	467	434	355	369	339	302	177
Flexed-	$\bar{X}$	18.4	17.8	19.3	21.5	21.1	18.7	17.6	16.4	16.5	15.8	15.8
arm hang	s	21.7	15.6	16.1	19.0	17.8	14.9	14.6	14.3	13.7	14.0	13.6
	N	364	633	580	497	472	436	353	367	338	297	174
50-yard	$\bar{X}$	10.68	10.01	9.68	9.22	8.89	8.75	8.66	8.67	8.49	8.45	8.51
run	s	1.15	0.89	0.98	0.95	1.0	0.93	0.93	0.93	0.90	0.90	0.77
	N	364	632	574	496	474	433	355	366	335	292	165
300-yard	$\bar{X}$	87.6	81.7	79.1	76.4	74.1	72.5	71.9	73.1	72.4	72.0	72.9
run	s	10.1	8.2	8.3	9.6	8.9	7.2	7.8	7.9	8.4	6.6	6.7
	N	360	627	571	495	470	430	353	363	334	288	162

Table C–5. Basic Statistics for the Physical-Performance Test for California (Revised)—Boys

Test		Age								
		10	11	12	13	14	15	16	17	18
Standing	$\bar{X}$	59.3	62.7	66.7	70.4	76.2	80.9	83.5	86.2	86.9
long	s	9.2	8.4	9.0	10.5	11.1	10.7	11.3	10.4	11.2
jump	Md	60.3	63.5	67.3	71.5	77.4	81.8	84.9	87.2	88.0
	Q_1	55.0	57.9	61.9	65.3	70.8	75.3	78.2	80.8	82.0
	Q_3	65.6	68.6	72.7	77.2	83.9	88.0	90.8	93.5	94.8
Knee	$\bar{X}$	25.1	28.7	36.6	41.4	45.1	48.1	49.8	50.4	49.5
bent	s	12.1	13.6	12.9	11.6	12.1	12.3	12.7	13.2	13.3
sit-up	Md	25.1	28.9	38.1	42.8	45.8	48.4	49.9	50.4	50.4
	Q_1	18.8	21.3	30.1	36.1	40.0	41.6	42.8	42.7	42.7
	Q_3	32.5	37.2	45.5	48.8	51.9	54.8	57.0	58.7	57.6
Chair	$\bar{X}$	15.4	17.0	18.5	22.9	26.7	29.1	34.0	35.7	35.4
push-up	s	11.3	12.0	12.1	13.2	14.4	14.0	13.9	14.4	13.7
	Md	14.1	15.3	17.1	21.0	25.5	29.4	34.9	35.2	35.1
	Q_1	7.5	9.2	10.4	13.9	17.5	20.4	25.5	26.3	26.2
	Q_3	21.8	23.9	25.6	31.1	35.3	39.7	43.0	46.6	46.3
Side	$\bar{X}$	13.2	14.4	15.6	17.0	18.5	19.3	19.4	20.0	19.9
step	s	4.0	4.4	4.8	4.1	4.3	5.0	4.8	5.0	5.0
	Md	13.8	15.1	16.3	17.6	18.9	19.7	20.0	20.4	20.5
	Q_1	11.7	12.6	13.7	15.2	16.4	16.8	16.8	17.5	17.4
	Q_3	15.8	17.2	18.6	20.1	21.4	22.6	22.9	23.4	23.5
Pull-up	$\bar{X}$	2.5	2.8	3.0	4.0	5.6	7.0	8.2	9.0	9.2
	s	3.1	3.3	3.4	3.8	4.2	4.7	4.7	4.7	4.9
	Md	1.9	2.4	2.7	3.8	5.5	6.9	8.4	9.3	9.8
	Q_1	0.7	0.7	0.9	1.4	2.7	4.0	5.3	6.3	6.4
	Q_3	4.4	4.8	5.0	6.5	8.9	10.4	11.6	12.5	12.6
Jog-	$\bar{X}$	11.5	12.2	12.2	12.9	13.4	13.8	14.0	13.7	13.8
walk	s	5.5	5.5	4.2	3.6	4.0	3.5	3.3	3.5	3.0
	Md	12.0	12.5	13.0	14.0	14.5	14.6	14.8	14.7	14.7
	Q_1	10.3	10.6	11.2	12.2	12.8	13.1	13.4	13.0	13.1
	Q_3	13.6	14.1	14.5	15.2	15.7	16.0	16.0	15.9	16.1
	N	1,069	1,104	1,199	1,277	1,206	1,132	1,232	1,178	1,084

Table C–6. Basic Statistics for the Physical-Performance Test for California (Revised)—Girls

Test		Age								
		10	11	12	13	14	15	16	17	18
Standing	$\overline{X}$	55.9	59.0	62.2	64.8	65.2	65.4	65.4	65.6	65.7
long	s	8.4	9.6	9.0	10.1	10.4	9.8	9.3	9.2	9.8
jump	Md	56.7	59.4	63.2	65.3	65.6	66.3	65.9	66.5	66.4
	Q_1	51.6	54.3	57.2	59.9	60.8	60.6	60.5	60.8	60.6
	Q_3	61.7	64.9	68.8	71.1	72.4	72.2	72.0	72.2	72.2
Knee	$\overline{X}$	23.2	24.1	28.4	30.8	31.4	31.4	31.0	31.4	31.5
bent	s	11.0	11.1	10.5	10.0	10.3	10.3	10.0	9.9	9.9
sit-up	Md	23.1	23.6	29.9	31.6	32.5	32.1	32.1	32.7	32.6
	Q_1	16.3	17.4	22.4	25.3	25.6	25.7	25.7	25.0	25.9
	Q_3	30.3	31.8	35.8	37.5	38.8	39.0	38.2	38.8	38.8
Chair	$\overline{X}$	9.4	9.1	8.2	7.6	7.2	6.4	5.5	5.5	6.4
push-up	s	9.3	9.7	9.0	7.8	7.5	7.7	7.3	5.9	7.7
	Md	7.8	7.4	6.1	6.0	5.6	4.9	4.0	3.0	4.7
	Q_1	3.5	2.9	2.5	2.5	2.1	2.0	1.3	1.5	1.8
	Q_3	13.3	12.9	11.6	11.2	11.1	9.9	8.4	8.8	9.5
Side	$\overline{X}$	12.9	13.6	15.6	15.8	15.8	16.0	16.0	16.3	16.2
step	s	5.1	4.5	7.2	4.1	3.5	3.6	4.0	3.2	3.5
	Md	13.4	14.3	15.8	16.5	16.4	16.8	16.4	16.7	16.5
	Q_1	11.3	11.8	13.3	14.3	14.4	14.6	14.4	14.7	14.7
	Q_3	15.3	16.3	17.9	18.4	18.4	18.5	18.5	18.9	18.8
Pull-up	$\overline{X}$	1.8	1.6	1.2	1.2	1.2	1.0	0.7	0.4	0.6
	s	5.6	5.5	3.6	4.4	4.4	4.1	3.3	2.2	2.5
	Md	0.8	0.7	0.7	0.6	0.6	0.6	0.6	0.6	0.6
	Q_1	0.4	0.3	0.3	0.3	0.3	0.3	0.3	0.3	0.3
	Q_3	1.8	1.5	1.5	1.2	1.1	1.0	0.9	0.9	0.9
Jog-walk	$\overline{X}$	10.0	10.6	10.7	10.7	10.8	10.6	10.0	9.8	9.7
	s	5.0	4.8	4.0	3.0	2.8	3.2	2.6	2.9	2.9
	Md	10.6	11.0	11.2	11.5	11.3	11.1	10.8	10.7	10.6
	Q_1	9.2	9.4	9.8	10.1	10.1	10.0	9.5	9.4	9.3
	Q_3	12.1	12.6	12.6	12.7	12.6	12.4	12.0	11.8	11.7
	N	1,060	1,102	1,148	1,164	1,115	1,112	1,145	1,128	1,089

APPENDIX D

Illustrative Physical Education Attitude Inventory

WEAR PHYSICAL EDUCATION ATTITUDE INVENTORY [1]

Directions—Please Read Carefully: Below you will find some statements about physical education. We would like to know how you feel about each statement. You are asked to consider physical education *only* from the standpoint of its place as an activity course taught during a regular class period. No reference is intended in any statement to interscholastic or intramural athletics. People differ widely in the way they feel about each statement. There are no right or wrong answers.

You have been provided with a separate answer sheet for recording your reaction to each statement. (a) Read each statement carefully, (b) go to the answer sheet, and (c) opposite the number of the statement place an "x" in the square *which is under* the word (or words) which best express your feeling about the statement. After reading a statement you will know at once, in most cases, whether you *agree* or *disagree* with the statement. If you *agree*, then decide whether to place an "x" under "agree" or "strongly agree." If you *disagree*, then decide whether to place the "x" under "disagree" or "strongly disagree." In case you are undecided (or neutral) concerning your feeling about the statement, then place an "x" under "undecided." Try to avoid placing an "x" under "undecided" in very many instances.

Wherever possible, let your own personal experience determine your answer. Work rapidly, do not spend much time on any statement. This is not a test, but is simply a survey to determine how people feel about

[1] Carlos B. Wear, "The Evaluation of Attitude Toward Physical Education as an Activity Course," *Research Quarterly,* XXII, No. 1 (March, 1951), 114.

physical education. Your answers will in no way affect your grade in any course. In fact, we are not interested in connecting any person with any paper—so please answer each statement as you actually feel about it. *Be sure to answer every statement.*

Statements

1. If for any reason a few subjects have to be dropped from the school program, physical education should be one of the subjects dropped.
2. Associations in physical education activities give people a better understanding of each other.
3. Physical education activities provide no opportunities for learning to control the emotions.
4. Engaging in vigorous physical activity gets one interested in practicing good health habits.
5. Physical education is one of the more important subjects in helping to establish and maintain desirable social standards.
6. The time spent in getting ready for and engaging in physical education class could be more profitably spent in other ways.
7. Vigorous physical activity works off harmful emotional tensions.
8. A person's body usually has all the strength it needs without participation in physical education activities.
9. I would take physical education only if it were required.
10. Participation in physical education activities tends to make one a more socially desirable person.
11. Participation in physical education makes no contribution to the development of poise.
12. Physical education in schools does not receive the emphasis that it should.
13. Because physical skills loom large in importance in youth it is essential that a person be helped to acquire and improve such skills.
14. Physical education classes are poor in opportunities for worthwhile social experiences.
15. Calisthenics taken regularly are good for one's general health.
16. A person would be better off emotionally if he did not participate in physical education.
17. Skill in active games or sports is not necessary for leading the fullest kind of life.
18. It is possible to make physical education a valuable subject by proper selection of activities.
19. Physical education does more harm physically than it does good.
20. Developing a physical skill brings mental relaxation and relief.
21. Associating with others in some physical education activity is fun.

22. Physical education classes provide nothing which will be of value outside of the class.
23. Physical education classes provide situations for the formation of attitudes which will make one a better citizen.
24. There should not be over two one-hour periods per week devoted to physical education in schools.
25. Physical education situations are among the poorest for making friends.
26. Belonging to a group, for which opportunity is provided in team activities, is a desirable experience for a person.
27. There is not enough value coming from physical education to justify the time consumed.
28. Physical education is an important subject in helping a person gain and maintain all-round good health.
29. Physical education skills make worthwhile contributions to the enrichment of living.
30. No definite beneficial results come from participation in physical education activities.
31. People get all the physical exercise they need in just taking care of their daily work.
32. Engaging in group physical education activities is desirable for proper personality development.
33. All who are physically able will profit from an hour of physical education each day.
34. Physical education activities tend to upset a person emotionally.
35. Physical education makes a valuable contribution toward building up an adequate reserve of strength and endurance for everyday living.
36. For its contributions to mental and emotional well-being physical education should be included in the program of every school.
37. Physical education tears down sociability by encouraging people to attempt to surpass each other in many of the activities.
38. I would advise anyone who is physically able to take physical education.
39. Participation in physical education activities makes for a more wholesome outlook on life.
40. As far as improving physical health is concerned a physical education class is a waste of time.

Table of Squares and Square Roots for Numbers from 1 to 1,000

N	N^2	$\sqrt{N}$	N	N^2	$\sqrt{N}$	N	N^2	$\sqrt{N}$	N	N^2	$\sqrt{N}$
			30	900	5.4772	60	3 600	7.7460	90	8 100	9.4868
1	1	1.0000	31	961	5.5678	61	3 721	7.8103	91	8 281	9.5394
2	4	1.4142	32	1 024	5.6569	62	3 844	7.8740	92	8 464	9.5917
3	9	1.7321	33	1 089	5.7446	63	3 969	7.9373	93	8 649	9.6437
4	16	2.0000	34	1 156	5.8310	64	4 096	8.0000	94	8 836	9.6954
5	25	2.2361	35	1 225	5.9161	65	4 225	8.0623	95	9 025	9.7468
6	36	2.4495	36	1 296	6.0000	66	4 356	8.1240	96	9 216	9.7980
7	49	2.6458	37	1 369	6.0828	67	4 489	8.1854	97	9 409	9.8489
8	64	2.8284	38	1 444	6.1644	68	4 624	8.2462	98	9 604	9.8995
9	81	3.0000	39	1 521	6.2450	69	4 761	8.3066	99	9 801	9.9499
10	100	3.1623	40	1 600	6.3246	70	4 900	8.3666	100	10 000	10.000
11	121	3.3166	41	1 681	6.4031	71	5 041	8.4262	101	10 201	10.050
12	144	3.4641	42	1 764	6.4807	72	5 184	8.4853	102	10 404	10.100
13	169	3.6056	43	1 849	6.5574	73	5 329	8.5440	103	10 609	10.149
14	196	3.7417	44	1 936	6.6333	74	5 476	8.6023	104	10 816	10.198
15	225	3.8730	45	2 025	6.7082	75	5 625	8.6603	105	11 025	10.247
16	256	4.0000	46	2 116	6.7823	76	5 776	8.7178	106	11 236	10.296
17	289	4.1231	47	2 209	6.8557	77	5 929	8.7750	107	11 449	10.344
18	324	4.2426	48	2 304	6.9282	78	6 084	8.8318	108	11 664	10.392
19	361	4.3589	49	2 401	7.0000	79	6 241	8.8882	109	11 881	10.440
20	400	4.4721	50	2 500	7.0711	90	6 400	8.9443	110	12 100	10.488
21	441	4.5826	51	2 601	7.1414	81	6 561	9.0000	111	12 321	10.536
22	484	4.6904	52	2 704	7.2111	82	6 724	9.0554	112	12 544	10.583
23	529	4.7958	53	2 809	7.2801	83	6 889	9.1104	113	12 769	10.630
24	576	4.8990	54	2 916	7.3485	84	7 056	9.1652	114	12 996	10.677
25	625	5.0000	55	3 025	7.4162	85	7 225	9.2195	115	13 225	10.724
26	676	5.0990	56	3 136	7.4833	86	7 396	9.2736	116	13 456	10.770
27	729	5.1962	57	3 249	7.5498	87	7 569	9.3274	117	13 689	10.817
28	784	5.2915	58	3 364	7.6158	88	7 744	9.3808	118	13 924	10.863
29	841	5.3852	59	3 481	7.6811	89	7 921	9.4340	119	14 161	10.909

N	N²	√N	N	N²	√N	N	N²	√N	N	N²	√N
120	14 400	10.954	170	28 900	13.038	220	48 400	14.832	270	72 900	16.432
121	14 641	11.000	171	29 241	13.077	221	48 841	14.866	271	73 441	16.462
122	14 884	11.045	172	29 584	13.115	222	49 284	14.900	272	73 984	16.492
123	15 129	11.091	173	29 929	13.153	223	49 729	14.933	273	74 529	16.523
124	15 376	11.136	174	30 276	13.191	224	50 176	14.967	274	75 076	16.553
125	15 625	11.180	175	30 625	13.229	225	50 625	15.000	275	75 625	16.583
126	15 876	11.225	176	30 976	13.267	226	51 076	15.033	276	76 176	16.613
127	16 129	11.269	177	31 329	13.304	227	51 529	15.067	277	76 729	16.643
128	16 384	11.314	178	31 684	13.342	228	51 984	15.100	278	77 284	16.673
129	16 641	11.358	179	32 041	13.379	229	52 441	15.133	279	77 841	16.703
130	16 900	11.402	180	32 400	13.416	230	52 900	15.166	280	78 400	16.733
131	17 161	11.446	181	32 761	13.454	231	53 361	15.199	281	78 961	16.763
132	17 424	11.489	182	33 124	13.491	232	53 824	15.232	282	79 524	16.793
133	17 689	11.533	183	33 489	13.528	233	54 289	15.264	283	80 089	16.823
134	17 956	11.576	184	33 856	13.565	234	54 756	15.297	284	80 656	16.852
135	18 225	11.619	185	34 225	13.601	235	55 225	15.330	285	81 225	16.882
136	18 496	11.662	186	34 596	13.638	236	55 696	15.362	286	81 796	16.912
137	18 769	11.705	187	34 969	13.675	237	56 169	15.395	287	82 369	16.941
138	19 044	11.747	188	35 344	13.711	238	56 644	15.427	288	82 944	16.971
139	19 321	11.790	189	35 721	13.748	239	57 121	15.460	289	83 521	17.000
140	19 600	11.832	190	36 100	13.784	240	57 600	15.492	290	84 100	17.029
141	19 881	11.874	191	36 481	13.820	241	58 081	15.524	291	84 681	17.059
142	20 164	11.916	192	36 864	13.856	242	58 564	15.556	292	85 264	17.088
143	20 449	11.958	193	37 249	13.892	243	59 049	15.588	293	85 849	17.117
144	20 736	12.000	194	37 636	13.928	244	59 536	15.621	294	86 436	17.146
145	21 025	12.042	195	38 025	13.964	245	60 025	15.652	295	87 025	17.176
146	21 316	12.083	196	38 416	14.000	246	60 516	15.684	296	87 616	17.205
147	21 609	12.124	197	38 809	14.036	247	61 009	15.716	297	88 209	17.234
148	21 904	12.166	198	39 204	14.071	248	61 504	15.748	298	88 804	17.263
149	22 201	12.207	199	39 601	14.107	249	62 001	15.780	299	88 401	17.292
150	22 500	12.247	200	40 000	14.142	250	62 500	15.811	300	90 000	17.321
151	22 801	12.288	201	40 401	14.177	251	63 001	15.843	301	90 601	17.349
152	23 104	12.329	202	40 804	14.213	252	63 504	15.875	302	91 204	17.378
153	23 409	12.369	203	41 209	14.248	253	64 009	15.906	303	91 809	17.407
154	23 716	12.410	204	41 616	14.283	254	64 516	15.937	304	92 416	17.436
155	24 025	12.450	205	42 025	14.318	255	65 025	15.969	305	93 025	17.464
156	24 336	12.490	206	42 436	14.353	256	65 536	16.000	306	93 636	17.493
157	24 649	12.530	207	42 849	14.387	257	66 049	16.031	307	94 249	17.521
158	24 964	12.570	208	43 264	14.422	258	66 564	16.062	308	94 864	17.550
159	25 281	12.610	209	43 681	14.457	259	67 081	16.093	309	95 481	17.578
160	25 600	12.649	210	44 100	14.491	260	67 600	16.125	310	96 100	17.607
161	25 921	12.689	211	44 521	14.526	261	68 121	16.155	311	96 721	17.635
162	26 244	12.728	212	44 944	14.560	262	68 644	16.186	312	97 344	17.664
163	26 569	12.767	213	45 369	14.595	263	69 169	16.217	313	97 969	17.692
164	26 896	12.806	214	45 796	14.629	264	69 696	16.248	314	98 596	17.720
165	27 225	12.845	215	46 225	14.663	265	70 225	16.279	315	99 225	17.748
166	27 556	12.884	216	46 656	14.697	266	70 756	16.310	316	99 856	17.776
167	27 889	12.923	217	47 089	14.731	267	71 289	16.340	317	100 489	17.804
168	28 224	12.961	218	47 524	14.765	268	71 824	16.371	318	101 124	17.833
169	28 561	13.000	219	47 961	14.799	269	72 361	16.401	319	101 761	17.861

N	N²	√N	N	N²	√N	N	N²	√N	N	N²	√N
320	102 400	17.889	370	136 900	19.235	420	176 400	20.494	470	220 900	21.679
321	103 041	17.916	371	137 641	19.261	421	177 241	20.518	471	221 841	21.703
322	103 684	17.944	372	138 384	19.287	422	178 084	20.543	472	222 784	21.726
323	104 329	17.972	373	139 129	19.313	423	178 929	20.567	473	223 729	21.749
324	104 976	18.000	374	139 876	19.339	424	179 776	20.591	474	224 676	21.772
325	105 625	18.028	375	140 625	19.365	425	180 625	20.616	475	225 625	21.794
326	106 276	18.055	376	141 376	19.391	426	181 476	20.640	476	226 576	21.817
327	106 929	18.083	377	142 129	19.416	427	182 329	20.664	477	227 529	21.840
328	107 584	18.111	378	142 884	19.442	428	183 184	20.688	478	228 484	21.863
329	108 241	18.138	379	143 641	19.468	429	184 041	20.712	479	229 441	21.886
330	108 900	18.166	380	144 400	19.494	430	184 900	20.736	480	230 400	21.909
331	109 561	18.193	381	145 161	19.519	431	185 761	20.761	481	231 361	21.932
332	110 224	18.221	382	145 924	19.545	432	186 624	20.785	482	232 324	21.955
333	110 889	18.248	383	146 689	19.570	433	187 489	20.809	483	233 289	21.977
334	111 556	18.276	384	147 456	19.596	434	188 356	20.833	484	234 256	22.000
335	112 225	18.303	385	148 225	19.621	435	189 225	20.857	485	235 225	22.023
336	112 896	18.330	386	148 996	19.647	436	190 096	20.881	486	236 196	22.045
337	113 569	18.358	387	149 769	19.672	437	190 969	20.905	487	237 169	22.068
338	114 244	18.385	388	150 544	19.698	438	191 844	20.928	488	238 144	22.091
339	114 921	18.412	389	151 321	19.723	439	192 721	20.952	489	239 121	22.113
340	115 600	18.439	390	152 100	19.748	440	193 600	20.976	490	240 100	22.136
341	116 281	18.466	391	152 881	19.774	441	194 481	21.000	491	241 081	22.159
342	116 964	18.493	392	153 664	19.799	442	195 364	21.024	492	242 064	22.181
343	117 649	18.520	393	154 449	19.824	443	196 249	21.048	493	243 049	22.204
344	118 336	18.547	394	155 236	19.849	444	197 136	21.071	494	244 036	22.226
345	119 025	18.574	395	156 025	19.875	445	198 025	21.095	495	245 025	22.249
346	119 716	18.601	396	156 816	19.900	446	198 916	21.119	496	246 016	22.271
347	120 409	18.628	397	157 609	19.925	447	199 809	21.142	497	247 009	22.294
348	121 104	18.655	398	158 404	19.950	448	200 704	21.166	498	248 004	22.316
349	121 801	18.682	399	159 201	19.975	449	201 601	21.190	499	249 001	22.338
350	122 500	18.708	400	160 000	20.000	450	202 500	21.213	500	250 000	22.361
351	123 201	18.735	401	160 801	20.025	451	203 401	21.237	501	251 001	22.383
352	123 904	18.762	402	161 604	20.050	452	204 304	21.260	502	252 004	22.405
353	124 609	18.788	403	162 409	20.075	453	205 209	21.284	503	253 009	22.428
354	125 316	18.815	404	163 216	20.100	454	206 116	21.307	504	254 016	22.450
355	126 025	18.841	405	164 025	20.125	455	207 025	21.331	505	255 025	22.472
356	126 736	18.868	406	164 836	20.149	456	207 936	21.354	506	256 036	22.494
357	127 449	18.894	407	165 649	20.174	457	208 849	21.378	507	257 049	22.517
358	128 164	18.921	408	166 464	20.199	458	209 764	21.401	508	258 064	22.539
359	128 881	18.947	409	167 281	20.224	459	210 681	21.424	509	259 081	22.561
360	129 600	18.974	410	168 100	20.248	460	211 600	21.448	510	260 100	22.583
361	130 321	19.000	411	168 921	20.273	461	212 521	21.471	511	261 121	22.605
362	131 044	19.026	412	169 744	20.298	462	213 444	21.494	512	262 144	22.627
363	131 769	19.053	413	170 569	20.322	463	214 369	21.517	513	263 169	22.650
364	132 496	19.079	414	171 396	20.347	464	215 296	21.541	514	264 196	22.672
365	133 225	19.105	415	172 225	20.372	465	216 225	21.564	515	265 225	22.694
366	133 956	19.131	416	173 056	20.396	466	217 156	21.587	516	266 256	22.716
367	134 689	19.157	417	173 889	20.421	467	218 089	21.610	517	267 289	22.738
368	135 424	19.183	418	174 724	20.445	468	219 024	21.633	518	268 324	22.760
369	136 161	19.209	419	175 561	20.469	469	219 961	21.656	519	269 361	22.782

N	N²	√N	N	N²	√N	N	N²	√N	N	N²	√N
520	270 400	22.804	570	324 900	23.875	620	384 400	24.900	670	448 900	25.884
521	271 441	22.825	571	326 041	23.896	621	385 641	24.920	671	450 241	25.904
522	272 484	22.847	572	327 184	23.917	622	386 884	24.940	672	451 584	25.923
523	273 529	22.869	573	328 329	23.937	623	388 129	24.960	673	452 929	25.942
524	274 576	22.891	574	329 476	23.958	624	389 376	24.980	674	454 276	25.962
525	275 625	22.913	575	330 625	23.979	625	390 625	25.000	675	455 625	25.981
526	276 676	22.935	576	331 776	24.000	626	391 876	25.020	676	456 976	26.000
527	277 729	22.956	577	332 929	24.021	627	393 129	25.040	677	458 329	26.019
528	278 784	22.978	578	334 084	24.042	628	394 384	25.060	678	459 684	26.038
529	279 841	23.000	579	335 241	24.062	629	395 641	25.080	679	461 041	26.058
530	280 900	23.022	580	336 400	24.083	630	396 900	25.100	680	462 400	26.077
531	281 961	23.043	581	337 561	24.104	631	398 161	25.120	681	463 761	26.096
532	283 024	23.065	582	338 724	24.125	632	399 424	25.140	682	465 124	26.115
533	284 089	23.087	583	339 889	24.145	633	400 689	25.159	683	466 489	26.134
534	285 156	23.108	584	341 056	24.166	634	401 956	25.179	684	467 856	26.153
535	286 225	23.130	585	342 225	24.187	635	403 225	25.199	685	469 225	26.173
536	287 296	23.152	586	343 396	24.207	636	404 496	25.219	686	470 596	26.192
537	288 369	23.173	587	344 569	24.228	637	405 769	25.239	687	471 969	26.211
538	289 444	23.195	588	345 744	24.249	638	407 044	25.259	688	473 344	26.230
539	290 521	23.216	589	346 921	24.269	639	408 321	25.278	689	474 721	26.249
540	291 600	23.238	590	348 100	24.290	640	409 600	25.298	690	476 100	26.268
541	292 681	23.259	591	349 281	24.310	641	410 881	25.318	691	477 481	26.287
542	293 764	23.281	592	350 464	24.331	642	412 164	25.338	692	478 864	26.306
543	294 849	23.302	593	351 649	24.352	643	413 449	25.357	693	480 249	26.325
544	295 936	23.324	594	352 836	24.372	644	414 736	25.377	694	481 636	26.344
545	297 025	23.345	595	354 025	24.393	645	416 025	25.397	695	483 025	26.363
546	298 116	23.367	596	355 216	24.413	646	417 316	25.417	696	484 416	26.382
547	299 209	23.388	597	356 409	24.434	647	418 609	25.436	697	485 809	26.401
548	300 304	23.409	598	357 604	24.454	648	419 904	25.456	698	487 204	26.420
549	301 401	23.431	599	358 801	24.474	649	421 201	25.475	699	488 601	26.439
550	302 500	23.452	600	360 000	24.495	650	422 500	25.495	700	490 000	26.458
551	303 601	23.473	601	361 201	24.515	651	423 801	25.515	701	491 401	26.476
552	304 704	23.495	602	362 404	24.536	652	425 104	25.534	702	492 804	26.495
553	305 809	23.516	603	363 609	24.556	653	426 409	25.554	703	494 209	26.514
554	306 916	23.537	604	364 816	24.576	654	427 716	25.573	704	495 616	26.533
555	308 025	23.558	605	366 025	24.597	655	429 025	25.593	705	497 025	26.552
556	309 136	23.580	606	367 236	24.617	656	430 336	25.613	706	498 436	26.571
557	310 249	23.601	607	368 449	24.637	657	431 649	25.632	707	499 849	26.589
558	311 364	23.622	608	369 664	24.658	658	432 964	25.652	708	501 264	26.608
559	312 481	23.643	609	370 881	24.678	659	434 281	25.671	709	502 681	26.627
560	313 600	23.664	610	372 100	24.698	660	435 600	25.690	710	504 100	26.646
561	314 721	23.685	611	373 321	24.718	661	436 921	25.710	711	505 521	26.665
562	315 844	23.707	612	374 544	24.739	662	438 244	25.729	712	506 944	26.683
563	316 969	23.728	613	375 769	24.759	663	439 569	25.749	713	508 369	26.702
564	318 096	23.749	614	376 996	24.779	664	440 896	25.768	714	509 796	26.721
565	319 225	23.770	615	378 225	24.799	665	442 225	25.788	715	511 225	26.739
566	320 356	23.791	616	379 456	24.819	666	443 556	25.807	716	512 656	26.758
567	321 489	23.812	617	380 689	24.839	667	444 889	25.826	717	514 089	26.777
568	322 624	23.833	618	381 924	24.860	668	446 224	25.846	718	515 524	26.796
569	323 761	23.854	619	383 161	24.880	669	447 561	25.865	719	516 961	26.814

N	N²	√N	N	N²	√N	N	N²	√N	N	N²	√N
720	518 400	26.833	770	592 900	27.749	820	672 400	28.636	870	756 900	29.496
721	519 841	26.851	771	594 441	27.767	821	674 041	28.653	871	758 641	29.513
722	521 284	26.870	772	595 984	27.785	822	675 684	28.671	872	760 384	29.530
723	522 729	26.889	773	597 529	27.803	823	677 329	28.688	873	762 129	29.547
724	524 176	26.907	774	599 076	27.821	824	678 976	28.705	874	763 876	29.563
725	525 625	26.926	775	600 625	27.839	825	680 625	28.723	875	765 625	29.580
726	527 076	26.944	776	602 176	27.857	826	682 276	28.740	876	767 376	29.597
727	528 529	26.963	777	603 729	27.875	827	683 929	28.758	877	769 129	29.614
728	529 984	26.981	778	605 284	27.893	828	685 584	28.775	878	770 884	29.631
729	531 441	27.000	779	606 841	27.911	829	687 241	28.792	879	772 641	29.648
730	532 900	27.019	780	608 400	27.928	830	688 900	28.810	880	774 400	29.665
731	534 361	27.037	781	609 961	27.946	831	690 561	28.827	881	776 161	29.682
732	535 824	27.056	782	611 524	27.964	832	692 224	28.844	882	777 924	29.698
733	537 289	27.074	783	613 089	27.982	833	693 889	28.862	883	779 689	29.715
734	538 756	27.092	784	614 656	28.000	834	695 556	28.879	884	781 456	29.732
735	540 225	27.111	785	616 225	28.018	835	697 225	28.896	885	783 225	29.749
736	541 696	27.129	786	617 796	28.036	836	698 896	28.914	886	784 996	29.766
737	543 169	27.148	787	619 369	28.054	837	700 569	28.931	887	786 769	29.783
738	544 644	27.166	788	620 944	28.071	838	702 244	28.948	888	788 544	29.799
739	546 121	27.185	789	622 521	28.089	839	703 921	28.966	889	790 321	29.816
740	547 600	27.203	790	624 100	28.107	840	705 600	28.983	890	792 100	29.833
741	549 081	27.221	791	625 681	28.125	841	707 281	29.000	891	793 881	29.850
742	550 564	27.240	792	627 264	28.142	842	708 964	29.017	892	795 664	29.866
743	552 049	27.258	793	628 849	28.160	843	710 649	29.034	893	797 449	29.883
744	553 536	27.276	794	630 436	28.178	844	712 336	29.052	894	799 236	29.900
745	555 025	27.295	795	632 025	28.196	845	714 025	29.069	895	801 025	29.917
746	556 516	27.313	796	633 616	28.213	846	715 716	29.086	896	802 816	29.933
747	558 009	27.331	797	635 209	28.231	847	717 409	29.103	897	804 609	29.950
748	559 504	27.350	798	636 804	28.249	848	719 104	29.120	898	806 404	29.967
749	561 001	27.368	799	638 401	28.267	849	720 801	29.138	899	808 201	29.983
750	562 500	27.386	800	640 000	28.284	850	722 500	29.155	900	810 000	30.000
751	564 001	27.404	801	641 601	28.302	851	724 201	29.172	901	811 801	30.017
752	565 504	27.423	802	643 204	28.320	852	725 904	29.189	902	813 604	30.033
753	567 009	27.441	803	644 809	28.337	853	727 609	29.206	903	815 409	30.050
754	568 516	27.459	804	646 416	28.355	854	729 316	29.223	904	817 216	30.067
755	570 025	27.477	805	648 025	28.373	855	731 025	29.240	905	819 025	30.083
756	571 536	27.495	806	649 636	28.390	856	732 736	29.257	906	820 836	30.100
757	573 049	27.514	807	651 249	28.408	857	734 449	29.275	907	822 649	30.116
758	574 564	27.532	808	652 864	28.425	858	736 164	29.292	908	824 464	30.133
759	576 081	27.550	809	654 481	28.443	859	737 881	29.309	909	826 281	30.150
760	577 600	27.568	810	656 100	28.461	860	739 600	29.326	910	828 100	30.166
761	579 121	27.586	811	657 721	28.478	861	741 321	29.343	911	829 921	30.183
762	580 644	27.604	812	659 344	28.496	862	743 044	29.360	912	831 744	30.199
763	582 169	27.622	813	660 969	28.513	863	744 769	29.377	913	833 569	30.216
764	583 696	27.641	814	662 596	28.531	864	746 496	29.394	914	835 396	30.232
765	585 225	27.659	815	664 225	28.548	865	748 225	29.411	915	837 225	30.249
766	586 756	27.677	816	665 856	28.566	866	749 956	29.428	916	839 056	30.265
767	588 289	27.695	817	667 489	28.583	867	751 689	29.445	917	840 889	30.282
768	589 824	27.713	818	669 124	28.601	868	753 424	29.462	918	842 724	30.299
769	591 361	27.731	819	670 761	28.618	869	755 161	29.479	919	844 561	30.315

N	N^2	$\sqrt{N}$	N	N^2	$\sqrt{N}$	N	N^2	$\sqrt{N}$	N	N^2	$\sqrt{N}$
920	846 400	30.332	940	883 600	30.659	960	921 600	30.984	980	960 400	31.305
921	848 241	30.348	941	885 481	30.676	961	923 521	31.000	981	962 361	31.321
922	850 084	30.364	942	887 364	30.692	962	925 444	31.016	982	964 324	31.337
923	851 929	30.381	943	889 249	30.708	963	927 369	31.032	983	966 289	31.353
924	853 776	30.397	944	891 136	30.725	964	929 296	31.048	984	968 256	31.369
925	855 625	30.414	945	893 025	30.741	965	931 225	31.064	985	970 225	31.385
926	857 476	30.430	946	894 916	30.757	966	933 156	31.081	986	972 196	31.401
927	859 329	30.447	947	896 809	30.773	967	935 089	31.097	987	974 169	31.417
928	861 184	30.463	948	898 704	30.790	968	937 024	31.113	988	976 144	31.432
929	863 041	30.480	949	900 601	30.806	969	938 961	31.129	989	978 121	31.448
930	864 900	30.496	950	902 500	30.822	970	940 900	31.145	990	980 100	31.464
931	866 761	30.512	951	904 401	30.838	971	942 841	31.161	991	982 081	31.480
932	868 624	30.529	952	906 304	30.855	972	944 784	31.177	992	984 064	31.496
933	870 489	30.545	953	908 209	30.871	973	946 729	31.193	993	986 049	31.512
934	872 356	30.561	954	910 116	30.887	974	948 676	31.209	994	988 036	31.528
935	874 225	30.578	955	912 025	30.903	975	950 625	31.225	995	990 025	31.544
936	876 096	30.594	956	913 936	30.919	976	952 576	31.241	996	992 016	31.559
937	877 969	30.610	957	915 849	30.935	977	954 529	31.257	997	994 009	31.575
938	879 844	30.627	958	917 764	30.952	978	956 484	31.273	998	996 004	31.591
939	881 721	30.643	959	919 681	30.968	979	958 441	31.289	999	998 001	31.607

Index